Health and Medicine through History

Health and Medicine through History

From Ancient Practices to 21st-Century Innovations

VOLUME 2: 19th through 21st Centuries

Ruth Clifford Engs, Editor

GREENWOOD

An Imprint of ABC-CLIO, LLC
Santa Barbara, California • Denver, Colorado

Library of Congress Cataloging-in-Publication Data

Names: Engs, Ruth Clifford, editor.
Title: Health and medicine through history : from ancient practices to 21st-century innovations / Ruth Clifford Engs, editor.
Description: Santa Barbara, CA : Greenwood, [2019] | Includes bibliographical references and index.
Identifiers: LCCN 2018055964 (print) | LCCN 2018056496 (ebook) | ISBN 9781440858925 (eBook) | ISBN 9781440858918 (set : alk. paper) | ISBN 9781440858932 (volume 1 : alk. paper) | ISBN 9781440858949 (volume 2 : alk. paper) | ISBN 9781440858956 (volume 3 : alk. paper)
Subjects: | MESH: History of Medicine
Classification: LCC R131 (ebook) | LCC R131 (print) | NLM WZ 40 | DDC 610—dc23
LC record available at https://lccn.loc.gov/2018055964

ISBN: 978-1-4408-5891-8 (set)
978-1-4408-5893-2 (vol. 1)
978-1-4408-5894-9 (vol. 2)
978-1-4408-5895-6 (vol. 3)
978-1-4408-5892-5 (ebook)

23 22 21 20 19 1 2 3 4 5

This book is also available as an eBook.

Greenwood
An Imprint of ABC-CLIO, LLC

ABC-CLIO, LLC
147 Castilian Drive
Santa Barbara, California 93117
www.abc-clio.com

This book is printed on acid-free paper ∞

Manufactured in the United States of America

For Jeff Graf and Jeff Franz

Contents

Part 4 20th Century and Beyond

Ruth Clifford Engs

PART 3

19th Century

Deborah Brunton

1

Key Factors in Health and Wellness

Throughout history, health has depended on four main factors. Diet was very important to maintaining good health. People who were hungry or lived on a very narrow range of foods were less able to resist disease and to recover from illness. Those who ate adequate amounts of a range of nourishing foods were more likely to remain well. Hygiene also played a part in preventing disease: individuals who had access to generous supplies of clean water could regularly bathe, keep their homes clean, and wash their clothes. Those who could not were exposed to "filth diseases"—infections transmitted by contaminated water or parasites. Location—where people lived—and their occupations also affected their risk of exposure to disease and injury. Finally, the ability to obtain medical care helped to ensure recovery from illness. Access to a good diet, clean water, a healthy environment, and medical care varied widely around the globe and changed radically during the 19th century. The social, cultural, economic, and political changes associated with modern life wrought their effects on people's health and their ability to maintain their well-being in many, sometimes unexpected ways.

HEALTHY AND UNHEALTHY DIETS

Then, as now, a plentiful and reasonably varied diet was one of the keys to a long and healthy life. During the 19th century, most of the world's population lived by some form of subsistence farming. On all continents, peasant families or larger tribal groups worked together to cultivate crops on small areas of land, tend to grazing animals on open ground, and gather native plants and fruits. Most of the food produced in this way was eaten within the family group: any surplus was sold or exchanged to obtain items that they could not make for themselves, such as metal tools or high-quality fabrics. The diet of subsistence farmers was often monotonous, based around starchy foods such as rice, potatoes, or wheat, with some seasonal fruits and vegetables but with only small amounts of protein from meat, eggs, and milk. Diet varied with the seasons: in the Northern Hemisphere, food was plentiful in summer and autumn but often ran short in early spring.

Overall, so long as there was enough food to go around, the diet of subsistence farmers was basically healthy.

If crops failed due to bad weather or the upheaval caused by wars, then hunger and disease was the result. Famines occurred in every continent during the century, and their impact could be devastating. When the monsoon rains failed in Rajputana in India in 1869, over a million people died from hunger and disease. In China, several millions died from starvation following the Taiping Rebellion between 1850 and 1864. Even the populations of European countries, who enjoyed a moderate climate and relatively high levels of prosperity, did not escape from hunger. Ireland was devastated by famine in the 1840s. The population had grown rapidly in the early part of the century, but many were entirely dependent on growing potatoes to survive. When disease repeatedly struck the crop in the wet summers between 1846 and 1848, almost one million people died of hunger or disease, and a further million emigrated. Overall, the population fell by around a quarter.

People living in towns had to buy food. Poor workers could afford only cheap, filling foods and lived on a monotonous diet. Laborers all over Asia survived on a diet of rice. In mid-century Britain, bread with margarine and tea with sugar (providing a quick pick-me-up of calories and caffeine) was the staple diet of factory workers. Better-off families were able to buy a wider range of foods. They too ate staple foods, such as grains, that were imported from the countryside. They could afford to eat meat, from animals brought to cities for slaughter, and enjoyed a variety of vegetables grown in market gardens close to towns and cities. The wealthy classes enjoyed exotic foods that were shipped in by road, rail, and sea.

The diets of people everywhere, but especially those living in urban areas, benefited from improved transport. One of the features of the 19th century was the increased volume and speed of movement of goods and people around the globe, thanks to steam-driven ships and railways. In the later 19th century, the global trade in food brought access to a wider range of foods and brought down prices of items that previous generations had regarded as luxuries. In the 1890s, housewives in London, Paris, or Berlin bought meat shipped from South America, mutton from Australia, and tinned salmon from Canada. Bread from the local baker contained wheat from Canada, sugar came from plantations in the West Indies, and relishes contained spices from India and Java. The demand for luxury foodstuffs tempted producers and retailers to increase their profits by bulking out foods with cheap fillers or by adding materials to improve their appearance. Such adulteration could be lethal: red lead was added to cocoa, while pickled vegetables, relishes, and sweets were colored using chemicals containing arsenic and copper.

New Foodstuffs

Global travel brought new foodstuffs to populations around the world. Potatoes were introduced to New Zealand from Europe and America. A more productive crop than native roots, the potato increased the amount of food available and allowed the Maori people to trade with passing ships. Some new foods were a mixed blessing. Corn or maize had been introduced to Europe and North America from South America in the 16th and 17th centuries and remained an important part of the diet of small farmers in Italy and the southern United States in the 19th century. Unfortunately, the traditional method of preparing dried maize by soaking it in a solution containing lime was not transferred. This process ensured that niacin (vitamin B3), an important nutrient, was accessible to the body. In hard times, when farmers and their families were forced to rely on a diet of dried maize, they developed pellagra, a debilitating disease that caused skin lesions, weakness, and even death. Transporting food over long distances required high levels of processing to prevent it from going bad but sometimes removed important nutrients. Polished "white" rice kept better than unprocessed "brown" rice but contained little vitamin B1. Sailors and laborers working in factories in Asia, who ate a diet based on white rice, suffered from beri-beri, a disease that caused weakness, weight loss, and heart failure.

While most of the world's population was concerned about getting enough to eat, a small section of the population in Europe and America worried about eating too well: that they ate too much rich food and as a result became ill. Many chose to follow simpler, more "natural" diets such as the one promoted by an American, the Reverend Sylvester Graham. According to Graham, eating meat irritated the digestive system and nerves, leading to excessive sexual energy and a whole range of ailments. He advocated a diet of vegetables, whole meal bread, and the fiber-rich crackers that still bear his name. The 19th century also saw the arrival of low-carbohydrate diets designed to reduce weight.

Toward the end of the century, food supplements were heavily marketed through advertisements in newspapers. A vast array of pills, potions, and tonics promised to protect and improve health, promoting vigor, energy, and vitality by ensuring the correct functioning of the organs and building up stores of nervous energy. Some acted on specific parts of the body, purifying the blood or stimulating the liver. Others claimed to have a more general effect. One advertisement proclaimed: "HOOD'S SARSAPARILLA which makes rich, healthy blood and thus gives strength and elasticity to the muscles, vigor to the brain, and health and vitality to every part of the body. Hood's Sarsaparilla MAKES THE WEAK STRONG" (Ueyama 2010). Very few of these potions can have done the consumer much good, although cod liver oil was sold from 1870s as a general tonic, well before it was understood to be a source of vitamin D.

HEALTH AND HYGIENE

A second crucial factor in keeping well and avoiding disease was access to a plentiful supply of clean water for drinking and washing. Throughout the world, in Africa, Asia, Europe, and the Americas, there was a long association between dirt and disease. In rural areas, where people lived in fairly small, stable communities, they chose to site their homes close to natural sources of water such as streams and rivers. If there was no convenient natural source, householders dug wells or built tanks to store rainwater. Living quarters were arranged to ensure that water supplies were not contaminated by dirt, feces, or domestic refuse. In Indian and African villages, water was stored uphill of latrines and rubbish dumps. Zulu people collected their water upstream of villages and away from the parts of the rivers used for bathing and washing.

While access to a plentiful supply of clean water gave populations the opportunity to bathe and wash their clothes, the frequency of washing was also dictated by cultural factors. In Africa, many peoples bathed daily and took great care to keep their bodies and hair clean and free from parasites. By contrast, travelers in Eastern Europe criticized the indigenous peasant farmers for rarely bathing and for living in filthy conditions. Religious rites also affected when and how often people washed: followers of Islam washed their heads, arms, and feet before praying.

In cities, getting access to clean water was often difficult, as rapid urban growth put a great strain on traditional systems of water supply. At the beginning of the 19th century, there were relatively few large cities in Europe and Asia. Over the course of the century, new cities grew up around important transit points and industrial sites, and existing centers grew in size. The population of London increased from 800,000 inhabitants in 1801 to over 6 million in 1901. Gradually, societies moved from being predominantly rural to largely urban. In 1800, less than one-fifth of the European population lived in towns: by 1900, over half made their lives in urban areas. In Britain, over 80 percent of the population lived in towns by the end of the century. (With such rapid change, it is easy to overlook the continuities of life: at the same time, less than 1 percent of the African population lived in urban centers.)

In cities, the traditional sources of water—rivers, reservoirs, and wells—could not keep up with the demands of growing populations. In many towns, the supplies became seriously polluted by rubbish, excrement, and industrial refuse. Wealthy residents could avoid the problem by digging their own wells or by building tanks to allow water to settle and clear before use. The poor migrants to towns had no choice but to take dirty water from rivers and canals or spend time standing in line to obtain piped water from a public well.

Better-off residents of cities, who enjoyed access to plentiful supplies of clean water, could afford to follow medical practitioners' advice to bathe regularly as means of removing dirt and sweat from the skin and stimulating the body. They had servants to carry water and, later in the century, had the space and resources to build laundries and bathrooms within their homes. For the poor, who had to carry home water from a river or pump in buckets and jugs, keeping clean was exhausting and time consuming, and it is not surprising that many people rarely, if ever, bathed.

From the 1860s in Europe and America, as scientific medicine identified bacteria as the cause of many diseases, there was an increasing concern with keeping the body and the environment clean. Women took on the responsibility for keeping their homes free of germs and disease. The appearance of cleanliness was not enough to ensure that their homes were safe. "From the cellar, store-room, pantry, bedroom, sitting room and parlor; from decaying vegetables, fruits, meats, soiled clothing, old garments, old furniture, refuse of kitchen, mouldy walls, everywhere, a microscopic germ is propagating" ("Decomposition" 1874). Only thorough cleanliness, proper ventilation, and disinfection would stop disease and death from visiting the home.

General levels of hygiene improved in the late 19th century, when city governments made enormous investments in building new reservoirs and laying pipes to bring in greater amounts of clean water. As a result, many more homes were connected to water supplies. The poorest could wash themselves at public baths and clean their clothes in public washhouses. Messages about hygiene gradually spread down the social scale through pamphlets and lectures. Schoolchildren were taught to keep their faces and hands clean. Sales of soap soared: it was one of the first branded consumer products. Regular washing must have made life healthier by cutting down exposure to bacteria and infections; it also helped reduce the incidence of skin complaints and parasites such as lice and fleas.

CLEANLINESS AND THE ENVIRONMENT

Efficient removal of refuse and waste was also important in maintaining health. Traditional forms of housing were often designed around concepts of hygiene. In African villages, houses were grouped in compounds, with each dwelling separated from its neighbors by a small patch of ground. Houses were sited on higher ground, away from animal enclosures so that no contamination reached them. Refuse was regularly removed from living areas, and feces were disposed of very carefully. In some cultures, human excrement was placed in pits and doused with boiling water. In others, all feces were buried well away from the houses, for fear that it would be stolen and used in witchcraft to cause harm to the community.

In urban areas in the West and in Asia, the large and growing numbers of people packed into small areas put strains on traditional systems of waste disposal. These relied on householders keeping their own homes clean and taking responsibility for disposing of the debris, ashes, and excrement produced in the home. Domestic refuse and excrement was often collected and sold to local farmers to fertilize their fields. City authorities were responsible for keeping the streets clean, by employing cleaners to gather refuse and by maintaining drains or ditches to carry away rainwater. As towns grew, these systems broke down. In 19th-century cities in Europe, India, and North Africa, refuse piled up in the streets and filled the rainwater ditches. In Beijing and other Chinese cities, travelers noted that the old drainage systems were not maintained, rubbish was not collected, and cemeteries with shallow, badly dug graves were situated close to homes. Even the air of cities became increasingly polluted by smoke from domestic fires and from factories.

Reformers, eager to whip up support for sanitary improvements, provided graphic and dramatic accounts of the levels of filth in cities. The Reverend Andrew Mearns described the slums in London:

> [C]ourts reeking with poisonous and malodorous gases arising from accumulations of sewage and refuse . . . many of them which the sun never penetrates, which are never visited by a breath of fresh air, and which rarely know the virtues of a drop of cleansing water . . . Eight feet square—that is about the average size of many of these rooms. Walls and ceiling are black with the accretions of filth which have gathered upon them through long years of neglect. (Mearns 1883, 7)

In the early part of the century, the bad smells, or "miasma," arising from dirt and rotting matter were blamed for producing a range of diseases. By 1900, it was understood that these complaints arose from a number of causes, but their transmission was fostered by filthy conditions. Water supplies polluted with bacteria passed in human excrement exposed town dwellers to simple stomach upsets and deadly infections such as cholera, characterized by violent diarrhea, cramps, and, in many cases, a rapid death, and typhoid that caused high fever and delirium. Crowded and dirty living conditions allowed body lice to spread from person to person, carrying typhus fever with its rashes. Epidemics of these diseases regularly struck every city, even prosperous capitals and trading centers. Other diseases were endemic or present all the time. In densely crowded housing, respiratory complaints—tuberculosis, bronchitis, and pneumonia—were readily transmitted from person to person through the air, damaging the lungs and causing many deaths. Infection rates peaked in the winter months, when urban residents huddled indoors to escape the cold. Many city children had permanently bowed legs from rickets. The disease was caused by a lack of vitamin D (manufactured in the body when exposed to sunlight) that affected bone development.

In cities, wealthy residents avoided the worst health risks by making their homes in new suburbs, built away from the densely populated slums and factories and often situated on hills. In Britain, the most desirable homes tended to be on the west side of towns, where the prevailing winds blew away smoke and pollution. In London, the upper classes lived in the fashionable West End, while the East End was a working-class area. Wealthy homes had large rooms with many windows that allowed the air to circulate and that let in sunlight. They boasted the latest sanitary facilities: bathrooms equipped with baths and showers with hot and cold running water and flushing lavatories. Over time, building regulations passed by town authorities ensured that houses built for residents lower down the social scale had similar facilities. Building codes stipulated the width of new streets (to help circulate air through built-up areas), set minimum sizes of rooms, and required all dwellings to have piped water and sinks.

Town and city authorities helped householders to keep their dwellings clean by installing drainage and sewerage systems and organizing the collection and disposal of domestic refuse. They also launched new initiatives to improve the public spaces by introducing regular street cleaning.

CLIMATE AND HEALTH

The Moving World

Nineteenth-century developments in transport, especially reliable and efficient steam engines in ships and on railways, allowed travel on an unprecedented scale. Small numbers of European and American explorers mapped the African and Asian continents, and much greater numbers of European soldiers fought indigenous peoples, bringing vast areas under the control of colonial governments. In their wake came administrators to govern the local populations, settlers to set up farms, and missionaries to spread the Christian faith. Better transport increased the numbers of settlers in older European colonies, including Canada, Australia, and New Zealand. New industries and agriculture in the colonies brought a demand for migrant labor, to tend crops for the European market such as rubber, tea, and cotton, and to labor in mines and factories. Men from the Caribbean moved to Latin America in search of work, laborers from India settled in South Africa, and over half a million Chinese and South Asians found employment in the Americas. Men from China traveled the world as sailors and settled in "China-towns" from Vancouver to Liverpool.

Moving around the globe or even within a region could be very dangerous. On sea voyages, ships ran into bad weather and were wrecked or were delayed so long that supplies of food and water ran out. In the crowded conditions on emigrant ships, disease spread rapidly among the closely confined passengers. Travel on the railways too brought risks. The unprecedented speeds of over 40 miles per hour terrified many passengers, and some doctors feared that such rapid travel would damage the nervous system. The boilers on early steam locomotives occasionally exploded, killing drivers and railway staff. Trains derailed and collided, and the flimsy carriages gave passengers little protection. Rail travel even had its own medical condition called "railway spine." It was suffered by passengers who escaped apparently uninjured from crashes but later reported symptoms that were attributed to jarring. These would now be diagnosed as post-traumatic stress.

HEALTHY AND UNHEALTHY CLIMATES

Travelers arriving at their destinations were exposed to a whole new range of hazards. In Europe and America, it was generally accepted that different races were adapted to live in particular climates. White people were suited to cool, temperate climates, while black and other races of color were much more tolerant of heat and humidity. Moving to a new and unfamiliar climate therefore posed serious risks to health. For example, Bengal in India was seen as a particularly unhealthy place for Europeans. The heat, humidity, and wide variations of temperature between seasons were believed to affect the blood and organs, particularly the liver, undermining the health of settlers. The forests and lakes were full of "miasma," or bad air, that caused fevers and other complaints. Altitude also had an important effect on health. In Peru, Archibald Smith, a Scottish physician, concluded that the even temperatures and high humidity of the coastal regions made the immigrant population weak and subject to stomach complaints. The high mountains were also bad for new arrivals who experienced headaches, vertigo, and nausea. Although all unfamiliar climates were unhealthy in some ways, some were more dangerous than others. West Africa, where settlers and soldiers died in huge numbers, was nicknamed the "white man's grave"; but life in the countryside of Australia or South America was relatively healthy. It was certainly more conducive to good health than living in the slums of European cities, and British charities paid for orphans to emigrate to Australia and New Zealand in part to give them the opportunity of living in healthy surroundings.

Various techniques were adopted to mitigate the effects of moving to a new and potentially dangerous climate. In the early decades of the century, new arrivals were advised to take time to acclimatize by spending some time in areas where the climate was more like that of their homeland, and only gradually moving into less healthy locations. Settlers sought to protect their health by carefully choosing the sites of their new homes. Ideally, settlers' homes should be shaded from the sun, built away from dense vegetation and damp areas, and open to breezes but not strong winds. By the middle decades of the century, doctors were losing faith in the concept of acclimatization. Instead, they recommended minimizing the time spent in the unhealthiest areas. In India, European soldiers and administrators moved away from the heat and humidity of the plains to the cooler climate of the hills for a few weeks or months each year, as a way to maintain and restore their well-being.

Similar concerns drove European families to escape the heat and polluted atmosphere of the city for a few weeks or months during the summer by traveling to the seaside, mountain resorts, or spa towns. There, the mild climate, mineral waters, and fresh air helped to build up health and strength before the winter with its colds and other minor ailments. By the end of the century, working-class families saved hard to afford a day or two in the country or by the coast, partly for pleasure but also because they believed that the air would "do them good."

By the end of the century, climate was no longer blamed for high levels of mortality among settlers in Africa and Asia. Instead, deaths were linked to a range of "tropical" diseases associated with warm climates, such as kala-azar, sleeping sickness, yellow fever, enteric fever, and dysentery. Some hot, dry climates were even seen as healthy for Europeans. A handbook aimed at potential settlers in Queensland, Australia, claimed that "although the heat makes out-door work arduous and uncomfortable, such work can nevertheless be carried on throughout the summer without injury to men of steady and temperate habits" (Hughes 1891, 35). The heat was not entirely without its dangers; settlers were warned that drinking alcohol in such a hot climate could lead to insanity.

EXPOSURE TO DISEASES AND INJURIES

Travel to a new continent, or a new country, brought people into contact with unfamiliar diseases. American and European travelers to Asia and Africa were exposed to a range of unfamiliar diseases to which they had little or no resistance. Many did not survive long: half the British soldiers sent to the Gold Coast of Africa in the 1820s died there. But there were also risks of exposure to new diseases for people traveling much shorter distances. Many rural populations suffered from a fairly small range of diseases particular to their location. For example, before the 19th century, the peoples of southern Africa were fairly healthy because they lived far away from ancient trade routes. With the arrival of European travelers, they came into contact with infections such as whooping cough, polio, tuberculosis, and cholera. Europeans, who moved from the countryside into towns and cities for work or to trade, had a similar experience and were exposed to infections such as smallpox, tuberculosis, and measles that were endemic in large urban populations.

Diseases moved around the globe with travelers. The increasing numbers of people making long journeys, and the greater speed of travel, allowed infections to move between continents. In the 18th century, someone boarding a ship while harboring an infection such as smallpox or measles would probably remain on board long enough for the disease to run its course. With steamships cutting journey times from weeks to days, passengers arrived at their destination suffering from infections that they then spread to the local population. Cholera was endemic in South Asia but traveled around the globe in repeated pandemics during the 19th century. From 1855, plague moved across China and India, and as far as Australia and the United States. Diseases that were relatively mild in Europe, such as influenza and measles, had a devastating effect on unexposed populations on Pacific islands. These infections, combined with conflicts, the loss of land and resources, and social disruption, halved the native populations of Hawaii and New Zealand. Patterns of disease also shifted in response to man-made changes to the environment. In Malaya and India, the clearing of forests for the creation of sugar, cotton, and rubber plantations, and the introduction of irrigation systems, provided ideal conditions for mosquitoes to breed and resulted in the spread of malaria.

Occupations carried their own threats to life and health. Farmers working on the land risked injury from by being kicked by farm animals and from accidents when using sharp tools such as scythes. In towns, builders fell from ladders; carters and dockworkers, who moved heavy goods using muscle power, were crushed by barrels and bales. In factories and workshops, the moving parts of machines were often exposed, and women workers in particular were in danger of being caught by the hair or clothing and pulled into the mechanisms. Miners were killed and injured in rock falls and died from exposure to dangerous gases.

As if this were not enough, city life brought new threats of serious injury. Pedestrians traveling through the streets were knocked down by horse-drawn and motorized traffic. Town dwellers had to learn how to get on and off omnibuses and tramcars safely. Stress is often associated with the pace of present-day urban life, but it was also recorded in the 19th century. People suffered from new nervous conditions, such as neurasthenia, believed to be caused by rapid transport and the intense pace of work.

ACCESS TO MEDICAL CARE

Regardless of how carefully they guarded their health through diet, hygiene, and lifestyle, at some point almost everyone fell ill and sought medical help to cure their ailments. Although medical knowledge is usually associated with groups of experts who specialize in healing, in the past (as now), everyone had some basic knowledge of disease and remedies, called folk or popular medicine. Such medical knowledge was acquired through personal experience of ill health, from family and friends or practitioners and, increasingly over the 19th century, through printed books. It allowed people to deal with their own minor ailments and injuries and those of family members. Ailments might be treated using special foodstuffs such as a nourishing soup. Local herbs or medicinal plants bought from a traveling merchant or local shop were made into infusions to be drunk or used to

In this late-19th-century photograph, a Japanese physician feels the pulse of his patient to diagnose the cause of her illness. Such highly trained practitioners charged high fees and attended only the very wealthy. (Alinari Archives/Getty Images)

wash wounds. Poultices (pastes made of seeds, vegetables, or earths) were applied to encourage the healing of swellings and other injuries.

Even small communities had one or two people with a special knowledge of healing, learned through experience or from other practitioners, who provided help in return for some form of payment. They offered different types of treatment. Many were herbalists, who prepared medicines and gave advice. In many cultures around the world, disease was often believed to have its roots in an excess of blood. Barbers or bloodletters cut open veins to release a controlled amount of blood and allow the body to recover its normal functions. In cases of broken or dislocated limbs, a bonesetter would be consulted. In many cultures in Asia, Africa, and the Americas, a sick person could ask for help from a healer who used spiritual or supernatural means to diagnose and treat illness caused by spirits or by sorcery.

Wealthy members of society living in towns were able to consult what we might recognize as a professional doctor: a healer who had spent a long time acquiring a theoretical knowledge of how the body worked in health and illness, and who practiced medicine as a full-time occupation. These practitioners charged much higher fees than local healers, reflecting the investment in their training, their sophisticated knowledge, and their high social status. They visited patients in their homes, diagnosed their ailments, and directed treatment. Over the century, the numbers of these elite practitioners increased. More people began to access their help, either paying for their own treatment or obtaining help through charities and hospitals.

Public Health

While individuals were largely responsible for looking after their own health, over the course of the 19th century, governments and other institutions played an increasing role in helping them to do so. Particular groups of people such as members of the military or prisoners were subjected to close regulation of their diet, exercise, bathing, and living conditions in barracks, ships, and prisons. Public health regulations protected the wider population. Regulations on the quality of food sold by shopkeepers helped to ensure that customers did not buy milk or meat that was unfit for consumption. Governments set limits for working hours and rules to protect workers from dangerous machinery and from exposure to hazardous substances. They began to improve sanitation, introducing supplies of clean water and installing drainage systems to carry away wastewater. To control outbreaks of disease, they established quarantines, isolated and cared for the sick, and provided immunization against smallpox. While the degree of state involvement varied from place to place, by the end of the century, public health regulations had begun to make an impact, helping people to live longer, healthier lives.

The expansion of medical care to the general population was one of the justifications for colonial rule. Medicine was seen as a part of the "civilizing mission" of European governments and charities.

> I have been on horse back through the country a great deal attending to sick Natives and every where the Natives have hailed me with delight and have expressed themselves grateful to the Government for having sent me amongst them . . . before ten years pass over many a savage heart will be won over to the British Government and many a Father and Mother or Husband and Wife will bless the benevolence and wisdom of that Government which entered in spirit into the sickness and sufferings of the black savage lying neglected and forlorn on the cold damp ground and suggested a remedy. (Fitzgerald 1856)

2

Education and Training

In the 19th century, many forms of medicine were practiced around the world in different cultures. The majority of the global population used some form of folk medicine—different ranges of therapies used to treat particular ailments or diseases caused by spirits or by witchcraft. These varied from simple homemade remedies for minor ailments such as colds or stomach upsets, to treatments offered by healers skilled in the preparation and use of herbal medicines or rituals to cure supernatural diseases. A smaller number of people were able to afford the services of practitioners trained in a medical system—a body of knowledge that explained how the body worked and why and how illnesses occurred, and thus gave a logical explanation of how to cure any problems. Among the most important and widely used medical systems practiced around the world were Western or scientific medicine (used in Europe and North America), Chinese medicine, Ayurvedic medicine (practiced in India) and Unani medicine (practiced in India and North Africa).

All systems of medicine were based on a body of texts, often dating back many centuries, but they were not ancient and unchanging bodies of knowledge. Medicine constantly developed as doctors added new observations or reinterpreted the conclusions made by earlier generations of practitioners. In the 19th century, this development was given a new impetus by global travel that brought about contacts between different medical systems and exposed practitioners to new approaches to medicine and different methods of practice.

NON-WESTERN MEDICAL SYSTEMS

Although each of the major non-Western systems of medicine, Chinese, Ayurvedic, and Unani, were quite different, they shared some fundamental principles. Practitioners of all three systems believed that health reflected the smooth functioning of the body: illness occurred when there was some disruption to the body's fundamental processes—the flow of fluids or energies, or the processing of food within the body. A number of factors tipped the body from a state of health to one of illness: lifestyle (particularly diet, but also exercise and sleep patterns), strong emotions, and changes to the environment.

CHINESE MEDICINE

Chinese medicine dates back over 2,000 years. Ancient texts, written around 200 B.C.E., defined the central concepts of medical theory: yin/yang (opposing or complementary qualities) and the five phases (wood, fire, earth, metal, and water—each associated with a specific form of action or transformation within the body). Although Chinese medical theory referred to organs within the body, practitioners were concerned with the function of these organs rather than their structure. The five yin organs, the heart, liver, spleen, lung, and kidney, manufactured and stored qi (pronounced "chee")—a form of energy or spirit. The six yang organs, the small intestine, large intestine, gallbladder, urinary bladder, stomach, and *sanjiao* (triple burner) were responsible for the regulation of body processes such as digestion and breathing. Health was dependent on the smooth circulation of qi through channels spread throughout the body. Disease occurred when the yin/yang balance was disrupted, affecting the flow of qi that could become stagnant, or blocked in a particular place. This was caused by diet, environmental factors such as cold, internal factors including emotions, or external factors including the invasion of bad qi arising from the environment. Disease was also widely believed to be caused by spirits or ghosts.

Chinese medicine is often portrayed as static and unchanging, but the late 18th and 19th centuries were a time of lively debate on the causes and treatment of diseases. Different schools of thought were developed by prominent scholar physicians and continued by their pupils. Doctors debated the merits of classical and modern authors, and the role of cold damage and warm pathogens in causing disease. Cold damage theory ascribed all diseases to internal, external, or environmental factors, while warm factor theory claimed that some disease was caused by pestilential qi entering through the mouth and nose and attacking the body's own qi. Chinese practitioners also debated the true function of internal organs. In his book *I-lin kai-ts'o* (*Correction of Errors from Medical Literature*), Wang Ch'ing-jen complained of the contradictions in existing texts produced by earlier writers.

> When they spoke of the lung, [they said] it is empty like a beehive and has no opening at its lower side. Inhaling fills it, exhaling empties it. Now, if it is said [in one place that the lung] has no opening below, how can it be said elsewhere that the lung has twenty-four holes pointing into all directions as passageways for the influence of the body's depots? (Unschuld 2010, 213–214)

Wang Ch'ing-jen called for new research to achieve a better understanding of anatomy. Styles of medical practice also varied between practitioners. Each had a particular area of expertise and style of prescribing. Some were known for their use of strong drugs to attack the causes of disease: others favored milder remedies that supported the body.

Treatment aimed to restore the smooth circulation of qi, or to get rid of bad qi and to build up good qi, and thus return the patient to health. Drugs were used to manipulate the functioning of the body's systems. Each drug was categorized by its character—hot, cold, or cool—and which organ it affected. Drugs were used to break up and disperse blockages of qi or remove excess heat or cold. Practitioners also restored the circulation of qi and removed blockages by acupuncture (the insertion of needles at points along the channels of the body) or moxibustion (burning small pellets of vegetable material on the skin).

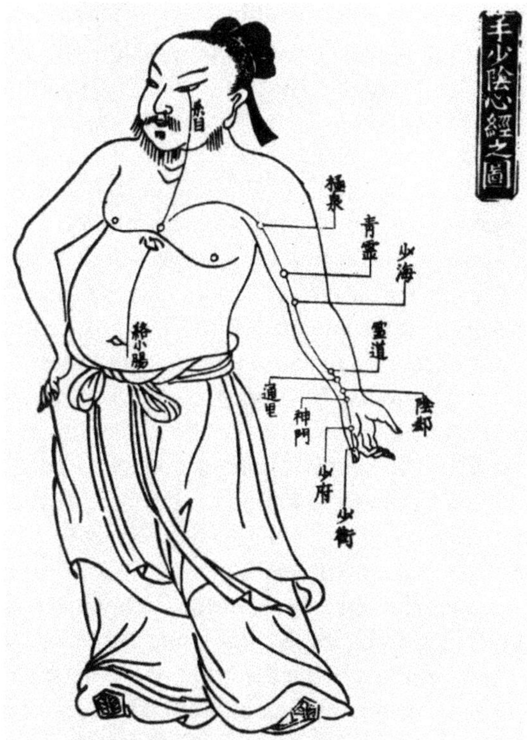

This diagram shows acupuncture points on the arm and body along one of the channels where qi flows around the body. By inserting needles at each point, doctors stimulated specific organs or encouraged the movement of qi. (National Library of Medicine/WHO photo)

Diet was an important form of therapy. Foods, like drugs, were categorized as hot, warm, cool, or cold and had particular qualities that related to the body's internal systems. Crab, for example, was characterized as cold and salty, while mutton was hot and sweet. In hot weather, it was important to eat cooling foods—vegetables and fruits, such as melon—and avoid hot foodstuffs such as meat and oily dishes that would cause the body to overheat. The bad effects of eating too much of one type of food at one meal could be balanced at the next: so the effects of a rich dish of mutton at dinner could be countered the next day by a meal of soup made with cool green vegetables. Some dishes could boost health. "Guarding life soup" containing the herb angelica and dahlia root was recommended to strengthen the body and calm the spirits.

Chinese Practitioners

There was a wide range of practitioners in China. The elite were learned scholar physicians, many of whom came from families who had practiced medicine for several generations. Learned practitioners had a deep understanding of medical theory drawn from texts. They trained as pupils under an established practitioner, who guided their studies and tested their developing knowledge. Pupils learned how to diagnose illness and prescribe treatment by observing their teacher at work. Diagnosis was made by listening to the patient's description of his or her symptoms, by feeling the pulse to read the flow of qi, and by close scrutiny of the face, tongue, and breathing. These signs indicated the deeper changes within the body and allowed practitioners to identify the nature of the illness, what parts of the body were involved, and whether the ailment was in its early or later stages—disease was easily cured in its early stages but at a later point required more vigorous treatment. Accurate diagnosis was vital: one symptom, such as a fever, could be caused by quite different underlying changes within the body, and the wrong therapy would make the problem worse.

Learned practitioners charged high fees: only wealthy patients could afford their services. Many specialized in treating one or more types of ailment, such as fevers or external complaints. The most common specialism was in treating children's illnesses. This required a high level of skill as children could not explain their symptoms to the doctor, so he had to rely on his ability to observe the patient and read the pulse. In the 19th century, the Chinese state no longer regulated medicine by requiring practitioners to pass examinations, so practitioners were ranked by their reputation for curing difficult cases. Famous doctors were praised for their skill and charged higher fees. They attracted patients suffering from complex cases who had failed to find a cure from other practitioners.

Alongside the highly trained scholar physicians were a much larger number of other practitioners. While some made use of theoretical concepts, such as the effects of lifestyle on the body or the balance of hot and cold, they did not possess the deep understanding of medical theory of learned practitioners. For this reason, learned practitioners dismissed them as dangerous quacks, offering worthless cures and cheating their gullible patients. Street healers (*shi yi*) diagnosed illnesses, prescribed medicines, and practiced acupuncture and moxibustion. Itinerant doctors offered quick, cheap cures for diseases, especially skin and eye complaints; extracted teeth; and treated wounds. Other types of practitioners had more practical skills. Drug sellers worked in shops, making up the prescriptions written by learned practitioners and handing out medical advice, or sold simple remedies for common ailments from a stall or on the street. Midwives helped women in childbirth, using medicines and massage. Shamans and priests exorcised disease-causing demons. Knowledge of medicine was spread widely through Chinese society. Patients too had some basic understanding of medicine that they used to devise treatments for their own minor ailments and to judge the skill and ability of practitioners.

AYURVEDIC MEDICINE

Ayurvedic medicine was widely practiced in India and Asia, particularly but not exclusively among those of the Hindu faith. It too had a long history: Ayurvedic medical texts dated back to the fourth century B.C.E. In this system, the body was believed to be composed of seven basic substances (chyle or fluid, blood, flesh, fat, bone, marrow, and semen). These were subject to the action of three *doshas*—*vata*, *pitta*, and *kapha* (wind, bile, and phlegm)—that regulated movement and transformations (for example, digestion) and stabilized the body by actions such as lubricating the joints. Each *dosha* was found throughout the body but was linked to particular organs. Thus *vata* was associated with the large intestine, *pitta* with the stomach, and *kapha* with the heart. The *doshas* corresponded to two of five fundamental elements: ether (or space), air, fire, water, and earth. For example, *vata* was linked to ether and air. A natural slight imbalance of the *doshas* affected the body shape, health, and character of each individual. Those with a *pitta* constitution were of medium height, slept lightly, and were prone to eye infections. The balance of *doshas* was not fixed: they varied according to age (infants had more *kapha*, old people more *vata*), the time of year, and even the time of day.

When healthy, the body, mind, and spirit were all in a state of harmony. Disease was the result of a significant imbalance within the body, usually an excess of one or more *doshas*. Disease could be caused by many possible factors—by changes in the season and temperature; by inappropriate behavior, such as too much or too little exercise; or by eating the wrong sort of foods. Illness could also be caused by supernatural forces. Children were particularly at risk of attacks by demons and had to be protected by prayer and rituals.

When diagnosing disease, practitioners examined the body and its secretions to gain an insight into what was happening inside the body: they noted the quality of the pulse and the appearance of urine, feces, and the eyes and tongue to determine the state of the *doshas*. Treatment aimed to remove the disease and also to restore the body's natural healthy processes. Medicines were used to counter imbalances of the *doshas*. Drugs were categorized by *rasa* or taste—sweet, sour, salt, pungent, bitter, and astringent—each with different effects. Sour medicines helped digestion and the healing of wounds. In addition, practitioners prescribed vomiting, laxatives, and enemas to remove toxins from the body. For example, laxatives or purges were prescribed in cases of fever, leprosy, female diseases, cholera, jaundice, and wounds. Bloodletting was used to remove an excess of blood or bad blood.

The position on the body where the blood was removed was specific to each type of ailment. Patients suffering from diseases of the ear had blood taken from the ear; in cases of madness, blood was removed from a vein on the chest. In theory, every course of treatment had to be tailored to the individual constitution of the patient; but in practice, standard preparations were often prescribed for common ailments.

As well as curing illnesses, Ayurvedic medicine provided techniques to preserve health and prolong life through diet, exercise, and massage to strengthen the body and mind. Personal hygiene was very important. Texts recommended brushing the teeth twice a day, washing the face and hands, massaging the skin with oils, and exercising.

Elite Ayurvedic practitioners, called *vaids*, learned medical theory by memorizing classic texts, often in the form of short rhymes. They acquired the skills of diagnosis and prescription by observing the work of established practitioners. Distinguished practitioners attracted numbers of pupils, and in the early 19th century, small schools of Ayurvedic medicine were based in the courts of Indian rulers. In the late 19th century, medical students attended colleges, modeled on Western universities. Alongside learned practitioners were other, less well-educated and sometimes self-taught practitioners who possessed a basic level of knowledge and charged lower fees. Drug sellers had an understanding of medical theory to help them make up medicines. Other practitioners had practical skills. Although elaborate surgery was described in ancient Ayurvedic texts, 19th-century surgeons carried out a limited number of procedures, including removing cataracts from the eye, bloodletting, and treating injuries. Midwives (*dais*) looked after women in childbirth.

UNANI MEDICINE

Unani medicine was derived from ancient Greek medical knowledge that spread into the Arabian Peninsula in the medieval period and was developed and elaborated by Islamic scholars. One of the central texts of Unani medicine was the *Kitab al-Qunan* (*Canon of Medicine*) by Ibn Sina (known as Avicenna in the West), completed around 1025. In the 19th century, Unani medicine continued to be practiced in North Africa, and it had spread eastward to India where it was used by the Muslim population. According to this system of medicine, health depended on a balance of four fluids or humors—*dam* (blood), *balgham* (phlegm), *safra* (yellow bile) and *sauda* (black bile)—that were produced by digestion. Each substance displayed two of four fundamental qualities—hot, cold, wet, and dry. Blood, for example, was hot and wet. As in Ayurvedic medicine, everyone had a slight natural imbalance of the humors that determined their character. The quantity of humors and their flow around the body was affected by six factors: air, food and drink, movement and rest, sleep and wakefulness, eating and evacuation, and emotions. Eating the wrong type of foods, or not getting enough sleep, or moving too quickly between hot and cold environments caused an imbalance or a blockage in the flow of humors and caused illness. Diseases caused by an excess of hot humors—blood and yellow bile—were categorized as hot; those associated with an increase in phlegm or black bile were cold complaints.

When an imbalance occurred, the body naturally tried to restore a healthy equilibrium. Practitioners aimed to support this healing process through diet, medicines, massage, and bathing. Therapies aimed to counter the effects of disease. Hot diseases, such as fevers, were treated with cooling medicines and foods including green fruits, cucumbers, and seeds. Where the flow of the humors had become blocked or corrupted humors had formed in the body, purging medicines and bloodletting were prescribed to remove them.

Unani Medical Practice

Elite practitioners (*hakims*) diagnosed illness by noting the quality of the pulse (*nabz*), the patient's breathing and general appearance, and the body's excretions, all of which gave clues to the internal workings of the body. As well as understanding the body and disease, successful *hakims* had to have a thorough knowledge of pharmacy, in order to prescribe and make up medicines for their patients. They also needed to possess patience, to be sensitive and caring, and to behave in a correct manner. Students wishing to become elite practitioners went through a formal training. They acquired knowledge of medical theory from texts, and they learned about practice by observing their teachers conducting consultations with patients. Pupils studied with established practitioners, who helped them to understand and memorize key texts that described the workings of the body and the treatment of diseases from those affecting the head to those attacking the feet. At the end of their training, their teachers certified that they had acquired the skill required of a good practitioner. One certificate (*ijazah*) from the mid-19th century declared:

> I taught him many books, lesson by lesson . . . Thereafter he worked on diagnosis of diseases and examination of urine and pulse, under my supervision. I found him intelligent and skillful. He possesses wisdom as is demanded of a physician. (Siddiqui 1980)

However, there were no rules about the qualifications required to set up as a doctor, and it was possible for anyone to simply read some books and begin practice.

There were a range of practitioners within Unani medicine. One traveler recorded that in the city of Hyderabad in India, there were "educated Hakeems [*sic*], following hereditary profession, uneducated quacks, the Hujams or barber caste who form the surgeons of India, herbalists of the shepherd caste, druggists, oculists, lithotomists, fakeers, midwives and leech-women" (Smith 1859). While the *hakims* possessed a thorough knowledge of medical theory, the other groups possessed practical skills, in bloodletting, surgery, or making and selling medicines.

Although Unani medicine had a long history, it adapted to new political and social circumstances. In India, in the early 19th century, Unani medicine was practiced by a small elite, attached to the courts of local rulers, who learned their medicine from books written in Arabic. In the late 19th century, in part as a reaction against colonial rule, Unani went through a revival. Old texts were translated from Persian and Arabic, languages used only by scholars, into Urdu, a language that was much more widely understood. New texts were written that retained the central tenets of Unani knowledge but opened up the study of medicine. They emphasized how, by reading, anyone could learn medicine. They described practical techniques to maintain health and treat simple ailments and brought a new spiritual dimension to medicine. Allah was portrayed as a physician: through his guidance, men could learn how to be healthy. Practitioners fought back against Western criticism of Unani medicine as irrational and unscientific. They pointed out that Western medicine (which they called "doctory") had a shared history with Unani medicine and that Western surgery was based on techniques described in medieval Arabic texts. They attacked Western medicine for failing to understand the fundamental processes within the body and claimed that Western medical treatments countered symptoms rather than treated the underlying causes of illness.

WESTERN MEDICINE

Western or scientific medicine, the predominant form of medicine practiced in Europe and North America, went through a radical transformation in the

19th century. Until the 18th century, practitioners followed humoral medicine. Like Unani medicine, it was derived from ancient Greek ideas and saw health as dependent on a balance of four humors—blood, yellow bile, black bile, and phlegm. In the late 18th century, practitioners began to abandon this system in favor of scientific or Western medicine. This was a major revolution in medical thinking: instead of seeing illness as a consequence of an imbalance of fluids, disease was now understood to be the result of malfunctions in the solid organs and tissues of the body. The new understanding emerged through anatomical research that mapped the structures of the healthy body in ever greater detail and linked symptoms in life to the effects of disease on the organs and tissues. For example, Jean Corvisart, a French practitioner and one of the leading researchers in heart disease, described the case of

> A wheelwright [who] . . . felt, after a violent effort, a sharp pain in the right side of the thorax. Immediately there ensued oppression, cough, and spitting of blood . . . the pulse strong, full, regular and frequent; the strokes of the heart violent, dry and hurried, but regular . . . The patient died three months [later] . . . On dissection . . . the inferior lobes of the lung [were] . . . hard, and gorged with black blood . . . the heart was twice its natural size. (Corvisart 1812, 80)

After 1850, research shifted from the dissection room to the laboratory. Using improved microscopes, practitioners investigated ever smaller anatomical structures, such as the nerves and muscle fibers. Through analysis and experiments, they explored the chemistry of the body and the function of organs.

This new approach to disease led to new techniques of diagnosis. As well as observing outward signs—the color of the skin, the quality of the pulse, and the excretions—to understand what was going on inside the body, practitioners used instruments to see inside the body. In 1816, René Laennec, a French doctor, discovered that by applying one end of a tube of paper to the chest and pressing his ear to the other end, he could hear sounds from the lungs. Laennec's stethoscope (the name comes from the Greek word "*stethos*," meaning "chest," and the French "*scope*," meaning "an instrument for viewing") made it possible for practitioners to visualize the changes caused by lung and heart disease in the living patient. As one contemporary put it, Laennec "placed a window in the breast through which we can see the precise state of things within" (Forbes 1838). By the late 19th century, doctors had an array of new technologies to see into the body. Ophthalmoscopes, invented in 1851, and laryngoscopes, developed in 1855, allowed them to peer into the eye and throat. Most dramatically, X-rays, discovered in 1895, graphically revealed broken bones.

Experimental techniques developed in the laboratory provided further new ways to diagnose illness. Diseased tissues were examined under the microscope to determine whether tumors were benign or malignant. Chemical analyses of blood and urine revealed problems with the kidneys or liver. Samples of body fluids could be cultured in the laboratory to identify disease-causing bacteria. Not all doctors welcomed the new array of diagnostic tests: some felt it was too easy to become reliant on technologies and that practitioners would lose the old skills of diagnosis at the bedside that relied on touch, vision, and experience.

Western Medical Training

The place of anatomy as the key to understanding the body and disease was reflected in the curriculum taught in medical schools and universities. Throughout the century, students learned in groups, through lectures, textbooks, demonstrations, and hands-on dissection. The basic shape of the curriculum remained constant: students first acquired a thorough grounding in anatomy and science before studying medical subjects, although the range of courses shifted and expanded. In the early 19th century, medical students began their studies with courses on anatomy, chemistry, and botany before progressing to the theory and practice of medicine and materia medica (the study of drugs). At the end of the century, students were taught anatomy, chemistry, and biology and then moved on to medical sciences such as physiology, biochemistry, and histology (the study of cells). In addition, students received clinical training in hospitals. They "walked the wards," observing patients, and the treatments carried out by hospital staff, and listening to short lectures on particular cases. Toward the end of their studies, students worked as junior staff, honing their skills in diagnosis and learning how to prescribe medicines and to apply treatments.

At the end of their training, students had to pass a rigorous set of examinations to prove their competence. In many countries, this was a requirement for them to be allowed to practice as a qualified practitioner. Most medical students went on to some form of general practice, treating the ailments of the general population. A small number specialized in a particular area of medicine, such as surgery or pediatrics. Doctors worked alongside nurses and pharmacists, who had their own forms of training, and competed for patients with unqualified quack doctors, who had no formal education and sold medicines and treatments.

Unorthodox Medicine

Not everyone welcomed the new, scientific approach to the study of health and disease. Many patients and practitioners turned to a range of new, more "natural" systems of medical practice. Homeopathy, devised by Samuel Hahnemann, a German practitioner, in the 1800s, used very small doses of drugs to produce symptoms similar to the complaint that the practitioner wanted to cure—the principle that "like cures like." Herbalism was a system of treatment based on the principle that all disorders were caused by obstructed perspiration and were cured by medicines to cause vomiting, purging, or sweating. Others argued that only water offered a truly "natural" source of healing. From 1829, Vincenz Priessnitz, an Austrian farmer, popularized hydropathy, or the "water cure." Patients drank copious amounts of water, were wrapped in wet sheets, and given cold baths and showers to balance the heat and cold within the body and to encourage natural healing processes. Hydropathy proved popular among the European upper classes: Charles Darwin went through several "water cures" to try to relieve his chronic stomach complaints. Knowledge of these systems of unorthodox medicine was spread through books, one-on-one training, and unorthodox medical schools.

Homeopathic medical schools taught the usual medical curriculum and the use of homeopathic rather than orthodox therapies.

FOLK MEDICINE

Systems of medical knowledge allowed practitioners to deal with any form of illness. From the visible symptoms, they worked out what was going wrong inside the body and therefore what type of treatment would restore the body's healthy function. Folk medicine was based on repertoires of particular treatments for specific ailments. In a few cultures, there were elements of a theory of body function; in southern African medical cultures, many types of swellings were attributed to an accumulation of blood, while excess bile was believed to cause stomach complaints, but in most cultures, there was no overarching theory that explained the causes and cure of illness. Many forms of folk medicine were very ancient; in parts of Central America, there were elements of Aztec medicine in 19th-century practice. But folk medicine, like medical systems, changed in response to social and cultural developments. In Mexico, native practitioners incorporated plants and animals introduced by the Spanish into their medicines, as well as the idea of a hot/cold balance from humoral medical theory. In Kazakhstan, in the Russian steppes, native people used a mix of shamanistic medicine and Islamic medicine.

Folk medicine provided treatments for many conditions—herbal medicines for internal complaints, bonesetting for injuries, drugs and massage to help in childbirth, and rituals and medicines to counter diseases sent by supernatural forces. Often, different practitioners dealt with different types of therapy. In Bantu-speaking West Africa, for example, there were *nganga mbuki* (herbalists), *nganga nkisi* (magicians or spiritual healers), *nganga ngombo* (diviners, who diagnosed disease), *nganga kilauki* (practitioners who dealt with skin complaints), and *nganga mpansu* (who treated mental illness). In Kazakhstan, shamans or *baksy* performed rituals to cast out spiritual disease, while other healers used herbal medicines, mare's milk, and saltwater baths to treat physical ailments.

The most common form of folk medicine used plant-based remedies to treat ailments. Some herbalists possessed a huge body of knowledge: in southern Africa, over 3,000 different plants were used in medicine. Herbal medicines could be drunk in the form of teas, inhaled as powders, used to bathe the skin and to cleanse wounds, or added to the water in a steam bath. For example, plains Indians in America drank yarrow tea as a tonic, took preparations containing the bark of the poplar tree as a laxative, applied poultices of poplar leaves to infected wounds, and chewed seneca root to relieve toothache. Most healers used indigenous plants gathered in the immediate area or grown in a garden, but some traded medicines over long distances. In the Andes in Bolivia, herbalists gathered medicinal plants indigenous to their area and traveled from Argentina to Peru, to practice and to trade their medicines with people living at different altitudes. Earths, minerals, and animal products, such as the fat of snakes, also had medicinal uses.

Spiritual healers dealt with illness caused by supernatural factors: by witchcraft, gods, ghosts, or the spirits of ancestors. In order to treat these patients, the healer had to diagnose the problem, and work out why it had happened, in order to affect a cure. Disease caused by sorcery might be prompted by a social dispute between individuals or families that had to be resolved before the patient could recover. Ancestor spirits might send illness if they felt neglected, and the disease would be cured by making offerings. Spiritual healers had a complex role: they were not just healers but have been described as friends, pastors, and psychiatrists as well as doctors. Many worked to protect the health of the whole community as well as individuals, protecting chiefs from harm or calling up rain in times of drought.

Wooden *agere-Ifa* (divination bowls) were used by the Yoruba people of Nigeria to hold palm nuts used in ceremonies to determine the cause of misfortunes, including illness. (Werner Forman/Universal Images Group/Getty Images)

Supernatural disease was diagnosed through communication with the spirit world. Healers might enter a trance state or use various forms of divination. In Kenya and Tanzania, practitioners diagnosed illness by throwing shells or other objects from a special divination gourd or basket called an *enkidong.* The final position of each object was controlled by the spirit world and indicated the cause of disease. Among the Xhosa people of southern Africa, disease could be a sign that the spirits were trying to communicate with the living. Sufferers and their families went to an *igqirha* or diviner, who contacted the spirits and found ways to pacify them. If witchcraft was suspected, an *igqirha elinukayo* found out who had cast the spell and removed the material used to cause the illness by sucking it out of the patient's body. In other cultures, supernatural complaints were treated by rituals that often included drumming and dancing.

Skills in these forms of medicine were acquired in different ways. Herbalists, bonesetters, and midwives trained with experienced practitioners. Knowledge was passed down through families or from healer to pupil. In Africa, aspiring healers traveled long distances to train with skilled practitioners and brought back new treatments to their own communities. Spiritual healers learned how to conduct rituals and interpret divination objects from experienced practitioners. In some cultures, they acquired powers through visions or dreams. Among Plains Indians in North America, healers acquired a spirit helper who helped them to diagnose illness and to perform curing rituals through a dream or vision. The knowledge of how to use plants for healing was also passed from the spirit world through dreams. Among Xhosa healers in southern Africa, the end of the training period was marked by rituals and celebrations, during which the spirits would give some sign that they accepted the new healer.

THE COEXISTENCE OF MEDICAL SYSTEMS

Throughout the 19th-century world, practitioners using different forms of medicine worked alongside each other. Patients were happy to turn to different forms of medicine in search of a cure. In Europe, patients tried folk remedies, and if this approach did not cure the problem, they sought help from a practitioner of Western or unorthodox medicine. Similarly in Africa, a sick person might visit a herbalist and then a spiritual healer. In the 19th century, the range of medical treatments on offer expanded in many countries, as Western medicine spread to Africa and Asia, where it was practiced alongside Chinese, Unani, Ayurvedic, and folk medicine.

In the early part of the century, practitioners of Western medicine found some common ground with other systems of medical ideas. Western and Unani practitioners agreed that miasma—bad air—was the cause of epidemics. One Egyptian practitioner, trained in both Unani and Western medicine, saw a common foundation in the two systems:

> Medicine is twofold, traditional (qadam) and modern (jaded). Traditional medicine consists of Greek medicine, and modern medicine comprises Greek medicine plus anatomy, pathology and some branches of mathematics, natural sciences and pharmacology, geology, physiology, botany etc. (Ruznameh-ye 'elmi 1887)

Non-Western treatments were adopted by Western practitioners. European-trained doctors working in India acknowledged that Ayurvedic practitioners possessed valuable knowledge of medicines used to cure unfamiliar local diseases. Chinese acupuncture enjoyed a brief vogue in both Europe and America, where it was used for pain relief, although practitioners were unsure how it worked.

Patients in many parts of the world called in Western doctors when their own healers failed to cure their ailments. Western surgery was particularly valued as European, and American practitioners carried out a greater variety of more complex operations than their non-Western counterparts. In India and Egypt, traditional Unani techniques for treating cataracts in the eye were replaced by techniques drawn from Western surgery. Some Chinese practitioners argued that Western understandings of public health were better than those of their own medicine, but their traditional medicine was better at curing most internal diseases.

Medicine on the Pacific island of Samoa shows how care could be divided between Western and indigenous medicine. At the beginning of the 19th century, the Samoans believed that disease was caused by the gods who had been offended in some way. They treated illness with prayers and rituals and a limited number of herbal medicines. These treatments failed to cure Western diseases such as influenza, whooping cough, mumps, and measles that were brought to the island by missionaries in the 1830s. As a result, the Samoan people redefined their medicine and split disease into two categories. Samoan illnesses (*ma'i samoa*) had existed before contact with the missionaries and were treated by indigenous healers (*foma'i* and *fogau*) using medicinal plants. The diseases introduced by missionaries were defined as *ma'ipapalagi* and were treated with European medicines.

CONFLICTS BETWEEN MEDICAL SYSTEMS

By the second half of the century, as Western understandings of the body and of disease completed their move away from humoral to scientific medicine, European and American practitioners became increasingly skeptical that non-Western medicine had any value. Western practitioners associated their medicine with reason, science, and progress, while Chinese, Ayurvedic, and Unani medicine were seen as irrational, superstitious, and unable to progress because of practitioners' reverence for ancient texts. One European doctor working in mid-19th-century China described the "absurd notions of attributing diseases to wind, breath, water or sweat" and found local medical practices both laughable and dangerous (Rogaski 2004: 94). There was a two-way traffic in criticisms of medical systems. Chinese practitioners generally dismissed Western medicine, complaining that the recently discovered bacteria were no different from the long-established understanding of pestilential qi.

The spiritual aspects of non-Western medicine came in for particularly harsh criticism from Western practitioners. African beliefs about the supernatural causes of illness were dismissed as "superstition" and indigenous practitioners seen as no better than quacks, duping their patients with useless or even dangerous medicines. Some African colonial governments tried to outlaw native medicine, punishing "witchdoctors" and banning sales of herbal medicines. Similarly, in Latin America, Western practitioners tried to get local practitioners (*curanderos*) banned from practicing, although with little success. Although many Western practitioners assumed that indigenous forms of medicine would die out and be replaced by scientific medicine, non-Western medicine not only survived but thrived. Patients welcomed the option of consulting practitioners using different systems of medicine, and they were happy to consult the type of healer they felt best able to deal with their illness.

3

Religion and Medicine

Around the globe, different cultures had different understandings of the relationship between the physical and the spiritual world that fundamentally shaped ideas about health and medicine. Some people saw ill health as the result of purely physical processes—some malfunction within the body's chemistry or damage to its structures. Others understood ill health to be caused by supernatural forces that punished individuals for breaking some religious rule, by spirits or gods associated with a particular disease or by the ghosts of ancestors who were unhappy about the behavior of the living.

In the 19th century, all cultures recognized that disease had both physical and supernatural causes. In Africa, Asia, and Australia, native peoples understood the world to be full of spirits, and diseases and injuries were often, although not exclusively, caused by supernatural forces. In Christian Europe and the Americas, most disease was understood to arise from purely physical causes and was treated by drugs and surgery; however, for some religious groups, ill health was sent by God and prayers could result in miraculous healing.

CHRISTIANITY AND HEALING

In the 19th-century Christian West, medicine and spirituality were, in theory, clearly separated: disease and injury occurred in the physical body, and the immaterial soul had no influence on health. The physical body was cared for by doctors and nurses, while priests cared for the soul. In practice, however, the separation between religion and medicine was by no means so clear cut. Different sects and denominations within the Christian faith had different understandings of the role of God in causing disease and of faith as a means of cure. Many doctors and nurses had a deep faith and found a model for their lives in Christ the physician.

Healing and the Catholic Church

In Catholic teaching, the body was a temple for the Holy Spirit: health was a gift from God, and therefore everyone had a responsibility to care for his or her body. Pain was sent from God, possibly as a punishment and had to be accepted. If bravely borne, suffering could cleanse the soul and be a sign of grace. Injuries and illness could be cured by medical treatment or through divine intervention. Miraculous healing occurred through prayer to the Virgin Mary and to saints. Particular saints were able to intercede for specific conditions, often related to the forms of their martyrdom. People suffering from eye diseases prayed to St. Lucy, who had been blinded; those with toothache appealed to St. Apollonia, who had been tortured by having her teeth pulled out. Churches throughout Europe and the Americas displayed proof of the power of prayer in the display of ex-votos—objects left in thanksgiving for recovery from illness, injury, or danger. Votive objects took the form of a small model of the body part that had been healed—a hand, or leg, or eye—or a picture showing the patient at the moment of healing.

In the 19th century, many sick and injured people made pilgrimages to healing shrines in search of cures. One of the most important healing sites, at Lourdes in southwest France, was established in 1858 after a local girl, Bernadette Soubires, experienced a series of visions of the Virgin Mary. By the end of the century, hundreds of thousands of pilgrims visited the shrine every year. Lourdes was not the only new pilgrimage center set up at this time. The small town of Knock in Ireland also became a site of pilgrimage after a vision of the Virgin Mary, St. Joseph, and St. John the Evangelist appeared in 1879.

Protestant Healing

The Protestant churches saw rather different relationships between faith and healing. A few branches accepted that direct divine intervention could cause or cure illness. Disease was sign of sin and a gift of grace to improve spiritual life. For example, Charles Haddon Spurgeon, a prominent English Baptist preacher, declared the following:

> I venture to say that the greatest earthly blessing that God can give to any of us is health, *with the exception of sickness* [emphasis in original]. Sickness has frequently been of more use to the saints of God than health has . . . A sick wife, a newly made grave, poverty, slander, sinking of spirit, might teach us lessons nowhere else to be learned so well. Trials drive us to the realities of religion. (Spurgeon 1973)

Most Protestants rejected the idea that God sent disease directly, but rather they believed that he had devised rules for healthy living, and that breaking those rules would lead to illness. A simple diet, exercise in the fresh air, a regular pattern of work and rest, and cleanliness would ensure health. ("Cleanliness is next to Godliness" was a popular proverb in the 19th century.) Disobeying these rules by eating to excess (especially meat), drinking alcohol, smoking, and staying up late exposed the body to infections and illness: sin thus led directly to disease. Ill health was cured by returning to a healthy and righteous lifestyle. Prayer did not cure illness but aided the healing process by strengthening the mind and spirit and giving courage.

While most Protestants called in doctors in times of illness, members of some sects opposed some or all aspects of orthodox medicine. Vaccination against smallpox caused widespread concern. Parents feared that a procedure that prevented attacks of smallpox interfered with God's right to inflict disease. Members of the Mormon, Methodist, and Seventh-day Adventist churches favored unorthodox medicine such as homeopathy and herbalism, with their simple remedies and rejection of modern excesses. The Christian Science movement rejected all forms of medicine. Followers believed that illness and pain were not real but were produced by fear, ignorance, or sin and were cured by getting rid of these false beliefs through prayer.

Faith in the Time of Cholera

Religious faith came to the fore during the fear and panic spread by epidemics. When cholera swept Europe and the United States in the middle of the century, the new disease was widely interpreted as a punishment sent from God. While it was generally accepted that the disease was transmitted through the atmosphere (or, later, in the water supply), it was also believed that those who followed an immoral or irregular lifestyle were particularly susceptible. The disease therefore struck drunkards and prostitutes, and there was almost a sense that it cleansed society of its unproductive, criminal members. A pamphlet published in Oxford, England, on the 1854 epidemic reported

> A woman woke in the agony of cramps with intense and sudden collapse . . . in the hospital she died. Her room was cleaned out: the woman that cleaned it had next night the cholera. She and her husband were drunk in bed. The agony sobered *her*, but her husband went reeling about the room: in a room below were smokers and drinkers. Then a woman of the streets [a prostitute] in her gaudiness came to see her. They would not hear reason but drank more spirits. The victim of the disease cried out to the end that her soul was everlastingly lost; and she died. (Acland 1856)

When respectable citizens fell victim to the disease, it was assumed that they must have sinned in some unknown way. Not surprisingly, respectable families often tried to hide cases of cholera that occurred in their households.

Faced with such danger, people turned to religion for help. Clergymen of all denominations visited the sick despite the risk of infection, dispensing prayers and practical advice on a healthy diet and lifestyle. Protestant churches held extra services to pray for the victims of cholera, issued special prayers, and organized fast days, when the faithful were asked to reflect on their sins. In Catholic communities, people flocked to churches to pray for protection against the disease and for help for those who were infected. Religious images were carried in processions between shrines. St. Gennaro, a fourth-century saint, was credited with bringing to an end a devastating cholera outbreak that struck Naples in southern Italy in 1884.

Christianity and Medical Care

Christian churches of all denominations played an important role in providing medical care to the poor in the 19th century. Even though governments began to take responsibility for the welfare of populations at this time, the number of faith-based charities increased and the scope of their work expanded.

At their simplest, churches provided care through their clergy. In rural areas, where there were few doctors, priests and clergymen provided advice to the sick poor and distributed medicines. They also organized care within their parish, encouraging members of their congregations to donate food and fuel to the sick. Members of Catholic and Protestant orders provided care to the poor on a larger scale in hospitals or though home visits. The 19th century saw the founding of new Catholic orders of monks and nuns, many of them dedicated to caring, such as the Sisters of Mercy, set up in Ireland in 1831, and the Little Sisters of the Poor, established in France in 1834. Protestant sisterhoods, similar to their Catholic counterparts, were also founded from the 1830s, including the Nursing Sisters of St. John the Divine and the All Saints Sisters of the Poor in London. Alongside these orders, voluntary groups such as the Society of St. Vincent de Paul, established in Paris in 1833, carried out similar work among the poor.

The services of nursing sisters were in high demand, reflecting the good standard of care they offered. In the early 19th century, nursing was a rather haphazard, often poor-quality service provided by working women with little medical knowledge or by convalescent hospital patients. By contrast, the nursing sisters had a strong commitment to their work: they saw nursing not as a job but as a vocation and a way of expressing their faith. They were also well trained: the

Members of religious orders were an important source of medical care, especially to the poor. While many nuns nursed in hospitals, they also treated patients suffering from minor illnesses, such as eye infections, in clinics or dispensaries. (National Library of Medicine)

religious orders established new forms of nurse education. Trainees (often called probationers) observed the work of experienced nurses and learned to carry out nursing tasks under their supervision. These forms of training were taken up by secular nursing organizations, helping to transform nursing into a profession by the end of the 19th century, with a distinct body of skills, recognized qualifications, and a hierarchical organization. Nursing orders provided staff for some of the most prestigious hospitals, including King's College and University College Hospitals in London and St. Mary's Hospital (the forerunner of the Mayo Clinic) in Rochester, Minnesota. Catholic and Protestant nursing sisters even served on the battlefield, tending to sick and wounded soldiers during the Crimean and Franco-Prussian wars.

Religious organizations also played an important role in organizing and delivering hospital care. For hundreds of years, churches had encouraged members to offer help to those unable to support themselves—the old, the poor, the sick, and the mentally ill. In the 19th century, this duty was increasingly fulfilled by donating money to hospitals and dispensaries. During this period, large numbers of hospitals were founded and run by religious institutions, both Catholic and Protestant, especially in North America. Members of religious orders provided nursing care and were responsible for all aspects of the administration of the institution, from patient admissions, to purchasing supplies, to raising funds. These institutions served the local population or particular social groups. For example, in North America, Lutheran hospitals served German-speaking immigrants from Europe. Religion played an important role in hospital life. In Catholic institutions, beds were arranged so that patients could see altars and observe mass. Prayers were said and hymns sung in the wards. Chaplains or priests would talk to patients and give religious instruction; they would also administer the sacraments to the dying and baptize weak infants.

Medical Missionaries

Religion and medicine came together in the work of medical missionaries. The Catholic Church had sent out missionaries to the Americas since the 16th century, many of whom undertook some form of medical work. Protestant missionaries with some medical training had occasionally been sent from Europe to convert indigenous people to Christianity in the 18th century. In the 19th century, however, there was a new emphasis on medicine within mission work. Many more trained missionaries were sent out, especially to Africa and Asia, where they established hospitals and dispensaries.

Peter Parker, the first qualified medical missionary, began work in Canton in 1835. His Ophthalmic Hospital offered minor surgery, such as cataract operations and the removal of small tumors, and proved popular, treating almost 2,000 patients in its first year. From the 1860s, medical missionaries were sent out by both Protestant and Catholic churches to offer advanced forms of Western medical treatment. Mission hospitals grew from small affairs often staffed by a single doctor, to become large institutions with state-of-the-art equipment such as X-ray machines. Nevertheless, the numbers of medical missionaries were always small.

In the 1870s, Protestant churches (who were the largest operators) sent out only 20 qualified missionaries to India and a further 15 to China. Missionaries with little or no medical training also provided free drugs and advice to local people as a means of attracting listeners and as a humanitarian gesture. As one missionary later put it, "every missionary became a quack doctor! He could not help himself. You cannot say 'poor fellow' and pass on, when you know that a dose of salts or a grain or two of quinine a day might bring back health" (Sackett n.d.).

Medical missions were seen as a means of spreading the religious message in areas where it had proved difficult to convert local people. Missionaries held short religious services in the waiting area for potential patients and their relatives. During and after treatment, they would also talk and pray with patients. In India, where efforts to convert the male population met with limited success, female medical missionaries were employed to go into the *zenana* (the women's quarters) and treat women and children. By the end of the century, roughly half of all missionary doctors working in India were women.

Western medicine, particularly surgery, was popular among indigenous people, who recognized that it was more effective than their own medicine in dealing with some conditions. However, few abandoned their use of indigenous medicine but chose the type of medicine that was best able to help them. In China, patients went to a mission hospital as a last resort when Chinese medicine had failed, especially in cases requiring surgical treatment or difficult births. Patients were equally reluctant to abandon their religion and convert to Christianity. In 1874, one missionary society reported it had made just 12 converts from over 400,000 patients. Large numbers of converts were not made until the end of the century.

CONFLICTS BETWEEN RELIGION AND MEDICINE

Missionaries were often hostile to indigenous medicine. Those in Africa interpreted indigenous medicine as a form of religion: they called local healers "witch-doctors" and described their rituals as "pagan" or satanic. Equally, native peoples interpreted the actions of missionaries in their own terms. Missionaries in China complained that local people believed that they had magical powers and were able to ward off evil spirits and to deal with cases of "fox possession" in which the body of the patient was invaded by a spirit. The practice of baptizing very sick children led to a belief that the baptism caused their death. In Tianjin, China, in 1870, a group of Catholic nuns who ran an orphanage were massacred, following rumors that they were kidnapping children and using their body parts to make medicines.

There were also conflicts between medicine and religion in the West. In the Catholic Church, elaborate funerals, with the body on display in an open coffin, served to demonstrate piety, and burial inside the church and close to an altar was sought after as a means of helping to release the soul of the deceased from purgatory. By the mid-19th century, medical practitioners condemned both practices as unsanitary and likely to spread disease. They advocated short and simple funeral rites followed by burial in a cemetery well away from populated areas.

There was also conflict over the relationship between intense religious experiences and mental illness. In North America, doctors debated whether religious experiences could be a form of mental illness or could induce mental disturbance in susceptible individuals. The early 19th century saw a wave of evangelical revivals, where preachers called on congregations to confess their sins and dedicate themselves to God in readiness for the Second Coming of Christ. Such events were often highly emotional, with people wailing, singing, and dancing for hours or even days. For a few people, the heightened emotional states at these meetings were followed by bouts of mental illness, and they were confined in asylums suffering from "religious insanity." Doctors attributed their condition to nervous over-stimulation combined with an underlying mental weakness. In hindsight, the prevalence of religious insanity in the 1840s in North America was produced by a combination of the popularity of religious revivals and the building of large asylums where, for the first time, doctors saw much greater numbers of patients suffering from mental illness.

ISLAMIC RELIGIOUS MEDICINE

Religion played a central place in medicine in the Islamic world, particularly in the later 19th century. Allah was the supreme healer; he had created disease but also placed the means of curing illness in the world and given people understanding so they could seek out cures. Therefore when sick, Muslims sought the help of physicians with specialist knowledge of the body and disease. Illness could also be cured by spiritual means, through prayers and miracles. The Qur'an offered advice on how to stay healthy, especially through observing good hygiene. These parts of the text, and the sayings of the prophet Muhammad, his family, and his followers, were gradually expanded into a body of medical ideas known as prophetic medicine. It recommended simple remedies, such as honey or cumin seeds for treating internal complaints, or the use of scarification—a method of removing small amounts of blood from the body through scratches made on the skin. The Qur'an itself was believed to have healing powers—the sick benefited from hearing, reading, or reciting the text. Religious remedies were used alongside physical therapies: a 19th-century text on cholera, for example, contained sections on medicines and on prayers for the prevention and cure of the disease.

As well as illness arising from physical causes, the Qur'an also attributed ill health to the work of evil spirits, or jinn. Jinn were usually invisible (although they could assume the shape of animals) but bad smells were a sign of their presence. If offended in some way, they took revenge by causing illness, and large numbers of jinn could work together to produce epidemics. The actions of jinn were prevented by the use of amulets consisting of holy texts written on pieces of paper and attached to clothing. Particular substances including silver, gunpowder, and pungent herbs could also ward off jinn.

BUDDHISM AND MEDICINE

In Buddhist thinking, illness and suffering were facts of life. They were caused by physical factors such as diet, lifestyle, and climate, but also by spirits; or they were sent as a form of punishment for bad actions or patterns of thought. Buddhist practices, including meditation, helped to ensure good physical and spiritual health. For illnesses with a physical cause, followers sought medical advice usually from a practitioner of Ayurvedic medicine. For diseases linked to the patient's spiritual condition, they had to meditate and pray to deities associated with healing. Maladies associated with evil spirits were prevented by wearing amulets: spells or Buddhist religious texts were written on slips of paper and attached to clothing, or they were burned and the ashes mixed with water and given to the patient to drink. Some Buddhist teachers and monks possessed special healing powers that were a sign of their purity and faith, and they treated illness with a combination of medicines, meditation, and exorcism.

MEDICINE AND TAOISM

Supernatural forces also played an important role in health and medicine in Chinese religions, including Taoism (or Daoism), a religious and philosophical movement popular in the 19th century. Illness was caused by physical factors such as poor diet, climate, or an inappropriate lifestyle and treated using medicines. Diseases were also caused by spirits or ghosts, especially the spirits of ancestors who felt neglected when families failed to venerate their memory. They possessed the bodies of the living, resulting in mental or physical illness or even death.

Divination was used to diagnose these diseases and to direct treatment: spirits were persuaded to write on a board covered in sand, or a divining stick was passed over a patient and used to produce a charm or prescription. Charms, often in the form of spells or religious texts written on slips of paper, were used to cure or to ward off supernatural disease. Spirits were also chased away by loud noises or were persuaded to depart by offerings of food, incense and prayer. One such ceremony was reported by a Westerner in 1847. At his neighbors' house, the family

> commence[d] beating drums and gongs, and set out a feast, in the superstitious belief that some deceased member of the family is starving in the world below, and that, in revenge of their neglect, his spirit has come to feed on the body of the sick person. Hence they seek, by the bribe of a feast, and the intimidation of sounds, to expel [the spirit]. (Smith 1847)

Particular gods were linked to sickness and healing. For example, *T'ou-Shen Niang-Niang* was a goddess of smallpox in China and was widely worshipped in temples and at home shrines to prevent or cure the disease. (Smallpox was also attributed to supernatural forces in Japan. A demon was believed to cause the disease, and pictures of *Tametomo*, a 12th-century hero who was believed to have driven away the smallpox demon, were hung in the rooms of victims to help in their recovery.) The sick also prayed to healing gods, such as the Medicine King or the Empress of Heaven, to ask for relief or protection from disease. The Empress of Heaven and her associated deities were believed to be particularly effective in preventing illness among children and women. During epidemics, whole communities joined in seeking divine help. Auspicious days were chosen for prayers to halt the disease, images of gods were carried through the streets, and fireworks were set off to help drive away the illness.

HINDUISM AND MEDICINE

Particular gods were also associated with healing and with particular diseases in the Hindu religion. These included *Jvarasura*, the fever demon, *Ghentukarna*, the god of skin diseases, and *Sitala*, the goddess of smallpox. *Sitala* was an important goddess, with many temples and shrines dedicated to her. It was believed that smallpox patients were possessed by the fiery goddess, whose presence was associated with high fevers. The disease was treated by rituals and offerings. Ritual and physical treatment overlapped—images of the goddess were washed and fanned while patients also received cooling food and drinks and were bathed in cold water.

Rituals around smallpox had a long history, but when cholera became an important cause of death in India in the early 19th century, new deities emerged in response to the threat. The goddess *Ola Candi* or *Ola Bibi* may have been associated with dysentery, but in the 19th century, she emerged as the goddess of cholera. In other areas, cholera was associated with new deities known as *kala mari* (black death). Representations of the deity were paraded and sacrifices made to try to please her and thus prevent outbreaks of cholera. During epidemics, objects or animals dedicated to the goddess were driven out of the village in the hope that doing so would also drive away the disease. In a number of areas, young women appeared, claiming to be possessed by a spirit associated with the disease. In 1818, a woman appeared:

> Her whole body and her scanty apparel were daubed and clotted with the dingy red and ochry yellow powders of the Hindoo burial ceremonies . . . in one hand she held a drawn sword, in the other an earthen vessel containing fire (the one probably a symbol of destruction, the other of the funeral pyre) . . . her phrenzy [sic] seemed beyond human control; and as she bounded along, she denounced certain destruction to all those who did not immediately acknowledge her divinity. (Kennedy 1846)

The panic caused by cholera prompted inhabitants to reach out to more than one religion in search of some power to control the terrible disease. When cholera struck a village in Konkan, in western India, the people initially asked the Catholic priest for help. When he proved ineffectual, a Hindu ceremony was performed.

SPIRITUAL MEDICINE IN AFRICA, THE AMERICAS, AND THE PACIFIC

In many cultures in Africa, South and Central America, and throughout the Pacific Ocean, the supernatural played an important role in everyday life. Gods, spirits, and ghosts were believed to influence many aspects of life—the weather, the success of crops, and the health and well-being of individual people and of groups. Every culture had a different understanding of the identity of spirits involved in health and disease, but there were some broad similarities. Many cultures recognized that disease was sent by gods or by spirits of ancestors and animals, or it was caused by magic. Native American peoples also attributed disease to soul loss and to unfulfilled desires. Certain complaints were associated with supernatural causes. In southern Africa, fevers, coughs, and diarrhea had natural causes, while spirits or ghosts were responsible for causing chronic ailments that failed to respond to herbal medicines, diseases that came on very suddenly, or illnesses that caused unconsciousness.

Different cultures had their own types of spiritual healers. Among many peoples, there were diviners, who used spiritual means to diagnose the causes of illness, exorcists and shamans or "witchdoctors," who communicated and negotiated with the spirits that caused disease in order to effect a cure. Among Native American tribes, medicine men both diagnosed the spirit responsible for illness and performed rituals to cure the complaint. In some cultures, natural therapy overlapped with supernatural medicine. In New Zealand, *tohunga* healers used a mix of herbal medicines and rituals, as did the *curanderos* of Latin America. Among some indigenous American peoples, medicine men drove away disease by giving the patient bitter medicines that the spirits found unpleasant.

Healers were powerful people, often set apart in some way from the rest of their community. In some cultures, healers were "chosen" by the gods: the !Kung people of the Kalahari Desert believed that the god *Hishe* bestowed healing powers, and healers were visited by the god in dreams or visions. In *ngoma* medicine, practiced in southern Africa, people were called to become healers by illness sent by ancestral spirits. Being cured of this initial illness was the first step in becoming a healer.

Many types of healers also trained with an established practitioner, who might be a family member. Training could last for several years and involved learning about the preparation and use of drugs, the performance of rituals, and communication with the spirit world. Often training involved a purification process and required the trainee to follow special rules of diet and lifestyle. In Ghana, the first stage of training for Akan healers involved washing with infusions of herbs to strengthen their bodies and increase their spiritual powers; washing the eyes allowed them to "see" the unseen. The training process of *ngoma* healers included ritual song and dance, drumming, making medicines, and sacrifices that established a bond between healer and the ancestral spirits. Finally, the new healer's status was established by an initiation ceremony.

Diviners diagnosed illness by spiritual means. In some cultures, the diviner would enter a trance in which he or she communicated with spirits. American medicine men would contact the spirit world to discover what spirit had caused the illness—each one responded to different remedies. In many African cultures, diagnosis was performed through various forms of divination. Among Zulu-speaking people of southern Africa, people seeking help were asked to beat on the ground with sticks and to respond to a series of questions posed by the diviner. The sounds made by the sticks helped the healer to determine the cause of the disease. In other areas, healers gained information from the position of objects thrown onto the ground. The final position of each object was controlled by the gods or spirits. *Ngoma* healers diagnosed using a selection of bones or shells, each of which had a particular significance, indicating something about the cause of illness.

Treatment took many forms, depending on the problem. Rituals were used to contact the spirits and ask for a cure. Drumming, shouting and singing drove out spirits or called back lost souls. Many rituals involved "casting out" the disease from the patient. While in a trance, a !Kung healer placed his hands on the patient, drawing out the disease and throwing it away. Illness caused by the spirits of deceased relatives or ancestors was cured by the performance of rituals or the sacrifice of animals to appease their anger.

Spiritual healers diagnosed and cured disease caused by gods, demons, or ghosts. This Dakota shaman is shown communicating with the spirit world by chanting and shaking a ceremonial rattle. (National Library of Medicine)

MAGIC AND MEDICINE

Disease could also be caused by humans using supernatural forces. In Hawaii and Polynesia, sorcerers were capable of *pule 'ana'ana* (praying to death) by sending evil spirits into a victim's body. In other cultures, sorcerers would "shoot" arrows or objects into the bodies of victims, causing pain and illness. In southern Africa, witches (*umthakathis*) caused illness and death by spreading "poison" on paths used by the victim or by using objects belonging to the victim as the base for a spell. Such cases required the intervention of a healer able to discover the source of the problem and undo the magic by rituals or countermagic. For example, foreign objects magically implanted into a person were removed through incisions or sucking.

Slaves transported from Africa to North America and the Caribbean took with them their beliefs in supernatural disease causation and traditional forms of healing. In Haiti, "conjure" or hoodoo was used by sorcerers to cause illness. Wasting diseases such as chronic exhaustion or loss of weight were thought to come from witches eating the soul or inhabiting the body. Disease-causing charms were made from substances with special powers such as earth from graveyards or the hair or nail clippings from the intended victim. When buried or hidden close to the target's home and activated by the spirits, they caused illness or even death. Conjurers diagnosed spirit illness by divination.

They might ask the victim to hold a silver coin: if it turned black, then this was a sign that the problem had been caused through magic. They would then hunt for the charm that had caused the illness, analyze it, and compose a counter-charm.

WESTERN VIEWS OF SPIRITUAL MEDICINE

In 19th-century Barbados, slaves and the descendants of slaves used "obeah" medicine, based on African traditions. Obeah healers prepared herbal remedies using local plants and provided supernatural cures. In the early 19th century, the plantation owners saw obeah as a threat to the health of slaves, and practitioners were punished. By the end of the century, it was dismissed as a form of quackery, practiced on gullible patients. One Western observer mockingly described it as follows:

> He [the obeah practitioner] charges a large sum, administers a large dose of powerful medicine extracted from the medicinal plants so numerous in the interior of this colony; throws the patient into a deep sleep, and then by an act of jugglery produces to the astonished and frightened relatives, a quantity of old rusty nails, glass, splinters, a dead frog or snake, and tells them that that has been the cause of the illness. (Overseers Manual 1896, 73)

As with other medical theories, ideas about supernatural or spiritual healing were not fixed; they changed in response to new circumstances. For example, in the Caribbean, conjure became mixed with evangelical Christianity. The ability to conjure was reinterpreted as a gift from God, and prayer was believed to cure illness. The similarities between evangelical religion and African rituals—the physical expression of belief through dancing and singing, and a sense of being possessed by the Christian Holy Spirit or ancestral spirits—helped in this process.

In Africa, colonial rulers attempted to control the work of spiritual healers, who presented a political problem. Healers were powerful people who had a strong influence over their communities, and they led uprisings in the Cape Colony in South Africa. But administrators faced a difficult situation. They could not acknowledge that witches caused harm by supernatural means, but they intervened when witches were condemned to death by local chiefs. They also sought to punish individuals who had murdered others by poison. In a number of colonies, colonial governments tried to ban all native healing by prosecuting and punishing healers. This simply drove the practices underground, and the rules were later relaxed.

4

Women's Health

In the 19th century, women's health was dominated by reproduction. Most women gave birth at some time in their lives, and many had numerous pregnancies. This was probably the most dangerous event in women's lives; they ran the risk of becoming ill or even dying from complications during pregnancy. Labor was even more dangerous, and a proportion of women died during or shortly after delivery. It was not surprising, then, that the discussion of women's health in medical texts around the world was dominated by issues surrounding reproduction—the menstrual cycle, pregnancy, and childbirth.

But women were not only patients; they were the most numerous providers of medical care. Women in every culture cared for sick family members; large numbers worked as healers and midwives, and during the 19th century, growing numbers entered the medical profession as nurses and doctors, which sometimes brought them into conflict with male practitioners.

WOMEN'S BODIES

In Western medicine, male and female bodies were seen to be fundamentally the same. With the exception of the reproductive system, all the organs of the body functioned in the same way. In some non-Western medical systems, the sexes were understood to be slightly different. In Unani medicine, all women were believed to have a natural imbalance in their humors that made their constitution colder and wetter than men. As a result, they were weaker, prone to cold diseases, became ill more quickly, and could not tolerate strong medicines. In Chinese medicine, women were dominated by yin—the quality associated with growth—while men had yang constitutions. Some Chinese doctors saw women as naturally sickly and prone to poor health.

Social or cultural expectations influenced women's health in many ways. Many cultures had an ideal female form that was attractive to men. Conforming to this ideal helped to ensure that girls made good marriages. In North Africa, for example, a thin figure was not seen as desirable. Slim women sought help from healers

Footbinding was widely practiced by the elite in China, although the practice was extremely painful and often resulted in infection and even death. Tiny feet and a swaying walk were thought to be highly erotic, and helped to ensure that girls married wealthy men. (Library of Congress)

who prescribed medicines to increase their weight. Achieving that perfect form, however, could damage the body. In some cultures in Africa and Asia, girls and women wore columns of metal neck rings to produce the appearance of a long and slender neck. The heavy rings deformed the collarbones and shoulders. In China, upper-class girls had their feet tightly bound from an early age to produce the appearance of tiny feet and a delicate, mincing walk. This very painful process displaced the bones of the feet from their normal positions and often caused ulcers and even gangrene. Opposition to the practice, led by Western missionaries and Chinese officials, led to an edict against foot-binding in 1902.

In Europe and America, women wore corsets—heavy undergarments reinforced with strips of bone or metal to compress their torsos into an attractive shape, with a small waist and a large bust and hips. At their most extreme, corsets could be used to achieve a waist measurement of just 18 inches. Most women saw nothing wrong with wearing corsets: they chose to wear them to follow prevailing fashions or to provide support to the back and waist during exercise. Corsets also had a moral meaning: uncorseted women were associated with "loose" morals and prostitution. Doctors warned that overly tight corsets were dangerous, resulting in deformed or broken ribs and causing fainting, liver damage, and even death.

Apart from complaints arising from these issues, women suffered from much the same diseases and injuries as men. Their domestic role exposed them to a higher risk of burns as they were usually responsible for cooking over open fires or on stoves. In European cities, women suffered from higher rates of tuberculosis infection, probably a consequence of poor diet and their indoor lifestyle. Women working in factories faced a particularly high risk of injury as long hair or skirts easily became caught up in the moving parts of exposed machinery, dragging them into the mechanisms with sometimes fatal consequences.

In some cultures in Asia and Africa, elite women had limited access to medical care. They lived segregated lives, with no contact with men outside their families.

If ill or injured, such women could not have a face-to-face consultation with a male doctor. Elaborate arrangements were put in place to get around the problem. Wealthy Chinese women sent a servant to describe their symptoms and consult with a doctor on their behalf. Or they sat behind a curtain and extended their arm through the material to allow the practitioner to feel their pulse but not see their face or body. If women patients were too embarrassed to describe their symptoms, practitioners gave them a small figure of a naked woman so they could mark the place where they felt pain.

WOMEN AND REPRODUCTION

When medical texts discussed women, they focused on reproduction. The lifecycle was divided into separate phases of puberty, childbearing, and menopause; and during adulthood, women's lives were punctuated by cycles of menstruation, pregnancy, and childbirth. All had the potential to undermine women's health.

Reproduction in Chinese Medicine

In Chinese medicine, the constant changes produced by women's reproductive systems posed a constant risk to their health. Blood (a term that covered all body fluids, not just the blood known to Western medicine) was the yin aspect of qi. It nourished the body and the fetus in pregnant women, formed breast milk, and was lost during menstruation. The loss of blood during the menses meant that women were at risk of a serious imbalance of qi and of blockages in the flow of blood, leading to a range of illnesses.

> Their monthly courses stop and go, now early, now late, [leading to] congestion and coagulation of blood, and blocking central pathways of circulation. The injuries that arise from this can't be fully enumerated. Cold and heat affect the organ systems, depletion (*hsu*) and repletion (*shih*) conditions interact, noxious blood leaks within, and the circulation vessels become worn out. (Pei chi ch'ien chin yao fang (1849), quoted in Furth 1986, 50)

Maintaining a regular menstrual cycle was crucial to both general health and fertility. Any increase or decrease in the normal flow, irregular bleeding, or pain were signs that something was wrong. Eating too much hot or cold food or exposure to cold could upset the menstrual cycle. Strong emotions were also dangerous. Anger caused barrenness, miscarriage, and blood disorders; resentment made the blood congeal, producing feelings of oppression, tightness in the chest, and loss of appetite. If blood was blocked, then it could produce a deformed fetus. "Ghost fetuses" were the result of dreams of having sex with ghosts or demons.

Books provided advice on how to deal with problems associated with menstruation. Written for a nonmedical audience and published by public-spirited laymen, they gave simple descriptions of common symptoms and explained their underlying causes. "Rushed and early menses indicate Heat. Receding and late menses indicate depletion. If Blood is stagnated, then it is proper to break it up. If Blood has dried up, then it is proper to replenish it" (Wu 1998). The texts recommended medicines to treat each condition. Betel nut was recommended for late menses, and green tangerine peel for pain. The books also recommended standard remedies, such as "At ease powder" or "Menses' regulating pills."

In China, the key to a safe birth was to avoid any stagnation or blockages to the flow of the blood within the body during pregnancy. Elite doctors monitored pregnant women, giving advice and prescribing medicines to maintain a balance of qi and blood. They recommended that pregnant women take gentle exercise, eat moderately, avoid anxiety, and repress sexual desire. "Hot" foods such as meat and oil and "cold" foods such as raw vegetables were considered dangerous.

As well as using medicines, diet, and lifestyle to ensure a healthy pregnancy and safe birth, women prayed to Chinese deities. Women who wanted to conceive prayed to *Bixia Yuanjun*, the goddess of Mount Tai, and made pilgrimages to the mountain to pray for children. Or they appealed to a Buddhist deity *Guanyin*, who was also associated with fertility. During labor, women prayed to Aunty Ge, the Divine Midwife.

Childbirth left women dangerously exhausted, depleted of blood, and vulnerable to ill health. Practitioners and popular texts recommended giving medicines to replenish qi and blood immediately after the birth. "Producing and Transforming Decoction," containing angelica, ligusticum root and peach pit, was given to break up the old blood and prevent "noxious dew"—blood left in the body after the birth. New mothers were told to stay indoors, keep warm, and eat strengthening foods.

Reproduction in Ayurvedic and Unani Medicine

Practitioners of Ayurvedic and Unani medicine shared the concerns of their Chinese counterparts that reproduction was potentially dangerous to health, as well as the need for an appropriate diet and lifestyle to ensure fertility and safe childbirth. In Unani medicine, regular menstruation was believed to be important for maintaining health. Irregular periods or the lack of menstruation were believed to cause the retention of menstrual blood within the uterus. This blood putrefied and moved to the heart and brain, causing hysteria. Patients fainted and experienced palpitations, and treatment included sweet smelling oils and sprinkling the patient with cold water. During pregnancy, women should follow a quiet life, pray regularly, and eat a good diet. Women who failed to conceive made pilgrimages to special springs or shrines or sought blessings from holy men. Unani medicine recognized that men could be responsible for women's failure to become pregnant, and medicines were prescribed to increase the chances of conception.

Ayurvedic medical texts advised pregnant women to avoid heavy work and any strenuous exercise. They should eat a diet appropriate to each stage of pregnancy, with milk during the early months and later a diet rich in ghee (clarified butter). They should avoid wine, large amounts of meat, and spicy foods. Women should abstain from sex in the later stages of pregnancy. Women had to take great care as their behavior affected the unborn child. They who ate too many sweets gave birth to delicate children; those who were angry and quarreled might have an epileptic infant. After the birth, new mothers were fed nourishing foods to help recover their strength and clean out the uterus, and medicines were given to purify the blood.

Reproduction in Western Medicine

In Western medicine, although the functions of the ovaries and uterus were poorly understood, doctors believed that the reproductive organs created the feminine character. In 1848, the distinguished German medical researcher Rudolf Virchow concluded

> The female is female because of her reproductive glands. All her characteristics of body and mind . . . the development of her breasts . . . the beauties of her hair . . . those depths of feeling, that unerring intuition, that gentleness, devotion and loyalty—in short, all that we respect and admire as truly feminine, are dependent on the ovaries. Take the ovaries away and we get the repulsive, coarsely formed, large-boned, moustached, deep-voiced, flat-breasted, resentful and egotistic virago. (Virchow 1856)

Their reproductive biology determined that women were physically weak, irrational, and emotional but with a strong moral sense and a natural instinct to care and nurture. Men's biology dictated that they were strong, rational, level-headed, and courageous, although prone to moral lapses.

Women's reproductive functions were understood to make their bodies inherently unstable and susceptible to a wide variety of illnesses. Although 19th-century medicine was increasingly concerned with the solid structures of the body, it retained older ideas about balance. The body was understood to contain a fixed amount of nervous energy; in women much of this energy was required to maintain the normal menstrual cycle. Any excessive demands on the supply of nervous energy produced irritation in the uterus and ovaries that spread via the spine and nerves throughout the body, and caused illnesses from hysteria, headaches, and coughs to cancer and epilepsy.

Women were particularly susceptible to poor health during periods of transition, such as puberty and menopause, or immediately after giving birth. Girls at the onset of puberty fell ill with chlorosis or "green sickness." Sufferers were depressed, listless, and thin, they often refused food, and their skin was pale with a greenish tint (hence the name). Because the ovaries had a close connection to the nervous system, women were susceptible to mental as well as physical illness. One leading authority on insanity wrote that during menopause, "every care or anxiety produce a more depressing and permanent impression on the mind. There is neither so much vital nor mental energy to resist the effects of the various adverse circumstances which it is the lot of most to meet" (Burrows 1828). From the 1870s, as a last resort, surgeons treated some mental conditions, such as convulsions, by removing the ovaries.

The large amounts of nervous energy required for reproductive functions dictated the type of lifestyle suitable for women. According to medical authorities, women's minds and bodies were fitted for a domestic role as a wife and mother. Going out into the world of work and engaging in hard physical labor or in jobs requiring intellectual skills went beyond women's natural capacities and threatened their physical and mental health.

> Miss C—— was a bookkeeper in a mercantile house. Like the other clerks, she was at her post, *standing*, during business hours, from Monday morning till Saturday night. Miss C—— . . . believed in doing her work in a man's way, infected by the not uncommon notion that womanliness means manliness. . . . When about twenty years of age, perhaps a year or so older, she applied to me for advice in consequence of neuralgia, back-ache, menorrhagia, leucorrhœa [menstrual disorders] and general debility. She was anemic, and looked pale, care-worn, and anxious. (Clarke 1875, 76–77)

Education also posed dangers. Around the time of puberty, any mental strain drained the reserves of nervous energy, preventing the development of a healthy reproductive system and leading to menstrual disorders, depression, nervous breakdowns, madness, and infertility. Women eager to go to university argued that girls could study safely, so long as time spent with their books was balanced by rest and exercise. This image of women as delicate creatures, compelled to limit their activities in order to maintain their reproductive health, was an idealized, middle-class image of womanhood; working-class women in homes, on farms, and in factories worked long hours at tasks that required a good deal of strength without damaging their ability to have children.

Despite these perceived threats to women's fertility in Europe and North America for much of the 19th century, large families were the norm, with 8 or 10 children not uncommon. Many women spent a large part of their life between the ages of 20 and 40 pregnant or with a small infant. Many women did limit their family size in some way by avoiding sex for a period after giving birth or breastfeeding for long periods. Rubber condoms were available after 1850. Many women wittingly or unwittingly used drugs to induce an early abortion when their periods stopped; newspapers and magazines regularly carried advertisements for medicines to ensure regular periods or remove "stoppages." Doctors played only a minor role in looking after women during pregnancy or after birth. They simply advised them to eat a good diet of simple foods, to exercise (walking was often suggested as a suitably gentle activity), and to rest during pregnancy and for at least a month after the birth.

WOMEN AS CAREGIVERS

Throughout the world, in all cultures, women played a central role in protecting the health of their families. In most societies, they ran the household, growing and gathering fruits and vegetables, helping to raise the livestock to supply eggs, milk, and meat, and buying food. Women's ability to produce and cook food and to budget determined how well-nourished their families were. They also took primary responsibility for hygiene by sweeping out the home, collecting and disposing of refuse, and washing clothing.

Women were the primary caregivers of the sick. When family members fell ill, women nursed their children, husbands, siblings, or parents, making them comfortable by keeping their bedding clean and preparing suitable foods. Women also made simple medicines: a warm drink, a cool bath for fever sufferers, or a poultice to treat a swelling. This role in caring for family members meant that women were important consumers of medical services. All around the world, women bought remedies to treat minor ailments from a local herbalist or shop or by mail order. Buying medicines through the post was not confined to the West; by the end of the century, Western and traditional medicines were sold in this way across Africa and Asia. If these measures failed, or the case was thought sufficiently serious, it was often women who decided to seek the help of a doctor or healer.

Women were guided in this role by advice books. A reduction in the costs of paper and printing brought books and pamphlets offering advice on diet, nursing, and childcare within the reach of many families around the world. In India, books of Unani medicine encouraged women to take responsibility for their own health and that of their families and advised them how to buy medicines and when to consult doctors. Books and magazine articles written by Western-trained doctors gave a new scientific gloss to the traditional role of mothers to identify, treat, and prevent illness within the family. In Europe, the United States, and many other countries where Western medicine was practiced, doctors gave out expert advice to mothers. In Egypt, for example, doctors advised women on how best to clean their houses and to prepare foods. Many manuals included advice on childrearing, encouraging women to breastfeed and to allow their children to play and exercise in the open air.

WOMEN AS HEALERS

While almost every woman cared for sick family members, a smaller but still significant number worked as healers, providing skilled services in return for money or goods. In many cultures, both men and women worked as healers using various forms of folk medicine. In American and African societies, women herbalists treated illnesses using plant-based remedies, performed bloodletting and scarification to remove blood from the body, treated wounds, and set broken limbs. In some cultures, women combined the treatment of physical ailments with work as spiritual healers. In Mexico, for example, female *curanderos* practiced among the indigenous population, curing physical ailments and illness caused by witchcraft. Sorcerers caused illness by implanting foreign objects such as beetles, feathers, and other small objects in the body. These were drawn out by massage or sucking. For physical illnesses, *curanderos* used herbal remedies and rituals that combined Christian prayers and symbols with much older practices from Aztec medicine. One *curandera* was reported to make the sign of the cross over the liver, stomach, and heart, the three important organs in ancient Aztec medicine, as part of her healing rituals.

MIDWIVES

In very few cultures, women were expected to deliver their own babies without help; but in most societies around the globe, women helped each other during

In many cultures, midwives encouraged delivery by getting the mother-to-be to pull downwards on a suspended rope, or by pressing on the abdomen. This illustration shows techniques used in the United States in the mid-19th century. (Hulton Archive/ Getty Images)

labor. Female friends and family members provided physical and emotional support while midwives—women with special knowledge and experience of childbirth—supervised the birthing process. Most midwives learned through experience, by giving birth themselves, through training with an experienced midwife, and by observing births. In some parts of the world, such as Persia, midwifery was a hereditary occupation, passed down from mother to daughter. Although midwifery was a recognized specialist role, it was a part-time job for most women. In rural areas with a small population, the local midwife might deliver a few babies a year. Midwives in towns attended more births but still combined this role with other work. In some cultures, midwives also worked as healers. In North Africa, midwives treated wounds and illnesses among women and children.

Midwives supported the mother-to-be through the labor, helped to deliver the baby, cut the umbilical cord, and often stayed to help look after mother and infant for a few days. In China, for example, midwives gave drugs to stimulate contractions, offered food and drink, and massaged the mother-to-be to help the labor progress. Once the birth was imminent, they would support the mother in a standing position and catch the infant. Native American midwives massaged the mother to help deliver the baby, to move the infant into a safe presentation, and to expel the placenta. Various plant medicines were used to increase contractions, to ease pain, and to control bleeding. After the birth, a bandage or belt was tied around the mother's abdomen to promote recovery. In the Congo, midwives tapped women on the head with a broom if their labor was prolonged: a symbolic action to sweep the child out of the womb. Iranian midwives encouraged labor by giving the mother-to-be tea made with carrot seeds and sage. Ayurvedic midwives speeded up labor by massaging the abdomen, giving drugs to induce vomiting or getting the mother to pound grain in mortar and pestle in the hope that the exertion would encourage the contractions.

Rituals were a very important means of ensuring the safety of mothers and infants at a very dangerous time. In every society, large numbers of women died when they were unable to deliver because of the size or position of the baby, or from blood loss. In the days following birth, many more succumbed to fever caused by infections usually unwittingly transmitted by the birth attendant. Many more suffered injuries such as tears or a prolapsed uterus. Even in Europe in the late 19th century, where birth was relatively safe, around four in every 1,000 women died as a result of childbirth.

In many cultures, women gave birth in a special space from which men were excluded. Among the Blackfoot people of North America, birth took place in an isolated *tipi*. In India, among Hindus, birth took place in a small, warm, dark room (*aturghar*). Performing rituals was an important part of the midwives' role. In many cultures, midwives said prayers for a safe delivery. Among Australian aboriginal people, women attendants performed ritual songs to ensure a safe birth. In Persia, metal objects were attached to the bed to avert the evil eye. In Jewish homes, the key of the synagogue might be placed under the pillow to promote a safe labor. In India, Hindu midwives (*dais*) cut the umbilical cord with a knife smeared with cow dung. In Iran, the demon *Al* was kept away from women in childbirth by metal objects. Iron was thrown into the water used to wash the newly delivered infant as a means of keeping away the evil eye.

Midwives and Western Doctors

In the West, midwives had traditionally delivered babies, and they remained the main source of help for women in rural areas and for the poorer classes throughout the 19th century. Middle-and upper-class women increasingly chose to have a doctor present at the birth. In the case of a difficult labor, doctors could deliver the child using forceps (midwives did not, as a general rule, use instruments to help delivery) and they gave anesthetics, such as chloroform, to ease the pain. From the 1840s, surgeons could repair tears and other injuries caused by the birth, and by the end of the century, they successfully performed cesarean sections to save the lives of the mother and child.

Although doctors took an increasing role in childbirth, most women continued to give birth at home, and only the very poorest women had their babies in maternity or "lying-in" hospitals. In return for their care, medical students were allowed to observe the birth and deliver the baby under supervision. Lying-in hospitals had a dreadful reputation for high mortality, largely due to epidemics of puerperal fever after delivery. The disease killed around one in 20 patients at *La Maternité*, the largest lying-in hospital in Paris, roughly seven times the mortality rate for women giving birth at home. This institution had an exceptionally bad record: in other European hospitals, outbreaks of the disease were controlled by thorough cleansing.

Western doctors were increasingly critical of the skills of midwives all around the world. They portrayed traditional midwives as superstitious, ignorant, and a danger to both mother and infant. Indian *dais* came in for particular condemnation. Colonial doctors complained that they were dirty, clumsy, and ignorant, endangering the lives of infants and mothers by their traditional practices, such as pressing on the stomach to hasten delivery and pulling on the head or limbs to extract the baby. Such criticism was not confined to Western doctors. In China, elite practitioners complained that midwives created problems when they tried to rush the birth.

The solution was better education. By 1900, midwives working in European towns and cities were trained by attending lectures and courses at a local hospital or college. Midwives in rural areas might have had some training from a local doctor. Efforts to introduce midwives trained in Western medicine were made around the world. The National Association for Supplying Female Aid to the Women of India, a charity set up under the patronage of Lady Dufferin, the wife of the viceroy, established programs to educate new midwives in local hospitals. In Egypt, under the Ottoman viceroy Muhammad Ali, a school of midwifery was founded in 1831. Similar initiatives were established in the Caribbean, Cuba, South America, Latin America, and Malaya. The new training strongly discouraged midwives from following traditional practices, such as delivering women in dark, overheated rooms, or from performing rituals around cutting the umbilical cord or burying the placenta. Instead, teachers emphasized the need for fresh air and cleanliness, and for midwives to monitor but not intervene in labor. It instilled the need to follow Western practice by calling in a doctor if there were any complications.

In some parts of the world, the training brought immediate results. A program to teach midwives in Iceland to use sterile implements to cut the umbilical cord drastically reduced cases of infection. Elsewhere, women were reluctant to employ Western-trained midwives who did not follow traditional rituals or use local remedies. In Java, for example, local women disliked the way that Western-trained midwives ignored the local beliefs that an infant and his or her placenta were siblings and that they should not cut the umbilical cord until the placenta had been delivered.

WOMEN AS NURSES

While most female healers combined caring with other work, women in the West were able to make careers in medicine as doctors or as nurses. This was part of a wider movement of women into higher education and the workplace, where they took up many of the new "white collar" jobs, working in shops and as typists, clerks, and teachers. At the beginning of the 19th century, hospital nursing was provided by members of religious orders, convalescent patients or poorly paid nurses, who were really domestic servants responsible for cleaning, cooking, and laundry work, rather than providing medical care. Nursing emerged as a profession toward the end of the century as the high standards of care and training of the religious orders were transferred to a new body of career nurses.

The development of trained nurses reflected the need for more medically trained staff in hospitals to care for acutely ill patients and those recovering from surgery. In the early part of the century, training was based around the development of character and self-discipline, rather than medical knowledge. Trainee nurses absorbed a culture of order and method, keeping wards scrupulously clean, feeding and washing patients, and administering medicines. In the later 19th century, the nurses' role expanded to include more medical tasks. They began monitoring the patient's condition, dressing wounds, and assisting surgeons in the operating theater. Their training was expanded to include formal teaching in medicine; new recruits attended lectures on anatomy, physiology, and pharmacy. This shift was controversial; there were concerns that nurses might encroach on the work of doctors, gaining an ability to cure but losing their capacity to care.

WOMEN AS DOCTORS

Although women were free to become healers, midwives, and nurses, very few were able to access formal training in medical theory and work as learned practitioners. In China, a handful of women who belonged to medical families received an education from their male relatives. They wrote books and practiced medicine, mostly among female patients. In India, too, a very small number of women were educated in Unani medicine and attended women in their segregated quarters. In Egypt, women briefly had the opportunity to enter medicine through an initiative to train midwives. Graduates from the School of Midwifery were trained not only to attend births but as doctresses (*hakima*) providing basic medical care to communities. They treated injuries, dispensed medicines, vaccinated against smallpox, and tackled public health problems.

In Europe and North America, medicine was a male monopoly as women were excluded from medical schools and universities. In the second half of the century, women attempted to enter the medical profession, but they faced a hard battle. Although nursing fitted with the ideal of women's natural capacity for caring, the intensive study required to graduate as a doctor and the capacity to make quick, calm decisions when faced with seriously ill or injured patients was thought by many (both men and women) to be beyond the ability of women.

> Women are neither physically nor morally qualified for many of the onerous, important and confidential duties of the general practitioner, nor capable of the prolonged exertions or severe exposures to all kinds of weather which a professional life entails; nor capable of keeping the social secrets of patients, which are often dearer than life. (The Lancet 1873)

A concerted push by women to obtain medical training began with an American, Elizabeth Blackwell, who was awarded a medical degree in 1849 from Geneva College in New York State. She inspired and encouraged women in mainland Europe to emulate her. Although elite universities in Switzerland and France began to grant degrees to women in the 1860s, in other countries, women struggled to gain qualifications. In Britain, a small group of women, headed by Sophia Jex-Blake, managed to study at the prestigious Edinburgh Medical School despite violent opposition from some staff and students. Jex-Blake and her colleagues were jeered at and jostled, and on one occasion, the male students pushed a live sheep into their classroom. At the end of their studies, although the women passed their exams, the university refused to grant them their degrees. Women did not graduate from Edinburgh until the 1890s.

Even when they had overcome the hurdles of medical training, women doctors faced further difficulties in pursuing their careers. Prestigious posts in hospitals were closed to them, and few male patients were willing to go to a female doctor. Many women doctors were forced to take poorly paid posts or to work among poor women and children in small dispensaries or hospitals. Other graduates went abroad to work in the colonies where there were greater opportunities to practice.

WOMEN AND WELFARE

Middle-and upper-class women in Europe and North America played an important role in setting up charitable schemes to care for the health of the poor at home and abroad. Women had a limited role in political life in the 19th century—very few could vote in elections or sit on the governing bodies of institutions—and they justified these activities as an extension of their traditional caring role within the home. Women founded and helped to run charities to provide medical care to women and children and to give advice and free or cheap baby milk and food to infants and mothers, and they organized holidays for slum children to improve their health. The Dufferin Fund in India not only trained midwives, it also provided free Western medical care to large numbers of Indian women. By the beginning of the20th century, Dufferin-funded institutions were treating around two million women a year.

Charities set up by women played an important role in shaping government welfare policies. In Britain, Ladies Sanitary Societies supported the public health work of local and national governments by education campaigns among the poor. They distributed pamphlets, organized lectures and employed home visitors to spread the gospel of fresh air and cleanliness among the working classes. (The word "gospel" is appropriate: their strategies were copied from religious groups.) In Argentina, elite women founded the Beneficent Society (*Sociadad de Beneficencia*) in 1823 to provide a hospital for women, care for orphans, and educate girls. The society helped to set a new agenda for social welfare and participated in running government institutions.

Women were also active in reining in governments if they felt that health policies had gone too far. In the 1870s, the Contagious Diseases Acts, designed to control venereal disease through the compulsory treatment of prostitutes provoked strong opposition among middle-class women in Britain. The Ladies National Association for the Repeal of the Contagious Diseases Acts, led by Josephine Butler, argued that the legislation unjustly targeted women, who were the victims of disease, while their male clients went free. The society played a major role in securing the repeal of contagious diseases legislation in Britain and in its colonies.

5

Infant and Children's Health

Attitudes to children in the early 19th century were very different from the present day. In some ways, children were treated as if they were small adults. Around the world, children worked from a very early age. Within the family, children as young as five or six looked after even younger siblings or helped to look after animals and tended crops. When a little older, they might go out to work for an employer. In Europe and North America, children were treated as adults by the legal system. The youngest convict transported from Britain to a penal colony in Australia was just 10 years old: she had stolen clothing. By 1900, attitudes had changed radically. It was widely accepted that childhood was a special period of life, when children should be allowed time to play, to be educated, and to grow and develop physically and mentally.

These two contradictory attitudes—that children were just the same as adults, and were very different—was reflected in the understanding of children's health in all cultures around the world. Babies and infants were thought to be much more delicate than adults and needed constant care to keep them in good health. Children suffered from a range of "childhood diseases" and were very susceptible to illness caused by supernatural forces. At the same time, medical systems understood children's bodies to work in the same way as those of adults. Children were therefore given the same therapies and medicines (albeit in smaller doses). Only in Western medicine, practiced by European and American physicians, did children's health emerge as a specialty by the end of the 19th century.

PROTECTING BABIES' HEALTH

Throughout the world, newborn babies were seen as delicate creatures, going through a massive and potentially dangerous transformation between life in the womb and life outside as an independent individual. In many cultures, infants were purified immediately after birth. Among indigenous North American peoples, babies were washed in water in which herbs had been boiled. In Europe, newborn infants were given castor oil or butter to clean any fetal material from the digestive tract. Ayurvedic texts recommended that babies should be washed and then given salt and butter to cause vomiting, in order to clear out any substances in the gut left from life in the womb. In China, babies were believed to be at risk from illness caused by "fetal poison" produced by material from the womb left clinging to the infant at the time of birth. If infants inhaled any fetal matter, they suffered from conditions such as "goose mouth" or "wood tongue." Fetal poison also caused a range of illness in infants, including jaundice. If the baby was exposed to cold and dampness, the poison produced "navel wind" that caused convulsions and could kill. To help reduce the effects of fetal poison, midwives cleaned babies' mouths immediately after birth and gave them purifying tonics.

In the days and weeks after birth, infants remained at risk of illnesses caused by spiritual and physical influences. In many cultures, mothers and infants were kept isolated for a set period. In Asia, mothers and their babies remained in the birthing room for several weeks. In Persia (now modern Iran), baby girls were kept indoors for 40 days, baby boys for 90 days, to protect them from the evil eye. In the Caribbean, infants were kept indoors to protect them from witches. In China, mothers and babies were isolated for a month after the birth. Even then, infants were seen as not completely developed; over the next 18 months, Chinese children were open to all sorts of malign influences that could enter through the pores of the skin or the navel. To keep these out, babies were kept wrapped up and the navel covered.

FEEDING AND HEALTH

In most cultures, breast milk was seen as the best, most nourishing food for infants. Ayurvedic practitioners, however, recommended that the breast milk produced in the first few days after birth should not be fed to infants. Mothers should delay breastfeeding but instead feed their babies a mixture of honey and water. Mothers who breastfed their babies had to take care to ensure that their milk was plentiful and nourishing. In different medical cultures, from Europe to China, women were advised to eat simple foods and avoid rich or spicy dishes. In Asia, mothers were warned that if they ate inappropriate foods, causing an imbalance of *doshas* within their bodies, then their milk would reflect this imbalance and cause their babies to become ill.

Emotions and behaviors were also thought to affect the quality of milk. New mothers should avoid stress and agitation as these had a bad effect on the quantity and quality of their milk. Moral qualities could be transmitted through breast milk, so mothers should not drink alcohol or have frequent sex, for fear that their children would become drunkards or prostitutes. Chinese practitioners warned against the bad effects of "ghost milk" produced by nursing mothers who became pregnant. In Ayurvedic medicine, milk produced by pregnant women was believed to cause coughs and indigestion. Infant feeding was strongly influenced by culture. In most societies, mothers tried to ensure that they produced plenty of milk, but in Burma, it was traditional for pregnant women to restrict their diet to rice and dried meats and to avoid eating fresh vegetables. As a result, their babies were very small at birth, and mothers produced very little breast milk.

Diet was crucial to the health and development of infants. When first weaned, infants in cultures around the world were fed on bland, starchy foods such as rice, like this baby in Japan, ca. 1800. (Hulton Archive/Getty Images)

For women who were unable to breastfeed their infants, or chose not to because they needed to go back to work after the birth, there was the option of employing a wet nurse to feed their children. Wet nurses were usually either poor women whose infants had died or unmarried mothers, willing to place their own infants in a foundling hospital in order to earn some money by nursing another women's child—in effect, selling their milk. Women registered as wet nurses through agencies, advertised their services in newspapers, or were recommended by medical practitioners. In the Americas, slave women were often used as wet nurses. Mothers who employed a wet nurse had to be extremely careful that the women were healthy and of good character, to ensure they had a plentiful supply of good milk and would not pass on harmful influences to their infants. Wealthy women preferred to have their wet nurses live in their homes with the other servants so that they could supervise their activities. Poorer women sent their infants out to live with their wet nurses. Often this led to the death of infants, as nurses took on many children in order to increase their income and provided a poor standard of care.

The alternative to wet nursing was to wean babies on to bland, sweet, starchy foods. In Europe and North America, infants were fed cow's milk, thickened with flour and sweetened with sugar, or bread soaked in milk. In Asia, they received well-cooked rice or porridge. These diets often led to illness as they were not very nutritious. Parents often gave babies inappropriate foods, such as tea, potatoes, or beans, that they were unable to digest; and the food was often contaminated with dirt. This caused vomiting and diarrhea and in serious cases, it led to dehydration and convulsions and was a major cause of infant death. Treatments given to sick babies including purgatives (in the West) or emetics to induce vomiting (recommended by Ayurvedic practitioners) can only have made the problem worse. In the West, a better understanding of infant nutrition and of the need to keep feeding utensils scrupulously clean emerged only at the end of the century.

The stomach upsets that accompanied weaning onto a range of solid foods often coincided with the emergence of teeth. As a result, in many cultures, teething was thought to be a particularly difficult and dangerous time in an infant's life. In the West, doctors claimed that the growing teeth set up an inflammation in the gums, producing fevers, diarrhea, rickets, convulsions, and even death. They recommended cutting the gums to "release" the teeth. Ayurvedic practitioners advised applying medicines to gums to encourage the teeth to erupt.

Poor diet was a problem for older children, too. Throughout the world, children in rural areas suffered when food supplies ran short. Small children were among the first to die during famines, and lack of food permanently stunted the growth of children who survived. Urban children—middle class as well as poor—developed rickets, which prevented the bones from developing properly and left children with permanently bowed limbs. Rickets is now known to be caused a lack of vitamin D; it was prevalent among city children who rarely ate milk or eggs that contain the vitamin, and lived in streets where sunlight (which allowed the body to generate vitamin D) was cut off by the thick pall of smoke. In Europe and North America, children's diets gradually improved over the 19th century, reflected in a gradual increase in average height. Progress was slow and unsteady. In Britain, children's heights increased up to 1850 but then slipped back, before recovering toward the end of the century. This reflected a complex interaction between wages, the price of food, and actions to tackle disease.

PROTECTING CHILDREN'S HEALTH

Around the world, families did their best to keep their children in good health and to protect them from natural and supernatural diseases. Chinese infants were protected by *Zhang Xia*, whose arrows kept away any demons that might harm the child. The names of the Eight Immortals were embroidered on children's caps to ensure that they lived a long life, and protective spells were written on paper and pinned to their clothing. To protect children from attack by spirits or the evil eye, Iranian mothers bound a cloth over their infants' eyes for the first 10 or 15 days after birth. Children were given amulets to wear, as described by an early 19th-century traveler:

> They hang about the child's neck . . . a bangle, the colour of a turquoise, which . . . serves to annul the glance of an evil eye. They also insert paragraphs of the Koran into little bags, which they sew on the child's cap, or on its sleeve, esteeming them as great preservatives against sickness. (Morier 1818)

Slave mothers hung lockets containing camphor around the necks of their children to ward off "bad airs."

Children were seen as being naturally healthy; however, some individuals, through illness, accident, or a poor constitution inherited from their parents, were delicate and needed extra care. Books on childcare encouraged European and American mothers to ensure that their children had a good diet, with plenty of milk and meat, but not too much food, as this led to flabby, soft flesh. Children should sleep in well-ventilated rooms, spend time outside in the fresh air, and avoid spending long periods studying or reading. Many were regularly dosed with medicines. Mild laxatives such as castor oil or syrup of figs were given to maintain their digestive health. Similar advice was handed out to mothers in China, by practitioners who warned them not to be overprotective of their infants. Children should not be overfed, as this led to digestive upsets, or dressed in too many clothes.

CHILDREN'S ILLNESSES

Children suffered from many of the same diseases as adults. They caught respiratory infections such as pneumonia and tuberculosis; the latter was responsible for as many as a quarter of the deaths among older children. They were exposed to diseases spread through contaminated water, such as typhoid fever and cholera, and those transmitted by insects, including yellow fever and malaria. While yellow fever was not a major cause of death among children, who acquired some immunity against further attacks, malaria was a significant killer of older children, who were worn down by repeated bouts of fever.

Children were also exposed to the risks of illness and injury in the workplace. Children joined the labor force when very young, helping out in the family home. In Europe, large numbers of children worked in factories; in 1839, half of all British factory workers were under age 18. Children in Africa worked on farms, industries, and mines sometimes as slaves or unfree labor. They made up a major part of the workforce on colonial plantations. Children working on farms fell from wagons; they were kicked by animals and injured by tools. In mines, they risked death from noxious gases or roof collapses. A wide range of medical problems were associated with long working hours in cotton mills and other factories, including stomach disorders, ulcers, and deformed limbs as well as poor general health. In glass factories, for instance

> [T]he hard labour, the irregularity of the hours, the frequent night-work and especially the great heat of the working place (100 to 190 Fahrenheit), engender in children general debility and disease, stunted growth . . . Many of the children are pale, have red eyes, often blind for weeks at a time, suffer from violent nausea, vomiting, coughs, colds and rheumatism . . . The glass blowers usually die young of debility or chest infections. (Engels 1845)

Childhood Diseases

In addition to all this, children suffered from "childhood diseases"—a set of infectious diseases that conferred immunity to further attacks later in life, and hence were rare in adults. They included smallpox, chicken pox, measles, mumps, whooping cough, scarlet fever, and diphtheria. At the beginning of the century, most of these diseases were found in Europe and North America; by the middle of the 19th century, they had moved around the world with settlers and traders. Doctors struggled to understand why children caught these diseases only once. Western practitioners speculated that there was some factor in the blood that was activated by the infection and expelled during the course of the disease. Chinese practitioners believed that measles and smallpox were caused by fetal poison—material left in infants' bodies after birth. When activated by some external influence, the poison caused disease. Children suffered from measles and smallpox only once because during the course of these illnesses, the fetal poison was carried out of the body through the skin in the form of a rash.

Childhood diseases were of varying severity. Mumps and chicken pox were relatively mild diseases, although, like all these diseases, they were more serious among populations that had had no previous exposure to the infection. Scarlet fever killed many older children, breaking out in epidemics when as many as one-sixth of patients died. For reasons that are still not clear, the incidence of the disease and the number of deaths declined toward the end of the 19th century. Measles too killed huge numbers of children, especially those who were poorly nourished. According to one European doctor: "In healthy children among the well-to-do class the mortality is small: in the tubercular and wasted children to be found in workhouses, hospitals and among the lower classes, the mortality is enormous . . . [it] amounts to 9 or 10 percent" (Fifty-fourth Annual Report 1883: 12). In addition, the complications associated with measles permanently damaged the sight and hearing of many children. Whooping cough was particularly dangerous for infants, killing many young children. The initial symptoms were not serious, but patients developed uncontrollable fits of coughing, followed by a whooping sound as they gasped for air.

> To a weakly child the disease is necessarily a formidable one; the exhaustion produced by the constant muscular efforts, the frequent vomiting which prevents a proper amount of food from being assimilated ...often reduce the child to a feeble and emaciated condition. It can easily be imagined that forty or fifty attacks of coughing every twenty-four hours produce great muscular exhaustion. (Ashby and Wright 1899)

When ill, children were given the same sort of care as adults. The children of wealthy families were attended by learned doctors. Most children were taken to a local healer best able to deal with their condition—a herbalist, bonesetter, drug seller, or spiritual healer. Children's bodies were thought to work in the same way as adults': they too became ill through an imbalance of humors or *doshas*, a blockage in qi, a malfunctioning organ, or the presence of an infection. Consequently, they received the much same treatment as adults to try to restore balance and help the natural healing process. Around the world, feverish children were sponged with cold or tepid water to make them more comfortable and treat the "hot" disease. Bathing in warm water was advised as a way of helping a rash to appear (this was seen as a positive development and part of the natural course of disease). Poultices were applied to the chest if there was difficulty in breathing or to the neck in cases of sore throat. Diet was an important part of treatment. In the West, children were given bland foods—such as rice puddings—to help build up their strength. Children were given the same types of medicines as adults. In Europe and America, children submitted to bloodletting and were prescribed purges and drugs to induce vomiting. In Ayurvedic medicine, children's illnesses were treated by rebalancing the *doshas* using vomits, purges, and bloodletting with leeches.

Texts reminded practitioners of the need to use small doses of mild, astringent drugs that were often mixed with honey to make them more palatable. In Unani medicine, children were given laxatives and emetics to remove bad material from the body and other medicines to help rebalance the humors.

Folk remedies were used to treat children in Africa, Asia, and the Americas. They were also popular in the West, where they were used alongside orthodox medicine well into the 20th century. For example, children were passed under the belly of a donkey or a piebald horse to cure or prevent whooping cough. The procedure was so popular that donkey owners charged a regular fee. Alternatively, sufferers were advised to breathe in the warm air rising from the ground where a sheep had slept, or from a distillery or (a more modern version) from a gasworks.

During the 19th century, children were protected from the risks associated with smallpox by inoculation or vaccination. Smallpox was particularly unpleasant; sufferers developed a high fever and then a rash (or "pocks") that covered the face and hands. As many as one in 10 of all children died of smallpox, and those who survived were left with scarred and pitted skin. In the 18th century, children in Europe, North America, and India were protected from dying from smallpox by inoculation—deliberately infecting them with the disease. For reasons that are still not understood, the mortality from inoculated smallpox was considerably less than that from a naturally acquired case of the disease. After 1798, children were protected against catching smallpox by vaccination, infecting them with cowpox. Cowpox was a mild disease—vaccinated children had few if any symptoms—and the procedure prevented them catching smallpox. Western practitioners encouraged the use of vaccination all around the globe, but many parents were reluctant to submit their infants to the procedure. Some viewed vaccination as "unnatural" and claimed that many children suffered from side effects or even died as a direct result of the procedure. They also worried that other diseases were passed on through the vaccine. In India, Hindu parents refused to allow the use of vaccine taken from calves, as the cow was a sacred animal.

By the end of the century, Western doctors had a successful treatment for only one childhood infection: diphtheria. Diphtheria victims developed a sore throat and fever. In severe cases, a membrane developed in the throat, blocking it and leaving patients unable to swallow or breathe. Around a quarter of all patients died. In 1884, the bacterium responsible for diphtheria was identified, but further research revealed that the membrane was not directly caused by the bacteria, but by a toxin released from it into the blood. In 1890, the German researcher Emil von Behring produced an antitoxin made from the blood of horses injected with diphtheria toxin. The first ever effective specific treatment for a childhood disease, diphtheria antitoxin caused a huge sensation. Its use spread rapidly around the world and death rates from the disease began to fall. Von Behring was awarded the first Nobel Prize in Medicine for his work.

Supernatural Disease

In many cultures, children suffered from illnesses caused by supernatural forces. Chinese babies who cried a lot were thought to be possessed by spirits.

Shocks could cause "fright" (*jing*) or "soul loss" that brought on a range of problems, from irritability to convulsions. In serious cases, spiritual healers had to conduct ceremonies to call back the child's soul. In Ayurvedic medicine, diseases caused by spirits and demons were recognizable by their very sudden onset, with symptoms such as fits or convulsions. They were treated with a combination of baths, prayers, and offerings. In North Africa, illness caused by the evil eye—a look from a person who wished the recipient ill luck or ill health—was cured by prayers and blessings from a holy man.

Specific demons were associated with particular illnesses. In China, smallpox was caused by the goddess *T'ou-Shen Niang-Niang*. She was believed to select pretty children as victims, so children were given ugly masks to wear, to trick the goddess into leaving them alone. Praying to the goddess provided protection from smallpox and helped victims to recover from the disease. When a child was infected, a shrine was set up within the home. Offerings were made on set days as the illness progressed. On the 14th day, when most sufferers were on the road to recovery, a ceremony was performed before the shrine. The infected child sat in front of the shrine.

> On top of his head is then put a small piece of red cloth, and . . . parched beans are taken from before the goddess and laid upon this red cloth, whence they are allowed to roll off . . . [this] indicates the strong desire that the pustules should dry up and become in appearance like the parched bean! (Doolittle 1865, 15)

CHILD DEATHS

Despite the care of parents, doctors, and healers, in the 19th century, huge numbers of children died early in life. In Europe, as many as one in four or one in five children died in their first year. Such statistics are not available for non-Western countries, but the level of child deaths must have been similar and higher during epidemics or periods of social upheaval. National figures mask wide variations: well-fed infants born into middle-class families had a much better chance of survival than those born to poor mothers, and those born in the country were less likely to die than children born in densely populated cities. Infants died from injuries caused during birth, from congenital defects, or from infections caused by cutting the umbilical cord with dirty instruments. Later, they fell victim to diarrhea, convulsions, and respiratory diseases. Once children reached the age of four, they stood a better chance of survival, although they were at risk from a range of infectious diseases.

In the past, when so many children died early in life, it is often assumed that parents did not become emotionally attached to their offspring, but research shows how deeply mothers and fathers felt about child death. They were slightly less upset by the death of babies—perhaps because they had been members of the family for a relatively short time. But the death of older children, whose characters and potential were clearly established, was devastating. Even poor parents did their best to have a proper funeral for the child and to mark the site of the grave in some way.

THE RISE OF PEDIATRICS

In Europe and America, doctors had become interested in children's illnesses in the 18th century; however, few if any specialized in treating children until the late 19th century. The first area of children's medicine to emerge was orthopedics, the surgical correction of deformed limbs. From the 1830s, surgeons repaired "club foot"—a condition in which the foot turned inward so that the child walked on the side of the foot or ankle. By cutting the tendon, the foot was released into a more normal position. From the 1860s, with the development of anesthetics and antiseptic surgery, doctors were able to successfully treat joints infected by tuberculosis. Although much better known as a disease of the lungs, the tubercle bacterium also attacked skin and bones, resulting in abscesses and swellings. Surgeons cleaned away the infected bone and then placed the joint in a splint to help it to heal in a more normal position and allow it to regain movement.

The establishment of children's hospitals allowed doctors to treat large numbers of children and to conduct research into the incidence, course, and outcomes of children's diseases, thus paving the way for pediatrics to emerge as a specialist field. Until the 19th century, children were generally excluded from general hospitals but received care as outpatients at clinics or dispensaries. The first hospital specifically for sick children opened in Paris in 1802. It was followed by hospitals

The Great Ormond Street Hospital in London, one of the first institutions for sick children, opened in what had once been a grand mansion. In the friendly and informal wards, patients were cared for and entertained while receiving treatment. (National Library of Medicine)

in Germany and Italy in the 1830s and 1840s, and the Great Ormond Street Hospital in London opened in 1855. Thereafter, these institutions spread throughout the world. Most children's hospitals were small. To deal with the huge demand for care, some opened outpatient departments or introduced home visiting schemes, where nurses treated children at home. The hospitals treated a wide range of conditions—fevers, rheumatism, skin diseases, respiratory complaints, and rickets. In these hospitals, children from poor families received care very similar to that provided to middle-class children at home. Rest, a good diet, and nursing were the basis of care. Children often stayed in hospitals for weeks or months, and some hospitals had convalescent homes, where children could continue to regain strength when they no longer needed medical care.

Although set up to treat children suffering from chronic conditions, children's hospitals regularly had to deal with outbreaks of infectious diseases. An outbreak of measles in the Benevolent Asylum in Sydney, Australia, in 1867 affected over 250 patients and killed many of those children admitted with other diseases. The solution was to create separate wards for infectious diseases and to take steps to ensure that staff members did not transfer infection. The fear of infection meant that many institutions strictly limited the number of visitors coming on to the wards; as a result, hospitalized children might not see their parents for days or weeks.

THE STATE AND CHILDREN'S HEALTH

Over the 19th century, governments in the Americas, Europe, and in African and Asian colonies increasingly intervened to protect the health of children. This was prompted by the introduction of accurate recording of births and deaths, which revealed the high levels of infant mortality for the first time. Governments were motivated to act by a mix of humanitarian and political concerns. Because of their age, children had little power or influence, and it was increasingly accepted in the late 19th century that, when exposed to unnecessary risk or suffering, it was right that the state should step in to protect them. Governments were also concerned about population size. At a time when European states were fighting over national boundaries and territory overseas, it was vital that nations had a large and healthy population to provide men for the army and a workforce to support a healthy economy. In North America, there were fears that the white, native-born population was being swamped by high immigration from southern Europe. In Latin America, new governments set up following the wars of independence saw good infant health as a measure of national well-being.

Governments and charities around the world identified the same root cause of high infant mortality: poor and ignorant mothers who were incapable of raising healthy children. The authorities took two basic approaches to the problem. In some countries, such as France, charities and local government provided a range of services to help poor mothers such as maternity benefits so they could take time off work, midwives to attend the birth, and free and cheap meals. New mothers also received advice on child rearing; their infants received free milk and free treatment from doctors and nurses. The French model inspired other governments to act, but many chose a different approach, focusing on the need to educate mothers. In Britain, classes in childcare, cookery, and hygiene were offered at welfare centers. Babies were weighed and examined by nurses and doctors to check that they were developing normally, but parents had to pay for any medical treatment. The provision of infant welfare spread around the globe at the end of the century. Schemes were adopted in the newly independent states of South America and Latin America and in colonial Africa, where the ruling powers portrayed children as the victims of malnutrition, tropical diseases, and poor mothering. Welfare schemes to teach mothers how to feed their infants and keep them clean were part of the project of bringing civilization to "primitive" peoples.

The high mortality among children sent out to wet nurses was also a cause of public concern. To ensure that the children were well looked after, and that the wet nurses received adequate payment, local governments set up official bureaus of wet nurses. In France in 1874, a national law required that all children sent to be wet-nursed had to be registered. Similarly, wet nurses were licensed in Sao Paulo, Brazil, from 1879, although the law was frequently ignored.

In the middle of the century, European governments passed a series of laws to protect children from the bad effects of factory work, and in the process defined the period of childhood as the first 13 years of life. The number of hours that children could work was gradually restricted. In Britain, under the Factory Act of 1847, children between the ages of 13 and 18 could work a maximum of 63 hours per week. The following year, the figure was reduced to 58 hours per week, and by 1870, it was accepted that children should not be employed in full-time work. Children were also banned from the most dangerous trades, such as working underground in mines; however, children working at home or in small workshops enjoyed less protection from workplace dangers or exploitation. Restricting the hours children could work did not give them free time; there was simply a shift from paid work to attendance in schools. In the 1870s, a further wave of regulation made schooling compulsory to ensure that children received a basic education and were taught norms of behavior and moral codes.

Governments throughout the world joined the effort to protect children from disease. By the late 19th century, doctors were required to notify local authorities of cases of childhood diseases so that the victims could be isolated to prevent the spread of infection. Governments also joined the crusade against smallpox. In many countries, vaccination was made compulsory for all children. Laws were first introduced in the German states of Hessen and Bavaria as early as 1807, in Sweden in 1816, in England and Wales in 1853, and parts of India from 1877. While this legislation increased the numbers of children undergoing vaccination, the introduction of compulsion aroused protests in many countries, including India, Britain, Canada, and Brazil. Parents objected to governments telling them they must have their children vaccinated and felt that these decisions should be left to the family. A small number even went to jail rather than have their children vaccinated.

6

Diseases

The 19th century saw the most radical changes in patterns of disease in human history, driven by rapid social, political, and cultural developments. In the industrialized world, huge numbers of people moved into cities in search of work, bringing them into contact with a range of infections they might never have encountered in the countryside. Diseases began to travel in new ways; infections that had existed in particular locales for hundreds of years were spread within regions and around the globe by increasingly mobile populations traveling by steam-powered railroad and ship. European soldiers and adventurers, intent on exploring and conquering in Asia and Africa, encountered (often fatally) indigenous diseases. People from India, Africa, and the Americas moved to new countries to work in mines, on plantations, and in factories. The man-made expansion of disease prompted new efforts at control. People tried to stop the spread of diseases by religious ceremonies, cleansing of the environment, better personal hygiene, and enforced isolation of infected individuals. As a result, by the end of the century, some epidemic diseases had been brought under a measure of control.

CHANGING PATTERNS OF DISEASES

Disease and Urbanization

The 19th century was a century of urbanization, when populations moved from living on the land to living in the town where they found new forms of work. New cities were established and old cities expanded around the world, especially in Europe, the Americas, and Asia. Urban life impacted on the incidence of disease in many ways. Immigrants coming into cities from rural areas were exposed to new infections to which they had little or no immunity. All urban residents came into contact with large numbers of people every day, and many were exposed to contaminated food and water, allowing the rapid transmission of diseases including typhoid and cholera. Many forms of work brought particular hazards to health, such as exposure to carcinogenic chemicals.

Not surprisingly, 19th-century cities were unhealthy places, regularly swept by waves of infectious disease. The most common disease in early 19th-century urban records is "fever." Many of these cases would now be diagnosed as typhus, a bacterial infection spread by body lice that caused chills, a high fever, and a rash. Typhus had long been associated with wars, when large numbers of soldiers lived together in filthy conditions, and with famine. The disease claimed huge numbers of the Irish population when they were struck by the potato famine in 1845–1848. The disease traveled with Irish immigrants to Canada, where more than 20,000 people died between 1847 and 1848. But typhus was also a regular feature of city life. Fever broke out every few years in the poorest parts of towns across Europe and North America, often in the winter when populations rose due to an influx of agricultural laborers seeking work.

Urban dwellers also suffered from epidemics of respiratory diseases, including bronchitis, pneumonia, and influenza. Flu is still a common disease—many of us are familiar with the symptoms of chills, fever, and aching joints. The history of flu is dominated by the pandemic—the global epidemic—that swept around the world in the aftermath of the First World War, killing more people than the conflict itself. However, outbreaks of flu were closely linked to urbanization; major epidemics began in the 18th century with the growth of urban living. Death rates for flu were relatively low, but because the disease attacked so many people, it killed large numbers, mostly among the young and the old. Over a million people died in the 1889–1890 pandemic of so-called Russian flu (named for its origin in Eastern Europe).

Epidemics killed large numbers in short periods, and their dramatic impact means that they often dominate contemporary records. But endemic diseases—those infections that were present all the time—claimed more victims in total. Tuberculosis, a bacterial infection, was by far the biggest killer of the 19th century, causing up to one in four deaths in Europe, mostly among young adults. Tuberculosis commonly affected the lungs. Victims suffered from a chronic cough, fevers, and weight loss (hence the common name of the disease "consumption") over months or years. In its later stages, sufferers coughed up blood from their badly damaged lungs. In the crowded living and working conditions in cities, the infection spread rapidly. Well-fed, healthy individuals were able to fight off the infection, but anyone weakened by poor diet, bad living conditions, and long hours of work was highly susceptible to the disease.

Global Diseases

Diseases had been traveling between continents with explorers and adventurers since the 15th century, but the 19th century saw the emergence of new patterns of disease transmission. Areas of the globe were opened up to exploration and trade for the first time, particularly in Africa, exposing travelers and indigenous peoples to novel diseases. Infections spread over longer distances. With the advent of steamships, journey times decreased, and passengers incubating infections, who would previously have become ill during a long sea voyage, now disembarked still apparently healthy but carrying the seeds of disease. In addition, many more people were traveling, increasing the chances of transmitting infections.

In previous centuries, diseases from the Old World had been exported to the New World, with devastating effects. Indigenous populations, especially those isolated on islands or in mountainous and desert regions, had no previous exposure and therefore little resistance to European diseases such as influenza, measles, smallpox, syphilis, and typhus. In the 19th century, indigenous peoples in North and South America continued to die in large numbers from the onslaught of these diseases. Island populations in the Pacific were exposed to European infections for the first time. The population of Hawaii fell from well over 250,000 in the late 18th century to around 73,000 by 1853, as a consequence of syphilis (which reduced the birth rate), measles, whooping cough, influenza, and smallpox. Some commentators interpreted the decline of indigenous populations as proof of their inherent weakness and the superiority of white races.

In turn, Old World and American populations began to suffer from diseases brought from the African continent. Yellow fever had existed in Africa for centuries where it was a mild illness, mainly affecting children. In the late 18th and early 19th centuries, it spread through many parts of the Americas and southern Europe. Yellow fever is caused by a virus transmitted by mosquitoes that stowed away in the water supplies carried on ships. Victims suffered from high fever and liver damage that caused the skin to turn yellow. A letter written in 1897 describing a case of the disease recorded "the skin was a bright yellow hue: tongue and lips dark, cracked and blood oozing from the mouth and nose. To me the most terrible and terrifying feature was the 'black vomit' . . . it was as black as ink and would be ejected with terrific force" (Humphreys 1997, 87). A series of severe epidemics struck the southern United States in the late 19th century and decimated some towns: Memphis was almost abandoned after serious outbreaks in 1878 and 1879 caused many of its residents to move away to healthier locations.

The mass movement of people within Africa and Asia also disturbed existing patterns of disease incidence. Travelers moving long distances within the continent, the mass migration of people seeking to escape conflicts or to find work, deforestation, the establishment of large plantations, and better transport, all helped to spread a range of diseases. Some of these were introduced from abroad, such as cholera or plague, but most were indigenous parasitic diseases that had previously been limited to specific areas. Sleeping sickness, for example, was endemic to some parts of the Congo but spread across wide areas in an epidemic from 1900. Hundreds of thousands died in the Congo basin and Uganda. Malaria too, spread into new areas of Africa and Asia over the century.

Cholera and Plague

The most dramatic incursions of foreign diseases in the 19th century were the repeated pandemics of cholera and plague. Cholera spread around the globe from its roots in India in repeated epidemics throughout the century. The first cholera pandemic occurred between 1816 and 1826, affecting China, Japan, North Africa,

Honoré Daumier's image captures the horror of the 1832 cholera epidemic in Paris. A working man collapses; a woman flees, covering her nose and mouth to avoid the infectious miasma; and corpses are carried away. (National Library of Medicine)

and Russia. The second and third pandemics, from 1827 to 1835 and from 1839 to 1852, spread even further, reaching into Europe and to North and South America. Two more pandemics occurred before the end of the century. The movement of cholera graphically revealed the new global networks of trade and migration. The disease followed shipping routes, from India to China, the Persian Gulf, and the Caspian Sea. The spread of the first and fourth pandemics were hastened by international pilgrimages: the first by Hindu pilgrims traveling home from a gathering at the Ganges in India and the fourth by Islamic pilgrims returning from Mecca in the Arabian Peninsula.

The slow, inexorable movement of cholera—it took several years for the second pandemic to travel from Asia to Europe, and then a further two years to spread across the continent—contrasted with the character of the disease itself. It struck without warning and developed at incredible speed; newspapers reported on healthy people preparing to go about their daily routine in the morning who were dead by evening. Victims suffered from violent vomiting, diarrhea, and muscular cramps, and as the body became extremely dehydrated, the face sank and the skin and lips turned blue. In the absence of good records (and the reporting of deaths even in well-administered countries broke down under the pressure of the epidemics), it is impossible to calculate accurately the total mortality from cholera, but it was clearly huge. Between 1848 and 1849, cholera claimed over 50,000 victims in Britain alone; the first two outbreaks of the disease in the United States caused around 150,000 deaths, and the toll in China, India, and Russia ran into the millions. It has been estimated that cholera killed around 15 million people between 1817 and 1865.

Just as cholera was declining, the world was hit by a pandemic of plague. Plague, or the Black Death, as it was also known, had spread to Europe in the 14th, 17th, and 18th centuries, but in the 19th century, its movement was enhanced by global travel. The outbreak of plague originated in southern China and Mongolia around 1855. From 1886, the disease moved via shipping routes to Hong Kong and India, then to Egypt, San Francisco, South Africa, and Australia by 1900, with isolated outbreaks in European ports. Victims developed fever and characteristic swellings or "buboes"; the tips of the fingers became gangrenous and turned black. The death toll was horrific: in Hong Kong, around 100,000 people died within a few months in 1894; 400,000 people had died in India by 1900. The outbreak did not end until the 1950s, killing several million people around the world.

UNDERSTANDING DISEASE

The increase in epidemics over the 19th century forced medical practitioners to consider how a disease could suddenly appear, infect large numbers of people, and then disappear. In China, learned practitioners had two main theories as to the cause of epidemics. Cold damage theories blamed climatic factors, particularly excessive cold or wind, for producing a pathogenic qi. This entered the body via the pores, producing fevers. Warm factor explanations, which were more generally accepted by practitioners, held that epidemic diseases including cholera and plague were caused when environmental factors came together to produce pestilential qi that entered through the nose and mouth.

> Then the hot qi of heaven descends, the humid qi of the earth rises, and people are stuck in the middle of these qis, and are subjected to the qi that results from the earthly and heavenly qis fermenting together. The emanation from the two qis enters through the nose, goes into the body, and results in a chaotic mixture of pure and impure, thus giving rise to cholera. (Shixiong 1838)

Pestilential qi was more likely to be generated in warm air—this explained why cholera generally appeared in the summer—and in the filthy conditions found in dense, urban populations. Rats were linked to the appearance of plague; pestilential qi rose from the earth through their burrows and contaminated wells. When pestilential qi entered the body, it affected the blood (*xue*) and disturbed the healthy flow of the body's own qi. Symptoms varied according to where the qi entered the body, and where it stagnated within it.

While doctors discussed the role of qi, ordinary Chinese people continued to believe that epidemics were caused by supernatural beings. Armies of ghosts—the spirits of the dead who had not been given appropriate rituals at the time of their deaths—were believed to roam the land, attacking large numbers of people. They were sent by disease gods to inflict disease as a form of punishment for sin. The demons could not attack those who were honest and loyal and who gave money to the poor.

Elsewhere, medical practitioners were also divided as to whether epidemics had natural or supernatural causes, and the mechanisms by which diseases spread. In India, Ayurvedic practitioners debated if the spread of cholera was linked to environmental factors, such as monsoon rains, or whether it was contagious and spread by people attending religious gatherings, or whether the pilgrims were in some way particularly susceptible to the disease. Practitioners of Unani medicine in North Africa suggested that cholera was caused by celestial factors such as meteors, was a punishment sent by god, or was caused by evil spirits or jinn. These explanations of supernatural causes could be very elaborate, mirroring the different symptoms of disease.

> The first [jinn], *Aya'il*, had a list with the names of those condemned to death. Those who died barely stricken had been hit by the arrows of the second jinn *Ya'il*. Those who died on the first day after the sudden illness were hit in the heart by the arrows of the third jinn, *Haiha'il*. If an abscess appeared on the skin of the victim, it was the result of wounds from arrows of the fourth jinn, *Griha'il*. The fifth jinn, *Shaykha'il*, was armed with clubs and stones and killed by striking the victim in the heart, stomach or head, causing accumulation of blood in the mouth, altered reason, prolonged suffering, loss of speech and slow death. (Bertherand 1855, 431)

In parts of Africa, such as the Congo, epidemics were blamed on witchcraft.

In the West, practitioners rejected supernatural theories of disease causation but debated the mechanism by which epidemics spread through the population. Early 19th century practitioners understood that some diseases, such as smallpox, were contagious—they were transmitted by direct contact between infected and susceptible persons—although they did know exactly what agent was passed from person to person. Other epidemics seemed to appear spontaneously, breaking out in particular locations and thus were linked to environmental factors. Filthy conditions were seen as a prime cause of disease: most fevers were believed to arise through "miasma"—the unpleasant atmosphere caused by rotting organic matter. Thus epidemics such as cholera were most severe in dirty urban environments. One British doctor reporting on the first epidemic in India noted "the thickly populated and close lanes of Delhi suffered more than the rectangular and spacious streets of Jaipur. And again the low and nasty town of Saharanpur more than the city and cantonment of Meerut" (Jameson 1820, 116).

There was no hard and fast division between contagious and environmental diseases; the spread of a contagious disease might be enhanced by filthy conditions, or disease might arise from environmental conditions and then begin to spread from person to person. Doctors differed in their opinions as to exactly where a particular disease lay on a continuum between contagious and environmental transmission. In the 1840s, doctors in England tended to favor environmental causes for fever; their colleagues in Scotland and Ireland were more likely to believe that fevers were contagious. Western doctors also believed some groups were more susceptible to particular diseases. In the early part of the century, it was widely accepted that there was a hereditary component to the transmission of tuberculosis—a particular "constitution" handed down through the generations made some individuals more likely to succumb to the disease.

From the 1880s, a growing number of epidemic diseases were shown to be spread by bacteria. Louis Pasteur, a French chemist, had revealed the link between microorganisms and disease in the 1860s. Robert Koch, a German bacteriologist, led research into identifying the bacteria responsible for specific diseases. Koch discovered the bacterium that caused tuberculosis in 1882, and the following year, he isolated the cholera bacillus. Thereafter, the organisms responsible for major infectious diseases were uncovered at the astonishing rate of one every year for the rest of the century. In 1894, Western researchers working in Hong Kong discovered the bacterium responsible for plague was present in humans and in rodents, usually rats. The disease was transmitted when humans were bitten by an infected rat flea. Practitioners were unable to identify viruses (which are much smaller than bacteria) until the end of the century, so the agents responsible for many important diseases, including smallpox and influenza, remained mysterious.

In the past, historians believed that the so-called "germ theory"—the understanding that microorganisms caused illness—revolutionized thinking about disease causation. More recently, they have realized that doctors did not immediately switch to the idea that "germs" caused disease. Given the long association between dirt and ill health, many doctors were reluctant to believe that the environment played no part in disease transmission, and they continued to argue that it played some part in determining where and when diseases arose—especially as it was clear that bacteria were present in huge numbers and at all times. For example, it was suggested that yellow fever was spread by some "seed" or germ, but the disease would only appear if it found a suitable "soil"—dirty conditions and a humid climate. These debates over disease causation gradually declined over the last years of the century, after Koch developed a set of techniques for culturing and identifying disease-causing bacteria.

TREATING INFECTIOUS DISEASES

Although epidemics were different from other diseases in that many people were affected simultaneously, the treatment was much the same as for other ailments. Chinese practitioners believed that the pestilential qi responsible for outbreaks of disease had a slightly different effect on each individual depending on their lifestyle and constitution, and on where the invading qi came to rest within the body. As a result, individuals suffering from similar symptoms might receive quite different medicine and diet to correct the effects on the internal balance of qi within the body.

Unani practitioners in North Africa saw cholera as a hot disease and treated it with cooling medicines similar to those used in cases of dysentery, including herbs, honey, vinegar, and garlic. In cases of plague, they recommended bloodletting to remove the poisoned blood that had accumulated in swellings or buboes. Western practitioners treated diseases that caused vomiting or purging with medicines that mimicked this response, in the hope that clearing the digestive system of bad materials would help the natural healing process. Faced with the acute symptoms produced by cholera, Western doctors responded with their strongest treatments, including bloodletting and purgative medicines containing mercury. As it became clear that this therapy was rarely successful, practitioners switched to using milder therapies. Their treatment for the fevers associated with many infectious diseases was more successful. Quinine halted the violent shivering, while cold baths and bloodletting lowered the body temperature. Ayurvedic practitioners treated cholera with mild purgatives and later also prescribed alcohol—a medicine borrowed from Western practitioners.

Folk practitioners used specific remedies for each disease, sometimes combining natural and supernatural therapies. In the Yucatan peninsula in Mexico, shamans sought to expel smallpox from the body, but they also treated the itching associated with the rash with soothing herbs and roots. They treated the diarrhea and vomiting accompanying cholera with lemonade, herbs and a drink made from fermented corn.

PREVENTING AND CONTROLLING DISEASE

Debates about disease causation were hugely important because they underpinned different strategies to control disease: if a disease was spread by contagion, then it could be halted by isolating infected people and destroying goods that might carry the infection; if disease was a punishment sent by gods or spirits, then only prayers and offerings would have any effect.

Individuals adopted a number of strategies in an attempt to avoid catching epidemic diseases. People left infected areas. When cholera arrived in Europe and North America, people fled from the cities to the countryside, which was traditionally thought to be healthier. People were encouraged to keep themselves and their homes clean, to eat a simple diet, and to follow a healthy regimen of moderate exercise and rest. Practitioners warned against drinking alcohol, staying up late, and eating unripe fruits. Similar advice circulated in China when the nation was struck by plague, possibly inspired by Western medicine. Individuals were advised to wear clean clothes and shoes, which helped to prevent contact with the pestilential qi rising from the ground. To strengthen the body against the effects of pestilential qi, people should eat a good, simple diet and remain calm. Homes should be cleaned and ventilated and wells purified with garlic and other drugs. People living in the city should escape to the fresh air of the countryside. People also sought supernatural protection—they wore amulets on their clothing, placed them on their houses, and burned amulets and put the ashes into their wells. Unani practitioners recommended that to avoid plague, people should keep their blood pure by avoiding overexcitement and by inhaling sweet-smelling substances to strengthen the heart.

Collective Action

Epidemics also prompted collective responses, and the residents of villages, towns, and cities worked together to protect their communities from disease. When threatened by cholera, the inhabitants of rural communities in Finland stopped all travelers entering their villages for fear that they might bring the disease. In Chinese towns, festivals were held to ward off plague in which paper boats containing images of disease gods were burned or floated away as a means of expelling illness from the community.

> Every spring, in the towns and countryside, people pool their money in order to hold a Qing jiao. They use paper to make a dragon boat, spirit mediums use red ink to paint their faces like each god in the pantheon. They seek out the fugitives [ghosts] at each household along the way in order to exorcise epidemics. (Bijiexian zhi 1879)

Local healing gods were asked to do battle with the plague gods and keep the disease at bay. If plague arrived, gods from nearby towns and cities were invoked to strengthen the supernatural defenses. In India, too, public ceremonies and rituals were held to ward off cholera.

The arrival of cholera pandemics galvanized national and local governments to take action to protect the health of their populations. The temporary measures adopted against the disease often formed the basis for long-term strategies to deal with other diseases and inspired the creation of public health bodies to monitor and tackle disease within communities. The authorities faced a problem, however, in deciding what measures to implement, as doctors were divided as to whether cholera was contagious or arose from environmental conditions. When cholera first appeared in Russia and Austria-Hungary in 1830, the disease was believed to be contagious, so the governments set up quarantines at their borders and outside major cities. All travelers were stopped at quarantine stations where they were held for a period of time, and their goods and belongings were cleaned and fumigated. Only those believed to be healthy were given a certificate ("a clean bill of health") and allowed to continue on their journey. When cholera broke through the cordons, governments tried to stop its further spread by forcibly isolating infected people in special hospitals and requiring all cholera victims to be buried quickly and with few funeral rites.

Countries to the west of Russia benefited from this experience and adopted a mix of strategies to deal with cholera. In Britain, ships were quarantined. Anyone infected with cholera was offered care in their own home or in cholera hospitals. (Although sufferers were not required to go to the hospital, the local authorities often effectively forced them to do so.) Infected houses were fumigated. Alongside these measures to break the chain of infection, local agencies organized massive cleaning initiatives, sweeping and washing the streets of whole towns and getting rid of accumulated refuse. This combined approach—sanitary measures plus quarantines—was generally adopted throughout Europe and beyond in the cholera outbreaks of the 1840s and 1850s.

New information about how cholera was transmitted had surprisingly little effect on these control measures. In 1855, John Snow, a British physician, demonstrated that infection was carried in the water supply. He tracked cholera cases in a London neighborhood in 1854 and showed that people whose water supply was drawn from lower down the river Thames (where it had become contaminated by sewage) were much more likely to catch the disease than those drinking cleaner water taken upstream. Snow's findings were worked into existing ideas; the British authorities interpreted his work as a demonstration of the old premise that dirt (in this case carried in water) was linked to disease and thus supported the continued use of sanitary reforms.

Even Robert Koch's discovery that cholera was spread by bacteria shed in the body fluids of cholera patients and that the bacteria could be killed by disinfection did not produce a revolution in disease control practices. Koch's discovery made it practical to reinstate quarantines in a modified form. The sheer numbers of people and quantities of goods traveling around the globe made the old system of holding all passengers impractical, so quarantines were made more focused and much shorter. Only those travelers suffering from suspicious symptoms were sent to isolation hospitals, where further infection was checked by careful disinfection. Goods that had come into contact with cholera sufferers were also disinfected.

These Western methods of prevention were widely adopted but remained controversial. Some governments were suspicious of Koch's ideas and refused to abandon their belief that the environment played a role in the spread of cholera. Governments in India persisted with their sanitary policies, reassured by the inaccurate findings of their own experts that Koch's bacillus did not cause cholera. Unani practitioners in India were divided over the merits of measures used by British doctors against the spread of plague, such as disinfecting homes and isolating the sick. Some believed that they were necessary; others objected to the forcible isolation of the sick (especially of women) and argued that the failure of these measures to halt the outbreak was proof that Western doctors did not understand how plague affected the bodies of Indian people.

Disease controls also disrupted trade and were unpopular with the public. While European governments were able to enforce unpopular regulations on shipping, in Tunisia, Western methods of quarantine, isolation, and sanitary reforms were adopted only during cholera epidemics in the 1820s and 1830s under the leadership of a pro-Western ruler. They were abandoned in later epidemics following pressure from European traders who objected to the disruption caused by quarantines. In Europe and the United States, there were riots against the strict regulations on burial rites and the isolation of cholera patients in special hospitals. Rumors that patients would be killed and their bodies dissected prompted mobs to smash cholera ambulances and attack isolation hospitals. In Russia, government officials were accused of poisoning wells in order to kill off the peasant population.

SMALLPOX AND VACCINATION

For the vast majority of infectious diseases, sanitary measures and isolation were the only possible strategies of control. There was one exception: smallpox. Unlike any other 19th-century disease, it was possible to prevent smallpox by immunization. Smallpox was a horrible disease, now known to be caused by the *variola* virus. Victims were struck by a high fever and aches and pains. After a few days, the characteristic red spots began to appear, on the face and hands in mild cases, covering the whole of the body in serious ones. The spots gradually filled with a clear fluid that turned into pus. Many burst under the pressure of the patient's body, sticking the bedclothes to the skin and giving off a foul odor. It took several weeks for the spots to dry and heal. At the beginning of the century, about one in 10 people died of the disease. Those fortunate enough to survive had lifelong immunity to future attacks but were usually left disfigured with pitted skin where the spots had been.

Smallpox had become a global disease long before the 19th century. It had been present in Africa and Asia from ancient times, was recorded in Europe in the medieval period, and reached the Americas through European travelers in the 16th century. Smallpox had no respect for status; rich and poor alike suffered from the disease. In the 17th and 18th centuries, when the disease seems to have acquired a particularly virulent form, royal victims included European kings and queens and emperors of China and Japan. By 1800 in Europe, smallpox had become primarily a disease of children, except in isolated communities where it continued to attack adults.

Parents in India prayed to the smallpox goddess, Sitala, to protect their children from the disease or to recover from it. The goddess is shown carrying a broom and a pot of water for ritual cleansing. (National Library of Medicine)

Although smallpox posed a terrible threat, it was also a disease amenable to control. Remarkably, not one but two forms of immunization were available in the 19th century. The first was inoculation or variolation. This involved deliberately infecting a child with smallpox. Although it sounds extremely dangerous, and some recipients did die as a result of variolation, records consistently show that the death rate for inoculated smallpox was much lower than for the naturally acquired infection. (It is not clear why this should be so.) Various techniques to transmit the disease had been developed in different cultures around the world. In Asia and the near East, practitioners scratched or pierced the skin and then rubbed on some of the dried crusts from the smallpox spots; in China, patients inhaled a powder made from the scabs; in some parts of rural Europe, children simply held some smallpox crusts in the hand. Inoculation was often carried out by special groups of practitioners. In India, they were known as *tikaders*; they traveled from village to village in the spring, inoculating children, supervising their care during the bout of smallpox, and praying to the smallpox goddess Sitala to ensure a safe outcome. The use of inoculation varied around the world; the procedure was popular in India but was rarely practiced in China.

The second form of immunization was vaccination: infecting children not with smallpox but with cowpox, a related virus that conferred immunity but caused only mild symptoms. The procedure was developed by Edward Jenner, an English medical practitioner, in the late 18th century. Like many other doctors, he knew that women who milked cows rarely suffered from smallpox and were famous for their fine, smooth complexions. Jenner took this observation a stage further in 1796, infecting a boy with cowpox and then with smallpox. The inoculation had no effect. While Jenner proved that vaccination was effective, he did not understand how it produced immunity. He published his findings in 1798 and spent much of the rest of his life promoting vaccination through letters and publications and by sending out supplies of vaccine. This was crucial to the spread of the new procedure; cowpox was a rare disease, so new vaccine was collected from the fluid-filled spot that appeared on the arms of vaccinated children. Later, larger supplies of vaccine were produced by inoculating calves; this also ensured that the vaccine did not transmit other human diseases such as syphilis.

Vaccination spread with extraordinary speed. By 1800, it had been introduced across Europe and in America; 20 years later, vaccination had spread through the British Empire to India and Australasia, and to Spanish America. By the late 1850s, it was practiced in Japan and Asia. Initially, vaccination was used by the upper classes, who could afford to employ a practitioner to carry out the procedure. Free vaccination provided by charities and governments helped to spread the practice. States encouraged its use by passing laws to stop the older practice of inoculation that was blamed for spreading smallpox, or by making vaccination compulsory. Vaccination greatly reduced the number of deaths caused by smallpox. In Europe, the frequency of smallpox epidemics declined sharply with the introduction of vaccination, and by the end of the century, smallpox was no longer a major cause of death. Vaccination did not become popular in all countries. In India, Hindu parents objected to having their children immunized with vaccine taken from a cow, a sacred animal. Elsewhere, parents disliked taking their children to an unfamiliar (often a Western-trained) practitioner.

To overcome this prejudice, the rulers of Bhopal employed local Unani practitioners to vaccinate. In some medical cultures, vaccination was rejected completely because it made no sense within indigenous medical knowledge. In the Yucatan peninsula of Mexico, where local practitioners treated smallpox by driving the disease out of the body, deliberately inviting the infection into the body seemed a dangerous and pointless practice.

Vaccination represented a huge leap forward in disease control, but it did not immediately lead to immunization against other diseases. The new vaccines against epidemic diseases were developed around a century later, based on Pasteur's findings that the virulence of microorganisms could be weakened to the point where they could safely be injected into animals, triggering a response that protected against further attacks of disease. In 1892, Waldemar Haffkine, a Russian bacteriologist, developed a cholera vaccine that came into use in India toward the end of the century. In 1897, Almoth Wright, a British researcher, devised a vaccine against typhoid fever; however, there were doubts over its efficacy, and it came into general use only very slowly.

THE IMPACT OF PUBLIC HEALTH

The 19th century saw huge changes in people's experience of disease, in disease patterns and in mortality. Toward the end of the century, the number of pandemics declined and deaths from infectious diseases fell over much of the globe. As a result, life expectancy began to increase and the degenerative diseases we associate with modern life, such as heart disease and cancer, began to become significant causes of death.

The contribution of public health to the decline in epidemics has been debated by historians for many years. There is no doubt that governments around the world responded to epidemics by introducing public health policies to protect the lives of their people. But sanitary reforms were slow and patchy. While the governments of large cities could afford large infrastructure projects, such as building new reservoirs to provide clean water, the authorities in smaller towns and villages could not. The population of rural communities continued to use contaminated water from rivers and wells, and the authorities had to rely on individuals to keep their villages clean.

As a result, it is difficult to be certain of the overall effectiveness of measures to control disease, even in Europe, where we have good records charting the mortality from infections and the actions taken against them. In the 1960s, historians concluded that medical treatment had done little to cure or prevent disease and that the saving of life was due to economic factors—higher standards of living and, in particular, a better diet. These arguments have, in turn, come under scrutiny as demographers have developed more sensitive analyses of 19th-century data. They have concluded that public health initiatives made a significant impact in reducing the number of deaths from waterborne diseases, such as cholera and typhoid fever. Efforts to reduce overcrowding in city housing, to isolate cases of tuberculosis, and to prevent infant diarrhea also helped to reduce high urban death rates. Now it is clear that the conquest of infectious disease was a slow process, affected by many factors including incomes, diet, education, and individual choices as well as public health policies.

7

Occupational and Environmental Hazards

At the beginning of the 19th century, both the natural and built environment was full of hazards to health. People were at risk of injury from natural disasters, extreme weather, and wild animals. In some cultures, supernatural beings living in wild places caused disease. In all medical systems, temperature and humidity were believed to affect the normal functioning of the body, so certain climates and the changing seasons left the body susceptible to poor health. Occupations brought their own risks of injury from tools and machines or from exposure to damaging dust and chemicals.

Over the century, global travel, the expansion of cities, and the development of industry added to the numbers of people exposed to injury or illness. Settlers struggled to survive in unfamiliar climates and when exposed to new diseases. The growing population of towns and cities faced diseases that spread through the urban environment, and the expanding industrial workforce was at risk of injury from machines and chemicals used in manufacturing processes. As an understanding of the potential dangers of the workplace emerged, governments began to fight back, introducing regulations to protect workers' health.

NATURAL HAZARDS

In the 19th century, the natural world was full of potential danger. Around the world, farmers and people foraging for wild foods were at risk of encounters with wild animals. Large animals such as lions, bears, and elephants claimed some victims, but far more people died from the bites of poisonous snakes and insects such as scorpions and spiders. Even more suffered from diseases carried by insect vectors, including malaria and yellow fever.

Human populations were at risk from natural disasters. The eruption of the volcano Krakatoa in Indonesia in 1883 killed at least 30,000 people and disrupted weather patterns around the world for several years. In 1854, over 10,000 people died in a series of earthquakes in Japan. Although such events were dramatic, they affected relatively few people. Unusual patterns of weather—abnormally

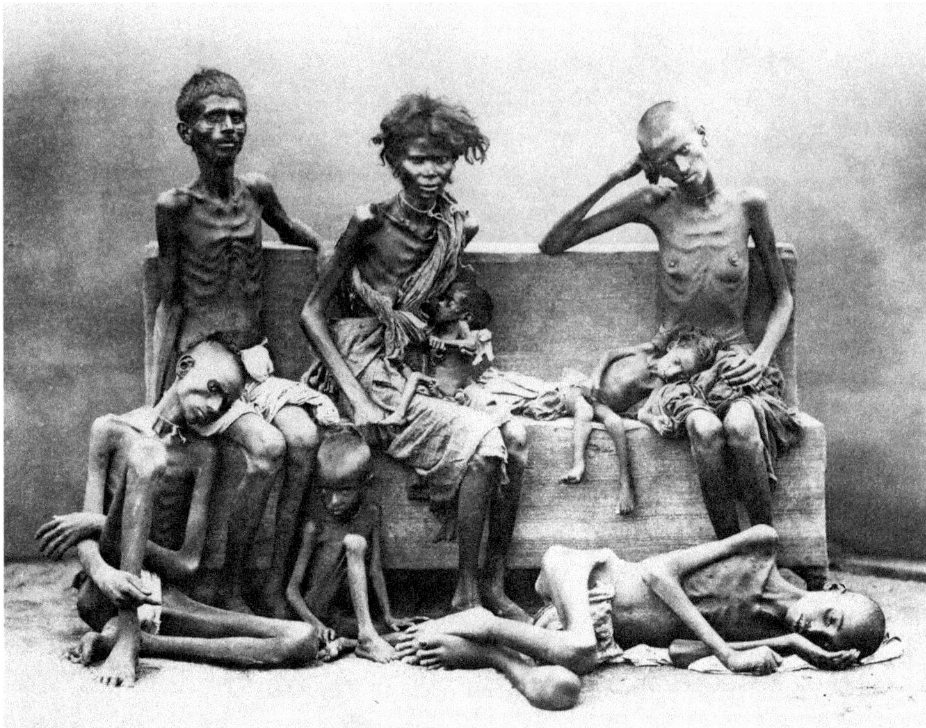

In 1876, severe drought and crop failures resulted in a famine across southern India. Over five million people perished as a result, as the British government continued to export grain and did little to support the local population. (W. W. Hooper/Royal Geographical Society/Getty Images)

wet or dry seasons—affected far greater numbers by disrupting farming. Both droughts and floods could lead to famines. Lesthoto in Southern Africa, for example, suffered from serious droughts in every decade of the 19th century. These were always followed by famine because food production was reduced and large amounts of food could not be transported into the region to make up the shortfall. Famines also arose in the aftermath of conflicts over land and resources. The Boer people in South Africa, the descendants of Dutch settlers, fought indigenous tribes for access to farming land, killing cattle and burning crops to force them to move away.

Developments across the 19th century both ameliorated and exacerbated the impact of famine. Improved farming methods meant that famines became rare in Europe and North America. The last European famine occurred in Finland in 1866, when cold and wet weather led to crop failures. Global trading networks and improved transportation allowed governments to buy and ship foods into famine areas. However, in the Madras famine in India in 1877, the situation was made worse because local farmers grew grain for export: even when large numbers were starving, food continued to be shipped out to the world market.

HEALTH AND THE NATURAL ENVIRONMENT

Climate and landscapes also posed a risk to health. In all the major systems of medical knowledge—Chinese, Ayurvedic, Western, and Unani medicine—the body was seen as constantly interacting with the environment. Consequently, environments had a fundamental role in maintaining health and causing disease. Each medical system understood this interaction in different ways, although they identified similar factors—heat, cold, and moisture—as the main risks to health.

Environment and Chinese Medicine

In Chinese medicine, health was the product of the smooth flow and functioning of the body's qi: blockages or stagnation of qi caused disease. Disruption to the body's qi was often the result of eating the wrong sort of diet or an irregular lifestyle, but qi was also affected by six external factors—heat, cold, damp, wind, dryness, and summer heat. In warm weather, qi moved toward the surface of the body; in winter, it became sluggish and dormant. Thus certain diseases tended to appear at different seasons—cold diseases in winter and hot complaints in summer.

Diseases caused by different environmental factors had their own particular characteristics. Wind diseases appeared suddenly and produced symptoms in the upper part of the body, such as shaking of the head and itching. Cold diseases were associated with feeling chilly, with excretions such as a runny nose and the stagnation of body fluids, causing pain. Damp diseases were associated with exposure to moisture from wearing wet clothes, living in damp conditions, or periods of rainy weather. Sufferers felt heavy and stiff and experienced pains in the joints, nausea, and lack of appetite. Heat diseases such as fevers were caused by exposure to sun and high temperature. In Chinese medicine, not everyone reacted in the same way to the same external factors. Yang helped to keep the body warm from within, and individuals with little yang were therefore more prone to developing cold diseases.

Pestilential or noxious qi was associated with environmental conditions, but there was some debate over its origins. According to one school of thought, the pestilential qi responsible for plague was believed to arise from the earth, finding its way to the surface through rat burrows. Other doctors claimed pestilential qi was generated from filthy conditions. Flies were attracted to qi arising from filth, hence filth and flies were present during outbreaks of disease. Some practitioners suggested that pestilential qi appeared spontaneously but only became active when combined with other environmental factors such as filth, warm air, or changes in the seasons.

Environment and Ayurvedic Medicine

In Ayurvedic medicine, the body was seen as a microcosm of the world. The three *doshas*—*kapha*, *vata*, and *pitta*, the fundamental factors or substances determining health—were made up of the same basic elements—ether, air, earth, fire, and water—as the rest of the world. The climate and environment thus affected the bodies of inhabitants. People living in moist, swampy areas near rivers and jungles had soft, fleshy bodies and suffered from diseases associated with *kapha* and *vata*. In dry areas, with little vegetation and hot, dry winds, the people had thin, strong bodies. Travelers moving between areas of different climate had to take care to adjust their bodies to the new conditions by managing their diet and patterns of sleep and work.

Seasonal changes in temperature caused the *doshas* to increase and decrease. If not countered by diet, drink, dress, behavior, and medicines appropriate to the season, this natural variation in the level of *doshas* could become extreme and tip over into illness. Sushruta, the author of one of the classic texts of Ayurvedic medicine, recognized categories of disease associated with the seasons. In spring, *kapha* began to accumulate and was removed by drugs to induce vomiting. To stay healthy, diet should consist of light, digestible foods such as barley and wheat. Heavy, oily foods were to be avoided. People should take exercise and bathe in cool water. During summer, *kapha* decreased and *vata* increased. To maintain a balance within the body, people should eat cold and bitter foods, wear light clothes, bathe in cold water, and avoid physical exertion. In winter, when the weather was cold, heat moved into the center of the body. In cold weather, the body was better able to digest rich foods, such as meats, oil, and sweets. Ayurvedic texts advised against eating light foods that increased the *vata dosha*. People should use hot water for washing, stay in warm rooms, and massage the head with oil.

Environment and Unani Medicine

In Unani medicine, environment played a crucial role in determining health and illness. Health was a reflection of a balance of four fluids or humors (*akhlat*) within the body. These were associated with four qualities—hot, cold, wet, and dry—and the four elements—earth, air, fire, and water. Blood, for example, was hot and wet and associated with air; bile was hot and dry and linked to fire. Climate was one of the six external factors that acted on the internal balance and thus played a crucial part in maintaining health and in causing disease. Classic Unani texts stressed the effects of wind, heat, cold, and moisture on the body and on health. Living in a hot climate encouraged the production of the hot humors within the body, producing diseases such as fevers. Exposure to cold increased the production of phlegm and black bile, leading to respiratory illnesses.

Environment and Western Medicine

Although Western practitioners developed a scientific understanding of the body in the early decades of the 19th century, older ideas about health and the environment, based on humoral medicine, coexisted with these newer ideas. Practitioners maintained a belief that environmental factors were intimately linked to body function and thus to health and disease.

Temperate climates, without extremes of temperature, in Europe and the Americas were essentially healthy, but reckless behavior could still put the body at risk. Engaging in physical activity on a warm day and then drinking cold water, or moving from an overheated room to the cold air outside without putting on warm clothes, was believed to bring on fevers and inflammation. During the early 19th century, doctors warned of the risks of wearing thin, fashionable silk and cotton clothing and extolled the benefits of warm wool and flannel garments. They were also concerned about the quality of air. Cool, clean, moving air, found in the countryside, was good for health, but the warm stuffy air found in homes and public buildings, heated by fires and candles and full of the products of respiration, was unhealthy.

Europeans faced much greater risks to their health when they moved from a familiar temperate climate to warmer tropical areas in Asian and African colonies. Heat was believed to affect the blood and the liver, producing a wide variety of conditions from acute fevers and dysentery to nervous disorders and chronic weakness. A combination of warmth and moisture was even more dangerous. Jungles, rivers, ponds, and swampy areas in hot climates generated "miasma," or bad airs, that caused fevers. These could be fatal and caused misery to travelers. One settler in the southern United States described how he "had the shakes until I was shook pretty near out of myself. I got so I did not have the strength to shake any longer: just lay and shivered outside and was burning up inside. Oh so thirsty! I felt as if I could lie and let a good sized spring branch run right into my mouth" (Keefe and Morrow 1988, 122–123). It was not until the end of the century that these fevers were recognized as attacks of malaria, spread by mosquitoes that bred in warm, stagnant water. In some areas, winds were also a risk to health. Seasonal hot winds were particularly feared, such as the dust-laden *simoon* of North Africa, or the *julo* or *badé sumoon* of India that was reputed to kill. Even if settlers survived the heat, fevers, and wind, they still could not escape the deleterious effects of foreign climates: the children born to settler parents were weak and prone to illness.

Unhealthy environments could be improved by agriculture. Initially, cutting trees and leaving them to rot down added to the amounts of miasma, but once planted with crops, the air became clear and healthy. Draining swamps helped to get rid of miasmas. Planting trees, especially varieties of eucalyptus, was recommended as a means of removing moisture from swampy, saturated soils and releasing it into the air.

The climate of particular areas produced specific local forms of disease. Fevers were common diseases in Europe and the Americas, but in India their symptoms were particularly violent and they did not respond to the usual treatments. As a result, doctors named diseases after their location, such as "Bengal fever" found in northeastern India. Local practitioners used this geographical specificity to claim a special competence to treat local diseases. Archibald Smith, a Scottish doctor working in Peru, engaged in a debate with José Manuel Valdés, a local practitioner, over the merits of bleeding in the treatment of dysentery. Smith claimed that bloodletting was unsuitable for patients from coastal cities but could be used on the strong indigenous people of the Andes. Valdés was scornful of

Smith's knowledge, claiming that although Andean people could resist the cold and carry out hard physical labor, their constitutions were naturally weak and they could not bear such strong therapies.

Coping with Unhealthy Climates

In the early 19th century, doctors were optimistic that settlers could adapt to their new surroundings through a process of "seasoning" or acclimatization. New arrivals should arrive in the coolest season, when the climate was similar to that of their homeland, and move into hotter and wetter areas very slowly. Justus Post, who moved from Vermont to the Mississippi Valley in the 1810s, warned:

> Emigrations to this or any other country should be made in the fall . . . otherwise the arrival would be made in the heat of summer, when even the fatigues of travelling in the heat of the sun would be sufficient to produce disease. You must not place your heart on a farm at the mouth of the Ohio [River] . . . —you must come to that point by degrees—it is in too low a latitude (37°) for a man of 45° north to strike the first dash—you will find the country above the Missouri to suit you and the people of your country best. (Post 1816)

As part of becoming acclimatized, newcomers expected to suffer from one or more bouts of fever, after which their bodies were able to come to terms with the new environment. To help the process, settlers were advised to eat a bland diet, avoid raw vegetables, get regular hours of sleep, and avoid alcohol. Frequent doses of quinine helped to ward off fever.

By the middle of the century, such optimism had evaporated. Doctors became convinced that different races were adapted to living in particular climates. The ill health suffered by Europeans settling in the tropics came about because their bodies were naturally adapted to a temperate climate. The bodies of people indigenous to tropical regions, such as African slaves and Indian laborers, were physiologically different from whites. A slave of African descent was able to tolerate heat because

> His head is protected from the rays of a vertical sun by a dense mat of woolly hair, wholly impervious to its fiercest heats, while his entire surface, studded with innumerable sebaceous glands, forming a complete excretory system, relieves him from all those climatic influences so fatal, under the same circumstances, to the sensitive and highly organized white man. Instead of seeking to shelter himself from the burning sun of the tropics, he courts it, enjoys it, delights in its fiercest heats. (Van Evrie 1861, 256)

It was widely believed that black people were immune to the fevers associated with warm climates but were more susceptible to diseases associated with unfamiliar cold weather. Thus they suffered from high rates of respiratory infections in winter. In retrospect, some African slaves had a degree of genetic immunity to malaria, but many had to go through the same "seasoning" to develop tolerance of the local strains of the disease as white settlers. Slaves in the West Indies and southern United States, and Indian laborers on plantations in Indonesia, actually suffered from much the same diseases as Europeans—malaria, fevers, dysentery, and cholera.

Now practitioners recommended that the best way for Europeans to survive in hot climates was to limit their exposure to dangerous heat and miasma. In the southern United States, settlers avoided living and working on low-lying swampy land, preferring to set up their new homes on drier slopes. In summer, plantation owners moved away from their mansions to the sea or to the hills, where the climate was cooler and they could enjoy fresh breezes. They were unconsciously imitating Native American people living around the Mississippi who moved away from rivers during the summer season. In India, British administrators and soldiers were periodically moved to "hill stations" where, it was hoped the more agreeable climate would counteract the effects of the heat during the rest of the year. Even this was not sufficient to protect the health of children, and many were sent home to attend schools in Europe.

In an effort to work out which areas were suitable for European settlement, doctors gathered data on a wide range of environmental factors in the new colonies. Almost every aspect of the landscape was relevant to the issue. Investigators exhaustively described

> [T]he surface and elevation of the ground, the stratification and composition of the soil, the supply and quantity of the water, the extent of marshes and wet ground, the progress of drainage; the nature and amounts of the products of the land; the condition, increase or decrease, and prevalent diseases of the animals maintained thereon; together with periodical reports of the temperature, pressure, humidity, motion and electricity of the atmosphere. (Martin 1856, 99)

Another strategy was to adapt the European lifestyle to a new context. John Dudgeon, a Scottish doctor who lived and worked in China, joked: "Europeans come to China, and they eat, and they drink, and they eat, and then they die, and afterwards wire home that the climate killed them" (Dudgeon 1877, 36). A typical European diet included plenty of meat and alcohol. Both of these foodstuffs were believed to heat the body and predispose it to fevers. Dudgeon argued that Europeans should follow the example of the Chinese people and eat a diet of beans, rice, and vegetables, with no meat or alcohol. Other doctors disagreed; different diets were suited to different races. European settlers should modify their diet, eating less meat and more vegetables, rather than make radical changes. They should also adapt their clothing and wear light, loose garments rather than the usual heavy European dress, and rest during the heat of the day. Regular bloodletting, especially at the change of seasons, helped to keep the body healthy.

The connection between environment and disease was not broken until the end of the century, when doctors working in the new field of tropical medicine began to identify the organisms responsible for the diseases previously linked to the climates of India and Africa. In 1898, Ronald Ross proved that malaria was not the result of miasma but was caused by a parasite spread by mosquitoes. In 1900, the transmission routes of elephantiasis and of yellow fever were also described. As a result, the diseases of tropical regions were no longer seen as an inevitable consequence of living in hot climates but were a set of illnesses that could be prevented by appropriate sanitary measures.

Environment and Folk Medicine

Folk medicine did not have explanations for how aspects of the natural world influenced the internal functions of the body, but indigenous people in Africa and America still identified risks to health originating in their environment, both natural and supernatural. Native American peoples believed that the world was full of spirits, many of which could cause disease if not shown respect. A fisher who wasted his catch or a hunter who did not ask the spirits for permission to kill animals by praying or making ritual offerings might be struck down with illness. In southern Africa, Zulu people refused to go into forests that were reputed to be inhabited by witches. As forests were inhabited by tsetse flies, this taboo provided protection against sleeping sickness.

People also had cultural practices that helped to protect against environmental disease. Native American people moved away from rivers in the summer, when mosquitoes were prevalent. Zulu people built their settlements well away from swampy ground. Their houses had floors made of cow dung, and smoky fires were used for cooking; both these practices helped to repel insects. Houses that became infested with insects were burned. The people disposed of excrement in pits in the ground well away from living quarters, or covered it with boiling water.

ENVIRONMENTAL CURES

While some environments produced disease, in every culture, particular climates and natural products were used to heal the body. A wide variety of natural substances were used in therapy. Mud and earths were collected to make poultices to treat injuries and skin complaints, and many minerals had medicinal uses. Plants formed the main source of drugs in every culture. Hot springs and waters impregnated with minerals had long been used as a form of therapy by indigenous peoples in Africa and the Americas; this is the origin of the place name "Indian Springs" still found in North America. Mineral waters were believed to be particularly effective in curing diseases of the liver—a frequent problem in hot climates—and settlers bathed in the water of mineral springs used by local peoples. On the island of Guadeloupe in the Caribbean, thermal mineral springs traditionally used by indigenous peoples became sites for hydropathic bathing establishments for settlers. There, soldiers and administrators spent time recovering their health by drinking and bathing in the waters. Mineral waters were also used in 19th-century Europe to treat a variety of ailments, especially skin complaints. Natural springs became centers for spa towns—therapeutic resorts where the sick came to drink and bathe.

European and American people, wealthy enough to be able to travel freely over long distances, sought out healthy climates to cure their ailments. Coastal resorts were initially built to allow the sick to bathe in saltwater and to breathe sea air. Over time, they became sites primarily for leisure, although they never entirely lost their therapeutic identity. A seaside holiday was a chance to take in sea air and provided a chance to relax and "recharge the batteries." Living in a sunny, dry, airy environment was recommended as a cure for tuberculosis. Sanatoria were set

Bathing in water rich in minerals was believed to cure diseases and to improve health and well-being. These patients bathing in water from a sulphur spring might have been seeking relief from skin diseases or rheumatism. (Corbis Historical/Getty Images)

up throughout the world in appropriate situations—on the coasts of California, on Pacific islands, and on European mountains where the resinous smell given off by pine trees was believed to add to the therapeutic qualities of the air.

HEALTH AND THE URBAN ENVIRONMENT

Around the globe, towns and cities were seen as inherently unhealthy. In Western medicine, dirt was seen as a direct or indirect cause of disease, and 19th-century cities were filthy places. Huge amounts of refuse were generated by homes and businesses. In small communities with a fairly static population and active local government, these could be removed efficiently. Sweepers carted away street and household refuse from built-up areas. Privies and cesspools were emptied by night-soil men and the contents used as manure on nearby fields. However, when urban populations expanded rapidly, these mechanisms broke down. There was too much excrement to use on the land, and old rubbish dumps were quickly filled. Householders began to deposit their refuse on the streets, in empty spaces, and in rivers, often polluting water supplies. In the early part of the century, doctors warned that rotting refuse generated miasmas that caused fevers and other diseases; by the end of the century, they understood that dirt helped to spread infections via contaminated water or dirty living conditions.

City dwellers were also exposed to the danger of air pollution. Coal was used to fuel industrial processes (tall factory chimneys dominated the skyline of many towns) and to heat homes. The resulting smoke pollution was visible to all; it blocked out sunlight so that plants could not grow and children developed rickets.

The air of towns smelled of smoke, and people's eyes stung from the sulfur released from the coal. Every surface became coated with particles of soot, so much so that the industrial north of England was nicknamed "the Black Country." Constant exposure to smoke pollution increased deaths from respiratory diseases; bronchitis was the most common cause of death in industrial areas in the late 19th century. Even more dangerous was smog, when smoke and fog combined to make a dense, choking atmosphere, sometimes lasting for days. In Britain, such smog was called a "pea-souper" after a type of thick, yellowish soup. During periods of smog, the numbers of traffic accidents rose, and deaths from respiratory complaints rocketed.

Certain spaces within cities were associated with pollution and disease, especially graveyards. As the population of urban areas expanded, so did the numbers of bodies requiring burial within churches or their adjoining cemeteries. These became overcrowded, with new bodies crammed into shallow graves on top of older burials. The custom of visiting the graves of recently deceased relatives so as to stay close to the body was increasingly seen as a health hazard.

In the second half of the century, urban authorities throughout Europe and the Americas began to tackle the health hazards associated with urban life. Reformed systems of street sweeping and refuse collection reduced the amount of rubbish on the streets. New sewer systems removed excrement beyond the city limits for processing and disposal. Large cemeteries were built away from town centers, and from the 1880s, a growing number of people chose to have their bodies cremated after death. City authorities could do little to reduce smoke pollution; burning coal was vital to many industries, and factory owners were reluctant to take any measures that might reduce the efficiency of their operations. Smog and smoke remained health hazards for urban dwellers well into the 20th century.

Other cities around the world were equally filthy, but local doctors did not necessarily see this as a source of ill health. Western observers complained of the filthy conditions in Chinese cities and were surprised that the inhabitants nevertheless seemed to be healthy. Although some Chinese practitioners believed that filth was associated with pestilential qi and disease, the inhabitants of Chinese cities were apparently fairly tolerant of dirt. Indeed, they valued excrement as a fertilizer and collected it from homes and the streets to sell to local peasant farmers. They probably escaped some urban diseases through the practice of treating water to make it pleasant to drink. Water collected from wells and rivers was stored for some days so that dirt or sediment collected in the bottom of the vessel. It was then treated with alum (potassium aluminum sulfate) to make it clear and was boiled before use.

OCCUPATIONAL HAZARDS

In addition to the hazards posed by the natural world and the built environment, workplaces brought their own sets of dangers. In every culture, certain occupations were known to carry risks.

Agricultural Hazards

By far the most common set of dangers was those associated with agriculture. Subsistence farmers, growing crops to feed themselves and perhaps to trade, used simple tools. Even so, they received cuts, bruises, or even broken bones from sickles, axes, and plows. Animals were an essential part of many farms: they provided meat and milk and the motive force to pull carts or plows. But even well-trained animals could be dangerous and unpredictable; riders fell from horses and camels, workers were trampled by cattle and run over by carts. Where farmers lived in close proximity to their animals, they were likely to pick up parasites and diseases such as anthrax.

The risks of injury increased when farming became industrialized. Where farmers could sell to a big market, they began to use machinery to till the soil and raise crops. Steam engines or "traction engines" were used on large farms in Europe and North America to pull plows and run threshing machines. Smaller machines, such as reapers to cut grain crops and mills to process vegetables, were powered by horses. Both large and small machines presented new dangers as it was all too easy for fingers, hands, or whole limbs to be caught in the moving parts and cut or torn off.

In addition, agricultural workers suffered from spending long hours outdoors. In cold climates, a large proportion of farm laborers developed chronic ear infections that led to deafness. Workers on rice, cotton, rubber, and coffee plantations in tropical parts of Asia and Africa endured very poor health. Many of these plantations were worked by indentured laborers from India, who signed up for a period of two or three years. Little money or attention was given to building good living quarters for them. Workers were packed into huts or barracks, working long hours with few rest periods. They suffered from high rates of tuberculosis, from cholera and dysentery spread through contaminated water supplies, from parasitic infections such as hookworm picked up from the damp soil, and from deficiency diseases such as beri-beri from a poor diet. Not surprisingly, mortality rates were high.

Industrial Hazards

Diseases and injuries were known to be associated with particular occupations throughout the 19th century. The first occupational disease, a form of cancer found among chimney sweeps, was identified as early as 1775. Workplace hazards to life and health were found not only in the industrialized West. Mining for minerals, metals, coal, and precious stones took place around the world. Regardless of the depth of the mines, and whether hand tools or cutting machines were used, all miners faced the risk of lung disease from inhaling dust. "Miner's lung" was first recorded in Europe in the early 1830s. Workers developed a chronic cough, breathlessness, and chest pains, and many died. The disease was characterized by the black phlegm coughed up by victims, full of particles of dust. Postmortem examinations revealed the damage.

> When cut into, both lungs presented one uniform black carbonaceous colour, pervading every part of their substance. The right lung was much disorganised, and exhibited in its upper and middle lobes several large irregular cavities . . . The cavities contained a good deal of fluid, which, as well as the walls of the cavities, partook of the same black colour. (Gregory 1831, 389–394)

While "black lung" was associated with miners, especially coal miners, many other groups of workers suffered from similar illnesses. Stone masons, bakers, and textile workers all labored in dusty conditions and experienced high death rates from respiratory illnesses. Workers in the metal industries breathed in dust and grit from machines used for sharpening and grinding. Many went blind from small particles of metal that became lodged in their eyes.

Industries exposed workers to a variety of toxic substances. Women working in match factories developed "phossy jaw," a disease that ate away at the bones of the face due to contact with phosphorus. Mercury compounds, used in the hat and fur trades and in silver mines as an agent to separate metal from ore, caused damage to the nerves. One of the most common occupational diseases was lead poisoning. Lead was used in many manufactured goods such as batteries and paint. Workers suffered from "lead colic"—an acute form of poisoning that caused severe stomach pains and seizures. Those who came into contact with lead over long periods suffered chronic poisoning that damaged the kidneys and blood and left them unable to fight off infections.

Many workers employed in occupations requiring physical strength, from farmers to builders, coal miners, dockworkers, and general laborers suffered from injuries. They were crushed by falling objects. Strenuous physical effort resulted in hernias, when part of the internal organs bulged through the muscular wall of the abdomen. Trusses—special bandages to support the injury—allowed sufferers to continue to work.

OCCUPATIONAL HEALTH

Tracing out the links between diseases and occupations was far from straightforward. Workers often developed symptoms years after exposure to toxins. Workers handling the same chemicals might fall ill after a short time or remain unaffected for long periods. Nevertheless, by the end of the century, doctors in the West had described many of the most common industrial hazards, and governments—particularly those in Europe—had begun to pass legislation to limit the dangers. Regulation had little effect, however. Many of the new laws advised factory owners to take action but did not require them to install ventilation or provide special clothing. Workers did not always welcome measures to protect their health. Safety goggles, gloves, or masks might protect their eyes, hands, and lungs, but they were uncomfortable to wear for long periods and slowed the pace at which they could work and thus reduced their wages. Given the lack of effective treatment for most occupational illnesses, many workers chose to take the risk and to earn high wages in dangerous workplaces for a limited time and then change jobs if they became ill.

8

Surgery and Medical Procedures

In the present day, surgery is a specialist branch of medicine, concerned with repairing injuries to the body and treating disease by the removal of malfunctioning tissues. Surgeons enjoy high status within the medical profession and work exclusively in hospitals. This modern form of surgery emerged in the 19th century in Europe and North America. In 1800, in many medical cultures, manual procedures were carried out by groups of healers (called surgeons in the West but with a variety of names in non-Western cultures). They treated complaints on the outside of the body—injuries, skin diseases, and abscesses—and performed various procedures aimed at curing internal diseases, such as bloodletting and acupuncture. A few carried out major operations, such as the removal of bladder stones, but only as a last resort when patients' lives were in danger.

While these forms of surgical practice continued in non-Western cultures throughout the 19th century, in Europe and North America, surgery underwent a revolution. Scientific medicine saw illness arising from some problem within a particular organ, and it allowed practitioners to develop new procedures to treat illness by the removal of diseased tissue. The discovery of anesthetics and the development of antiseptics enhanced these developments, ensuring greater levels of success. As a result, surgery moved onto center stage in medicine and surgeons became medical heroes, no longer dealing with minor complaints but treating serious, acute disease.

SURGERY OUTSIDE THE WEST

Surgical Practitioners

In many (although not all) cultures, medical practice was divided between healers, who dealt with internal diseases, and surgical practitioners, who treated injuries and ailments that affected the surface of the body. In Chinese, Unani, and Ayurvedic medicine, learned practitioners, trained in medical theory, diagnosed disease and prescribed medicines and other therapies. They regarded any form of manual work as demeaning to their status as learned men and left the application of mechanical treatment to surgical healers. In Unani medicine, for example, bloodletting might be prescribed by a learned *hakim*, but because touching the patient's body (except to take the pulse) was not appropriate behavior for an elite practitioner, the bloodletting was performed by a *jarrah*—a surgical practitioner. In systems of folk medicine, there was no distinction between learned and surgical practitioners. Many healers diagnosed, prescribed, and carried out surgical treatments, although some, such as diviners and spiritual healers, did not perform manual therapies.

Surgical practitioners could specialize in a single form of treatment or offer a range of therapies. In Costa Rica, for example, most practitioners were barber-surgeons or bloodletters (*sangradores*). (At first glance, this seems an odd combination of occupations, but both barbering and bloodletting required the use of sharp instruments.) Bloodletting was a popular therapy and was the mainstay of their work, but some practitioners also lanced abscesses, extracted teeth, cauterized wounds, and practiced bonesetting. A few forms of surgical therapy were highly specialized. The removal of bladder stones, small masses of material that formed in the urine and irritated the bladder, was a very dangerous operation requiring great skill. The condition was relatively rare and was treated by a small number of specialist itinerant practitioners, who traveled over large areas to treat patients.

Surgical practitioners acquired their skills and knowledge by observing the work of experienced practitioners and learned to practice under their supervision. In Costa Rica, they were called *empíricos* (a term with the same root as the English word "empirical"), reflecting the importance of experience and observation, rather than theory, in their practice. Although surgical practitioners were distinguished by their mechanical skills, many often possessed some basic knowledge of medical theory. In China, acupuncture was prescribed by a learned doctor but was carried out by healers skilled in the techniques of inserting the needles and with some understanding of the actions of qi and a knowledge of the points to use in order to achieve the desired effect.

Practitioners carrying out surgical procedures had an uneasy relationship with practitioners formally trained in medical theory. Learned physicians frequently complained that surgical practitioners did not confine their practice to the exterior of the body but attempted to take over their role by diagnosing illness and prescribing treatment. Given their limited understanding of how the body worked, this often had disastrous results. In many places, physicians tried to impose some form of regulation on surgical practitioners, by requiring them to have evidence of their training and limiting their practice to manual procedures. These efforts rarely succeeded. Usually, surgical healers who dealt with simple cases were ignored or tolerated by the local authorities, unless their practices were dangerous to patients. In times of emergency, such as during epidemics, local governments sometimes employed surgical healers to treat patients under the supervision of formally qualified practitioners.

SURGICAL PRACTICE

Surgical practitioners provided a wide range of therapies. These included manual procedures to treat injuries, by cleaning and closing wounds and setting broken and dislocated limbs. They cured lesions on the exterior of the body, lancing or applying medicines and poultices to swellings, and carried out therapies such as bloodletting, cautery, or acupuncture to treat internal complaints. Finally, some surgical practitioners dealt with eye diseases, operated for stones in the bladder, removed teeth, and carried out smallpox inoculation and later vaccination.

Wounds and Broken Bones

When confronted by wounds to the skin and flesh, surgical healers around the world used broadly similar treatments. They first cleaned the injury by washing it using plain water or water in which herbs had been boiled or by sucking to remove any blood and dirt. Various substances were applied to stop bleeding, including spiders' webs, the spores of puffballs and other fungi, and the roots and leaves of plants. Injuries were then bandaged with cloth or bark. If the wound was serious, practitioners in some cultures closed it by stitching the skin using sutures made of plant fiber or animal hair. In Africa, travelers described how biting ants were used to close a wound. The insects were encouraged to clamp their jaws over the edges of the skin and then the ant's body was twisted off, leaving the mouthparts in place.

A range of medicines were used to help healing. Minor wounds were allowed to heal spontaneously, but in the case of deep or complex injuries, practitioners often deliberately tried to induce infection as the formation of pus was seen as a necessary part of the healing process. Healers tried to prevent the surface of the wound from healing, while infection remained within the body. Ideally, wounds should heal from the bottom upward to achieve a complete cure. To encourage this, Native American healers blew a powder made from roots into wounds. In other cultures, healers prevented wounds from closing by inserting small pieces of reed, bark, or cloth into the flesh. This technique was particularly important in cases in which arrows or bullets remained in the body. If the object was close to the surface, it was removed using a knife or a magnet. If it was out of reach of instruments, healers induced infection to push the foreign object out of the wound.

In some cultures, medical theories were used to guide what medicines should be used in the treatment of injuries. In Unani medicine, the treatment of wounds drew on the principle of opposites. Weeping wounds should be treated with dry medicines. The wound should be "pressed so that the fluids ooze out. Then medicine should be applied on the wound with cotton wool wrapped on a slim rod . . . it should be allowed to dry . . . [then] medical ointment [marham]mixed with egg white is put on it. The wound should be washed with water boiled with fruits and herbs like dried pomegranate" (Khan 1878, 1258).

Broken or dislocated bones were treated using very similar techniques around the world. The damaged limb was straightened and massaged so that the ends of the bones moved back toward their normal alignment and then held in place with bandages and splints made of thin strips of wood or bones. In southern Africa, broken bones were supported with a cast made of clay, and in North Africa, gypsum plaster was used to make a cast. Medicines were used to help the healing process. Poultices or ointments were applied to help the bones to heal. In southern

Africa, herbal medicines were rubbed into incisions above the damage to encourage the ends of the bone to unite.

Skin Diseases and Abscesses

Skin conditions such as rashes and insect bites were treated with soothing applications. Native American peoples used bears' oil to prevent and to cure a variety of skin diseases. The rash caused by contact with poison ivy was treated with bruised leaves applied directly to the skin or with a lotion made from leaves boiled in water. Localized infections that produced swellings called boils or abscesses were treated with hot poultices. The heat was soothing, and the poultice encouraged the abscess to burst, letting the pus flow out. Alternatively, healers cut open the swelling or applied a caustic substance to make it burst. Ayurvedic texts applied medical theory to direct the best course of treatment. As tumors, boils, and ulcers developed under the skin, they were believed to reflect an imbalance of *doshas* within the body. Different imbalances produced different types of skin lesion: abscesses caused by an excess of *kapha* were white and with a copious discharge; those associated with *pitta* were yellow and burning. They were treated with a combination of external treatments, such as poultices, and internal medicines to deal with the underlying imbalance within the body.

Bloodletting and Cautery

Bloodletting—removing a controlled amount of blood from the body—was widely practiced around the world. In Ayurvedic and Unani medicine, the procedure was used to remove bad blood, or excess amounts of blood associated with a range of illnesses. Bloodletting was also used to treat local pain and as a general tonic. Many people chose to be bled at the end of winter or at the change of seasons to remove "worn out" or stagnant blood. In some forms of folk medicine, such as those practiced in southern Africa, bloodletting was used to remove accumulations of blood that were believed to cause swellings. Only Chinese practitioners rarely used bloodletting. Learned practitioners argued that bloodletting was pointless, as bad and good blood were released at the same time. Patients with too much blood should be treated with medicines to tackle the causes of the excess.

The techniques of bloodletting were very similar across all cultures. Cupping was used to remove small amounts of blood. The skin was scratched or rubbed, and then blood was drawn through it using pressure. African folk practitioners applied a vessel such as a cow's horn to the skin and sucked air out through a hole in the narrow end. In India, a glass or pottery vessel was heated and put on the skin. As it cooled, a vacuum formed, drawing out some blood. Small quantities of blood could also be removed using leeches. This technique had several advantages. The operation was relatively painless as when it bit, the leech injected a form of local anesthetic and an anticoagulant. The quantity of blood removed from the body was easily controlled by varying the number of leeches; each would suck out around a tablespoonful of blood and then drop off. Leeches could be applied to particular parts of the body, and they were often used to remove blood around swellings. When a larger amount of blood needed to be removed, in cases of serious internal illness, bloodletters cut open a vein, allowed the blood to flow until a sufficient amount was removed or until the patient fainted, and then applied pressure to stop the bleeding. The site chosen for bloodletting depended on the condition. When treating localized conditions, bloodletters opened a vein close to the site of the problem; so for headaches, blood would be taken from the head. For generalized conditions, such as fever, the practitioner would open a vein at any convenient point, usually on the arm.

Like bloodletting, cautery, or localized burning of the skin, was used to treat various ailments, including stomach complaints and skin lesions such as ulcers, and to stop bleeding. In Unani medicine and in some systems of folk medicine, it was also performed to relieve pain. In North America, indigenous healers used a burning reed, placed over a piece of thin wet leather, to produce a burn. In other tribes, practitioners placed a small piece of burning fungus or plant directly on the skin. In North Africa, surgical practitioners used a hot knife to lightly touch the skin over a painful joint or over the stomach to treat gastric pains.

Acupuncture and Moxibustion

In Chinese medicine, health was the product of a regular, smooth flow of qi, and blockages to the flow caused illness. Acupuncture was used to influence the flow of qi and cure internal diseases. Practitioners inserted fine needles into the skin along channels running throughout the body. The exact position of the needles stimulated different pathways or organs, and different combinations of points were used to treat conditions including pain, fevers, colic, and headaches.

Chinese medicine also made use of heat to stimulate the movement of qi, a process called moxibustion. Small pellets of moxa, dried material from the mugwort plant, were placed on the skin above the channels through which qi flowed. They were lit and allowed to burn, producing heat and a small burn or blister. The substance used for the moxa pellets was important—it needed to burn quickly so as to stimulate the body but not to cause serious damage to the skin.

Traditional Surgical Operations

Outside Europe and North America, surgical operations that required deliberately cutting open the body were not a major form of 19th-century medical practice. Although accounts of a range of operations appeared in ancient and medieval Chinese, Ayurvedic, and Unani texts, the evidence suggests that relatively few were regularly performed. Historians have suggested that these descriptions of operations may have been written to show off the skill and knowledge of the author, rather than to provide a practical guide for surgical practitioners.

In the 19th century, operations were carried out for a handful of very serious conditions, when treatment using medicines had failed. Operations to remove

In many cultures, a group of practitioners specialized in eye surgery, including operations for cataracts. This image shows an Indian eye surgeon at work, with his instruments and pots of medicines. (Wellcome Collection)

cataracts from the eye, and thus preserve sight, were carried out by specialist eye doctors in many cultures. In China, India, and North Africa, they used very similar techniques. A lancet or needle was inserted slowly into the eye, and the damaged lens pressed downward to push it out of the line of vision. In some cases, the lens was pierced to allow the fluid to flow into the eye. While the operation was often successful in restoring some sight, Western travelers reported that many patients later lost their eye to postoperative infections.

Operations on the internal organs were much more dangerous and were performed only as a last resort. Bladder stones caused acute pain and, if they prevented urination, could prove fatal. Patients usually tried taking medicines to break up the stone and allow the pieces to pass out naturally with the urine. Only if this failed were specialist practitioners called in to operate. Ayurvedic texts described how the patient was given alcohol before the procedure to dull the pain. A skilled surgeon located the stone by massaging around the bladder area. He then made a small incision through the abdomen and into the bladder, removing the stone with a hooked instrument. The surgeon had to be very precise in making the incision—cutting into the urethra or uterus caused dangerous complications.

Cesarean sections to save the life of an infant when the mother could not deliver it naturally were attempted only when the mother had died or was close to death. The operation seems to have been performed occasionally in many cultures but was rarely successful. A handful of 19th-century travelers reported seeing cesarean sections carried out by indigenous practitioners in Africa. In 1879, a British traveler witnessed the operation in Uganda in East Africa. He reported that the healer gave the patient alcohol to dull the pain before making the incision. Cautery was used to stop the bleeding and massage to make the uterus contract. The incision was dressed with a paste prepared from roots (Felkin 1884). Reports of similar operations came from Rwanda in Central Africa.

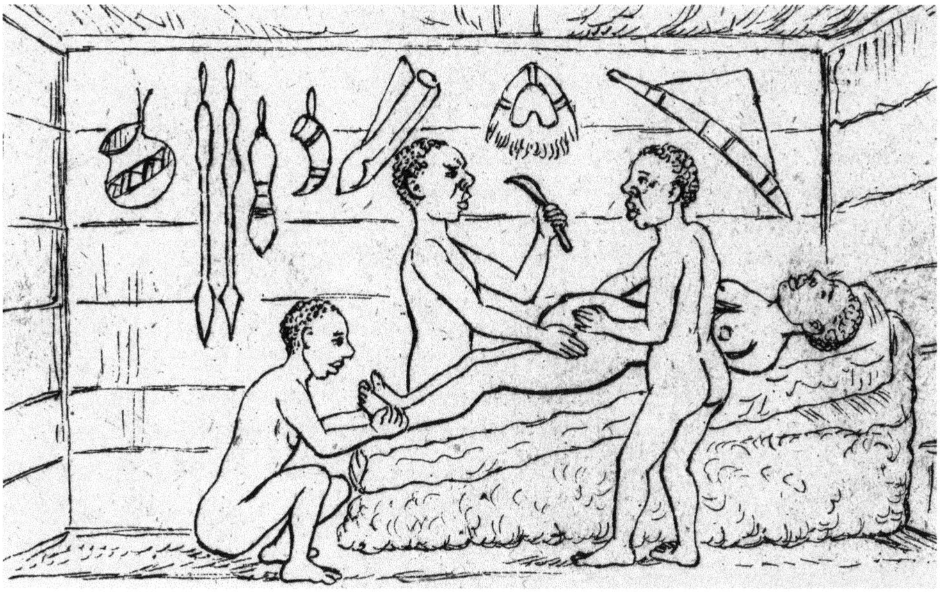

This drawing, made by a European observer in 1879, shows a group of indigenous practitioners in Uganda about to perform a caesarean delivery. (Wellcome Collection)

DEVELOPMENTS IN WESTERN SURGERY

Outside the West, practitioners continued to use this traditional repertoire of procedures during the 19th century; by contrast, in Europe and North America, surgery was revolutionized, going from a set of techniques to deal with a limited number of fairly minor conditions to procedures capable of treating a large number of serious or life-threatening diseases. In 1800, surgeons in the West performed procedures similar to those performed in the rest of the world: they treated injuries, dealt with diseases affecting the surface of the body, and let blood. They operated on cataracts in the eye and for bladder stones. Unlike non-Western surgical practitioners, they also routinely amputated diseased and damaged limbs.

In the early part of the century, the success of all surgical procedures was limited by pain, blood loss, shock, and infection. Even simple operations had a high mortality rate, and all were traumatic for the patient. Fanny Burney, the English novelist, recorded the experience of undergoing a 20-minute operation for breast cancer in 1811. The opium and alcohol she was given to reduce the pain clearly had only a limited effect.

> When the dreadful steel was plunged into the breast—cutting through veins—arteries—flesh—nerves—I needed no injunctions to restrain my cries. I began a scream that lasted unintermittingly [sic] during the whole time of the incision . . . when again I felt the instrument—describing a curve—cutting against the grain . . . while the flesh resisted . . . I thought I must have expired. (Porter 1997, 365)

The early decades of the century saw a number of improvements in surgical techniques. The treatment of broken limbs was helped by the development of bandages impregnated with plaster of Paris to make a secure and durable cast. Better tourniquets helped to reduce blood loss in cases of serious injury or during amputations. Survival rates after amputation increased as surgeons reduced blood loss and shock by operating more quickly. Amputation of the leg at the hip took around 20 minutes at the beginning of the century; by the 1830s, James Syme, a London surgeon, performed the same operation in 90 seconds.

New understandings of disease—that illnesses were often localized within one organ or tissue—developed in the early part of the century encouraged Western doctors to explore the possibility of treating these conditions by removing the malfunctioning part of the body. An operation to remove diseased tonsils was first carried out in 1828. Two American physicians Ephraim MacDowell and James Marion Sims pioneered the successful removal of ovarian tumors and the repair of tears in the vagina following childbirth in 1809 and the late 1840s, respectively. Nevertheless, it required a series of breakthroughs in the control of pain and infection before surgery could become a highly successful method of treating disease.

Anesthesia

From the early 19th century, practitioners knew that inhaling nitrous oxide (laughing gas) or the fumes from diethyl ether (usually called simply "ether") produced mild euphoria and reduced pain. Doctors had experimented with ether as an anesthetic in the early 1840s, but its use was established by a public demonstration in October 1846, when William Morton, an American dentist, removed a small tumor from the neck of an anesthetized patient. Word quickly spread. Ether anesthetic was used in Paris two months later, and shortly afterward, a leg amputation, the first major operation under anesthesia, was performed in London before an audience of medical students and practitioners. Ether presented a great advance on earlier attempts to control pain. When they breathed the fumes from an ether-soaked cloth, it brought a blessed unconsciousness to the patient. It also made the surgeons' job much easier, as they no longer had to operate on a screaming, struggling patient. The drug was not without its hazards. Ether was highly inflammable, unpleasant to inhale, and caused nausea and vomiting when the anesthetic effect wore off.

Practitioners therefore looked for other chemicals with similar effects. Just one year later, James Young Simpson, a Scottish obstetrician, tried inhaling chloroform, another organic chemical, and passed out. Within days, he began using the drug in his own practice and later published his findings. Chloroform was quickly adopted by European practitioners to ease the pain of childbirth and for surgical operations. Chloroform had the advantage of acting more quickly than ether, and patients did not go through a period of exhilaration before becoming unconscious. On the other hand, a slight overdose of chloroform was highly dangerous, as patients suffered fatal heart attacks. This problem was solved by developing inhalers that precisely controlled the amount of anesthetic given to the patient.

Both ether and chloroform induced general anesthesia. Local anesthetics, which dulled pain in a part of the body while the patient remained conscious, were first used in the 1880s. The numbing effect of chewing leaves of the coca plant had been known for centuries. Cocaine, the chemical responsible for this effect, was isolated in 1859, but not until 1884 was the drug applied to control the pain of eye operations and dental work. However, the problems associated with its use—several patients died, and more became addicted to the drug—meant that it quickly fell out of favor, and local anesthesia was not routinely used until new compounds such as procaine were developed in the early 20th century.

While anesthesia freed patients from excruciating pain, it was not without controversy. Doctors believed that pain was a natural response to injury and a stimulus to healing, and worried that incisions made under anesthesia would not heal properly. As a result, not all patients received anesthetics. A study of operations conducted in American hospitals in the decade after the introduction of anesthetics showed that men, especially soldiers, black men, and Irishmen, were believed to be able to stand the pain of operations and were less likely to receive anesthetics than women and children. Patients too had their concerns: would surgeons be tempted to carry out unnecessary procedures or experiment with new and unproven techniques on their unconscious subjects? Surgeons were optimistic (to modern eyes, hopelessly overoptimistic) about the benefits of the removal of organs. In the 1870s and 1880s, many women had their healthy ovaries taken out in the hope of curing nervous conditions such as hysteria.

Antisepsis and Asepsis

While anesthetics made operations safer and more bearable, patients were still at risk of developing fatal wound infections after surgery. Surgical wounds were exposed to contamination from many sources. Procedures were carried out in operating theaters, often in front of an audience of medical students, or on hospital wards or in patients' homes. These spaces were clean but not scrupulously so. Surgeons expected to be spattered with blood during surgery, so they operated wearing old clothes. Often they wore the same coat for many operations. Surgical instruments were wiped or washed but not sterilized. Sometimes infection became so prevalent that it affected the wounds of every patient in a hospital ward. The only way to deal with these outbreaks was to shut the ward and undertake a thorough cleansing, sometimes even stripping the plaster from the walls.

From the 1840s, some surgeons adopted a "cold water and cleanliness" strategy to combat infection, ensuring that instruments, the surgeons' hands, and the operating area were thoroughly scrubbed before each operation. In 1867, Joseph Lister, a Scottish surgeon, published the results of using antiseptic techniques—an approach that attempted to kill all germs in and around the wound. Lister's work was based on Louis Pasteur's observations that bacteria were responsible for putrefaction. He began to systematically disinfect everything that came into contact with a wound using carbolic acid. Lister experimented on cases of compound fractures that routinely became infected. Wounds were cleaned with carbolic acid and dressed with bandages soaked in the chemical. The surgeon's hands and all instruments were disinfected; even the air was disinfected using a fine spray of carbolic. Lister's results were spectacular. Compound fractures healed without infection, avoiding the need for amputation of the limb, and the death rate following amputations fell from 45 percent of all cases to just 15 percent.

Lister's methods were not immediately adopted by all medical practitioners. Some doubted whether invisible bacteria were really the cause of infection. Others found that Lister's procedures were difficult to use and that the carbolic acid disinfectant irritated the skin of surgeons and their patients. Over the following decades, his techniques were adapted, moving from antisepsis to asepsis (working in a germ-free environment). Operating theaters were redesigned: wooden floors and cabinets gave way to tiled or glass surfaces; windows and skylights were replaced with electric lights, and simple tables removed in favor of specialized operating tables. Steam was found to be a more effective means of disinfecting instruments than carbolic acid. Surgeons began to wear sterilized gowns, caps, and gloves, and students were banished from the operating room to enclosed viewing galleries.

The Rise of Surgery

The combination of anesthetics, antisepsis, and asepsis allowed surgeons to safely open up all parts of the body without risk of infection, to operate slowly and carefully, to remove the minimum of diseased and damaged tissues, and to control blood loss by clamping vessels. Improved suturing techniques allowed surgeons to reconnect the cut edges of skin and tissues inside the body. These techniques allowed surgeons to devise a range of new operations in the late 19th century. In the 1860s, surgeons mainly repaired limbs and dealt with superficial tumors. By the end of the century, they were carrying out complex operations to remove diseased tissue from the internal organs and thereby treat diseases such as appendicitis and duodenal ulcers. Surgeons could take out gallstones and kidney stones and remove tumors anywhere in the body, even from the brain and spinal cord. Often, new operations carried a high mortality rate, but as surgeons refined their skills and understanding, death rates fell. Mortality from removal of goiter (an enlarged thyroid gland) fell from 14 to less than 1 percent in around a decade.

Surgery offered the hope of a cure in previously untreatable conditions. Until the late 19th century, cancers of the breast and uterus had inevitably caused lingering and painful deaths. Early attempts to remove tumors usually proved unsuccessful—the patients either died as a direct result of surgery or the cancer returned within a few years. Toward the end of the century, surgeons began to have some measure of success as they realized the need to remove tissues around the tumor. However, survival rates rose only slowly. In 1870 in Vienna, one of the best centers for surgery, only eight of 170 women operated on for breast cancer were cured.

The number of patients undergoing surgery increased, not just as a result of the availability of new operations to treat a wider range of conditions. More patients were seen as suitable cases for surgical treatment. Prior to the introduction of anesthetics, women had been less likely to undergo operations because doctors feared that they were unable to stand the pain. Ether and chloroform removed this barrier, and many more women underwent surgery. Patients suffering from serious disease or injury, who had previously been expected to die and therefore were not operated on, could now be saved through prompt surgical intervention.

ORTHOPEDICS

Developments in surgery further advanced the creation of orthopedics as a new area of specialist practice. From the 18th century, a few doctors specialized in the treatment of deformed limbs and joints. They mainly practiced on "crippled" children, suffering from deformities such as curvature of the spine or club foot—a condition in which one or both feet were pointed inward or down, leaving the patient unable to place weight on the sole of the foot. A combination of splits, plaster casts, bandages, and massage were applied to gradually push the affected joint back into a more normal configuration.

Surgery opened up new possibilities for treating these conditions. From the 1830s, doctors developed an operation to treat club foot by cutting the Achilles tendon, thus allowing the foot to fall into a better alignment. With improved infection control, surgeons began to operate on bones. Limbs that had become bowed as a result of rickets, a deficiency disease linked to lack of vitamin D, were treated by cutting through the bone and allowing it to heal in a straighter form. Infections within bones and joints, often caused by tuberculosis, were now cured by opening the abscess and allowing pus to drain out. Surgery did not displace older, nonsurgical methods of treatment. The two were combined to treat many conditions, such as congenital hip displacement.

SURGEONS AND HOSPITALS

Developments in surgery had profound effects on the status of surgeons. Traditionally, surgeons, with their practical training in surgical procedures acquired through apprenticeship, had a lower status than university-educated physicians. Over the course of the 18th and 19th centuries, the relationship between the two groups changed radically. In the late 18th century, the training of the two groups came together. Surgeons began to attend lectures in medical schools, and physicians were taught anatomy and surgery. Gradually, a standardized curriculum covering both medicine and surgery became the norm in all medical schools. While most practitioners performed basic surgical procedures such as cleaning and stitching wounds as part of their medical practice, surgery emerged as a specialty within medicine. Following basic training, students wishing to become surgeons received further training in hospitals. As surgery became an option for the treatment of previously incurable diseases, the status of surgeons rose. By the end of the 19th century, surgeons were godlike figures, commanding respect, admiration, and high fees.

The rise of surgery also had a dramatic effect on the work of hospitals. In 1800, they were places of care, treating chronic disease among the poor with medicines, diet, and basic nursing. By 1900, hospitals had become centers for surgery, taking in patients suffering from acute illnesses and serious injuries. The role of nurses changed, too, as they began to assist in operating theaters and to care for very sick patients recovering from surgery.

SURGICAL EXCHANGES

New surgical techniques developed in Europe and North America were taken to non-Western cultures by colonial practitioners, especially medical missionaries. The superiority of Western surgery over the procedures traditionally used in Asia and Africa, in terms of both the range of conditions that could be treated and the success of operations, was quickly recognized. Patients flocked to hospitals and dispensaries offering Western surgery. In China, where indigenous practitioners performed very little surgery, medical missionaries attracted patients suffering from eye diseases and large tumors. In India, dispensaries treated broken bones, carried out amputations, and treated eye diseases and skin lesions. British surgeons taught Western techniques of cataract surgery to local eye doctors. Not all Western techniques were welcomed. Patients in many countries feared the use of anesthetics that seemed to produce a deathlike state.

There was a two-way traffic in surgical techniques: acupuncture was adopted from Japan and China by European practitioners in the early 19th century. However, European doctors struggled to understand the rationale behind the practice. Initially, they assumed acupuncture was a form of bloodletting. Instead of using the procedure to treat internal disease by manipulating qi, European practitioners used it to treat pain by inserting needles over painful joints in cases of gout or rheumatism.

DENTISTRY

At the beginning of the century, all around the world, dentistry was largely concerned with the treatment of toothache by the removal of painful teeth or application of medicines. Indigenous American peoples used hot poultices applied to the cheek or chewed the prickly ash bark to ease the pain. One traveler reported that a healer treated toothache by performing ritual songs and then scratching the skin over the aching tooth and sucking out the spirit that had caused the pain. In North Africa, toothache was attributed to worms inside the teeth, and it was treated by holding the mouth open to expose the painful tooth to the smoke from burning henbane seeds. If the pain became intolerable, the rotten tooth was extracted. In all cultures, this was performed by knocking out the tooth using a stick or by pulling it out using some form of tool.

More elaborate forms of dental treatment developed in Europe and North America in the late 18th century. As the upper classes grew more conscious of the appearance of their teeth, practitioners devised wire braces to pull displaced teeth back into line. Around the same time, practitioners developed artificial teeth to replace missing ones. Teeth, made of bone or ivory or taken from corpses on battlefields, were used in these primitive dentures. Teeth were taken from dead soldiers in huge quantities; they were shipped from the battlefield of Waterloo by the barrel. The use of soldiers' teeth was so common that all false teeth became known as "Waterloo teeth." These dentures were purely cosmetic; the plates were not firmly anchored to the jaw and had to be taken out when eating. Attempts were made to transplant teeth from the jaws of the poor into those of wealthy patients but failed.

For much of the 19th century, filling decayed teeth was a painful and expensive option affordable only to the middle and upper classes. It usually required several visits to remove the decayed material. Gold foil was then pounded into the cavity or an amalgam of mercury and silver pressed into the hole and then heated. In the late 19th century, filling teeth was made quicker and easier by improved drills; first by a foot-operated drill (based on the treadle mechanism used to power sewing machines) and later by more powerful electric machines. It became a routine practice following the discovery of local anesthetics.

Taking out a rotten tooth was a cheaper, simpler option. From the 1860s, it was also painless, as patients inhaled nitrous oxide anesthetic before the procedure. The inhalation of nitrous oxide (laughing gas) started as a form of entertainment. Horace Wells, an American dentist, was among many to note that it appeared to dull pain, and he had a tooth extracted by one of his students under nitrous oxide anesthesia in 1844. The problems of ensuring that patients received a standard dose—enough to kill the pain but not kill the patient—meant that the use of nitrous oxide did not become a routine part of dental practice for another two decades.

As patient demand for dental services grew, dentistry emerged as a new profession. In 1800, dentistry was practiced in the West by a few medical practitioners and by a larger number of people with little or no formal training. With the development of more complex equipment, dentists moved from working on the street to practicing in offices.

Dental schools were established to train students in knowledge of the mouth and teeth, techniques of filling and extraction, and giving anesthetics. The world's first dental school was established in Ohio in 1828 and the first dental college in Baltimore in 1840. Dentistry gradually took on the features of other professions, with standardized qualifications, professional societies, and journals where dentists exchanged information.

9

Mental Health

Mental illness (commonly called "madness" in the 19th century) was recognized around the world. The mentally ill displayed strange behaviors; madmen and women were unruly, were suicidal, ignored social codes by not dressing properly or by shouting, neglected their family responsibilities, or wandered about. However, different cultures understood mental illness in different ways. In Europe and North America, madness was thought to be fundamentally different from other diseases. Mental illness was seated in the mind and the brain. It was believed to be caused by a number of factors: disruption to the circulation or the functioning of nervous system, physical damage to the brain, or psychological trauma. All forms of mental illness were treated by specialist practitioners in institutions using medical and psychiatric therapy. Outside the West, the mind and body were perceived to be more closely linked. Mental illness was caused by the same factors as all other ailments—both physical and supernatural—and was treated with the same type of therapies, by healers who dealt with other diseases. Patients were cared for at home, not in special institutions.

MENTAL ILLNESS IN THE WEST

Theories of Mental Disorder

Within Western medicine, mental illness was defined by its symptoms. Sufferers displayed bizarre, irrational behaviors such as delusions, hallucinations, removing their clothing, wandering about, singing and shouting, aggression, and failure to deal with family or work responsibilities. In mild forms, such behaviors were tolerated by families and communities, who thought of them as simply odd or eccentric. If individuals became violent or unruly, families would conclude that he or she was mad and seek medical help. For example, in 1835, a mentally ill patient admitted into a hospital was described as being "restless melancholy, violent towards his life [*sic*], wandering about the country leaving his work & crying 'lost man.' [He] . . . refused food, and would have destroyed his wife and himself"

(Melling and Forsythe 1999, 119). A woman who entered an asylum in 1881 was reported to be "violent in word and action: never asks after her child; incessant talking, most absurdly singing" (Clark 1883).

During the course of the century, the definition of madness was extended to include idiocy and imbecility (in modern terms, forms of learning disability), nervous complaints, and even behaviors such as masturbation and homosexuality. Among women, strong sexual desires were labeled as nymphomania. Even high intellectual ability (again, especially among women) became suspect; genius and madness were seen as close allies.

It was generally accepted in the West that there was a clear division between the mind and the body, and thus a split between illness that afflicted the body and mental disorders that arose in the brain and affected the mind. In the 18th century, madness was interpreted as a loss of reason; the mad were like children or animals. The only means of cure was to force them to recover their rationality through punishment and restraint. The 19th century saw the emergence of new ideas about mental health and a debate over the causes of mental illness. There was little doubt that direct injury to the brain from a blow or a tumor produced mental illness. Puerperal insanity was acknowledged to follow childbirth.

For most physicians, madness was rooted in the brain and nerves and caused by the same basic phenomena as other ailments. In his 1812 book on diseases of the mind, Benjamin Rush, a Philadelphia physician and one of the founders of psychiatry in America, proclaimed: "the cause of madness is seated primarily in the blood-vessels of the brain, and it depends upon the same kind of morbid and irregular actions that constitute other arterial diseases" (Rush 1812). Other practitioners believed that the problem lay in irritation to the nerves and brain. Whether based in the circulation or the nerves, the triggers of mental illness were the same: exposure to extremes of heat or cold or prolonged mental or physical strain. Toward the end of the century, practitioners increasingly stressed the role of heredity in mental illness and mental disability. Brain damage accumulated down to the generations: parents with nervous conditions or suffering from alcoholism produced children and grandchildren who exhibited criminal behaviors and mental disorders.

Some physicians, led by J. C. Heinroth in Germany, believed that madness was a psychological, rather than physical, phenomenon. Extreme emotions or traumatic experiences such as bankruptcy, disappointment in love, or bereavements permanently disordered brain function. Those with a healthy constitution and regular lifestyle could bear such shocks; people with a family history of mental illness or lacking emotional control, drunkards, and gamblers were more likely to succumb to mental illness.

THERAPY AND INSTITUTIONS

In the 18th century, nearly all mad people were cared for at home; they were looked after within the family, and they received little medical treatment aimed at curing their condition. A tiny proportion of the mentally ill was confined in institutions, often called "madhouses." In the 19th century, while wealthy patients and people suffering from mild forms of mental illness continued to be cared for at home, a much greater number were treated in a new type of institution—the asylum. Rather than an institution of confinement and punishment, the asylum (as its name suggests) was a place of refuge and cure. The institution itself was seen as having a curative influence. It took patients away from the setting, lifestyle, and surroundings that had provoked their illness. The ideal asylum was located in the calm of the countryside, away from the stresses and bustle of the town:

> [It should be a] spacious building . . . airy, and elevated, and elegant, surrounded by extensive and swelling grounds and gardens. The interior is fitted up with galleries, and workshops and music-rooms. The sun and air are allowed to enter at every window, the view of shrubberies and fields, and groups of labourers, is unobstructed by shutters or bars; all is clean, quiet and attractive. (Browne 1837, 229)

Within the asylum, patients were subjected to a treatment regime. "Moral therapy" was developed at the end of the 18th century by a number of doctors and laymen—by Philippe Pinel in France, the Tuke family in England, and Vincenzo Chiarugi in Italy. It recognized that the harsh treatment meted out in early institutions was likely to provoke violent responses from inmates, and it took an optimistic view that most patients could be cured. Moral therapy was based on the idea that the mentally ill were not wholly irrational but capable of recovering their self-control. Asylum patients were not restrained (except in extreme circumstances, to prevent harm to themselves). Quiet entertainments, work, and an ordered routine were intended to divert the mind from irrational thoughts and behaviors. Patients were encouraged to return to conventional standards of behavior: to dress and converse normally, adopt hobbies, and take exercise. Good behavior was praised. In the asylum,

> The inmates all seem to be actuated by the common impulse of enjoyment, all are busy, and delighted by being so . . . There is in this community no compulsion, no chains, no whips, no corporal chastisement, simply because they are proved to be less effectual means of carrying any point than persuasion, emulation, and the desire of obtaining gratification. (Browne 1837, 230)

In practice, asylum staff used fear as well as a desire for praise to keep their charges in line: patients who persisted in displaying irrational behaviors were punished by scolding, loss of privileges, or confinement. Under such regimes, it was confidently predicted that most mad people would be cured, especially if they were admitted to the asylum in the early stages of their illness.

In many asylums, psychological therapy was combined with medical and physical treatments aimed at restoring brain function. For much of the century, tried-and-trusted therapies were applied. Bloodletting, medicines to induce vomiting and purging, and hot and cold baths were used to stimulate the circulation throughout the body, including the brain, and to reduce the excitement exhibited by unruly patients. Mechanical treatments were also used to affect the circulation. Benjamin Rush's "tranquillizer" was a chair in which the patient was completely immobilized, to stop any muscular movements and thus reduce the circulation. On the

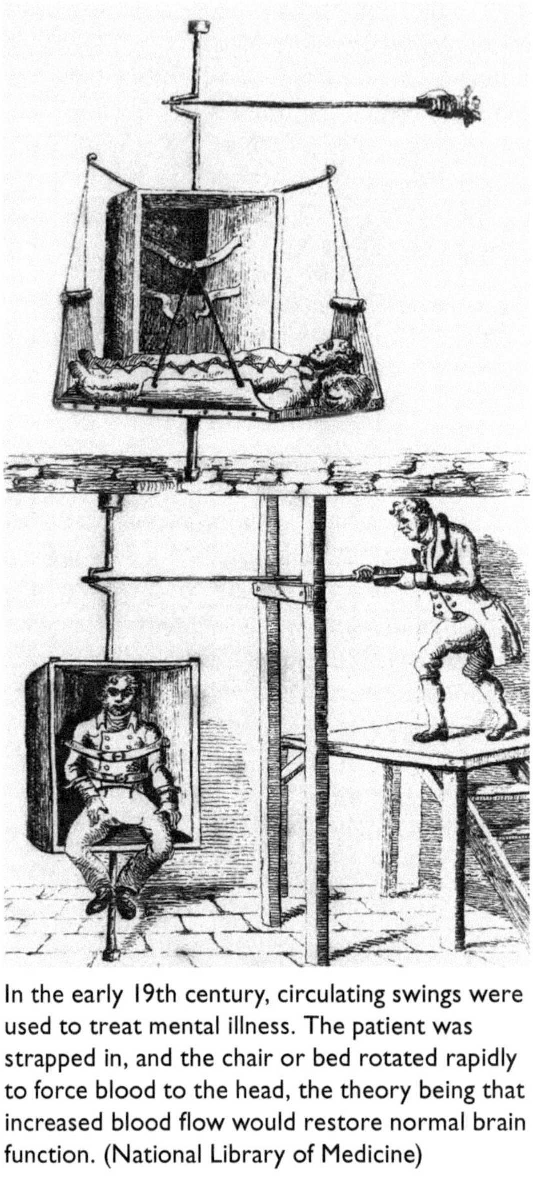

In the early 19th century, circulating swings were used to treat mental illness. The patient was strapped in, and the chair or bed rotated rapidly to force blood to the head, the theory being that increased blood flow would restore normal brain function. (National Library of Medicine)

"gyrator," the patient was whirled around, the circular motion forcing blood to the head. When none of these therapies proved successful, doctors turned to new drugs, including cannabis, amyl nitrate, and digitalis, along with mild electric shocks, to calm agitated or violent patients and to stimulate the morose.

THE RISE OF THE ASYLUM

The 19th century saw a huge increase in the numbers and size of asylums. In Europe and North America, local and national governments and charities funded institutions to treat the poor. In England and Wales, the number of publicly funded asylums rose from 23 in 1849 to 87 in 1904. At the same time, the average number of patients in each institution rose from fewer than 350 to almost 1,000. Some asylums were even larger: Colney Hatch Asylum had over 2,000 patients by 1860. In other countries, the boom in numbers came rather later; in Italy and Germany, public asylums grew rapidly in the last two decades of the century. Private asylums continued alongside the public institutions, serving a class of patients able to pay for care. They were always much smaller, sometimes with only a handful of patients.

Despite this building boom, there was never enough asylum accommodation. As fast as asylums expanded, so did the number of patients requiring treatment. The reasons for the rise in the numbers of the mentally ill were not clear. Contemporary commentators believed that mental illness was becoming more common due to a rise in alcohol abuse and to the stresses of industrial and urban life. Others suggested that more of the mentally ill were ending up in institutions as a result of changing attitudes among the public: families were less willing to care for the insane, or they were less able to look after a family member displaying awkward and disruptive behavior if they lived in cramped accommodation in a city and worked long hours in factories. On a more positive note, it was claimed that with improved treatment on offer in asylums, relatives were happy for patients to be admitted in the hope of finding a cure for their illness. There was also a perception that asylums were simply filling up with incurable patients as the initial optimistic estimates of the proportion of cases who could be cured by asylum therapy were never realized. In fact, studies by historians have shown that while some patients were institutionalized for many years, around a third were discharged within 12 months of their admission. In many cases, the extreme behaviors that had led to their committal had diminished, so patients could return to the family home. In some cases, families took their relatives out of the asylum even if they had shown little or no improvement. In addition, a substantial number of patients died within a year of entering an asylum, often from the conditions underlying their irrational behavior such as old age, syphilis, brain tumors, or strokes.

The growing size of asylums made it more difficult to treat patients. While active treatment was pursued in the smaller private asylums that cared for better-off patients, in huge state-funded institutions, there were too few staff for doctors or attendants to develop a relationship with their patients. As a result, asylums increasingly became places to confine the insane:

> Many asylums have grown to such a magnitude, that their general management is unwieldy, and their due medical and moral care and supervision an impossibility. They have grown into lunatic colonies of eight or nine hundred, or even of a thousand or more inhabitants, comfortably lodged and clothed, fed by a not illiberal commissariat, watched and waited on by well-paid attendants, disciplined and drilled to a well-ordered routine. (Arlidge 1859)

While a small number of patients worked within the asylum, helping with cleaning or in the laundry, the remainder had little to do with their time. Organized entertainments, such as dances and concerts, were few and far between, and visitors reported that wards of patients simply sat doing nothing. The large proportion of incurable patients seemed to prove that mental degeneration was the cause of madness in many cases. If asylums could not cure these patients, they could at least incarcerate them and prevent them from having children and perpetuating the problem.

One exception to the rule was the treatment of puerperal insanity. A form of mental illness that developed in the weeks following birth, it was attributed to the associated trauma and linked to poverty. The symptoms and treatment varied: women who became depressed were cared for at home or in maternity hospitals. Manic cases, in which women shouted, sang, or were violent, were more likely to be admitted to asylums. In the mid-19th century, treatment took the form of supportive therapy—rest, a nourishing diet, and stimulating medicines. Later, doctors treated the disease more aggressively, with drugs and force feeding. Most patients recovered within a few months.

PSYCHIATRY AND PSYCHIATRISTS

The asylum provided the arena for the emergence of a new specialty within medicine, concerned with the treatment of mental illness. In the early 19th century, patients suffering from mental illness were cared for by family, by laymen, by ministers of religion, and by doctors. As it was increasingly accepted that madness was a form of illness, medical men became the acknowledged experts in dealing with the condition. Although initially the opinion of family members was influential in deciding who should enter the asylum (and families also chose to take back their relatives), over time, the views of medical staff based on observation of patients became the main criteria for diagnosing mental illness. Patients were admitted to and discharged from asylums on the certification of one or two doctors. Once inside the asylum, medical superintendents were responsible for prescribing their treatment.

In the asylum, doctors had an opportunity to observe patients with a range of conditions, to identify patterns of symptoms, and thus to divide cases of mental illness into different types so as to allow better treatment. However, madness defied easy categorization. All doctors recognized a few broad classes of mental illness, such as mania, melancholia, dementia, idiocy, and epilepsy, but not all defined these forms of madness in the same way; individual doctors might label the same patient as suffering from idiocy or from melancholia. Different doctors subdivided these classes in different ways. Some categorized cases by the circumstances that provoked the illness, such as "wedding night psychosis" or "religious mania," others by the major symptom, as in "delusional disorder." Mental illness was extremely complex. While puerperal insanity was a clearly defined syndrome, doctors concluded that there were four types and followed a course of six distinct stages. Attempts to classify different forms of mental illness by tracking the signs of mental disease in damage to the nerves and brain also proved fruitless, although neurologists did succeed in identifying the areas of the brain responsible for particular functions, such as speech and movement of the limbs. A new taxonomy of mental illness was finally developed from clinical observations by Emil Kraepelin in the 1880s and 1890s. He argued that forms of mental illness should be identified by typical patterns of symptoms, rather than their cause, and for the first time defined manic depression (now known as bipolar disorder) and schizophrenia.

The asylum also provided a career ladder for doctors wishing to specialize in the treatment of mental illness. The first asylum superintendents were trained in general medicine and had some interest or experience in dealing with madness. Later practitioners received formal teaching in the subject at medical school, and they worked their way up a hierarchy of asylum posts. Alienists, as members of this new group called themselves (since they treated mental alienation), formed professional societies and founded journals to advance research into mental illness and to increase the status of their specialty.

The 19th century saw the rise of public concern about asylums. There were criticisms of the quality of care offered to patients. Autobiographies of former asylum patients complained about the brutal treatment inflicted by staff. Poor patients were particularly vulnerable, and in the United States, Dorothea Dix led a campaign for better care after discovering a group of patients confined in an unheated room in an asylum. In Britain in the mid-19th century, there were a number of notorious cases of wrongful incarceration in which families used the asylum to control unruly relatives. In many of these cases, the patients did display erratic behavior, but it was not clear if they were genuinely mad. Rosina Bulwer Lytton, wife of a famous English author, was briefly sent to an asylum after she launched a campaign of harassment that included sending obscene letters against her estranged husband. Ironically, her family probably hoped that keeping her out of the way would avoid a public scandal, but the case was widely discussed in the newspapers of the day. In another *cause célèbre*, Louisa Nottidge's family forced her into an asylum after she joined a highly unorthodox religious sect and gave away substantial sums of money to its leader. There was also public concern that patients who had recovered (or thought that they had recovered) from mental illness struggled to leave the asylum system. John Perceval, son of a British prime minister, was admitted to an asylum following a severe mental breakdown. After three years, he recovered, but he initially failed to persuade his doctors to release him. Once outside the asylum, he wrote two books, condemning the treatment he had received, and helped to found the Alleged Lunatics' Friend Society.

Nervous Disorders

Asylums were places of care mainly for those with severe forms of mental illness or for patients with no family able to take care of them. Milder forms of mental illness were diagnosed as "nervous disorders" and were treated at home or in private clinics. In North America, neurasthenia was a common diagnosis. Identified by George Beard in 1869, it was a form of nervous disorder brought on by excessive mental effort or a serious shock, such as involvement in a road or rail accident. Women were believed to be prone to hysteria; the condition was particularly common among middle-class women who had little to do and suffered from unstable emotions. Patients diagnosed with hysteria and neurasthenia displayed a wide range of symptoms, from ringing in the ears, headaches, and indigestion, to paralysis, claustrophobia, and exhaustion.

Silas Weir Mitchell, an American neurologist, devised a "rest cure" to treat nervous disease. He prescribed an extreme form of bed rest (patients were not allowed to get up, wash, read, or have visitors), a milk diet, and massage for several weeks or months to allow the overworked nerves to recover. In Europe, many patients with nervous conditions went for treatment at spas, where they drank and bathed in natural mineral waters in the hope of restoring the health of their nervous systems. Hand-cranked machines were used to give small electric shocks to the head or other parts of the body to stimulate the nerves. In the 1890s, Sigmund Freud developed psychoanalysis as a new therapy for hysteria. Trained in neurology, Freud rejected theories that located these diseases in the nervous system, arguing that nervous diseases resulted from a conflict between the conscious mind and unconscious desires and were ultimately rooted in traumatic (often sexual) experiences in childhood.

MENTAL ILLNESS OUTSIDE THE WEST

Non-Western medical cultures, in Africa, Asia, and the Pacific, recognized remarkably similar forms of mental illness to those described in Europe and North America. Mad people displayed strange, socially unacceptable behaviors: they were violent, went about naked (even in cultures where people normally wore very minimal clothing, refusing to wear anything was seen as very odd), or wandered about ignoring their familial responsibilities. However, cultures outside the West saw mental illness arising from the same causes as other diseases, so healers who dealt with other diseases provided treatment, not any special group of practitioners.

In most cultures, the mentally ill were kept at home, rather than in special institutions. People with violent forms of madness were restrained in some way—often chained up or locked in a small room—and given food and water. Care was often very limited. Missionaries in China reported that mentally ill patients lived in squalid, filthy conditions in sheds or other buildings close to the family home. The exception to home care was found in North Africa, where charitable *bimaristans* (or *maristans*)—hospitals for the sick and the mad—had been founded from medieval times. Early records show that mentally ill patients admitted to a hospital were treated using drugs and other remedies. By the 19th century, however, all efforts to cure seem to have stopped. Travelers reported that the *bimaristans* were simply places of confinement for patients who were likely to harm themselves or others. After a short stay, they were released back onto the streets.

MENTAL ILLNESS IN JAPAN AND CHINA

From ancient times, physicians in China and Japan (where a version of Chinese medical theory called *kampo* medicine was used) had recognized different forms of mental disorders. These included imbecility, hysteria (*yi zheng* or *yi bing*), madness (*kuang*), and epilepsy (*dian*). Doctors knew that women were susceptible to bouts of mental illness after giving birth. As in the West, people suffering from mental illness displayed unusual behaviors. A Japanese text of 1807 described the symptoms of madness (*kan*):

> [Sufferers] are frightened by the slightest sound and are suicidal. They try to hide to avoid persecution. They cannot sleep because of anxiety or they sleep badly, often having nightmares. They talk grandiosely and behave arrogantly. They wash their hands or clean up their room many times, because they hate dirt . . . They do one thing over and over again and cannot stop themselves. They feel guilty and suffer from regret and grief. (Shutoka 1807)

Japanese practitioners also described cases of anorexia nervosa in which patients refused to eat or ate very little. If forced to eat, they vomited.

Unlike doctors in the West, Chinese and Japanese physicians did not see mental illnesses as different from other physical ailments. Chinese authors ascribed mental illness, like other diseases, to climate, lifestyle, or strong emotions that in turn produced a disturbance in the yin/yang balance and in the circulation of qi. Madness was associated with an increase in yang, and epilepsy with increased yin. By the 19th century, doctors had largely abandoned the ancient belief that madness was caused by ghosts or demons, although such ideas still circulated among ordinary people. Practitioners debated exactly how the disease was produced, whether it was a cold or warm disease, and if it affected the heart, liver, or spleen. Since mental illness was caused by the same mechanisms as other diseases, the same therapies—drugs and acupuncture—were used to restore balance, to relieve the symptoms, and to help restore control over the emotions.

Japanese practitioners also held that mental disorders had the same roots as other diseases, and they too debated the seat of mental illness and the processes that produced mental disorder. Some attributed madness to stagnant qi; others to poisons produced within the body that became active following a traumatic experience. The poison or qi formed a hard accumulation that could be felt by palpation and affected the organs linked to thought. Practitioners were divided as to the seat of thought within the body; some believed it to be the heart, while others located it in the stomach. Physicians exposed to Western medical ideas that were introduced to Japan in the 17th century believed that the poison acted on the brain. Some practitioners also accepted the view held by many laypeople that madness could be caused by supernatural means, such as possession by a demon or fox.

Treatment was aimed at dispersing the stagnant qi or poison by moxibustion (burning small amounts of fiber on the skin to warm the qi) and drugs to provoke vomiting or sleep. Some doctors also recommending a form of psychotherapy (*isei-henki*):

> A 59-year old widow had been depressed since losing her eight children in a series of epidemics. She kept grieving over her misfortune, and wept night and day . . . Wada [a physician] was called in to examine her . . . he was unable to find any signs of physical disease. When Wada scolded her, with the intention of shifting her attention from the disease to him, the woman opened her eyes. Then Wada talked to her patiently. He said that her life and death were determined by Heaven's will, that everyone is destined to die sooner or later, and that it was pointless to be so upset . . . His psychotherapy . . . was effective, and the patient's fear of death disappeared. (Tokaku 2002)

Mental Illness in Ayurvedic Medicine

In Ayurvedic medicine, madness was thought to be seated in the heart, the organ associated with thought. Mental disorders shared the same basic cause as physical illness: they arose from an imbalance of *doshas* caused by the wrong diet, lifestyle, or strong emotions. Such an imbalance could cause many types of illness: mental illness occurred when there was some predisposing factor that drove the excess *dosha* toward the heart, causing malfunctions in the vessels carrying the *doshas*. Epilepsy, for example, was caused by a sudden blockage in these channels. Imbalances in the different *doshas* produced different types of madness: mental illness arising from *pitta* had symptoms such as anger, violence, sleeplessness, and obstinacy. The imbalance was treated with the same therapies as for physical illness: drugs, diet, and bathing with decoctions of herbs all helped to reduce the excess *dosha*, to purify the body and strengthen the nerves.

MENTAL ILLNESS IN AFRICA

In Africa, people saw madness in similar ways to those in the West. Mental illness was defined by a set of strange behaviors: hallucinations, disordered speech, going naked, or wandering about. Healers identified a range of types of mental illnesses including melancholy, fits, and epilepsy. However, where Western medicine associated mental illness with the mind and brain, African healers saw no division between the body and mind. Mental illness arose from the same range of causes as other ailments, responded to the same therapies, and was treated by the same healers. Madness could be caused by natural means and treated with herbal medicines. Some forms of mental illness were understood to be hereditary or to develop in old age. Sufferers might be confined in their homes to prevent them from wandering off or doing harm to themselves or to others. Mental illness could also be brought on by supernatural means—by sorcery, by spirit possession or sent by the gods as a punishment for breaking taboos. In these cases, after diagnosis through some form of divination, the complaint was cured by rituals and by sacrifices of animals to appease the supernatural being responsible for the illness.

Just as physical disease moved between cultures, so did mental illnesses. In Zululand in southern Africa, a new form of disease appeared in the late 19th century. *Indiki* possession was introduced from areas further north. Initially, it was supposed to be caused by the spirits of warriors killed in battle that had not received proper burial rites and affected both men and women. Later it was predominantly found among women and was associated with the spirits of dead male relatives. Sufferers displayed symptoms such as twitching, weeping, fits, and numbness. It was treated with medicines (some of them poured into the ear), rituals, and animal sacrifices.

Western Views of Mental Illness in Africa and Asia

Many Western writers claimed that mental illness was almost unknown in isolated indigenous societies in Africa and the Pacific region. They suggested that indigenous people lived simple, stress-free lives, and as a consequence, very few people succumbed to nervous diseases. Alternatively, they claimed that the brains and nerves of native peoples were less developed than those of Europeans and therefore not susceptible to the irritation that caused madness. Mental illness was believed to become more common following contact with Europeans as a result of exposure to new diseases, alcohol, and new lifestyles. Such an analysis fit with colonial ideas of indigenous people as "primitive" and unable to survive within the modern world. In fact, Western travelers did occasionally report instances of madness among indigenous people. One author reported that insanity was not uncommon among old male Australian aborigines. While family members were rather afraid of those elders who suffered from mental illness, they looked after them.

Madness was a problematic category for Western travelers. To some observers, the trance states that diviners used as a means of diagnosing illness were a form of madness. The colonial authorities associated *indiki* possession with witchcraft, but administrators were unable to decide if sufferers were displaying the symptoms of a nervous disorder such as hysteria were the victims of witchcraft, were the gullible dupes of people claiming to be witches, or were fraudsters who feigned possession in order to demand animals for sacrifice. In 1910, in an effort to control the outbreak of *indiki*, 11 women suffering from possession were put on trial for practicing witchcraft.

The Colonial Asylum

There were occasional suggestions that the *indiki* sufferers were mad and should be sent to an asylum for treatment. Asylum accommodation became available in European colonies in Africa and India from the early 19th century as part of the drive to civilize and to improve the lives of the indigenous population. The development of the asylum system followed the same pattern as in Europe and North America. In the later 19th century, colonial governments built asylums for the care of the poor Europeans—white soldiers, sailors, and workers—and for indigenous peoples. Over time, the number of asylums increased, and the institutions grew larger. Despite this, the number of asylum places relative to the population was tiny. Kissy Asylum in Sierra Leone took in patients from all over West Africa, but in 1887, it had only 70 beds.

In other respects, the colonial asylum was different from that in the West. There was much less demand for asylum accommodation from the families of the

The "lunatic asylum" at Kissy in Sierra Leone offered care to a small number of patients suffering from mental illness across West Africa. Only the most difficult patients, unable to find care within their families, entered such institutions. (Wellcome Collection)

mentally ill. Relatives preferred to treat the mentally ill at home using traditional remedies. Indigenous patients were usually admitted to an asylum by the police or through the law courts, after they had been arrested for some act of violence or had been found wandering and unable to look after themselves. Diagnosis was often based on the testimony of police officials and other white people. In asylums in New Zealand, for example, few if any doctors spoke Maori, and translators were often not provided.

Asylum organization mirrored colonial society. Patients were segregated by race and class. White Europeans were believed to succumb to mental illness as a consequence of living in an alien culture. "In England and other cold countries, attacks of Insanity generally arise from sudden reverses of fortune, keen disappointments, and other causes of deep mental depression, but in this country it is otherwise; here the attack may at almost every instance be traced to exposure to the sun; hard living and other irregularities" (India Office Records 1818). Asylums took European patients away from these dangerous influences, but if they failed to respond within a year, they were sent back to Europe and more familiar surroundings where, it was hoped, they might be cured. European patients were generally given good accommodation within asylums, often in rooms rather than large wards. In the Bombay Lunatic Asylum, the wing for Europeans had "cheerful and pleasing views . . . of the entrance to the harbour, bay, Malabar Hill and the adjacent country" (Asylum Superintendent 1850). Treatment was tailored to the colonial situation. European patients resented being restrained by Indian attendants, so staff resorted to older forms of physical restraint such as strait jackets and manacles. Recreational facilities such as magazines, board games, and bowling were provided for patients, and they were rarely expected to undertake any form of work as part of their therapy.

Relatively few asylum places were available for indigenous people, and those were reserved for the most serious cases. The causes of mental illness diagnosed in indigenous patients were broadly similar to European inmates, although their condition was sometimes linked to the colonial situation. In midcentury, madness in Maori patients was linked to the loss of land to white settlers. Accommodation in native asylums was not as good as that provided for European patients. Indigenous patients were accommodated on large and often crowded wards and sometimes slept on mats, or on the floor, rather than in beds. Inmates were separated according to their symptoms—whether they were quiet or violent, or recovering. This caused conflict in Indian asylums, where diagnosis took priority over the important distinctions of social group (caste) and religion. Like their European counterparts, indigenous asylum patients were encouraged to undertake activities. They were more likely to be prescribed some form of work than Europeans, and their pastimes were tailored to local tastes. Indian asylum inmates were allowed to play active sports, such as cricket and shooting with a bow and arrows, and to keep a variety of pet animals. In Delhi Asylum, the patients formed an orchestra and were taken to religious festivals. In New Zealand asylums, however, there seems to have been little attempt to fit asylum life to Maori culture, and many patients were reported to have become mute, passive, and withdrawn.

10

Drugs and Remedies

Drugs were the cornerstone of medical treatment in almost every culture in the 19th-century world. They were used in all systems of medicine and in folk medicine. A huge range of substances—plants, animal parts, minerals, metals, even earths and precious stones—were prescribed to cure illness, either singly or in combination. Drugs were available from a wide range of sources. Families made their own remedies in the home using plants or foodstuffs from the family garden or local countryside. The sick obtained medicines directly from their healers, from specialist traders such as druggists and pharmacists, from general retailers, and even by mail order. The 19th century saw a boom in sales of medicines: people with a little spare cash were increasingly eager to buy remedies to cure illness or to preserve health. As a result, drugs were traded around the world in ever greater quantities to satisfy this demand.

THE WORLDWIDE TRADE IN DRUGS

Locally sourced plants, animal products, and minerals were the backbone of medical preparations worldwide. Healers gathered indigenous plants growing in forests and open areas, and cultivated native plants in gardens. Practitioners were not limited to making use of local plants; seeds were bought and sold around the world, allowing healers to grow exotic species for use in medicines. Cultivation took place on both large and small scales, by individuals and by large companies. Cinchona trees, the source of quinine, were native to South America; but seeds were transported to India, Sri Lanka, and Java where plantations were established. Asia became the major center of quinine production.

Preserved plant material and other medicinal substances had been traded over long distances for hundreds, possibly thousands of years, carried by people, on pack animals, and by sailing ships. Traditional trading routes remained in use during the 19th century. In Africa, for example, traders gathered, dried, and carried plant and other materials for hundreds of miles, from mountainous areas down to the plains or from the coast to inland communities. New methods of transport made possible the shipment of much larger quantities of drugs within and between continents, and to ensure that they arrived quickly and in good condition. The raw materials for medicines flowed into Europe and North America from around the world. Aniseed, camphor, gamboge (the fruits and sap of a tree), rhubarb, china root, and green tea came from China. Nux vomica, belladonna, asafetida, senna, camphor, and castor oil were imported from India. Chinese traders brought asafetida and putchuck (the roots of a plant) from India, ginseng from the United States and Turkey, and mercury from Europe and North America. As the manufacture of pharmaceuticals became industrialized, prepared and packaged medicines were exported from Europe and North America back to Africa and India.

New plant-based drugs were also discovered in the 19th century. European and American botanists explored many regions of Africa and Asia, bringing home new plants for use in gardens and in medicines. In 1859, a botanist connected with David Livingstone's expedition in Malawi collected the seeds of the *kombe* plant. This was used by local peoples to prepare poisoned arrows used in hunting. Analysis of the seeds revealed a chemical that slowed the heart, which became the basis of strophanin, a heart medicine, marketed from 1885.

PHARMACOPEIAS

All the world's systems of medical knowledge—Western, Chinese, Ayurvedic, and Unani medicine—contained explanations of how drugs acted within the body to cure disease. Books of materia medica (medical substances) or pharmacopeias provided lists of drugs and medicines classified according to their source, action in the body, methods of preparation, and uses. Often these texts were illustrated with drawings showing the plant or animal source of the drugs, helping practitioners to identify plants growing in the wild or to check that they were being sold the correct dried or preserved materials and were not duped into purchasing an inferior substitute.

Chinese Medicines

Chinese pharmacopeias dated back thousands of years. The classic Chinese text on medicines was the *Shen nung Pen ts'ao ching*, written around 2700 B.C.E. Later books followed the same format but included many more medicinal substances, as the Chinese empire expanded and practitioners made contact with healers in other cultures. For example, *Dongchong xiacoa*, a fungus that attacked caterpillars, was probably adopted into Chinese practice from Tibetan medicine in the 18th century. Drugs were used to manipulate the circulation of qi around the body and hence to restore health. Medicines could remove blockages in the flow of qi, nourish the qi, warm the body, or reduce heat. All drugs were classified by five "tastes"—acrid, sweet, bitter, sour, and salty—and their nature, whether hot, cold, warm, or cool. These factors determined the effect they had within the body. Sour medicines stopped discharges such as diarrhea. Bitter drugs had a drying effect; they were used to treat diseases caused by dampness and to clear heat from the body.

Licorice root, for example, was sweet and promoted qi. Abalone shell was salty and cold; it nourished yin and was used to treat liver diseases. Pharmacopeias described medicines by these principles and the type of conditions they cured, rather than giving very specific uses or exact doses because in Chinese medicine, every patient was an individual. Disease was a product of their natural constitution, age, lifestyle, and circumstances, and medicines had to be tailored to take account of all these factors. In practice, Chinese practitioners and their patients did use standard remedies to treat common conditions, such as the "Strongly Replenishing Infusion of Ten Ingredients" or the "Powder for Arousing the Pulse." Drugs were usually taken in the form of pills, powders, or decoctions (medicines boiled in water, then cooled and strained).

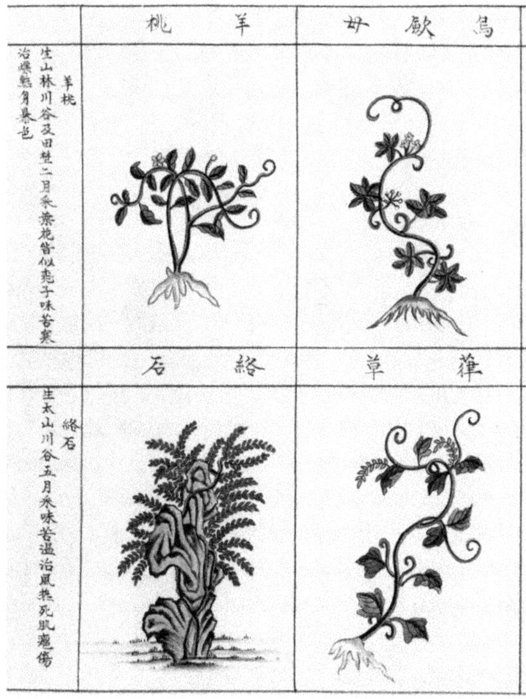

Illustration from a *Pen ts'ao*, a Chinese pharmacopeia, showing medicinal plants. Although published in the 19th century, this book follows the form and layout of ancient texts. (Societé Asiatique, College de France, Paris, France/Archives Charmet/Bridgeman Images)

Chinese medicine made use of a huge number of materials, usually in combinations in order to exert exactly the right effect within the body. Strong drugs were mixed with other substances to moderate their effects or with materials to help strengthen the body. Some drugs could help to direct medicines to particular organs, to ensure that they produced the maximum effect. Minerals and animal materials, such as sea horses, bones, and even excrement such as bat dung, had medicinal properties. Plants were a common source of medicines, and a single plant could have multiple uses. The leafy tops were prescribed for illnesses affecting the head and the roots for complaints in the lower parts of the body. A single drug could be used to treat different ailments. Licorice root (*gancao*) replenished qi in the spleen but also moisturized the lungs and stopped coughs, counteracted the fire poison that caused ulcers, relieved cramps, and was an antidote to toxic substances.

Ayurvedic and Unani Medicines

Ayurvedic and Unani medicine, like Chinese medicine, saw disease as an individual phenomenon. Medicines were categorized by a set of principles that defined their effect within the body. In Ayurvedic medicine, illness was caused by imbalance in three *doshas*—*kapha*, *vata*, and *pitta*. Diet, behaviors such as sleeping or exercise, heat, and cold all affected the *doshas* and could cause illness or be manipulated to restore balance to the body. Diet was the first means of curing disease; medicines were prescribed for more serious complaints. Ayurvedic practitioners mainly used plant-based medicines with a few animal and mineral substances. They were categorized by their qualities and effect on the *doshas*. Castor oil (extracted from the seeds of the castor oil plant) was heavy, hot, and sweet. It had a laxative effect and was used to treat a number of conditions, including hiccups, asthma, and gout. Urine was light, sharp, and hot, reduced *kapha*, and was used to treat colic, parasitic infections, and skin diseases. The types of medicines prescribed by practitioners varied across the country, taking account of the local climate and making use of plants found in the area.

Unani medicine, like Ayurvedic medicine, saw balance as the key to health and disease. However, rather than three *doshas*, Unani practitioners sought to control a balance of four humors. These had four essential qualities—hot, cold, wet, and dry—and drugs were also categorized by these qualities and by their potency, if mild or strong. For example, garlic was hot and dry and was prescribed in cases of fever, colic, or forgetfulness. The bruised bulbs were also used in ointments and poultices. The root and wood of the barberry shrub was hot and moist, acted on the spleen, and was used to treat dysentery. The oil of the camphor tree was cold and dry and was a brain tonic given to cure headaches. Unani medicines included a large number of animal and mineral substances alongside plant-based drugs. Musk, obtained from the glands of deer, was used as a tonic for the heart and brain, to combat inflammation, and to cure coughs. Drugs were taken singly or combined into medicines for a stronger effect. They were taken in the form of syrups, pills, powders, or decoctions.

Medicines in the West

In Europe and North America, knowledge of the body and disease was revolutionized during the 19th century. Research demonstrated that disease was not caused by changes in the humors but by malfunctions of the organs or tissues. While theories of the body changed rapidly in the early part of the century, a new understanding of the action of medicines developed more slowly. Doctors and their patients were reluctant to abandon tried-and-tested medicines that had been used for hundreds of years. For much of the 19th century, doctors continued to prescribe medicines that affected the body's excretions—by inducing sweating or vomiting—or controlled the symptoms of disease with the aim of making the patient feel better and allowing the body to heal itself. Practitioners were well aware that many of their medicines were of limited efficacy. Oliver Wendell Holmes, a distinguished American practitioner, reflected practitioners' cynicism when he concluded:

> [T]hrow out opium . . . throw out a few specifics which our art did not discover, and it is hardly needed to apply; throw out wine, which is a food, and the vapors which

> produce the miracle of anesthesia, and I firmly believe that if the whole materia medica, *as now used*, could be sunk to the bottom of the sea, it would be all the better for mankind,—and all the worse for the fishes [emphasis in original text]. (Holmes 1892, 202–203)

Over the century, practitioners gradually reduced their use of strong medicines such as mercury and antimony and replaced them with milder drugs given in smaller doses.

The uncertainty over the curative action of medicines was reflected in the organization of pharmacopeias. At the beginning of the century, medicines were listed by their effect on the body's excretions and secretions. Drugs were classified under categories such as sudorifics (inducing sweating), emetics (provoking vomiting), or purgatives (laxatives). Other drugs were listed according to their uses, such as carminatives (to combat flatulence), sedatives (to calm the nerves), and emollients (to soothe or soften the tissues). By the middle of the century, when practitioners had abandoned their belief in the importance of the body fluids in disease causation, authors shifted to producing alphabetical lists of drugs or classifications based on the diseases that they cured.

Many texts also provided detailed instructions on how to prepare drugs, revealing the long, arduous, and complex tasks required in making medicines. For example, the *British Pharmacopeia* for 1867 described how to make extract of opium, a relatively simple process.

> Take of
> Opium in thin slices......1 pound
> Distilled water......6 pints
> Macerate the opium in two of the pints of water for twenty-four hours, and express the liquor. Reduce the residue of the opium to a pulp, macerate it again in two pints of the water for twenty-four hours, and express. Repeat the operation a third time. Mix the liquors, strain through flannel, and evaporate by a water-bath until the extract has acquired a suitable consistence [*sic*] for forming pills (*British Pharmacopeia* 1867, 123).

Pharmacopeias also included recipes for medicines used to treat common minor complaints. European and American pharmacopeias were unusual in that they often included the appropriate dose for each drug. Unlike other systems of medical knowledge, Western medicine saw each case of a particular disease as fundamentally the same, and so each should be treated by standard amounts of a particular drug, adjusted according to the patient's body weight.

New Drugs

Before the 19th century, new drugs were discovered by rather haphazard means. Interested doctors experimented with substances often taken from folk medicines. In the 1780s, William Withering, an English doctor, proved the effectiveness of a traditional herbal medicine in the treatment of dropsy—fluid retention caused by heart failure. Withering worked out that the active ingredient in the medicine was derived from the foxglove plant. We now know that foxgloves contain digitalis that stimulates the heart. The 19th century saw the arrival of the pharmaceutical industry, bringing together large-scale production of medicines and research in company facilities or in universities to discover new drugs and systematically test their effects. German pharmaceutical companies set new standards of quality, introducing much greater standardization—they routinely tested the quality of each batch of medicines. Industrialized production also led to the introduction of new forms of medicine. Instead of the traditional liquid medicines and large, hand-rolled pills, pharmaceutical companies produced small machine-made pills and capsules that were much easier to swallow.

In these laboratories, the active ingredients within traditional medicines were isolated and identified for the first time. Preparations based on the bark of the cinchona tree had long been used to treat fevers, but the active substance, quinine, was not isolated until 1820. Similarly, opium was a traditional painkiller, produced from the dried sap of the opium poppy. Research into the chemistry of the plant revealed two painkilling chemicals, morphine (discovered in 1804) and codeine (isolated in 1832). Similar compounds were also discovered in other plants. Atropine, a drug used to treat gastric upsets, was isolated from deadly nightshade, and cocaine from the coca plant of South America.

In the late 19th century, research yielded completely new drugs, or synthetic forms of existing medicines. The discovery of the anesthetic effects of ether and chloroform prompted research into the medicinal effects of organic chemicals. Chloral hydrate, the first synthetic medicine to induce sleep, was created in 1869; and veronal, the first barbiturate drug, in 1903. The painkilling chemical in willow bark had been identified as early as 1826, but when isolated, it proved unsuitable as a medicine as it irritated the stomach lining. In 1899, Felix Hoffman synthesized a related compound, acetylsalicylic acid, which showed fewer side effects. Marketed as aspirin, it became one of the most popular medicines of the 20th century. Chemical dyes were an unlikely but fruitful source of new medicines. In 1856, an English chemist tried to synthesize quinine but succeeded in producing the first chemical dye used to color cloth. From 1880, dyes became the starting point for new drugs. Antipyrine, a drug similar to quinine, was produced in 1884 from a chemical used to make yellow dyes. Phenacetine and paracetamol came from similar sources and were used to reduce fevers and kill pain.

Unorthodox Medicines

Many of the medicines used in 19th-century Europe and North America produced extreme reactions. Vomiting after taking an emetic was reassuring (it was clear that the medicine was having an effect on the body), but it was uncomfortable and unpleasant. Even pure forms of drugs could have unpleasant side effects. A French traveler observed in 1850: “Quinine . . . does relieve fever quite rapidly, but when you have recovered from the disease, you still have to recover from the remedy . . . quinine inflames your bowel, blurs your vision, and causes so much hearing disorder that it sounds as though you could hear 36,000 bells in the ears” (Marmier 1852, 71–72).

It is perhaps not surprising that many people turned to alternative or "unorthodox" forms of medicine that used simpler, more natural therapies. Thompsonian medicine sought to cure all illness using a small range of medicinal herbs to regulate the heat within the body. These caused purging and vomiting but were perceived to be milder and more natural than the medicines prescribed by orthodox practitioners that contained poisonous substances such as mercury. Homeopathy, another popular unorthodox system of medicine, had no such unpleasant effects. Practitioners did use some strong, mineral-based drugs but in a very dilute form to stimulate the body's own healing responses.

Folk Medicine

Folk medicine, unlike systems of medical knowledge, did not have an underlying theory of body function and thus no explanation of the effect of medicines on the body. Instead, practitioners prescribed specific treatments for particular ailments. Many materials were used in medicines. Remedies incorporated local and exotic plants, earths, minerals, and animal products. In some cultures, healers made use of several hundred medicinal substances. Plants were a rich source of drugs, and all parts—roots, leaves, bark, and seeds—had their uses. Each was used in a variety of ways. For example, the leaves of trees or plants could be boiled in water to make an infusion, pounded to a paste with water or fat to make an ointment, squeezed to extract juice, rubbed directly on the skin, chewed, added to hot water in a steam bath, or burned and the smoke inhaled. In many cultures, plants were gathered at a specific time of year, in particular weather, and even at an exact stage of the lunar cycle to ensure their potency. Herbs were prepared in very precise ways; they could be dried quickly over a fire or in the sun or more slowly in the shade. Many medicines must have been discovered by a process of trial and error, but the medicine men of North American tribes received information about the use of drugs in dreams from spirit guides. In other cultures, the appearance or qualities of substances suggested their use. Zulu healers used plants with a red sap resembling blood to treat bleeding. The cause of ailments could also suggest a cure: medicines made from the flesh of snakes were applied to snakebites.

Indigenous people made use of local plants to treat disease. In the southern United States, the indigenous tribes used angelica root, a tender herb that grew only in warm areas, to treat stomach disorders. Among northern peoples, the buds and resin of pine and spruce trees that flourished in the cold climate were given for colds and respiratory ailments. Sometimes a single plant could cure several complaints. Preparations of the raw roots of butterfly weed were taken by native peoples in cases of respiratory diseases, and the dried and powdered roots were applied to wounds. Different groups of Native Americans used different plants for the same purpose. The Rappahannock prescribed wild ginger tea or bruised plantain leaves to treat fevers, while the Teton Dakotas used the root of little rattlepod. Equally, the same medicine was applied for different purposes by different peoples. The Cherokees used wild cherry bark during childbirth, the Ojibwas applied it to sores and for chest complaints, and the Poncas used it to treat diarrhea.

The use of medicines varied between cultures. Herbal medicines were the keystone of medical care throughout Africa and Asia, but Western travelers to the Pacific islands and in New Zealand reported that the indigenous people used only a few medicines. Maori people treated common digestive complaints, such as diarrhea or constipation, with plant juices, and they prepared ointments and salves containing extracts from leaves, berries, and bark to treat external complaints. Their limited use of medicines reflected their belief that most disease was caused by spirits, and as a result, they relied on rituals rather than drugs to treat illness.

PRACTITIONERS, APOTHECARIES, DRUGGISTS

Around the world, the 19th century saw an expanding market for medicines, which could be obtained through a variety of channels. Learned practitioners trained in Chinese, Ayurvedic, or Unani medical theory prescribed medicines for almost all their patients, tailored to their illness and designed to suit the constitution and lifestyle of each individual patient.

Prescribing was the key outcome of a medical consultation with an elite Chinese practitioner; patients were given a written prescription, which they took to a drug seller to be made up. Practitioners constantly adjusted their prescriptions to follow the course of the illness, sometimes changing them every day. When treating the Chinese emperor for smallpox in 1874, his doctors began by prescribing cooling remedies. As the disease ran its course, these were replaced by a mix of warming and cooling medicines to help replenish qi. The drugs prescribed for the emperor included milk vetch, magnolia bark, bamboo shavings, plantain, and ginseng. Patients often negotiated with practitioners over their prescriptions: they asked for medicines they did not like to be removed or for drugs that they believed were suited to their case to be included.

Ayurvedic physicians (*vaids*) and Unani *hakims* were trained in pharmacy and made up medicines as well as prescribing for their patients. Practitioners produced medicines in small amounts, with the dosage and composition adjusted to the age and strength of the patient. In Europe and North America, all doctors received training in the use of medicines as part of their education. Elite physicians prescribed, but did not prepare, drugs for their wealthy patients. Practitioners who served middle-and lower-class patients often kept a supply of commonly used drugs on hand and would make up their own prescriptions.

While textbooks stressed the need to prescribe for individual patients, in practice, physicians working in all medical systems often turned to standard medicines or favorite remedies. The composition of these medicines was often handed down from teacher to pupil: one Chinese remedy was called the "Ointment Medicine Secretly Transmitted by Master Feng." Even standard remedies were not rigidly specified. *Nushkas*, prescriptions written by famous Unani practitioners and sometimes published, could be made up with alternative ingredients, allowing the medicines to be adjusted to the individual patient.

Folk healers, too, provided medicines as part of a consultation. As well as knowing the identity of the raw materials for medicines, healers had to know where to find them, what parts to use, and how to store and prepare drugs so as to maximize their potency. Not surprisingly, in many communities it took several years to learn the preparation and uses of medicines.

Drug Vendors

Specialist drug sellers made up the medicines prescribed by Chinese and Western practitioners and sold standard remedies. Drug vendors were found in every medical culture and went by a variety of names. In India, *attars* prepared and sold Unani medicines; in the West, drug sellers were known as apothecaries (this was a traditional name that fell out of use during the century), chemists, pharmacists, herbalists, or druggists. They had some training in medical theory, but they learned the practical skills of preparing medicines through apprenticeships. The best druggists' shops carried a huge stock of drugs. One Western traveler wrote,

> The drug shops of China are large, and are commodiously fitted up. They have a great array of drawers and jars. Arranged much in the same way as in England; glass vessels are very rare. Different departments are allotted to separate classes of medicaments; care is taken to keep things in order; and there is a great degree of neatness and method in their appearance which would not be discreditable to a London laboratory. (Wilson 1846, 567)

Ordinary medicines were wrapped in paper, with instructions written on the outside. Expensive medicines, such as ginseng, were wrapped in red paper. Drug sellers had a comprehensive knowledge of the preparation and uses of medicines. Not surprisingly, many also offered medical advice as well as selling medicines. At the other end of the scale from the druggist in his well-stocked shop were street traders, who had a limited knowledge of medicine and sold a few herbs or a handful of general remedies.

As well as making up prescriptions, druggists made and sold standard preparations, such as laudanum, a medicine made of opium in alcohol, often devising their own variations on well-known remedies. In 1832, a druggist in the north of England advertised:

> His invaluable medicine BALSAM of HOREHOUND, for curing Coughs, Colds, Asthmas, Hooping [*sic*] Cough, Declines and Consumption, Also . . . his truly valuable and never failing Medicine for the Cholera Morbus, or Vomiting and Purging; and also his excellent medicines for Worms; all of which medicines . . . have obtained very high reputations, and can only be prepared by G. B. Reinhardt, as he is the sole possessor of his late Father's recipes. (*Wakefield and Halifax Journal* 1832)

Druggists carefully composed their medicines to suit their customers. South African drug sellers sold Western remedies to their European customers and compounded medicines including indigenous herbs aimed at the black population.

An increasing demand for medical care worldwide allowed drug sellers to flourish. In Europe and North America, druggist's shops were found in every town and city. Successful traders established chains of stores. In England, Boots' chemist shops expanded from a single market stall in 1849 to over 300 branches by the 1900s.

The mid-19th century saw a boom in pharmacies in the West, when people of all classes bought medicines for their minor ailments over the counter. This illustration shows an elegantly appointed shop carrying a wide range of drugs. (National Library of Medicine)

There was tension among druggists and between doctors. European practitioners complained that pharmacists were stealing their business by prescribing for patients as well as selling them medicines over the counter. Pharmacists, trained in making up prescriptions, complained that chemists selling popular over-the-counter remedies in bulk undercut their prices. This prompted a movement to improve standards of education in pharmacy and the development of new training courses and qualifications at colleges and universities. While qualified pharmacists enjoyed some advantages—they alone had the right to sell dangerous drugs and poisons—they never enjoyed a monopoly of trade. Throughout the century, anyone could set up a shop and sell medicines without any formal training.

These debates about competence were mirrored in India, where practitioners anxious to improve standards of care hit out at drug sellers with little knowledge of medicines. One writer complained that drug sellers had "ten to twenty pots, which have turmeric, tamarind paste, black pepper, and they begin dispensing medicines" (Alavi 2008, 253). Prompted by these concerns, practitioners set up an indigenous pharmaceutical industry in India, mass-producing Ayurvedic and Unani medicines of a consistently high quality that were sold at set prices. As they purchased manufacturing machinery from the West, they also adopted the forms of medicine used in Europe and North America—pills and powders—and standardized the strength of medicines.

PATENT MEDICINES

The 19th century saw a boom in the market for proprietary or patent medicines. (The term is a misnomer, as the medicines were not protected by legal patents.) The exact composition of these remedies was a secret, known only to the manufacturer, and they were heavily marketed. These were usually self-prescribed, rather than recommended by a medical practitioner, and were bought over the counter from druggists, grocers, or through mail order. Patent medicines had been developed in Europe in the 18th century but flourished in the 19th century with the development of the retail trade in medicines and in advertising.

Many remedies claimed to cure minor ailments and offered a cheap alternative to going to a doctor. Others were supposed to cure fatal diseases such as cancer, where doctors could offer little hope. Lydia Pinkham's Vegetable Compound, a mix of herbs and alcohol claimed to be a panacea—a cure-all. Advertisements claimed that the compound would

> [C]ure the worst forms of Female Complaints, all Ovarian Troubles, Inflammation and Ulceration[,] Falling and Displacement of the Womb, and consequent Spinal Weakness, and is peculiarly adapted to the Change of Life. . . . It dissolves and expels tumors from the Uterus . . . Bloating, Flooding, Nervous Prostration, Headache, General Debility quickly yield to it. . . . It quickly removes . . . Dizziness, Faintness, sleeplessness, flatulency, melancholy or the "blues" and headache. (*Sun* newspaper 1905)

The boom in sales of medicines was helped by a range of preparations aimed at people who were not ill but who felt they need to protect or boost their health. Pills, potions, and powders promised health and vigor by cleansing the body, or stimulating the nerves, or building up the blood. Bile Beans and Beecham's Liver Pills promised robust health, while Bromo-phosoph was a "brain food" that would restore vitality. Tonics, often in the form of wine fortified with drugs, were particularly popular at the end of the century to combat the exhausting pace of modern life. Many patent medicines were presented as modern and based on scientific research. Lactopeptine claimed to contain "ptyalin, pepsin and pancreatine" to help digest starch, protein, and fats, respectively. Exotic foreign remedies were also popular. "Sequah's Prairie Water," a medicine reputedly based on Native American remedies, was sold across Europe in the 1890s.

By the late 19th century, patent medicines were sold around the world, from Europe and North America to colonies in Africa and Asia, where they were manufactured by local firms. In southern Africa, for example, European remedies were sold in stores, by mail order, and by traveling peddlers to Afrikaner farmers, Europeans, and Africans. Many patent medicines were popular with Africans, as they claimed, like indigenous remedies, not to cure disease but to strengthen the body and purify the blood. Bizarrely, "Dr. William's Pink Pills for Pale People" proved particularly popular among black Africans.

MEDICAL EXCHANGES

Knowledge of medicines traveled around the world in the 19th century. Western remedies were brought to Africa and Asia by practitioners and settlers in the new colonies; migrant workers from India and China took their own medicines to the Americas and Africa. In late 19th-century southern Africa, where European farmers, soldiers, and administrators worked alongside migrant workers from India and China, a rich mix of indigenous, Western, Ayurvedic, and Chinese medicines were widely available. Such medical exchanges between different systems of medicine had a long history. Theriac or Venice treacle dated back to medieval times. It was a panacea, able to cure many diseases and counter poisons, and was reputed to contain as many as 70 ingredients, including the flesh of vipers. In the 19th century, Unani *hakims* in India were still importing and prescribing the medicine under the name "Treak farook."

With globalization, more and more doctors trained in different medical traditions came into contact and became aware of the remedies used in other medical systems. In India, Ayurvedic and Unani practitioners began to prescribe European medicines alongside their traditional remedies. In the early part of the 19th century, British doctors in India sought out local remedies as possible substitutes for expensive imported drugs. Over time, however, Western practitioners became skeptical about the efficacy of medicines used in other cultures.

MEDICINES AND PATIENTS

Patients were active consumers of medicine. In every culture, patients made their own medicines to treat everyday complaints using local plants and foodstuffs. When urbanization limited access to the wild plants that provided the raw materials for medicines, patients purchased ingredients or bought ready-made medicines. In Europe, even people who could afford to go to a doctor made use of homemade medicines. Whisky and hot water was a popular cure for colds; honey or jam dissolved in hot water soothed a tickly cough. Mustard added to a bath helped to warm patients suffering from chills, and poultices made from all sorts of materials, including animal dung or old bread, were used to treat boils.

While Western practitioners took a conservative attitude toward medicines used in other cultures, their patients were happy to try alternative medicines if their usual drugs failed. In North America, many turned to alternative medicines such as homeopathy. Unorthodox systems were popular not only because they represented a more "natural" approach to healing but because they were marketed as empowering ordinary people to become their own doctor. Kits of homeopathic and herbal medicines, along with books on their use, were sold by druggists. Settler families living a long way from towns and medical help turned to native herbal medicines, partly because they were easy to obtain, and also because it was generally believed that local remedies were particularly effective against local diseases. European farmers in South Africa were happy to try indigenous herbal remedies when their own remedies had failed. In Java, European settlers took local remedies for dysentery and used Chinese medicines to treat syphilis and diphtheria.

DRUG ADDICTION

The open market in medicines brought problems, as not only simple remedies, but poisonous or addictive drugs were readily available. Some medicines, such as opium, had a long history of both medical and recreational use. Opium was widely used in the Middle East, partly for pleasure and partly as a means of keeping healthy. In Unani medicine, opium was classed as a cold dry medicine, and doctors particularly recommended it for older people and those living in damp climates as a means of preserving their health. Tea also shared this dual identity; it was a hot and humid drug but also a pleasant drink. In the West, doctors prescribed large qualities of opium-based drugs, such as laudanum (powdered opium dissolved in alcohol) to reduce pain, stop spasms, and promote sleep. The drug was cheap and widely sold by drug vendors. When the hypodermic syringe was developed in the 1860s, morphine came into general use for pain relief.

Many patent medicines containing opium were sold as treatments for aches and pains, minor ailments, and insomnia. Dr. Collis Browne's Chlorodyne, a popular remedy for diarrhea, contained opium. It was even included in medicines aimed at children. "Soothing syrups" were advertised as a way to calm teething children and crying infants. Working mothers regularly gave their children these medicines to ensure that they slept through the night or during the day while they were out at work. Enormous quantities of opium were consumed. In Britain, imports rose from 41,000 pounds in 1839 to 114,000 pounds in 1852. In the United States, the increase in opium imports was staggering: from 24,000 pounds in 1840 to over 500,000 pounds in the 1890s.

Not surprisingly, many people became addicted. With no laws against drug taking, in the late 19th century, the recreational use of morphine was widespread, socially acceptable, and even fashionable. Plans to treat addicts were devised, based on a gradual withdrawal or the substitution of alternative drugs including cocaine. This, of course, simply created a new form of addiction. By the end of the 19th century, there was a public outcry against the use of opium in Europe and North America. Laws were passed to control the sale of opium by pharmacists and to stop the trafficking of the drug for recreational use. Newspapers mounted successful campaigns against the inclusion of opium in patent medicines, especially those intended for children.

11

War, Health, and Medicine

The 19th century was an age of political and social upheaval. The desire for power and new territory, the emergence of new nations from older groups of states, old nations conquering new territory in Asia and Africa, and independent nations breaking away from their colonial masters all provided the catalysts for conflict. War changed radically during the 19th century. Around the world, weapons became deadlier: rifles replaced muskets, spears, and clubs, and killing became distanced and impersonal. In the West, war was industrialized. Armies became massive organizations with complex administrations to mobilize and support huge numbers of troops. Factories supplied weapons, ammunition, and food. The boundary between soldiers and civilians was blurred; civilians became increasingly conscripted into armies, provided medical care, and produced the goods that supported soldiers in the field.

War affected people's lives and health in many ways. For those involved in fighting, often hundreds or even thousands of miles from home, there was the risk of wounds or disease. Civilians were caught up in conflicts, forced to defend their homes or trapped in besieged towns, suffering from artillery bombardments or rifle fire. Far more were affected economically. For farmers able to sell their crops to the army, war was a time of prosperity; for civilians close to the battlefields, war could be a disaster. Soldiers in the field would take cattle and crops to feed themselves, and retreating armies destroyed foodstuffs to ensure they could not fall into the hands of the enemy, leaving civilians to go hungry. Not surprisingly, epidemics and famines frequently occurred in the aftermath of war.

WARS BETWEEN WESTERN POWERS

In Europe and the Americas, nations fought each other for power and territory. The 19th century saw frequent conflicts as the map of Europe was redrawn. The old Ottoman and Austro-Hungarian empires began to crumble, and the new nations of Italy and Germany were formed from coalitions of small states. In 1848, there were unsuccessful popular uprisings all over Europe against old rulers.

These wars involved radically different types of conflicts, from set piece battles between huge armies (the Battle of Borodino in 1812, for example, involved around a quarter of a million troops) to guerilla warfare by Spanish civilians against occupying French forces during the Peninsular War of 1808–1813.

In the 19th century, wars became industrialized. Huge numbers of troops were delivered to the front lines by railroads and on steamships. They were supplied with weapons, ammunition, uniforms, and preserved and tinned food produced in factories. After 1854, the telegraph allowed rapid communications on the battlefield and brought news of war to homes within hours of the fighting. Weapons became more deadly. Muskets, accurate over relatively short distances and with a slow rate of fire, were replaced by high-velocity rifles. Artillery played a greater role in battles, while cavalry became redundant. Tactics changed, too; commanders abandoned the use of static formations of troops in favor of rapid maneuvers to attack defensive positions.

MILITARY MEDICAL SERVICES

Over the century, the medical care provided to soldiers steadily improved. Conscription—the compulsory enlistment of men into the armed services—was introduced during the Napoleonic Wars and continued thereafter in many European countries. As a result, a large proportion of the male population could expect to serve in the military at some point in their lives. While it was generally accepted that soldiers had to risk their lives when fighting, there was increasing public concern that they should be protected against disease and should receive good-quality medical care if hurt.

Soldiers and Disease

At the beginning of the century, armies suffered high levels of mortality even when not involved in fighting. Large barracks, where many soldiers lived, ate, and slept, provided a perfect environment for the spread of infectious diseases. From the 1850s, sanitary reforms, similar to those introduced in cities, were imposed on soldiers' accommodations. New barracks were built on healthier sites, away from swampy ground, with good drainage and ventilation and supplied with clean water. At the same time, new policies were introduced to improve soldiers' health. Regulations required soldiers to bathe regularly (initially at least every month) and to have their clothing laundered. Rations of alcohol were drastically curtailed, and soldiers were encouraged to drink beer rather than spirits. To reduce high levels of venereal disease, prostitutes visited by soldiers were required to undergo regular inspection and, if found to be infected, to enter hospitals for treatment. Vaccination against smallpox was made compulsory.

It was much more difficult to control disease when soldiers were on campaign. Camps were often set up quickly with little opportunity to dig latrines or secure clean water supplies. Officers lacked the time to enforce basic levels of personal hygiene among the rank and file. Typhoid fever was a constant scourge of armies in the 19th century, weakening Napoleon's forces in their attack on Russia in 1812 and causing huge casualties on both sides in the Crimean War of 1853–1856 and the American Civil War in 1861–1865.

BATTLEFIELD MEDICINE

The Organization of Care

Over the course of the century, the medical care provided to soldiers in the field was revolutionized. Haphazard and inadequate care was replaced by organized systems to rapidly evacuate soldiers through a hierarchy of medical posts where they received appropriate care. At Waterloo, the final battle of the Napoleonic Wars, fought on June 18, 1815, wounded soldiers received care at regimental medical posts. These temporary stations were set up just behind the lines. They had few staff, and during the battle, the supplies of medicines, dressings, and even clean water soon ran out. Soldiers with minor wounds walked, or were helped by comrades, to their regiment's medical post. The majority of the wounded remained on the field; at the end of the fighting, over 40,000 injured troops were spread over five square miles, and many waited for days to be discovered and given help. After the battle, wounded soldiers were cared for in temporary hospitals set up in nearby farms, villages, and towns. All available buildings—houses, churches, and stables—were pressed into service.

By the end of the century, a streamlined system of medical care for wounded soldiers had been developed, supported by more and better-trained medical staff. Mimicking industrial processes, the movement and treatment of wounded soldiers was broken down into a series of steps. When wounded, soldiers received first aid from their comrades; by the end of the century, all troops carried a field dressing in their uniforms. The injured soldiers were carried off the field by stretcher bearers to an aid post staffed by a medical officer. He re-dressed their wounds and carried out basic treatment to prepare the injured soldiers for the journey on to field hospitals away from the battlefield. These hospitals had a few hundred beds, a small staff, and basic equipment. Soldiers with minor wounds recuperated there and then returned to the fighting. The more seriously wounded were moved further away to larger and better-equipped general hospitals. Although a vast improvement over the care provided to earlier generations of soldiers, the system was not perfect. During the journey between each post, often over bad roads, the soldier-patients were jolted, causing wounds to reopen, and some troops bled to death before reaching their destination.

Dealing with Wounds

More rapid evacuation of troops and quicker access to care undoubtedly saved lives. The treatment of battle injuries also improved radically, reflecting broader improvements in surgery. In the early decades of the 19th century, soldiers suffered from cuts inflicted by swords and lances and from wounds from cannon fire, shrapnel, and musket balls. Treatments were limited. Surgeons probed wounds to remove shrapnel; they stitched cuts and set broken bones. Most wounds became infected, so when faced with a badly mangled limb, surgeons usually chose to amputate. The survival rate for amputations was poor—between 10 and 25 percent of soldiers died following the operation. Amputating quickly—within a day after being wounded—increased a soldier's chances of survival; if they had to wait longer, the chances of dying from infection increased. By the mid-19th century, treatment strategies remained the same, but wounded soldiers did have the benefit of anesthetics that allowed surgeons to operate more slowly and carefully. Later conflicts saw the introduction of improved techniques to control bleeding, using clamps, tourniquets, and elastic bandages. By the end of the century, surgeons had learned that efforts to remove bullets and shrapnel often introduced infection, so unless the object was in a dangerous position within the body, they simply dressed the wound and allowed it to heal.

Care was also better organized. At the siege of Sevastopol in the Crimean War, a Russian surgeon, Nikolai Pirogov, pioneered a system of triage, or sorting. Instead of treating all officers first and then ordinary soldiers on a first-come, first-served basis, Pirogov divided the wounded into three categories. Those who were too badly wounded to survive were put to bed and received basic nursing care. Those with fairly minor wounds were given a number and asked to wait. Soldiers likely to live after surgery were given priority. Leo Tolstoy, the Russian writer, visited the hospital and described what he saw:

> You are assailed without warning by the sight and smell of forty or fifty amputees and critically wounded, some of them on camp beds, but most of them lying on the floor . . . through the doorway on the left, that is the room in which wounds are bandaged and operations performed. There you will see surgeons with pale, gloomy physiognomies [faces], their arms soaked in blood up to the elbows, deep in concentration over a bed on which a wounded man is lying under the influence of chloroform, open-eyed as in a delirium and uttering words which are occasionally simple and affecting. The surgeons are going about the repugnant but beneficial task of amputation. (Tolstoy 1986)

Pirogov's system of triage was widely adopted and ensured that surgeons focused their efforts on the soldiers that could benefit from their care.

Mortality in War

Every war was different, in its length, intensity, and the types of weapons used, and consequently in the number of soldiers killed and the types of injuries they suffered. The muskets used in the Napoleonic Wars fired a large ball that caused terrible damage to flesh and bones. The high-velocity rifle bullets used in later conflicts caused less damage to the tissues, and as a result, the wounds healed better. The conditions in which troops lived and fought had a major impact on mortality. On Napoleon's retreat from Russia in the winter of 1812, over 350,000 French soldiers, around 95 percent of the army, died from cold and starvation. The total number of deaths caused by different conflicts varied widely. It is impossible to derive exact figures for the mortality caused by the Napoleonic Wars, fought between 1803 and 1815, but probably between 2.5 million and 3.5 million soldiers died. During the Crimean War, 25,000 British soldiers, 35,000 Turks, 100,000 French, and up to half a million Russians died.

Over the century, there was a clear trend in the proportion of deaths caused by wounds and disease. At the beginning of the century, soldiers were much more likely to die from disease than from injuries sustained in combat. During the Napoleonic Wars, the British lost 24 times as many soldiers to disease as to wounds. In the Crimean and the American Civil War, the ratio was five soldiers dead of disease to one from combat. In the Franco-Prussian War of 1870–1871, the Prussian army, with its well-organized medical services, lost 15,000 troops to disease and just 11,000 to wounds.

CIVILIANS AND WAR

Civilians suffered and died as a consequence of war, often in large numbers. In war zones, soldiers consumed local food supplies, disrupted trade, and brought infectious diseases so that epidemics and famines frequently followed war. An outbreak of plague in the wake of the Russo-Turkish War of 1806–1812 killed one-third of the inhabitants of Bucharest in Romania. At least a million (and perhaps as many as 3 million) civilians died during the Napoleonic Wars as both a direct and indirect result of the conflict. Civilians were engaged in war in many ways: they worked in factories, supplying the materials used by soldiers, and they played an increasing role in providing medical care.

Civilian Nurses

In army hospitals, nursing care was provided by untrained orderlies and ward sergeants helped by soldiers' wives and camp followers. Civilians had traditionally helped to look after wounded soldiers following battles. In the aftermath of Waterloo, Belgian civilians helped to set up temporary hospitals and provided bedding and assistance to the wounded. Female civilian nurses began working in military hospitals in the 1850s. In response to reports of dreadful hospital conditions, in 1854, the British Secretary at War sent a party of female nurses, led by Florence Nightingale, to the Crimea.

Nightingale's impact on the British army's general hospital at Scutari (some 200 miles from the main Crimean battlefields) has become the stuff of legend. At the time, Nightingale was presented as a saintly figure, performing hands-on care and transforming Scutari from a death trap, where soldiers were neglected and left to die from wounds and disease. In fact, Nightingale (as even her family acknowledged) lacked the caring qualities of a nurse, but she was a brilliant administrator. She reorganized the hospital supplies and helped to instigate a massive clean-up. The other nurses kept order on the wards, reportedly scolding orderlies into making improvements, and distributing food and medicines. Their efforts had little effect on mortality, however—soldiers continued to die in huge numbers from

Florence Nightingale (the central figure in this image) famously brought order to the chaotic conditions in the British military hospital at Scutari during the Crimean War. This ward, staffed by male and female nurses, is scrupulously clean, and the windows allow in fresh air. (Library of Congress)

typhoid, typhus fever, and dysentery. It was only when a sanitary commission discovered that the hospital's water supplies were contaminated by sewage that the death rates fell.

Female nurses also worked among French and Russian soldiers in the Crimea. French soldiers were cared for by nursing sisters from the Order of St. Vincent de Paul. In Russia, the Grand Duchess Elena Pavlova formed the Community of the Holy Cross, organizing teams of doctors and nurses to help Russian soldiers. The Crimean War set a pattern, and women formed a significant part of the medical workforce in later conflicts. In the American Civil War, women volunteered to serve as nurses, cooks, and cleaners for the Union army.

The Red Cross

Further civilian involvement in the care of soldiers came with the founding of the Red Cross. The movement was inspired by Henry Dunant, a Swiss businessman who witnessed the inadequate medical services provided to all combatants after the Battle of Solferino in 1859, one of the conflicts during the Italian War of Independence. Dunant wrote a pamphlet describing his experiences and concluded: "Would it not be possible, in time of peace and quiet, to form relief societies for the purpose of having care given to the wounded in wartime by zealous, devoted and thoroughly qualified volunteers?" (Dunant 1986). This was not a new idea—similar notions had been circulating since the end of the 18th century—but in the late 1850s, with growing concern for the welfare of soldiers, his ideas were swiftly put into practice. Over the next few decades, the Committee of the International Red Cross was formed in Geneva, and national Red Cross societies were formed throughout Europe, the Americas, the Ottoman Empire, and Japan. The new organization also drew up the first Geneva Convention in 1864, setting down rules for the treatment of sick and wounded soldiers and of civilian medical staff.

Initially, coordinating the civilian Red Cross Services with existing military medical services proved problematic. During the Franco-Prussian War, the French Red Cross Society worked separately from the army. While some of its volunteers undoubtedly helped many soldiers, its services were badly organized. The society sent out mobile field hospitals that were ill equipped, often over-or understaffed with untrained nurses, and rarely reached the battlefields when they were required. Civilians declared their homes to be Red Cross hospitals to escape the requirement to provide accommodation for soldiers, and society ladies set up hospitals as a means of proving their patriotism, regardless of where they were needed. By contrast, in Prussia, the work of Red Cross volunteers was closely coordinated with the army. The military medical services were highly organized, and Red Cross staff were used to complement the existing services. Red Cross nurses helped to staff hospitals and the hospital trains used to evacuate the wounded. They provided refreshments and manned re-dressing stations along the evacuation route. The Prussian approach provided the model for other national Red Cross societies in later conflicts.

War and Civilian Medicine

War is often portrayed as a laboratory, in which practitioners and administrators can experiment with new medical techniques and forms of organization that are later brought into civilian medicine. There were certainly examples of civilian medicine drawn from wartime experience. In the 19th century, army ambulance services provided the model for civilian services. But the relationship between civilian and military medicine was complex. Much that was learned in wartime, such as new techniques to deal with bullet wounds, was simply not applicable to civilian life.

War had an important although indirect impact on civilian health by inspiring investments in infant welfare programs. Around the world, governments equated population with power: a large population provided men for the army and workers for industry. However, in the West, birth rates were falling, provoking fears that the population might shrink. There were also fears about the quality as well as the quantity of manpower. Large-scale inspection of recruits and conscripts revealed a worrying picture of the health of nations, revealing that many volunteers were unfit for service because they were too short, had flat feet, or had poor teeth. To ensure that the next generation of men would be strong and healthy, governments and charities set up schemes to improve the health of infants. Mothers were provided with free milk and were taught how to look after their children. Babies were weighed and monitored to ensure that they grew at the correct rate.

WARS BEYOND THE WEST

Outside Europe and North America, wars took many forms. There were short conflicts between different groups or tribes of indigenous people, or between indigenous people and foreign settlers, over access to land and other resources. There were civil wars between large groups within a single nation, like the Taiping Rebellion in China, which lasted for several years. With increasing global travel and conquest, European armies fought many wars overseas, seeking to control rebellions in established territories. Haiti broke away from French rule and became an independent republic in 1804, and Mexico, Brazil, Argentina, and Chile gained independence from their colonial masters in the 1810s and 1820s. Armies also fought overseas to gain new colonies in Asia, Africa, and the Pacific. In 1838 and 1856, the British fought the so-called "Opium Wars" to force the Chinese government to permit trading by European merchants. These wars took many forms: pitched battles between forces of hundreds of thousands of troops, sieges of cities, skirmishes, and guerilla wars.

There was no clear division between Western and non-Western in these conflicts. Often, the combatants were a mix of foreign and indigenous fighters. Maori joined with British forces to fight anti-British Maori; the British army in India included large numbers of indigenous soldiers or *sepoys*. Non-Western armies, such as the imperial forces of Japan and China, adopted Western systems of command and weaponry. In other cultures, fighters used Western firearms alongside traditional weapons.

NON-WESTERN MILITARY FORCES

While wars between Western powers were usually fought with large bodies of well-trained and coordinated forces, the size of military conflicts in non-Western cultures varied radically. In India, the rulers of the Maratha Empire raised around 200,000 troops in the early 19th century to fight against the British East India Company. In the Satsuma Rebellion in Japan in 1877, an army of over 20,000 rebels, led by members of the traditional warrior class of samurai, fought against an imperial army of around 65,000 troops. By contrast, many disputes between indigenous peoples were relatively small scale. Among the Maori people of New Zealand, small groups of related people (*hapu*) frequently engaged in conflicts. One *hapu* could muster around 140 to 400 fighting men, but sometimes several *hapu* allied to attack another group. In the Indian Wars in North America, most tribes had hundreds rather than thousands of warriors, and large battles, such as Little Big Horn in 1876, involved perhaps 2,000 warriors (although it is difficult to arrive at a definite number).

When indigenous tribes unified under a single leader, they could support large and highly organized military forces. In the early 19th century, Shaka ka Senzangakhona, or Shaka Zulu, commanded an army of perhaps 15,000 troops, conquering an area of several thousand square miles in southern Africa. Shaka is often credited with inventing new tactics and introducing new weapons, and he undoubtedly developed the fighting capabilities of the Zulu tribes. Under his rule, Zulu warriors fought in named groups or "regiments" of 400 to 4,000 warriors, under an hierarchy of commanders. All young men had to serve in the king's army. They were called up for service at the age of 17 or 18, and they lived in a separate community, or barracks, associated with their fighting group or regiment. Each group had its own distinctive headdress and carried cowhide shields of a different color. In the barracks, they went through a period of training, including exercises in the use of weapons and in military tactics.

In conflicts involving indigenous groups, the division between civilians and combatants was never hard and fast. In cultures such as the Maori and Zulu, all adult men were likely to be involved in warfare at some point. In popular uprisings, such as the Haitian Revolution of 1791–1804, a large proportion of the slave population took part in the fighting. Women supported warfare behind the lines by growing and carrying food to be eaten on campaign and by helping the wounded. In some cases, they fought alongside men. Indian women helped to fight against American cavalry by frightening the soldiers' horses. In the Taiping Rebellion, there were separate units of female fighters, while Maori women worked alongside male warriors building defensive structures.

WEAPONRY AND TACTICS

The risks of death and injury to warriors depended on the type of weapons they faced. In the early 19th century, wars between indigenous peoples were often fought with traditional weapons that had been in use for hundreds or thousands of years. Maori fought hand to hand with stone clubs (*mere* or *patu*). From the 1810s, they traded with passing ships for iron tools, such as billhooks, which they also used in combat. Traditionally, Zulu warriors fought using light throwing spears and small shields, but under Shaka's rule, they added heavier stabbing spears (*assegai*) and clubs to their armory. Native American peoples fought with bows and arrows from horseback. All these weapons were most effective at fairly close range and capable of causing serious cuts, broken bones, or death.

Traditional weapons had a strong symbolic function as well as a practical one. The Japanese samurai were traditionally allowed to carry two swords, and the Satsuma Rebellion was sparked when the modernizing imperial government attempted to deprive warriors of this sign of their status. In the conflict, the rebels fought mainly with guns and artillery, but during the final battle, warriors made a last symbolic charge using their swords.

By the middle decades of the century, the risks of death or serious injury were increased by the use of firearms such as muskets, rifles, and artillery. In most conflicts, both sides had guns, but the quality of firearms often had a decisive impact. In the Taiping Rebellion in China, the rebels had older, less powerful rifles, while the imperial armies had better rifles and modern artillery pieces, purchased from Europe. Zulu and Maori fighters acquired muskets, but they were often old, required a long time to reload, and frequently malfunctioned. As a result, their guns were much less effective than might be expected. The Maori began to acquire muskets in the early 19th century, and when first introduced, they had a significant effect in combat, as coordinated volleys of fire killed large numbers and caused confusion. However, warriors quickly devised new tactics that reduced their effect. Guns were not fully integrated into Zulu ways of fighting. In battle, the Zulus used them rather like throwing spears, firing one shot, then continuing forward without attempting to reload. When they reached the enemy lines, they fought hand to hand with spears and clubs.

Fighters used an assortment of tactics. Many conflicts mirrored those of the West: in wars in India, China, and Japan, large armies fought battles in which one side set up defensive positions around a fort, city, or strategically important piece of ground, and the other attacked using artillery and infantry. The Chinese armies had traditionally mounted sieges, but they proved ineffectual when facing British and French ships and artillery during the Opium Wars. By contrast, the Indian Wars in North America involved a mix of battles and guerilla warfare that allowed small numbers of warriors to make best use of their mobility and limited weaponry to attack civilians or small groups of enemy combatants. While most battles were fought by soldiers on foot, cavalry forces took to the field in India, in northern China during the Nein Rebellion of 1851–1868, and in North America.

Indigenous people used elaborate fighting strategies, both defensive and offensive. Wars between Maori people usually took place around the community's *pa*, a defensive enclosure surrounded by fences, ramparts, and ditches. The local people would withdraw into the enclosure, with supplies of food and water, and defend the area against efforts to undermine or burn down the defensive walls. When firearms were introduced to Maori warfare, the *pa* was redesigned to absorb musket fire and to allow the defenders to fire out onto the enemy. Between 1845 and 1872, when facing British forces armed with modern artillery, Maori designers incorporated underground "bunkers" roofed with stones that allowed warriors to survive even heavy bombardments. At the Battle of Gate *Pa*, British troops entered the structure, believing all the fighters to be dead as a result of a fierce artillery bombardment. They fled in panic when Maori warriors suddenly appeared from their underground structures. Maori also devised completely new types of defensive structures to halt the progress of British troops—long lines of ditches and trenches, with redoubts. As soon as it became clear that the position could no longer be held, the Maori abandoned these positions to build new structures at other strategic points.

By contrast, the Zulu army used offensive tactics, splitting into three groups to encircle the enemy. This formation was called "the beast's horns." Young, mobile fighters moved around to the right and left, while the more experienced fighters remained in the center. Once in position, the warriors launched a rapid, coordinated attack. These tactics proved successful at the Battle of Isandlwana in 1879, when a Zulu army of around 20,000 warriors encircled and attacked a British army camp, killing large numbers of troops. From a defensive position, however, the British troops were able to make better use of their superior weaponry and defeat much larger forces of Zulu warriors. At Rorke's Drift, fought shortly after Isandlwana, around 140 British troops held off a force of 3,000–4,000 Zulu warriors.

The Zulu tribes had highly trained and disciplined warriors who fought using elaborate military tactics. This group of warriors display the distinctive shields and headdresses associated with different military subgroups, and carry spears. (Historica Graphica Collection/Heritage Images/Getty Images)

Medicine

Fighting groups drawn from indigenous peoples rarely had organized medical services. The highly organized Zulu army had healers to provide supernatural medicines as a form of preparation and protection. Before going into battle, warriors went through a process of purification: they drank medicines to make them vomit; then they were sprinkled with water containing substances including human flesh, to give them power and make them invincible. After the battle, the surviving Zulus went through a further purification process. Wounded Zulu warriors, like fighters from other cultures, had to find their own care. They walked or crawled or were carried away from the battlefield by comrades or family members. Many died from wounds on the field. Those who made it back to safety were treated by healers. Grasses, moss, and herbs were used to clean wounds and prevent infection. Zulu healers sewed up large wounds using sinews, but could do little for bones shattered by high-velocity bullets. In the years after the Zulu wars, travelers reported meeting veterans of the conflicts with multiple large scars, proving that at least some survived their injuries.

European troops serving overseas had the benefit of organized medical care, but even the best medicine could do little in the face of exotic and unfamiliar diseases such as yellow fever, to which troops had little or no immunity. Soldiers died in vast numbers. During the Indian Mutiny of 1857, the British army lost 9,467 soldiers; 586 were killed in the conflict, but 8,881 died from disease. The French lost 36,000 of their 39,000 soldiers sent to fight in Haiti in 1802–1803 to disease. Disease affected not only troops fighting in unfamiliar climates. Thousands of civilians and fighters died during an outbreak of plague spread through disruption to trade routes during the Muslim Rebellion of 1862–1877 in China.

MORTALITY IN NON-WESTERN CONFLICTS

Mortality in wars outside the West varied enormously. In a small skirmish, a handful of warriors might be injured and none killed. Rebel armies tended to suffer high mortality as they fought to the last. During the Satsuma Rebellion, around 18,000 of a total force of 22,000 rebel troops were killed or wounded. By contrast, the Japanese government army of 65,000 soldiers lost 6,000 killed and 10,000 wounded. Sieges of towns were very destructive. During the battle of Nanking in the Taiping Rebellion, 100,000 inhabitants died as fighting and fire swept through the city. During the Anglo-Boer War of 1899–1902, thousands of civilians were trapped alongside British troops in the besieged towns of Ladysmith, Mafeking, and Kimberley. Many were killed by shelling from the Boer artillery, and all suffered from the severe food shortages. The Boers besieging Ladysmith cut off the town's water supply, forcing the inhabitants to drink polluted water and causing outbreaks of typhoid and dysentery. Toward the end of the war, large numbers of Boer civilians, mainly women and children, were interned in over 100 concentration camps to prevent them from providing aid to the Boers' guerilla campaign. The camps were crowded and unsanitary, with inadequate shelter and food. Diseases, including measles and pneumonia, spread quickly. At least 28,000 women and children and around 20,000 black people died in the camps.

Several factors helped to reduce the death toll from conflicts between indigenous people. Wars were usually short because agricultural societies could not grow and store enough supplies to feed a large force of warriors for long periods. In addition, their fighting men were also farmers, and fighting had to stop during planting and harvesting seasons. In some conflicts between indigenous people, the rules of war were designed to avoid wholesale slaughter and to limit the number of deaths. Although the Maori people engaged in frequent conflicts, they had extremely elaborate strategies to reduce the number of casualties. *Taua muru* conflicts were far more common than full-scale wars. These conflicts were a means by which one group sought redress or punished another group but without outright war. Satisfaction could be achieved without bloodshed, by plundering food stores or destroying crops. Rituals, such as performing a *haka* (a war dance) or brandishing weapons replaced actual fighting. Muskets became part of this ritualized fighting: warriors would exchange symbolic volleys of fire or fire into the ground to prove their readiness to attack, without causing any injury.

Full-scale Maori wars involved up to several hundred warriors, with women and slaves to support them. Even in these conflicts, there were clear rules of engagement. In order to achieve a victory with limited bloodshed, chiefs sent out warnings before launching an attack or agreed before the battle not to kill more than a certain proportion of the defenders. Fighting stopped at dusk to allow the defenders to come out of the *pa* to forage for food and water. When one side sensed that they were likely to lose, they used peacemakers to find a resolution. This might involve giving up land and moving away from the area or presenting the victors with gifts such as canoes or clothing. The victors took prisoners or slaves, some of whom were killed and eaten. The rules of engagement were not always observed. A missionary, writing in 1845, noted

> The wars of the tribes are . . . generally conducted with moderation, and in accordance with established rules: this may arise partly from superstitious grounds; but when some act of more than usual atrocity has been committed by one party [i.e., the rules are broken by one side] it seems like a signal to proceed to acts of the greatest barbarity. But these cannot be regarded as mere acts of wanton cruelty; they are perpetrated with a view to intimidate the opposite party. (Hadfield 2003)

In conflicts between Zulu tribal groups, there was some element of ritual, and the disputes caused relatively few casualties. By contrast, the battles between British and Zulu forces were extraordinarily violent, as the Zulu warriors pressed on with their attacks. One Zulu described how, during a battle:

> We never got nearer than 50 paces to the English, and although we tried to climb over our fallen brothers we could not get very far ahead because the white men were firing heavily close to the ground into our front ranks, while the "by and bye" [artillery] was firing over our heads into the regiments behind us . . . Some of our men had their arms torn right off by [shells]. The battle was so fierce that we had to wipe the blood and brains of the killed and wounded from our faces, arms, legs and shields after the fighting. (Account of Chief Zimena 1929)

At the Battle of Isandlwana, around 1,300 of the 1,750 British defenders were killed along with around 1,000 Zulu warriors. At Rorke's Drift, the British suffered only 14 casualties, but the encounter ended with 350 Zulus dead and perhaps another 500 wounded Zulus massacred, in revenge for previous encounters. By March 1879, the huge death toll from repeated battles had decimated and demoralized the Zulus, who could no longer put a large army into the field.

12

Medical Institutions

While a one-to-one consultation between a fee-paying patient and an independent practitioner was by far the most common form of medical encounter, care provided through institutions became more frequent around the world in the 19th century. Institutions can be defined as organizations or structures developed for some social purpose. In the case of medicine, the range of institutions was very broad: they were responsible for organizing and delivering care to the sick, disease prevention, medical research, and training medical practitioners. Institutions were able to work in ways that individual practitioners could not. Large-scale projects, such as cleaning up the urban environment by instituting street cleaning or installing citywide drainage, required collective planning and financing. Only well-funded institutions could afford to buy new and expensive medical technologies, such as X-ray machines and operating theater equipment.

The growth in the range and numbers of medical institutions in the 19th century was driven by rapid and widespread social change. The movement of workers from the countryside to cities, factories, and plantations created a class of people who lacked family support in times of illness or injury. In rapidly growing and often unsanitary cities and towns, there was a need for measures to control and prevent disease. New welfare and medical institutions also reflected changing expectations of health services. Medicine was no longer a luxury available only to those able to pay: increasingly, governments acknowledged that they had a responsibility to ensure that their populations were not exposed to disease, while charities helped the poor to find care when they fell ill.

MEDICAL INSTITUTIONS IN THE WEST

In Europe and North America, institutions played a prominent part in providing medical services, especially in opening up access to high-quality medical care to all social classes. Churches and charities had a long tradition of providing care through hospitals and other institutions, and they continued and even increased these activities throughout the 19th century. However, much of the growth in the number of medical institutions and their expanding range of activities was due to the entry of the state into the provision of medical services. This brought huge new investments in hospitals, welfare programs, and especially public health reforms.

The Funding of Institutions

Churches and charities had traditionally organized care for the poor and sick, and they continued to play a leading role in this work throughout the 19th century. Protestant and Catholic churches collected money ranging from small donations at church services to major endowments of land or property to provide free treatment for poor patients in hospitals or in their own homes. Hospitals, dispensaries, and clinics catering to the poor and run by secular and religious charitable bodies were also funded through public donations. Toward the end of the century, these charities pioneered new services, such as welfare programs providing advice, medical care, and food to poor mothers and children, and schemes to educate midwives.

Donors gave money to these institutions for several reasons. There was a strong humanitarian or religious impulse to help people who could not afford to pay for treatment. Medical services also had a social or moral purpose. The hard-working poor or members of religious congregations were more likely to be given care than the improvident and impious. Education on hygiene not just served to control disease but also incorporated a message about the benefits of order and thrift. The donors also benefited; by contributing to medical charities, they demonstrated their generosity and concern for those less well off than themselves.

Over the course of the century, central and local government bodies began to provide medical and welfare services and programs of disease prevention and control funded through taxes. A growing number of institutions also provided medical services in return for fees. By the end of the century, wealthy patients were able to pay for treatment in hospitals, nursing homes, and clinics. Various forms of prepayment or insurance helped to spread the cost and opened up these services to a wider population.

HOSPITALS

Hospitals have a very long history. From medieval times, hospitals run by Christian churches had offered the old, the sick, and pilgrims a place to stay. Originally, hospitals offered only limited medical care, as they were primarily places of care and hospitality rather than of cure. Hospitals began to acquire their modern character in the late 18th century, gradually becoming centers for high-quality, modern medical treatment, staffed by well-trained practitioners and treating patients suffering from serious injuries and illnesses.

At the beginning of the 19th century, hospitals were confined to large towns and cities. A few were very large; the *Allgemeines Kranenhaus* in Vienna, opened in 1784, had 2,000 beds, but most institutions had accommodation for fewer than 100 patients. Hospitals were modeled on large country houses, with grand

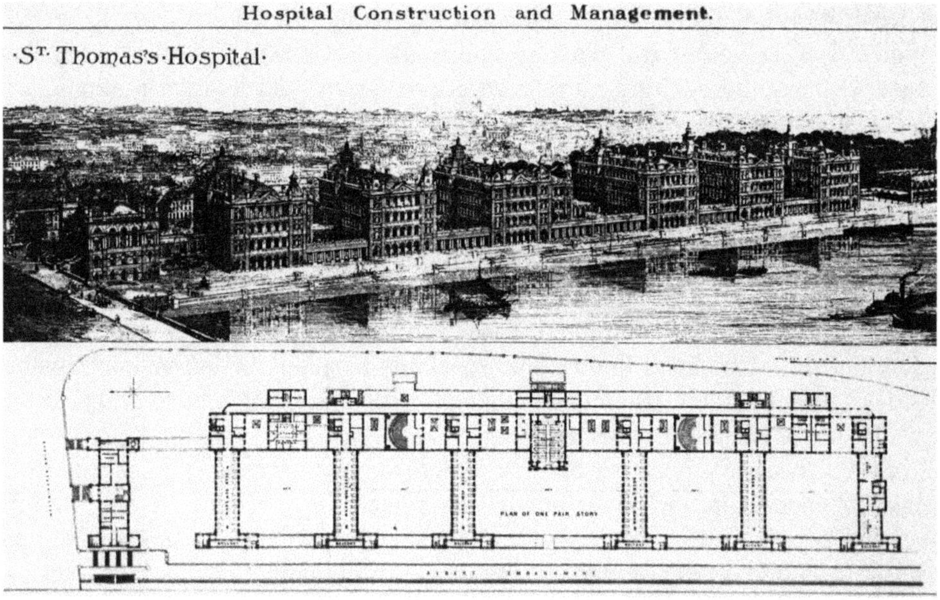

St. Thomas's Hospital, London, was opened in 1871 on the River Thames. It was one of the first medical institutions built on the pavilion plan, with long wards opening off a central corridor to prevent cross-infection between different groups of patients. (National Library of Medicine)

entrances (which usually housed the institution's offices), wings containing the patient's rooms or wards, and courtyards where patients could take exercise.

Over the century, the number of hospitals grew; by 1900, every town of any size had a hospital, while cities had several, and their average size also increased. Hospital design was transformed in an effort to combat the possible spread of infection. New hospitals were laid out using the pavilion plan. Large wards were housed in "pavilions"—buildings well separated from each other and laid out in such a way that staff and patients never passed through a ward to get to any other part of the hospital, thus avoiding any possibility of carrying contamination from one ward to another. The wards themselves were long and narrow, with many large windows that could be opened to provide a flow of fresh air to blow away bad smells and germs. Walls, floors, and furnishings were made of impermeable materials that could be kept scrupulously clean.

In the early part of the century, only certain types of cases were admitted to hospitals. The rules of the Infirmary in Huddersfield, a town in the north of England, declared:

> No person be admitted . . . who is able to pay for medical aid . . . no apprentices or servants . . . no soldier[s] . . . no woman advanced in pregnancy, no child under six years (except in particular cases, as fractures, cutting for the stone, amputations, couching, or where some other surgical operation may be required) or persons disordered in their senses, subject to epileptic fits, suspected to have the smallpox, measles, itch, or other infectious distemper, having habitual ulcers, syphilis . . . or those suspected to be in a consumption, or an incurable or dying state. (Brunton 2004, 25)

Charitable hospitals preferred to take in sick or injured adults likely to recover with a few weeks' rest and care and who would then return to work. Curing such cases boosted the institution's reputation and established its role in serving the local economy by helping to restore men and women to the workplace. This in turn helped to attract more funding.

The exclusive admissions policies of some general hospitals drove the creation of other hospitals. Specialist hospitals were founded to treat children, to care for patients suffering from fever and other infectious diseases, and for pregnant women to deliver their babies. Governments and charities funded the care of patients suffering from chronic diseases and requiring long-term care. With the development of medical knowledge, specialist hospitals or departments within general hospitals were also founded to treat particular conditions, such as diseases of the skin or of the ear, nose, and throat.

Over the century, hospitals became centers for the treatment of the most serious cases of illness and injury. An increasing number of patients were admitted for surgery, as the introduction of anesthesia and antisepsis allowed surgeons to treat severely injured patients and to operate for a greater number of conditions, such as stomach ulcers and appendicitis. Operating theaters became a crucial part of the hospital, developing from spaces designed to allow students to observe operations (sometimes crammed into lofts) to suites of rooms carefully designed to provide the best environment for surgery. Wooden floors and plastered walls were replaced with sterile glass and tile, and simple tables were replaced by special operating tables. Better lighting and equipment to sterilize instruments was installed. To deal with the increased number of surgical cases and patients suffering from acute illness, hospitals employed more and better-trained nurses. Over the century, nurses' work shifted from domestic care—cooking meals and keeping the ward tidy—to a more medical role, closely monitoring their patients and performing simple medical tasks as well as keeping patients comfortable and ensuring a high level of cleanliness.

For much of the century, hospitals treated the poor. In return for receiving free care, patients were expected to express their gratitude to the institution and its donors. Some were used as teaching material for medical students. Patients were subjected to a strict regime: there were timetables for meals, regular ward inspections, few entertainments, and little freedom to move around. Patients grumbled that an obsession with fresh air meant that wards were cold and drafty. In extreme cases, they rebelled. Lepers in a hospital in Lima, Peru, marched out to the viceroy's palace, protesting that the hospital's chief doctor was using them as guinea pigs for a new treatment.

Rich patients were formally excluded from charitable hospitals, and in any case, they did not want to be cared for alongside the poor. Instead, they were treated in their own homes, even undergoing surgery there. By the late 19th century, however, it was clear that hospitals offered much higher standards of care than were possible in a domestic setting. Private hospitals, private wards within general hospitals, and nursing homes were established to cater to middle-and upper-class patients able to pay for treatment.

Relatively few patients were admitted to hospitals; much larger numbers were treated as outpatients at hospitals, clinics, and dispensaries. In the 1890s, the large London teaching hospitals treated at least 10 times more outpatients than inpatients admitted to the wards—over 100,000 outpatients each year. Outpatient departments and dispensaries dealt mainly with patients suffering from minor illnesses, such as respiratory complaints and stomach upsets. Nurses and doctors (often junior members of hospital staff) offered basic treatments and prescribed simple medicines. Patients were seen on a first-come, first-served basis and, despite the very basic standard of care, were willing to stand or sit in line for hours to receive free treatment.

PREVENTATIVE MEDICINE AND PUBLIC HEALTH

While hospitals and other institutions offering treatment to the sick were funded by a mix of religious, charitable, and government support, the field of public health was dominated by the state. From the 1830s, across Europe and the Americas, governments developed increasingly extensive policies to protect the populations from the threat of disease, usually based on temporary measures mounted in response to epidemics. Generally, central government departments set policy, and municipal and regional agencies were responsible for putting it into practice. Governments in different countries engaged with public health and disease prevention to varying degrees. Some, like the United States, largely left responsibility for health in the hands of community or state authorities. In European nations, such as Britain, central government drove the public health agenda and helped to fund reforms. Progress was far from steady; an outbreak of disease often prompted communities to action, only for their enthusiasm to lapse as the danger passed. Nevertheless, public health programs grew in size and scope, driven by rising expectations that governments should protect their populations from disease.

The type of actions taken to prevent disease shifted over the century, reflecting changing medical knowledge. In the first half of the century, public health policies centered on sanitary reforms—large-scale projects to remove dirt from the urban environment by introducing street cleaning and refuse collection and citywide schemes of drainage, sewage processing, and water supply. Charities backed up these projects through health education, teaching the poor (especially women) about the need to keep their bodies, clothes, and homes clean. From the 1870s, germ theory permitted a more targeted approach. State and local authorities set up isolation hospitals to care for people suffering from infectious diseases and to prevent the spread of disease through the community. In an age when infections are largely controlled by immunization and antibiotics, it is easy to forget that at the end of the century, in some European countries, the majority of hospital beds were provided for patients suffering from infectious diseases.

From midcentury, doctors and public health administrators became increasingly aware of the link between disease and low standards of living; people who lived on a poor diet, had inadequate housing, and were unemployed were much more likely to fall ill than those who enjoyed better living conditions. This knowledge underpinned the development of welfare programs. States became involved in supplementing the free medical care provided through charities, ensuring that the poor had access to doctors and to basic medical treatments. Pensions were introduced to save the elderly from falling into sickness and poverty, and state-run health insurance schemes gave working men access to basic medical primary care. The first scheme was launched in Germany in 1888 and was copied in many European countries. Contributions from government, employers, and individual workers were pooled to pay for care provided by designated doctors. Governments also provided free medical aid to certain groups. Schoolchildren were subjected to regular medical inspection, to identify problems with teeth and eyesight, illnesses, and infestation with parasites such as head lice. Infants were targeted by government welfare programs that monitored their growth and provided assistance to mothers to ensure that their children grew into healthy adults.

INSTITUTIONS AND THE MEDICAL PROFESSION

Institutions played an increasingly important part in the lives and careers of medical practitioners during the 19th century. Doctors in Europe and North America trained in medical schools and universities, where they spent several years attending lectures, dissecting bodies, developing practical skills in laboratories, and observing practice on hospital wards. During their studies, as well as acquiring knowledge, students absorbed the ethos of the profession—the ethics and behavior expected of a doctor—and made contacts with their peers and with more senior practitioners.

In many (though not all) countries, separate institutions oversaw the training offered by medical schools, to ensure that practitioners trained in different institutions reached an acceptable level of competence. In Britain, this role was performed by the General Medical Council, formed in 1858. In the United States, there was much less oversight, and standards of medical teaching were largely left to market forces. Ambitious students paid more for the best teaching; students who chose to attend schools offering less rigorous training for lower fees were less likely to gain access to prestigious posts.

Institutions played an important role in building a medical career. Over the course of the century, newly qualified doctors increasingly began work in hospitals or dispensaries as junior staff, gaining experience in diagnosis and treatment. Most doctors then left institutional work to take up practice in the community, but the most ambitious climbed through a hierarchy of hospital posts, hoping to become a consultant or surgeon. Hospital posts were hard to come by, and some determined young practitioners solved the problem by starting their own small specialist hospitals as a way to build their expertise and gain a reputation. A few practitioners went on to study and work in research institutions. In Europe, these were mostly funded by governments, but the Pasteur Institute, one of the most prestigious institutions, was funded by public donations made in recognition of Louis Pasteur's work on vaccines to prevent disease.

INSTITUTIONS OUTSIDE THE WEST

Institutions played a less prominent role in medicine outside the West. Before the 19th century, medical care was provided by religious institutions and by hospitals supported by wealthy individuals. Practitioners at the courts of rulers in Asia trained small numbers of students. In the 19th century, as in Europe and North America, population growth and urbanization created a need for new institutions to offer care to members of a mobile population. Rulers and rich merchants were inspired to revive traditional institutions, to found new institutions modeled on traditional lines, and to establish Western-style institutions. Colonial governments and charities introduced Western institutions, such as hospitals, dispensaries, and medical schools. Western institutional care was not always popular with local populations; the most successful were those where care was adapted to the local culture.

TRADITIONAL WELFARE IN CHINA

During the 18th and 19th centuries, while state involvement in medicine gradually increased in Europe and North America, in China the role of the imperial government in health care declined. During medieval times, the state had appointed government doctors, set examinations for all practitioners, and countered epidemics by organizing the distribution of free medicines to the poor and setting up hospitals to care for the sick. The government gradually withdrew from these activities from the 16th century, and the gap was filled in part by charities set up by wealthy individuals, who wished to display their generosity and concern for social order as set out in Confucian teachings. In the 19th century, the need for such care increased, as the upheavals of the Taiping Rebellion, the famines of 1877–1879, and the movement of people from the countryside to the cities created migrants and refugees who lacked the family networks that usually provided support and care to the sick.

A variety of charitable institutions offered different forms of care. In the city of Tianjin, for example, wealthy merchants paid for orphanages and a hospital. The hospital developed from an institution to help ailing travelers and, by the 19th century, had become a sort of nursing home caring for the elderly. Donors also paid for the burial of corpses abandoned in the city streets. This was important for the physical and spiritual health of the community. Corpses could spread disease, and the spirits of the dead who did not receive full burial rites were believed to become "hungry ghosts" and cause disease among the living. As well as providing care and support, charitable institutions in China (like those in Europe) tried not to breed dependency and aimed to train the beneficiaries in correct ways of living.

> Throughout the ages, charities have been very concerned with providing food and clothing, considering this to be the highest good. However, these sorts of activities simply create a generation of lazy, apathetic people. How can we improve the simple and lazy nature of the Northerners and avoid bringing out their worst characteristics? . . . Our task is to ensure that each and every individual has his own work and can rely on his own efforts to support himself. (Rogaski 1997, 72)

The Hall for Spreading Benevolence in Tianjin was a charity set up to provide a home for impoverished widows and their children and for young women sold as servants or concubines. To ensure that the women followed the Confucian precept of chastity, women, boys, and girls were strictly segregated within the accommodation. Women could go outside the institution only with a female escort. The male children of widows were trained in a trade; the young women had to work in the institution's textile workshop.

RELIGIOUS INSTITUTIONS AND HEALING

Religious foundations served as centers of medical care in many cultures. Hospitals were attached to Christian convents and monasteries, where monks and nuns provided medical care alongside spiritual aid to the sick poor. Buddhist monasteries also had a long tradition of offering care, and some became famous as centers of healing. In China, the Bamboo Grove Monastery in Xiaoshan City had a long tradition of treating women's illnesses. The monks there had acquired special knowledge of how to treat these conditions in the 10th century from a stranger—actually a Buddhist deity in disguise—who gave the monks a book of remedies. In the 19th century, a few monks who resided in the monastery continued to practice medicine and enjoyed a reputation for successfully treating menstrual disorders, problems associated with pregnancy, and slow labors. Accounts of their treatments circulated widely through books published by grateful clients. Unlike learned Chinese practitioners, they did not use the pulse to diagnose illness but listened to a description of the patient's symptoms. They prescribed a range of secret medicines based on classical Chinese medicine and very similar to those described in standard medical texts, although some incorporated folk remedies and talismans.

The Bamboo Grove Monastery offered a form of healing similar to that provided by secular practitioners, but many religious institutions offered spiritual medicine. Buddhist and Hindu deities were believed to be capable of curing and preventing diseases and helping women to conceive and to have sons. Many of these gods were believed to have powers over particular diseases such as *T'ou-Shen Niang-Niang* and *Sitala*, the goddesses of smallpox in China and India, respectively. Those seeking help visited temples, monasteries, or pilgrimage sites associated with healing figures to pray, make offerings, or promise gifts should their wish be granted.

ADAPTING WESTERN INSTITUTIONS

Donors in Asia and Africa drew on both Western and traditional models when founding new institutions. Islamic cultures in North Africa had a long tradition of providing medical care through hospitals. Medieval *bimaristan* (or *maristan*) are often seen as the first true hospitals, as they had more medical personnel and placed a greater emphasis on curing patients than Christian hospices of a similar period. Islamic hospitals were traditionally funded by endowments of land; by the 19th century, these rarely provided enough income to support the institutions, and many had fallen into decay. While some hospitals remained open in Ottoman

Turkey, none had survived in Iran. During the 19th century, wealthy members of society looked back to this tradition and funded new hospitals either by making new endowments or through donations. The hospitals were modeled on those in the West and aimed to offer high standards of medical care.

In India, there was a long history of charitable giving to beggars, pilgrims, and travelers. In the 19th century, this was translated into support for new, Western-style institutions offering medical care. In the second half of the century, many dispensaries were founded by local governments within Indian states to provide medical care to the poor, offering basic medical and surgical treatments. Over time, government support declined, and wealthy local citizens were encouraged to donate to these institutions. While the dispensaries were organized along Western lines, the care was adapted to the local culture. Some dispensaries employed both Western-trained doctors and Unani hakims, thus allowing patients to choose the type of medical care they wished to receive. Hospitals offering only Unani medical treatment were founded in the early 20th century, as part of the more general revival and reform of Unani medicine. The female rulers of Bhopal in India founded several hospitals, including one for women living in seclusion (*purdah*) with only female staff. As in the West, these dispensaries not only served poor patients but provided valuable jobs for young Indian doctors, helping them to build their careers. For donors, the dispensaries provided a means for them to display their benevolence and a way of creating contacts with colonial administrators.

Adapting Care in Western Institutions

Western institutions that adapted care to the local culture proved very successful. Hospitals and dispensaries run by Christian missions flourished in China; by 1906, there were 241 dispensaries and 166 hospitals. Unlike Western institutions, in the Chinese hospitals the families of patients played an active and important role in treatment. Just as in an encounter with a traditional Chinese physician, relatives would accompany a patient seeking admission to the hospital, providing information on the course of the illness to help the doctor reach a diagnosis. A friend, servant, or family member accompanied each patient admitted to the hospital. They provided nursing and support to the patient, sleeping in the same room, preparing their food, and tending to their needs. They even accompanied patients into the operating theater. Compared to hospitals in the West, mission hospitals imposed few rules on their patients. They were free to sit up, move about, eat, talk, and even smoke as they wished.

The active participation of family members in hospital care was a mixed blessing. On the positive side, the support from relatives and friends helped to give Chinese patients (especially female patients) the confidence to seek help from Western doctors, and their labor allowed mission hospitals to care for large numbers of patients with very few staff. The Chinese Hospital in Shanghai had six wards for 30 patients, cared for by one missionary doctor and two Chinese assistants. However, family members also interfered with the course of treatment; sometimes they gave patients local remedies if they believed that the medicines provided by the mission doctors were inappropriate, and they often ignored the doctor's advice on diet.

Clinics offering free vaccination against smallpox were opened in many parts of Asia by colonial and indigenous governments, but the procedure received a very different reception in different countries. In Japan, vaccination was supported by local rulers and elite practitioners, and offers of free vaccination were readily accepted by the general population. The procedure was introduced to Nagasaki in 1849 and its use was spread by *ranpo* physicians—Japanese doctors trained in Western medicine. The practice was taken up by wealthy families, anxious to protect their own children against smallpox. They extended the benefits of vaccination to poorer families by funding vaccine clinics that attracted large numbers of children.

Similarly in China, the sponsorship of wealthy members of society ensured that institutions offering free vaccination attracted many clients. Vaccination was introduced to China in 1805, when a group of wealthy merchants and a surgeon working for the East India Company set up a clinic in Canton. The practice spread rapidly; between 1860 and 1911, 43 vaccination clinics were set up all over China. Initially intended for the poor, the clinics proved so popular that they opened their doors to all children. The procedure followed by Chinese clinics was similar to that in vaccine institutions in Europe but was adapted to fit with Chinese theories that smallpox was caused by "fetal poison," left in the body of children after birth. In the West, children were vaccinated at any time of year and at any point on the arm or leg. In China, vaccination was offered only at favorable seasons, in spring and autumn. The cowpox matter was placed on the Lesser Yang circulation tract, where it was carried to the kidney and thus helped to remove the fetal poison from the body.

In India, a failure to take account of local sensibilities meant that the vaccination was only gradually accepted by the indigenous population. Inoculation—the practice of deliberately infecting children with smallpox in the hope that they would have a mild form of the disease—was widely used within the local population. Vaccination was introduced to India in 1802, and European administrators assumed that the new, much safer procedure would quickly supersede inoculation. Their hopes were dashed. Vaccination proved unpopular because it did not fit with traditional practices. Whereas inoculation was practiced only at certain times of the year, and accompanied by prayers and special diets, vaccination was offered year-round, and vaccinated children were given no special treatment. Parents also resisted taking their infants to be vaccinated by unfamiliar practitioners employed by local governments. Hindus objected to a practice using vaccine that originated in cows—a sacred animal—and all respectable Indian families feared that their child might be vaccinated using material taken from the arm of a child from a lower caste.

Public Health

Around the world, Western medicine provided the model and the inspiration for public health initiatives. Many towns in China and North Africa had ancient systems of water supply and drainage as well as teams of night-soil men who collected excrement and other refuse to fertilize local farmland. However, as cities expanded, this infrastructure broke down. The population of Tehran in Persia (modern Iran) grew from a few thousand to around 200,000 in the 19th century. Travelers reported that

> [S]treams of water in dirty ditches called jubes, run through the centre of the streets . . . These ditches served at the same time for irrigation streams, drains and wash-tables, and in warm weather gave forth the most pestilential odour. Refuse of all sorts were thrown out in the streets, courtyards, or anywhere in the open. (Fraser 1826, 158)

Similar conditions were reported from other cities in Asia and South America; drainage ditches were blocked with waste, water tanks and rivers were polluted, and cemeteries were overcrowded.

The 19th century saw renewed initiatives to keep cities clean and well supplied with water, modeled on Western sanitary reforms, with the aim of increasing the comfort of inhabitants and as a means of reducing disease. Local and central governments set up permanent bodies to oversee public health issues, and to organize street cleaning, better water supplies, drainage, and sewage. Later, like Western governments, they turned their attention to improving child health and regulating housing. Rural areas, with their more scattered population, tended to lag behind in public health reforms, even though houses in the countryside were often overcrowded and unsanitary.

ADOPTING WESTERN INSTITUTIONS

Western institutions were also transplanted wholesale into Asia and Africa by colonial governments. Given the importance of hospitals in the West, it is not surprising that colonial administrators and indigenous rulers sought to introduce similar centers for care. For example, in Sri Lanka, a British colony from 1815, the colonial authorities established government-funded hospitals and dispensaries to care for the sick poor in the cities, modeled on those in Europe. Provision was extended to provinces by local welfare societies, funded by a mixture of charity and government support. In Africa, hospitals were funded by Christian missions, rather than governments. In Iran, new hospitals were established by a range of Western agencies, including missionaries, foreign legations, commercial companies, and charities such as the Russian Red Cross.

In Asia, the Pacific, North Africa, and South America, colonial governments tried to spread scientific medicine to their populations and ensure a supply of doctors for the army by setting up institutions to train practitioners in Western medicine. The first medical schools in South America were set up in Brazil in 1808 by the Portuguese royal family at Rio de Janeiro and Salvador da Bahia. Sydney Medical School, the first in Australia, began teaching in 1883. In China, mission hospitals acted as centers for medical training. Textbooks were published in Chinese languages in the 1850s. Formal training in Western medicine was available from 1866 when the first medical school was opened. However the number of students trained in Western medicine was very small—there were only around 300 graduates by the end of the century.

The teaching of Western medicine also spread to independent states where it was seen as "progressive" and as a means of ensuring the health of the population. Western-style medical training was available in Egypt at the *Dar al-fonun* from 1852, under the leadership of French practitioners and using French textbooks translated into Arabic. In Japan, the government founded medical schools modeled on those in Germany. By 1900, there were 14 medical colleges that had trained roughly one-half of all practitioners working in the country. Through Japan, Western medicine was introduced to Taiwan and Korea. Not all Western medical schools succeeded. A medical school founded in Lima, Peru, in 1808 was based on the outdated teaching of the University of Leiden in the 18th century. Not surprisingly, the school was widely criticized, and it closed in 1834.

In India, the colonial authorities experimented with the teaching of Ayruvedic and Unani medicine alongside Western medicine. Faced with a shortage of practitioners, in 1822, the Native Medical Institute was founded in Kolkata by the British East India Company to train students to work as assistants within the Indian Medical Service. Students were taught anatomy, medicine, and basic surgery using European texts translated into Indian languages and also Ayurvedic and Unani medicine. However, the initiative was short-lived, and the teaching of indigenous medicine was abandoned in 1835.

The Native Medical Institute was replaced by schools where the teaching was modeled on that of Europe. Like medical schools in France and other European countries, the Kolkata Medical College, founded in 1835, offered different grades of education. One group of students followed a standard curriculum, covering anatomy (including human dissection), theory and practice of medicine, pharmacy, chemistry, and materia medica. Lectures were given in English. Students in other classes studied a smaller range of subjects, with a greater emphasis on practical medicine, and were taught in Indian languages. Even though the curriculum followed that of Western medical schools, the content was adapted to the Indian context.

> It is . . . incumbent upon [the medical teachers] to teach their pupils the nature of disease and the principles of treatment, as regarded practically from an Indian point of view . . . Every Englishman, who has risen to the rank of a first-class practitioner in India, has learnt the necessity of unlearning many of the principles which he brought with him, and of cautiously adapting the rest of his store of knowledge to surrounding circumstances. ("Medical Education" 1855, 723)

Materia medica and pharmacy classes included teaching in the use of native medicinal plants.

Schools dedicated to teaching Ayurvedic and Unani medicine were not established until the late 19th century, as part of an effort to improve standards of medical knowledge and practice. Traditionally, Ayurvedic and Unani medicine had been taught on a very small scale. Rather than a large group of students attending lectures, a practitioner would train just a few students at a time, guiding their reading of classical texts and allowing them to observe the processes of diagnosis and prescription. From the 1880s, Indian practitioners set up Unani medical schools, as part of a drive to improve the status of the system. From 1872, a four-year course in Unani medicine was offered at the Oriental College in Lahore (in modern Pakistan). In 1889, teaching was also established in Delhi, India, at the *Madrasa-e-Tibbia*, and in Hyderabad.

13

Disease and Healing in the Arts

At first glance, medicine and the arts seem odd bedfellows; in the 19th century, medicine in the West was increasingly seen as a science. Nevertheless, medicine and the arts intersected at many levels. Images and objects used by practitioners in their work were designed to be not only functional but also beautiful, or they were decorated in ways that were pleasing to the eye and increased their healing power. In stories, images, and music, writers represented the diseases that terrified them and celebrated the healers who conquered them. As a result, the arts mirrored medicine in the 19th century—the new diseases that moved around the globe, the illness bred in the slums of growing cities, the power of new medical knowledge and practices, and the changing consumption of medical services.

IMAGES AND MEDICAL KNOWLEDGE

Around the world, practitioners made use of a wide range of objects and images to convey information about the body in their practice and to teach students. While some were provided strictly technical data, such as an X-ray plate, many others combined the practical and the aesthetic.

Western Medical Images

In the West, anatomical images had a long history of being more than purely practical. From the Renaissance, images of skeletons and dissected bodies were portrayed in a naturalistic manner, as if still alive. Skeletons appeared to look at skulls, like Hamlet in William Shakespeare's play, pondering on death. Dissected figures were drawn holding up their own skin to allow the viewer to examine the muscles and organs beneath. In the 19th century, beauty was sacrificed to utility. Complex backgrounds for anatomical figures disappeared as did all elements of the individuality of the dissected body such as the face, hair, and clothing.

At the same time, anatomical images began to reflect doctors' belief that disease affected particular organs or tissues. A new genre of images appeared, showing disembodied diseased organs such as a lung or kidney. Illustrators aimed for clarity; images were hand tinted or printed in color to show alterations to the appearance of the body parts caused by disease. Alternatively, the organs were shown injected with different colored waxes, to highlight different structures.

As surgery became more important within Western medicine, artists were employed to draw illustrations of different stages of an operation, such as the amputation of the leg. Images were also used to record different wounds and injuries. John Bell, a Scottish surgeon with considerable artistic abilities, produced a series of drawings of soldiers suffering from different types of wounds inflicted during fighting in the Crimean War. During the American Civil War, photography was used to record soldiers' injuries and the results of successful amputations. Although these images were intended simply as a record of the work of army doctors, they have a compelling quality and have been exhibited as artworks.

Asian Medical Images

In Asia, images and text often gave a pleasing appearance as well as conveyed technical information. In Tibetan medicine, which included elements of Unani medicine alongside Chinese and Ayurvedic ideas, practitioners used bloodletting charts. These gave practical information on where and when to let blood to treat various conditions, but they also incorporated images of gods and animals in complex and beautiful designs. Chinese medical texts included simple drawings of patients suffering from conditions such as skin diseases. Often rather stylized, the drawings showed the whole patient, rather than focus on portraying the symptoms in detail. Instead, the disease was described in the accompanying text, and words and image were laid out in a sympathetic and pleasing way. Books on acupuncture showed the points where the needles were to be inserted, in order to treat certain conditions. Sometimes, the charts were plain and very functional, showing the front and back of the whole body or a part of the body, such as an ear. In other works, acupuncture points and channels were illustrated using realistic paintings of figures, shown standing and with some of their clothing removed to reveal the relevant part of the body. The images shared the page with text describing the uses of the acupuncture points. Similar aesthetic considerations dictated the presentation of medicinal plants in Chinese texts. Drawings provided an accurate representation of the shape, the texture, and sometimes the color of fruits, flowers, and leaves alongside the associated text.

Chinese practitioners also made use of three-dimensional images. Carved ivory figurines of a woman lying on a couch were given to elite female patients, who could not expose their bodies to practitioners so that they could indicate where they felt pain. The ivory figures were simple but realistic. The women appeared to recline in natural positions in their carrying boxes, with calm facial expressions and elaborate carved hairstyles.

In Japan, traditional forms of visual media were used to help popularize vaccination, a new practice introduced from the West. Smallpox patients often had

In 19th-century China, it was not acceptable for male doctors to see the bodies of their elite female patients. Women used these ivory figures to indicate where they felt pain. (SSPL/Getty Images)

images of the warrior *Tametomo* defeating the smallpox demon hung in their rooms to aid recovery. To help popularize smallpox vaccination, a Japanese practitioner, Dr. Ryusai Kuwata, commissioned a woodcut in a similar style. This showed a child seated on a white cow, chasing away a smallpox demon with a spear. Text laid out around the image explained the new practice and urged parents to have their children vaccinated.

A remarkable set of images that bridge East and West were produced by Lam Qua, a Chinese painter trained in Western art. Between 1836 and 1855, he was commissioned by Peter Parker, an American medical missionary, to paint a series of over 100 portraits of patients suffering from huge tumors and growths that were subsequently removed at the Canton Mission Hospital. Parker took the paintings back to the United States to explain the work of the mission and to raise funds. Unlike anatomical drawings in the West, these were genuine portraits; while the images were dominated by distortion of the body caused by the tumor, they also showed the sitter's face and body and revealed something of their character.

ART AND SPIRITUAL MEDICINE

In the West, the objects and instruments used in scientific medicine were designed to be purely functional, with little or no consideration for decoration or aesthetic qualities. For example, at the beginning of the century, surgical instruments might have handles made of attractive wood, but they were otherwise quite plain: with the advent of antiseptic surgery, they were made entirely of metal that could be sterilized. By contrast, the objects associated with Western and non-Western spiritual medicine were often produced with great skill and elaborately decorated, in part to give them a pleasing appearance but mainly to enhance their healing powers.

Outside the West, healers were often people of great knowledge and power who had a particular role and status within their society. In many cultures, healers wore special clothing or carried objects that marked them out. Tibetan practitioners were immediately recognizable by their elaborately decorated clothing and hats. Among North American indigenous peoples, medicine men wore clothing that was painted, embroidered, or beaded with images of stylized animals or symbols. Healers also carried special objects. In many African cultures, healers carried special bags or containers for medicines, decorated in particular styles using materials including shells, beads, and metal. Others had decorated staffs or rattles used in healing ceremonies to communicate with the spirit world. In some cultures, healers wore masks. Among the Inuit of Canada, shamans wore masks representing the contorted features of a healing spirit.

HEALING OBJECTS

Divination was often used by healers to diagnose illnesses caused by supernatural forces—ghosts, spirits, or witches. Diviners threw small objects on the ground or a mat. As supernatural forces dictated where and how each object came to rest, healers discovered the cause of disease by interpreting their positions. Objects used for divination ranged from simple natural objects such as shells, stones, or seeds, to carved and decorated objects made of wood or bone. These took the form of decorated plaques or sometimes small animal figures, as particular spirits were associated with certain animals. The divining objects were kept in and thrown from special containers. In some cultures, these were simple baskets or gourds; in others, the bowls or containers were elaborately carved.

In many African cultures, two-or three-dimensional figures were used in medicine and are now highly prized for their artistic qualities. For African healers, the figures served to collect and hold supernatural power that could then be used to cure, prevent, or cause illness or injury. Figures were made of wood, bone, or clay and were often produced by professional carvers. They acquired their powers by being rubbed with medicinal substances, or by having medicines attached to or placed inside the figure, and through ceremonies. In some cases, they had to be activated by further ceremonies; the figures used by Yoruba healers would be "woken up" by having metal objects such as nails hammered into them or by setting off small explosions using gunpowder. Some medical figures were very simple. In Yoruba culture, *sigidi* figures were roughly shaped from clay mixed with medicines. When activated by ceremonies, they developed a spirit that could be controlled by a healer to cause illness or even to kill. Other figures, such the *minkisi* (singular *nkisi*) used by people in the Congo were carved from wood. They looked toward the sky and had partially opened mouths as if about to speak.

Some figures were quite plain, others elaborately decorated, with carved representations of chief's hats or headdresses and painted or decorated with fabric and feathers. *Minkisi* figures stored power from the spirits of the dead that was used to protect against illness or injury or to cause illness to strike other individuals. They were also used in rituals to protect warriors going into battle.

In many cultures, statues of pregnant or breastfeeding women, or women holding small children, were used to treat infertility and to help ensure a safe and speedy birth. The images were often highly stylized, emphasizing the belly, breasts, and female facial features. Among the Ashanti people, for example, women who wanted to conceive carried a wooden doll called an *akua mma*. The dolls had a simple, rudimentary body and limbs but large, carefully carved flat circular faces, narrow eyes, and curved brows, all features associated with Ashanti ideals of beauty.

African medicine figures linked the natural and supernatural worlds. In many religions, deities were believed to influence the lives and health of the living. Highly decorated images or figures of gods and deities associated with medicine, such as *Yakushi Nyorai*, the Buddha of healing, or deities linked to diseases such as cholera, were placed in Hindu and Buddhist temples. There, people offered prayers, food, and incense and requested the gods to protect them from disease or to cure them of their ailments. In China, carved figures of the Medicine King, often shown with a tiger and dragon, were given to temples by donors. The figures were made with a small cavity to contain a piece of paper with the name of the donor and a request for help.

Spiritual or supernatural healing often involved some form of ceremony. Music, in the form of drumming, chanting, and singing, played an important role in calling up or driving away spirits, or sending healers into trance states where they could contact the spirit world. Native American peoples carried out elaborate Thirst or Sun Dances, to seek healing for a sick person or to give thanks for a cure. In a large, specially built lodge, communities came together to dance, sing, blow through bone whistles, drum, and pray for four days. In parts of China, ceremonies were held each year to protect the community from disease. In southern China, communities held festivals to seek the protection of Marshal Wen against epidemics. For several days, parades were held that included drummers and people dressed as Marshal Wen and his entourage. In this form, the deity left his temples and patrolled the streets, chasing away any ghosts or evil spirits that might bring disease. At the end of the festival, there was a feast, and the disease demons were enticed on to a decorated bamboo and paper boat, fitted out with paper furnishings, tools, and food. This was towed out on to a river or the sea and set on fire. During the festival, actors performed plays, puppet plays, and operas that portrayed the chasing away of demons and ghosts. Such ceremonies were also held during outbreaks of disease, in an effort to expel the illness from the community. In eastern China, the Five Emperors were invoked to give protection against disease. Images of the emperors, shown as fierce and ugly figures with blue or black faces, red hair, and military costumes, were worshipped in temples.

Images were also widely used to prevent disease by chasing away demons or spirits from homes. In Japan, wooden or pottery models of *Shoki* the "Demon

Queller," a rather plump warrior with a fierce expression, were hung up to frighten away demons. In China, plaques painted with frightening demon faces and in the Nicobar Islands in the Indian Ocean, "scare devils"—wooden figures with wings, sometimes wearing Western dress—were used for the same purpose. In North Africa, people wore charms or jewelry with representations of eyes to deflect the malign influence of the "evil eye" that was believed to cause illness.

Containers used to store or to give medicines to patients were often highly decorated. The decoration was a means of imparting power to the medicines. Among North American peoples, bowls used to make up medicines or to give remedies to the sick were carved with animal symbols to give the medicine additional power. In Tanzania, plain gourds or calabashes were used to store foodstuffs, but calabash containers for medicine were decorated and had elaborately carved stoppers. Medicine containers were also made of special materials; antelope horn was used in Africa to make small vessels that were decorated with carvings of spirits and decorated with feathers. Carved rhino horn containers were used in Tibetan medicine. In other cultures, including China and Japan, decoration was used on medicine containers both to show the value of the contents and to present a pleasing appearance. Expensive medicines were stored in elaborately decorated chests or in decorated porcelain jars. In Japan, *inro*—small cases made of beautifully carved and painted wood or lacquer—were used for carrying medicines or snuff.

In Europe and parts of Africa, images of Christian saints and God were the focus for requests for healing or for protection from disease. In Ethiopia, priests from the Orthodox Church produced long scrolls to cure or prevent disease. Made from a long strip of parchment cut to the same length as the patient's body, the scrolls were covered with images of kings and prophets from the Old and New Testament and abstract designs, often incorporating eyes, to represent God or angels. Texts offered prayers and requested divine help for the owner of the scroll. Similar texts and images were also written on small pieces of parchment that were folded up and worn as amulets to prevent disease.

Paintings of saints, showing important events from their lives, were found in every Catholic church in Europe and the Americas. In the Eastern Orthodox Church, painted icons with stylized images of the Virgin and Christ were often heavily encrusted with silver or gold and precious stones. In the Western Catholic Church, figures of the saints and of the Virgin Mary stood in elaborately carved and painted chapels. In times of crisis, such as an epidemic, these images were the focus of prayers and were carried around a town or village to drive away the disease. Images were also left in churches as a sign of gratitude by people whose prayers had been answered. These votive objects took the form of small models of the part of the body that had been healed, such as a hand or eye, or paintings depicting the illness or injury and the intercession of a saint.

PRACTITIONERS AT WORK

Portraits of formally trained medical practitioners are found all around the world as both two-dimensional images and three-dimensional figures. Images of non-Western practitioners usually showed them at work, treating patients. In China, for example, there were many images of male doctors taking the pulse of a female patient. Similar scenes were depicted by Japanese *netsuke*, miniature sculptures used to attach objects to the belt of a kimono. These images present the doctor in a sympathetic light, but others criticized or made fun of learned doctors. In Japan, cartoons depicted incompetent doctors carrying out eye surgery likely to render the patient blind or practitioners trying to cure patients with impossible complaints such as a woman who wants to have her neck shortened. For Europeans traveling to the colonies, healers were part of a strange and exotic world, and they commissioned paintings of Ayurvedic practitioners at work, being consulted by patients and carrying out eye surgery.

In the West, the work of surgeons was celebrated in paintings epitomizing their new status as heroes of medicine. Thomas Eakin's paintings *The Gross Clinic* (1875) and *The Agnew Clinic* (1889) and Adalbert Seligmann's painting *Theodor Billroth Operating* (1899) all show distinguished surgeons in control of the operating theater. All are engaged in teaching, passing on their skills and knowledge to audiences of students. (It has been suggested that the artists drew on religious paintings when designing their work, with the surgeon as a Christ-like figure surrounded by acolytes.) The paintings were extremely realistic, showing the anaesthetized patient and surgical instruments (*The Gross Clinic* aroused controversy because it showed a very small amount of blood). The paintings reflect the development of surgical technologies in the use of ether or chloroform anesthetics and the shift to wearing special clothing. While Samuel Gross and his assistants wore ordinary street clothes, Billroth and his assistants were shown in surgical gowns, although they did not have masks or gloves.

PORTRAITS OF PRACTITIONERS

In the West, huge numbers of portraits of doctors were produced in the 19th century: as paintings, as printed images, and in fiction. The rising number of images reflected the shifting social status of medical men. For centuries, only wealthy individuals could afford to commission artists to paint portraits of themselves and family members. In the 19th century, professional men such as doctors could also afford painted or photographic portraits.

Doctors chose to be portrayed as learned gentlemen, usually soberly dressed, with a serious facial expression. Some were shown with objects linked to their careers including books, papers, or even medical instruments. Alexander Wood, a Scottish physician, chose to remind viewers of his role in the development of the hypodermic syringe: in his portrait, he holds an early syringe. The relatively low costs of photography allowed the creation of group portraits, reflecting the increasing importance of institutions in the careers of doctors and nurses. Medical and nursing students frequently owned class photographs, providing a permanent reminder of the school or hospital where they had trained. Group photographs of the staff of a hospital ward or surgical team reinforced the importance of working in a team.

DOCTOR AS HERO OR VILLAIN

Portraits of practitioners also appeared in novels and paintings for a general audience. Doctors appeared as heroes, dedicated to caring for their patients regardless of reward, or as villains using their knowledge to advance themselves financially or socially. The novelist Anthony Trollope presented a sympathetic portrait of the general practitioner in *Doctor Thorne* (1858). The title character was not a brilliant scholar, but he faithfully served the local community. Trollope accurately portrayed the social tensions within medicine in mid-19th-century Britain. The hero of the title is a provincial general practitioner who does not think it beneath him to dispense medicines and treat poorer clients as well as the local gentry. This gets him into a dispute with the established elite practitioners in the area. In this and other novels, Trollope shows the reader what he thinks of elite physicians by giving them ludicrous names such as Dr. Omnicrom Pie, Dr. Mewdew, and Dr. Fillgrave.

A similarly positive image of the doctor was provided by Luke Fildes's painting *The Doctor* (1890). The painting shows the ideal doctor, watching over a sick child in a poorly furnished room. Here the doctor is hard working (dawn is breaking, so the doctor has spent at least part of the night with his patient), and selfless (the poorly furnished interior suggests that he is not likely to be paid well for his efforts). Fildes was not the only artist to produce such positive images of practitioners; there was a genre of paintings of humanitarian doctors showing their compassion by their care for the living and respect for the dead.

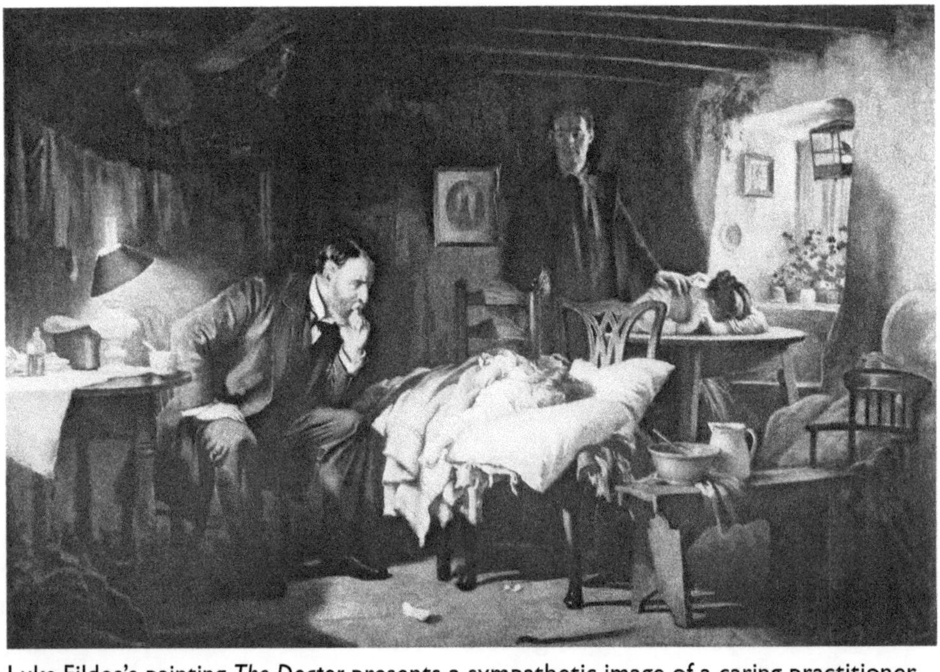

Luke Fildes's painting *The Doctor* presents a sympathetic image of a caring practitioner watching over a poor child, and it reflected the high regard for the medical profession in late-19th-century Britain. (National Library of Medicine)

Many portraits of doctors were much less respectful. Right through the century, cartoons portrayed medical men as greedy and incompetent, more concerned with their fees than ensuring that their patients recovered. Late-19th-century cartoonists also poked fun at women doctors: they were either so glamorous that male patients fell in love with them or rather masculine and unattractive. In Gustav Flaubert's *Madame Bovary* (1856), the doctor Charles Bovary is overambitious and lacking insight. Dr. Bovary is an *officier de santé*, a second grade of practitioner trained in a medical school but without taking a full degree course. Nevertheless, attempting to prove that he is abreast of recent medical developments, Bovary treats a local man's club foot by cutting the tendon—an operation far beyond his abilities. The wound becomes infected, and a more qualified doctor has to be called in to amputate the limb. His real downfall is not his medical ambition, but his choice of an unsuitable wife. Emma sees marriage to Bovary as a step up the social ladder but quickly becomes discontented with her dull life and dull husband, and she embarks on a series of affairs, runs up debts, and finally commits suicide.

Overambition was also the cause of the downfall of Tertius Lydgate, one of the main characters in George Eliot's *Middlemarch* (published in serial form in 1871–1872). Lydgate is anxious to pursue medical research through the observation of cases in a small, provincial hospital he has helped to establish. His career suffers as he spends more time on research than on the day-to-day work of treating patients, and his downfall is accelerated by his marriage to a self-centered young woman more concerned with social status than with professional reputation. Lydgate is forced to abandon his research and become a practitioner at a fashionable resort in order to make money.

A more extreme fate was meted out to the title character in Mary Shelley's *Frankenstein* (1818). It reveals a deep concern about doctors' knowledge of the human body. The hero, Dr. Victor Frankenstein, is a brilliant scientist who builds a "creature" from human body parts and brings it to life using electricity. (Shelley was making use of the discovery that electrical impulses ran along nerves, made in the 1790s.) Frankenstein's hideous creation is unable to integrate with society and wreaks a horrible revenge on its creator by murdering members of Frankenstein's family. In Robert Louis Stevenson's novella *The Strange Case of Dr. Jekyll and Mr. Hyde* (1886), research also proves fatal to its medical protagonist in a work that explores the tensions between outward Victorian respectability and inward uncontrolled passions. Dr. Jekyll, a respectable practitioner, develops a potion that he hopes will suppress the occasional evil urges that he struggles to control. Instead, the potion transforms him into Mr. Hyde, a cruel and violent man. At first, Jekyll is able to reverse the transformation, but increasingly Hyde takes over. At the end of the novel, Jekyll/Hyde commits suicide.

Sir Arthur Conan Doyle's stories of Sherlock Holmes neatly encapsulated the ambivalent views of medical men. Conan Doyle was trained as a doctor but turned to writing and, from 1886, produced a very successful series of stories featuring the detective Sherlock Holmes and his companion Dr. John Watson. The character of Holmes was inspired by Dr. Joseph Bell, one of Conan Doyle's teachers at medical school. Bell was a brilliant diagnostician, able to draw conclusions from apparently trivial features of the patient's appearance. Holmes approached his cases in the same manner. In "The Adventure of the Norwood Builder," Holmes instantly deduced that a client is a bachelor, a solicitor, a Freemason, and an asthmatic from his untidy clothes, the legal papers that he carried, a charm on his watch-chain, and his labored breathing. Holmes is a complex character, lacking in empathy. His friend and sometimes accomplice Watson is far more sympathetic and displays more feeling but is less insightful.

PATIENTS

Writers and artists also presented varying images of patients and practitioners. Many novels contained semi-comic characters obsessed with their health and petrified of falling ill. Mr. Woodhouse, the father of the heroine in Jane Austen's *Emma* (1815), spends much of the novel worrying about the effects of diet, temperature, and climate on his own health and that of his family and friends. Although Mr. Woodhouse's concerns are exaggerated for comic effect, he does reflect how middle-and upper-class people pursued good health by carefully monitoring their lifestyle and were willing to pay a practitioner for advice on preventing ill health as well as treating disease. The theme of the power of the paying patient over their practitioners continued through the century. Cartoons in magazines such as *Punch* portrayed fickle upper-class patients changing their doctors when offered a diagnosis they did not like and working-class patients and children showing little respect for the profession.

The patient did not have the whip hand all the time. The introduction of anesthetics aroused concern that doctors would take advantage of their helpless patients to carry out unnecessary or experimental surgery. The contrast between the powerful surgeon and the helpless patient was graphically represented in Henri Gervex's painting *Before the Operation* (1887). In a striking and disturbing image, a partially clad and anesthetized female patient is exposed to the gaze of a number of fully dressed doctors.

THE IMPACT OF DISEASE

In the West, art, literature, and music all dealt with diseases, particularly those that aroused fear among the public. Disease was rarely portrayed in simplistic ways; authors and artists offered changing and sometimes contradictory views of the same condition.

Cholera, a disease that arrived in Europe for the first time in 1830 and spread terror through the population, was the subject of many images. Colored engravings showed the horrific effects of cholera: attractive women became withered, blue corpses; people collapsed in the street, struck down with cramps and vomiting. Émile Loubon, a French painter, conveyed the fear that reached all sections of society in his *Emigration pendant l'epidemie de cholera a Marseille en 1850* (*Migration during the Cholera Epidemic at Marseilles in 1850*). The painting shows carriages, carts, and people on foot fleeing the city for the healthier countryside. Cholera was also the subject of cartoons, in which the disease appears as a person, dressed in strange, often oriental clothes, recalling the origin of the epidemics in India. Other cartoons satirized the ineffectual efforts of local authorities to deal with the emergency.

Disease was portrayed in novels as a way of analyzing social ills and drawing attention to the social conditions of the poor. In his novels and magazine articles, Charles Dickens exposed the dreadful living conditions in the rapidly growing slums of London and the diseases that bred there, ready to escape and infect the wealthy and respectable residents. In a famous passage in *Bleak House* (1852), a fictitious slum district called "Tom-all-alone" is portrayed as a person spreading infection.

> There is not a drop of Tom's corrupted blood but propagates infection and contagion somewhere. It shall pollute, this very night, the choice stream . . . of a Norman house, and his Grace will not be able to say Nay to the infamous alliance. There is not an atom of Tom's slime, nor a cubic inch of any pestilential gas in which he lives, not one obscenity or degradation about him, not an ignorance, not a wickedness, not a brutality of his committing, but shall work its retribution, through every order of society, up to the proudest of the proud, and to the highest of the high . . . Tom has his revenge. (Dickens 1996, 654, 657)

Dickens was warning his middle-class readers of the dangers of failing to help the poor of society, leaving them ill housed, ill fed, and diseased. In *Bleak House*, the diseases emanating from the slums claim two victims. Jo, the crossing-sweeper who lives in Tom-all-alone, dies of an unnamed disease, probably a respiratory illness. His death stands in for that of all poor people; Dickens ends the scene with the stinging rebuke "And dying thus around us, every day." Esther Summerson, a middle-class woman, catches smallpox from Jo and is left permanently disfigured.

Smallpox also causes the death of the title character of Émile Zola's *Nana* (1880). Nana is a courtesan, a prostitute with a string of upper-class lovers, who rises from the gutter to fame and fortune. At the end of the novel, smallpox robs her of her beauty and her life. Zola links the disease with Nana's roots in poverty and describes it returning her body to its social as well as its physical origins. Her dead body is described as

> [A] charnel–house, a heap of pus and blood, a shovelful of putrid flesh. The pustules had invaded the whole face, so that one pock touched the next. Withered and sunken, they had taken on the greyish colour of mud, and on that shapeless pulp . . . they already looked like mould from the grave . . . Venus was decomposing. It was as if the poison she had picked up in the gutters, from the carcasses left there by the roadside, that ferment with which she had poisoned a whole people, had now risen to her face and rotted it. (Zola 1972, 470)

The most common cause of death for much of the 19th century was tuberculosis. It was frequently depicted in art and in opera but in a strange, contradictory way. Tuberculosis sufferers were usually women, and the disease highlighted their feminine characteristics—they were frail, beautiful, and passive, their pale skin contrasting with their red lips. The disease was believed to heighten creativity (many writers suffered from TB) and was associated with sexual indulgence. The realities of the horrible death from tuberculosis—the pain, fever, and racking cough—were glossed over. In Giuseppe Verdi's *La Traviata* (first performed in 1853 and based on the novel *La Dame aux Camélias* of 1852) the heroine, Violetta, is an archetypal victim of tuberculosis. Her sexual availability (she is a courtesan) and her hedonistic lifestyle, filled with parties, gambling, and excitement, are signs that her unnamed illness is tuberculosis. Just as her lifestyle consumes money, diamonds, and lovers, the disease consumes her body and beauty. Violetta's passionate love for Alfredo, a student, takes her away from this life; but the disease cannot be halted, and she dies in the final scene.

La Traviata was written before the discovery in 1882 that tuberculosis was caused by a bacterium. Nevertheless, many of the features of the tuberculosis character and lifestyle remained in the public consciousness. Giacomo Puccini's opera *La Bohème* of 1896 is set in Paris in 1830 and the characters live in the cold, damp slum housing now understood to be linked to tuberculosis. Mimi, the heroine, works as an embroiderer, and she is already suffering from the disease when she meets Rodolfo. He is attracted to her fragile appearance and pale skin, those archetypal signs of the disease. Mimi later takes up with a wealthy protector—repeating the old association between tuberculosis and sex—but later leaves him and is reunited with Rodolfo just before her death.

Mental illness also featured in 19th-century literature. In Charlotte Brontë's *Jane Eyre* (1847), the mad and violent Bertha Rochester is portrayed as an object of fear, confined to the attics of Thornfield Hall. Brontë reflects medical and popular views of the causes of mental illness by linking her madness to heredity (Bertha's mother was also insane), to alcohol, and to race—Bertha was born in the West Indies. A more kindly view of the mad was provided by Dickens (and others) who described the inmates of asylums. In "A Curious Dance around a Curious Tree," published in the magazine *Household Words* in 1852, Dickens praises the humane treatment of patients in St. Luke's Asylum in London. In his description of a dance (dances were often held in asylums, as a means of encouraging patients to display "normal" behavior), he presents the inmates as slightly comical and endearing, rather than alarming.

In 1859, the wave of popular concern over the wrongful incarceration of women in lunatic asylums by family members seeking to control their money was also reflected in popular fiction. In Wilkie Collins' *The Woman in White* (serialized in 1859–1860), two women are wrongly locked away in private asylums. Anne Catherick is hidden away because she knows a guilty secret that might lead to a scandal. Laura Fairlie is locked up to get control of her money. In Mary Elizabeth Braddon's *Lady Audley's Secret* (1862), the plot of wrongful confinement is given a different twist. In the novel, the beautiful wife of Lord Audley is revealed to be a social climber who has abandoned her child, faked her own death, bigamously married Lord Audley, and then murdered her first husband to cover up her crimes. When her acts are discovered, rather than have her arrested, a doctor is called in, and he diagnoses madness brought on by stress as the cause of her criminal behavior. Lady Audley ends her life in a private asylum in France.

The Transforming Effect of Illness

The lasting impact of illness was a recurring theme in 19th-century novels. In Jane Austen's novel *Sense and Sensibility* (1811), the romantic, emotional Marianne Dashwood falls into a fever brought on by nervous strain when the man she loves abandons her. She survives her illness but becomes calmer and less impulsive and marries the older, rather grave Colonel Brandon. In a parallel story in *Persuasion* (1818), the young and headstrong Louisa Musgrave falls from a harbor wall and sustains a serious head injury. This transforms her into a thoughtful woman who becomes engaged to the book-loving Captain Benwick. Austen was not the only author to use illness in this way. Susan Coolidge's heroine in *What Katy Did* (1872) suffers a fall and serious illness that turn her from a boisterous tomboy into a calm and considerate young woman.

Novels did not faithfully reflect the incidence of disease. A complaint called "brain fever" appeared frequently in 19th-century literature. It was a genuine medical condition, identified as a form of inflammation, causing headaches and delirium, brought on by physical or mental stress. There is no data to suggest that it was particularly common or alarming, but for novelists it provided a dramatic device to emphasize the depth of emotional feeling. Emily Brontë had Catherine Linton in *Wuthering Heights* develop brain fever when forced to reject Heathcliff, and Gustav Flaubert described Emma Bovary suffering from the same condition when abandoned by her lover.

GLOSSARY

amulet
An object worn to protect against disease.

antiseptic
A substance used to kill bacteria on skin, in wounds, or on instruments. Antiseptic surgery refers to a method of surgery that uses antiseptics to kill bacteria and thus prevent infection.

aseptic
Free of disease-causing bacteria or other agents. Aseptic surgery refers to a strategy of operating in a bacteria-free environment to avoid infection.

Ayurvedic medicine
A system of medicine used in India from ancient times. Health reflects a balance of three *doshas*; disease is the result of an imbalance of these.

bloodletting
The practice of removing a controlled amount of blood from the body by various methods. Bloodletting was used in Western, Unani, Ayurvedic, and some forms of folk medicine.

Chinese medicine
A system of medicine practiced in China from ancient times that understood disease to be caused by a disruption to the flow of qi or blood (*xue*) within the body.

dais
Traditional midwives working in India and Asia.

divination
A means of diagnosing disease, especially if caused by supernatural forces, used in many systems of folk medicine.

doshas
Three substances (*vata, pitta, kapha*) within the body that influence health and disease in Ayurvedic medicine.

endemic
An infection present within a population at all times.

epidemic
A large number of cases of a disease breaking out within a population. Between outbreaks, epidemic diseases may be wholly or largely absent.

folk medicine
Systems of medicine that make use of a range of treatments to cure specific diseases, not underpinned by an overarching theory of how the body works in health and disease.

hakims
Learned practitioners trained in Unani medicine.

humors
Four fluids within the body that are understood to determine health and disease in Unani medicine.

jinn
A spirit capable of causing disease, found in North Africa.

miasma
Bad air arising from rotting organic materials, responsible for causing or helping to spread diseases.

pandemic
An outbreak of infective diseases that spreads over a large area or even around the world.

qi
The energy or force distributed through the body, understood to be responsible for health and disease in Chinese medicine.

Unani medicine
A system of medical knowledge based on Greek and Islamic ideas, practiced in India and North Africa. In Unani medicine, four humors are believed to determine whether the body is healthy or diseased.

vaids
Learned practitioners trained in Ayurvedic medicine.

Western medicine
The system of medical knowledge developed in Europe and North America. In Western or scientific medicine, disease is located in the solid organs and tissues of the body.

BIBLIOGRAPHY

Abugideiri, Hibba. *Gender and the Making of Modern Medicine in Colonial Egypt*. Burlington, VT: Ashgate, 2010.

Account of Chief Zimena, *Natal Mercury*, 1929. In *The Anatomy of the Zulu Army from Shaka to Cetshwayo 1818–1879* by Ian Knight, 220. Mechanicsburg, PA: Stackpole Books, 1995.

Acland, H. W. *Memoir on the Cholera at Oxford in the Year 1854, with Considerations Suggested by the Epidemic*. London, 1856. In R. J. Morris, "Religion and Medicine: The Cholera Pamphlets of Oxford, 1832, 1849 and 1854." *Medical History* 19 (1975): 265.

Alavi, Seema. *Islam and Healing: Loss and Recovery of an Indo-Muslim Medical Tradition 1600–1900.* New York: Palgrave Macmillan, 2008.

Alavi, Seema. "Unani Medicine in the Nineteenth-Century Public Sphere: Urdu Texts and the Oudh Akhbar." *Indian Economic and Social History Review* 42 (2005): 101–129.

Alpen, Jan Van, and Anthony Aris. *Oriental Medicine: An Illustrated Guide to the Asian Arts of Healing.* London: Serindia Publications, 1995.

Anderson, Robin L. "Public Health and Public Healthiness, São Paulo, Brazil, 1876–1893." *Journal of the History of Medicine and Allied Sciences* 41 (1986): 293–307.

Anderson, Stuart, ed. *Making Medicines: A Brief History of Pharmacy and Pharmaceuticals.* London: Pharmaceutical Press, 2005.

Anderson, Warwick. "Geography, Race and Nation: Remapping 'Tropical' Australia, 1890–1930." *Medical History* 44, supplement S20 (2000): 146–159.

Apple, Rima D. "Constructing Mothers: Scientific Motherhood in the Nineteenth and Twentieth Centuries." *Social History of Medicine* 8 (1995): 161–178.

Apple, Rima D., ed. *Women, Health and Medicine in America.* New York: Garland Publishing Inc., 1990.

Arlidge, John Thomas. *On the State of Lunacy, and the Legal Provision for the Insane.* 1859. In *The Faber Book of Madness*, edited by Roy Porter, 365. Boston: Faber and Faber, 1991.

Arnold, David. *Colonizing the Body. State Medicine and Epidemic Disease in Nineteenth-Century India.* Berkeley: University of California Press, 1993.

Arnold, David, ed. *Imperial Medicine and Indigenous Societies.* New York: Manchester University Press, 1988.

Arnold, David, ed. *Warm Climates and Western Medicine: The Emergence of Tropical Medicine, 1500–1900.* Atlanta, GA: Rodopi, 1996.

Ashby, Henry, and G. A. Wright. *The Diseases of Children, Medical and Surgical*, London, 1899, 314. In *Small and Special: The Development of Hospitals for Children in Victorian Britain* by Elizabeth M. R. Lomax, 119. London: Wellcome Institute for the History of Medicine, 1996.

Asylum Superintendent to Medical Board, February 28, 1850, quoted in Waltraud Ernst, "The European Insane in British India, 1800–1858: A Case Study in Psychiatry and Colonial Rule," in *Imperial Medicine and Indigenous Societies*, edited by David Arnold, 35. New York: Manchester University Press, 1988.

Attewell, Guy. *Refiguring Unani Tibb: Plural Healing in Late Colonial India.* Hyderabad, India: Orient Longman, 2007.

Bala, Poonam. *Imperialism and Medicine in Bengal: A Socio-Historical Perspective.* Newbury Park, CA: Sage Publications, 1991.

Bala, Poonam. *Medicine and Medical Policies in India: Social and Historical Perspectives.* Lanham, MD: Lexington Books, 2007.

Baldwin, Peter. *Contagion and the State in Europe 1830–1930.* New York: Cambridge University Press, 1999.

Ballara, Angela. *Taua: "Musket Wars," "Land Wars" or Tikanga? Warfare in Maori Society in the Early Nineteenth Century.* New York: Penguin Books, 2003.

Banerjee, Madhulika. *Power, Knowledge, Medicine: Ayurvedic Pharmaceuticals at Home and in the World.* Hyderabad, India: Orient Black Swan, 2009.

Barnes, Linda L. *Needles, Herbs, Gods, and Ghosts: China, Healing and the West to 1848.* Cambridge, MA: Harvard University Press, 2005.

Barry, Lorelle, and Catharine Coleborne. "Insanity and Ethnicity in New Zealand: Maori Encounters with the Auckland Mental Hospital, 1860–1900." *History of Psychiatry* 22 (2011): 285–301.

Belich, James. *The Victorian Interpretation of Racial Conflict: The Maori, the British, and the New Zealand Wars.* Montreal: McGill-Queen's University Press, 1989.

Bell, Leland V. *Mental and Social Disorder in Sub-Saharan Africa: The Case of Sierra Leone, 1787–1990.* New York: Greenwood Press, 1991.

Benedict, Carol. *Plague in Nineteenth-Century China.* Stanford, CA: Stanford University Press, 1996.

Benton, Edward H. "British Surgery in the South African War: The Work of Major Frederick Porter." *Medical History* 21 (1977): 275–290.

Berg, Manfred, and Geoffrey Cocks, eds. *Medicine and Modernity: Public Health and Medical Care in Nineteenth-and Twentieth-Century Germany.* Washington, DC: German Historical Institute, 1997.

Bertherand, E. *Médecine et Hygiène des Arabes.* Paris, 1855. In *Medicine and Power in Tunisia* by Nancy Elizabeth Gallagher, 56. New York: Cambridge University Press, 1983.

Bijiexian Zhi. 1879, 7: 9a. In *Bubonic Plague in Nineteenth Century China* by Carol Benedict, 117. Stanford, CA: Stanford University Press, 1996.

Bivins, Roberta E. *Acupuncture, Expertise, and Cross-Cultural Medicine.* New York: Palgrave in association with Centre for the History of Science, Technology and Medicine, University of Manchester, 2000.

Black, Jeremy. *War and the World: Military Power and the Fate of Continents 1450–2000.* New Haven, CT: Yale University Press, 1998.

Bordin, Giorgio, and Laura Polo D'Ambrosio. *Medicine in Art.* Translated by Jay Hyams. Los Angeles: J. Paul Getty Museum, 2010.

Branca, Patricia. *Women in Europe since 1750.* London: Croom Helm, 1978.

Bray, R. S. *Armies of Pestilence: The Effects of Pandemics on History.* Cambridge: Lutterworth Press, 1996.

British Pharmacopeia, London, 1867.

Browne, W. A. F. *What Asylums Were, Are, and Ought to Be.* Edinburgh: Adam and Charles Black, 1837.

Brunton, Deborah, ed. *Health, Disease and Society in Europe, 1800–1930: A Source Book.* New York: Manchester University Press, 2004.

Brunton, Deborah, ed. *Medicine Transformed: Health, Disease and Society in Europe, 1800–1930.* Manchester: Manchester University Press in association with the Open University, 2004.

Burnett, John. *Plenty and Want: A Social History of Diet in England from 1815 to the Present Day.* London: Scolar Press, 1979.

Burnett, Kristin. *Taking Medicine: Women's Healing Work and Colonial Contact in Southern Alberta, 1880–1930.* Vancouver: UBC Press, 2010.

Burrows, George Man. *Commentaries on Insanity*, 1828. In *Men, Women and Madness: Understanding Gender and Mental Disorder* by Joan Busfield, 149–150. London: Macmillan Press Ltd., 1996.

Busfield, Joan. *Men, Women and Madness: Understanding Gender and Mental Disorder.* London: Macmillan Press Ltd., 1996.

Bynum, W. F., and Roy Porter, eds. *Companion Encyclopedia of the History of Medicine.* New York: Routledge, 1993.

Bynum, W. F., et al. *The Western Medical Tradition, 1800 to 2000.* New York: Cambridge University Press, 2006.

Carter, Eric D. *Enemy in the Blood: Malaria, Environment, and Development in Argentina.* Tuscaloosa: University of Alabama Press, 2012.

Chang, Che-chia. "The Therapeutic Tug of War: The Imperial Physician-Patient Relationship in the Era of Empress Dowager Cixi (1874–1908)." PhD thesis, University of Pennsylvania, 1998.

Clark, A. Campbell. "Clinical Illustrations of Puerperal Insanity." *Lancet* 21, 1883: 98, quoted in Hilary Marland, "'Destined to a Perfect Recovery': The Confinement of Puerperal Insanity in the Nineteenth Century." In *Insanity, Institutions and Society, 1800–1914*, Joseph Melling and Bill Forsythe, eds., 146. New York: Routledge, 1999.

Clarke, Edward H. *Sex in Education; or A Fair Chance for Girls*. Boston: James R. Osgood and Company, 1875.

Cooter, Roger, ed. *In the Name of the Child: Health and Welfare, 1880–1940*. New York: Routledge, 1992.

Corvisart, Jean Nicholas. *An Essay on the Organic Diseases and Lesions of the Heart and Great Vessels*. Boston: Anthony Finley and Bradford and Read, 1812.

Cullen, Christopher. "Patients and Healers in Late Imperial China: Evidence from the Jinpingmei." *History of Science* 31 (1993): 99–150.

Cunningham, Andrew, and Bridie Andrews, eds. *Western Medicine as Contested Knowledge*. New York: Manchester University Press, 1997.

Curtin, Philip D. *Death by Migration: Europe's Encounter with the Tropical World in the Nineteenth Century*. New York: Cambridge University Press, 1989.

De Barros, Juanita. "Dispensers, Obeah and Quackery: Medical Rivalries in Post-Slavery British Guiana." *Social History of Medicine* 20 (2007): 243–261.

De Barros, Juanita, Steven Palmer, and David Wright, eds. *Health and Medicine in the Circum-Caribbean, 1800–1968*. New York: Routledge, 2009.

"Decomposition." *Sanitarian* 2 (1874): 316. In *The Gospel of Germs: Men, Women and the Microbe in American Life* by Nancy Tomes, 64. Cambridge, MA: Harvard University Press, 1998.

Derickson, Alan. *Black Lung: Anatomy of a Public Health Disaster*. Ithaca, NY: Cornell University Press, 1998.

Dickens, Charles. *Bleak House*. New York: Oxford University Press, 1996.

Digby, Anne. *Diversity and Division in Medicine: Health Care in South Africa from the 1800s*. Oxford: Peter Lang, 2006.

Digby, Anne. "Self-Medication and the Trade in Medicine within a Multi-Ethnic Context: A Case Study of South Africa from the Mid-Nineteenth to Mid-Twentieth Centuries." *Social History of Medicine* 18 (2005): 439–457.

Digby Anne, et al. *Crossing Colonial Historiographies: Histories of Colonial and Indigenous Medicines in Transnational Perspective*. Newcastle upon Tyne: Cambridge Scholars, 2010.

Dixon, Laurinda S., ed. *In Sickness and in Health: Disease as Metaphor in Art and Popular Wisdom*. Newark: University of Delaware Press, 2004.

Doolittle, J. *Social Life of the Chinese*, vol. 1, New York, 1865. In *The Greatest Killer: Smallpox in History* by Donald R. Hopkins, 137. Chicago: University of Chicago Press, 2002.

Dudgeon, John. *The Diseases of China, Their Causes, Conditions and Prevalence, Contrasted with Those of Europe*. Glasgow, 1877. In Shang-Jen Li, "Discovering 'The Secrets of a Long and Healthy Life': John Dudgeon on Chinese Hygiene," *Social History of Medicine* 23 (2009): 28.

Dunant, Henry. *A Memory of Solferino*. Geneva: International Committee of the Red Cross, 1986. In *Champions of Charity: War and the Rise of the Red Cross* by John F. Hutchinson, 18. Boulder, CO: Westview Press, 1996.

Ebrahimnejad, Hormoz, ed. *The Development of Modern Medicine in Non-Western Countries: Historical Perspectives*. New York: Routledge, 2008.

Ebrahimnejad, Hormoz. *Medicine, Public Health and the Qajar State: Patterns of Medical Modernization in Nineteenth-Century Iran*. Boston: Brill, 2004.

Echenberg, Myron. *Africa in the Time of Cholera: A History of Pandemics from 1817 to the Present*. New York: Cambridge University Press, 2011.

Elvin, Mark, and Liu Ts'ui-jung, eds. *Sediments of Time: Environment and Society in Chinese*. Cambridge: Cambridge University Press, 1998.

Engels, Frederick. *Condition of the Working Class in England in 1844*. Reprint, London: George Allen & Unwin, 1943. (Originally published 1845.)

Ernst, Waltraud. *Mad Tales from the Raj: The European Insane in British India, 1800–1858*. New York: Routledge, 1991.

Ernst, Waltraud, ed. *Plural Medicine, Tradition and Modernity, 1800–2000*. New York: Routledge, 2002.

Evans, Richard J. *Death in Hamburg: Society and Politics in the Cholera Years, 1830–1910*. New York: Oxford University Press, 1987.

Felkin, R. W. "Notes on Labour in Central Africa." *Edinburgh Medical Journal* 20 (1884): 922–930.

Fick, Carolyn E. *The Making of Haiti: The Saint Domingue Revolution from Below*. Knoxville: University of Tennessee Press, 1990.

Fifty-fourth Annual Report of the General Hospital and Dispensary for Sick Children. Manchester, 1883. In *Small and Special: The Development of Hospitals for Children in Victorian Britain* by Elizabeth M. R. Lomax, 119. London: Wellcome Institute for the History of Medicine, 1996.

Figes, Orlando. *Crimea: The Last Crusade*. New York: Penguin Books, 2010.

Fildes, Valerie, Lara Marks, and Hilary Marland, eds. *Women and Children First: International Maternal and Infant Welfare, 1870–1945*. New York: Routledge, 1992.

Fitzgerald, John Patrick. "Letter from Dr John Patrick Fitzgerald, Head of the Medical Department and Superintendent of the Native Hospital, to Colonel John MacLean, Chief Commissioner of British Kaffaria," April 13, 1856. In David Gordon, "A Sword of Empire? Medicine and Colonialism in King William's Town, Xhosaland, 1856–1891,"*African Studies* 60 (2001): 170.

Flint, Karen. *Healing Traditions: African Medicine, Cultural Exchange and Competition in South Africa, 1820–1948*. Athens: Ohio University Press, 2008.

Floor, Willem. *Public Health in Qajar Iran*. Washington, DC: Mage Publishers, 2004.

Forbes, John, *Preface to Rene Laennec, A Treatise on the Diseases of the Chest and on Mediate Auscultation* (n.p., 1838). In Stephen Jacyna, "Medicine in Transformation, 1800–1849," in *The Western Medical Tradition 1800–2000* by W. F. Bynum et al., 43. Cambridge: Cambridge University Press, 2006.

Fraser, James. *Travels and Adventures in the Persian Province on the South Banks of the Caspian Sea,* London, 1826. In *Medicine, Public Health and the Qajar State: Patterns of Medical Modernization in Nineteenth-Century Iran* by Hormoz Ebrahimnejad, 37. Boston: Brill, 2004.

Furth, Charlotte. "Blood, Body and Gender. Medical Images of the Female Condition in China." *Chinese Science* 7 (1986): 43–66.

Furth, Charlotte. "Concepts of Pregnancy, Childbirth and Infancy in Ch'ing Dynasty China." *Journal of Asian Studies* 46 (1987): 7–32.

Gabriel, Richard A., and Karen S. Metz. *A History of Military Medicine*. Vol. 2. New York: Greenwood Press, 1992.

Gallagher, Nancy Elizabeth. *Medicine and Power in Tunisia, 1780–1900*. New York: Cambridge University Press, 1983.

Garton, Stephen. *Medicine and Madness: A Social History of Insanity in New South Wales, 1880–1940*. Kensington, NSW: New South Wales University Press, 1988.

Genshiro, Hiruta. "Japanese Psychiatry in the Edo Period (1600–1868)." *History of Psychiatry* 13 (2002): 131–151.

Gilman, Sander L. *Disease and Representation: Images of Illness from Madness to AIDS*. Ithaca, NY: Cornell University Press, 1988.

Gilman, Sander L. "Lam Qua and the Development of a Westernized Medical Iconography in China." *Medical History* 30 (1986): 57–69.
Good, Charles M., Jr. *The Steamer Parish: the Rise and Fall of Missionary Medicine on an African Frontier.* Chicago: University of Chicago Press, 2004.
Gordon, David. "A Sword of Empire? Medicine and Colonialism in King William's Town, Xhosaland, 1856–1891." *African Studies* 60 (2001): 165–183.
Greenspan, Robert E. *Medicine: Perspectives in History and Art.* Alexandria, VA: Ponteverde Press, 2006.
Gregory, James. "Case of Peculiar Black Infiltration of the Whole Lungs, Resembling Melanosis," *Edinburgh Medical and Surgical Journal* 36 (1831): 389–394. In *Black Lung: Anatomy of a Public Health Disaster*, by Alan Derickson, 5. Ithaca, NY: Cornell University Press, 1998.
Grell, Ole Peter, Andrew Cunningham, and Robert Jütte, eds. *Health Care and Poor Relief in 18th and 19th Century Northern Europe.* Burlington, VT: Ashgate, 2002.
Hadfield, Octavius. "System of Government among the New Zealand Tribes," manuscript, Grey Collection, Auckland Public Library. In *"Taua: Musket Wars," "Land Wars" or Tikanga? Warfare in Maori Society in the Early Nineteenth Century* by Angela Ballera, 71. New York: Penguin Books, 2003.
Handler, Jerome S. "Slave Medicine and Obeah in Barbados, circa 1650 to 1834." *New West Indian Guide* 74 (2000): 57–90.
Hanson, Marta E. *Speaking of Epidemics in Chinese Medicine: Disease and the Geographic Imagination in Late Imperial China.* London: Routledge, 2011.
Hardiman, David, ed. *Healing Bodies, Saving Souls: Medical Missions in Asia and Africa.* New York: Rodopi, 2006.
Hardy, Anne. *The Epidemic Streets: Infectious Disease and the Rise of Preventative Medicine, 1856–1900.* New York: Oxford University Press, 1993.
Hardy, Anne. "Rickets and the Rest: Child-Care, Diet and the Infectious Children's Diseases, 1850–1914." *Social History of Medicine* 5 (1992): 389–412.
Harrison, Barbara. *Not Only the "Dangerous Trades": Women's Work and Health in Britain, 1880–1914.* London: Taylor & Francis, 1996.
Harrison, Mark. *Climates and Constitutions: Health, Race, Environment and British Imperialism in India, 1600–1850.* Oxford: Oxford University Press, 1999.
Harrison, Mark. "Differences of Degree: Representations of India in British Medical Topography, 1820–c1870." *Medical History* 44, supplement S20 (2000): 51–69.
Harrison, Mark. *Disease and the Modern World: 1500 to the Present Day.* Cambridge: Polity, 2004.
Harrison, Mark, Margaret Jones, and Helen Sweet, eds. *From Western Medicine to Global Medicine: The Hospital beyond the West.* New Delhi: Orient BlackSwan, 2009.
Helmstadter, Carol, and Judith Godden. *Nursing before Nightingale, 1815–1899.* Farnham, Surrey: Ashgate, 2011.
Henley, David. *Fertility, Food and Fever: Population, Economy and Environment in North and Central Sulawesi, 1600–1930.* Leiden: KITLV Press, 2005.
Hepler, Allison L. *Women in Labor: Mothers, Medicine, and Occupational Health in the United States, 1890–1980.* Columbus: Ohio State University Press, 2000.
Hillam, Christine, ed. *The Roots of Dentistry.* London: British Dental Association, 1990.
Hillier, S. M., and J. A. Jewell, eds. *Health Care and Traditional Medicine in China, 1800–1982.* Boston: Routledge & Kegan Paul, 1983.
Hochmuth, Christian. "Patterns of Medical Culture in Colonial Bengal, 1835–1880." *Bulletin of the History of Medicine* 80 (2006): 39–72.
Hodgson, Barbara. *In the Arms of Morpheus: The Tragic History of Laudanum, Morphine, and Patent Medicines.* Buffalo, NY: Firefly Books, 2001.

Hokkanen, Markku. *Medicine and Scottish Missionaries in the Northern Malawi Region 1875–1930: Quests for Health in a Colonial Society*. Lewiston, NY: Edwin Mellen Press, 2007.

Holmes, Oliver Wendell. "Currents and Counter-Currents in Medical Science," Address to Massachusetts Medical Society, in *Medical Essays 1842–1882*. Boston: Houghton Mifflin, 1892.

Homei, Aya. "Birth Attendants in Meiji Japan: The Rise of a Medical Birth Model and the New Division of Labour." *Social History of Medicine* 19 (2006): 407–424.

Hopkins, Donald R. *The Greatest Killer: Smallpox in History*. Chicago: University of Chicago Press, 2002.

Howard, Martin R. *Wellington's Doctors: The British Army Medical Services in the Napoleonic Wars*. Staplehurst, UK: Spellmount, 2002.

Hughes, Josiah. *Australia Revisited in 1890*. London, 1891. In Helen R. Woodcock, "'Our Salubrious Climate': Attitudes to Health in Colonial Queensland," in *Disease, Medicine and Empire. Perspectives on Western Medicine and the Experience of European Expansion*, edited by Roy MacLeod and Milton Lewis, 180. New York: Routledge, 1988.

Humphreys, Margaret. "Yellow Fever: The Yellow Jack." In *Plague, Pox and Pestilence: Disease in History*, edited by Kenneth F. Kiple. London: Weidenfeld & Nicolson, 1997.

Hutcheon, Linda, and Michael Hutcheon. *Opera: Desire, Disease, Death*. Lincoln: University of Nebraska Press, 1996.

Hutchinson, John F. *Champions of Charity. War and the Rise of the Red Cross*. Boulder, CO: Westview Press, 1996.

India Office Records, London, Medical Board to Government, November 30, 1818. In Waltraud Ernst, "Colonial Lunacy Policies and the Madras Lunatic Asylum in the Early Nineteenth Century," in *Health, Medicine and Empire: Perspectives on Colonial India*, ed. Biswamoy Pati and Mark Harrison, 148. London: Sangam Books, 2001.

Jackson, Mark, ed. *The Oxford Handbook of the History of Medicine*. New York: Oxford University Press, 2011.

Jameson, James. *Report on the Epidemic Cholera Morbus as it Visited the Territories Subject to the Presidency of Bengal, in the Years 1817, 1818 and 1819*. Calcutta, 1820. In *Islam and Healing. Loss and Recovery of an Indo-Muslim Medical Tradition 1600–1900* by Seema Alavi, 114. New York: Palgrave Macmillan, 2008.

Jankovic, Vladimir. *Confronting the Climate: British Airs and the Making of Environmental Medicine*. New York: Palgrave Macmillan, 2010.

Jannetta, Ann. *The Vaccinators: Smallpox, Medical Knowledge, and the "Opening" of Japan*. Stanford, CA: Stanford University Press, 2007.

Jennings, Eric T. "Curing the Colonizers: Highland Hydrotherapy in Guadeloupe." *Social History of Medicine* 15 (2002): 229–261.

Jolly, Julius. *Indian Medicine*. Translated by C. G. Kashikar. New Delhi: Munshiram Manoharlal Publishers Pvt. Ltd., 1977.

Jones, Margaret. *The Hospital System and Health Care: Sri Lanka, 1815–1960*. New Delhi: Orient Blackswan, 2009.

Katz, Paul R. *Demon Hordes and Burning Boats: The Cult of Marshal Wen in Late Imperial Chekiang*. Albany: State University of New York Press, 1995.

Kaur, Amarjit. "Indian Labour, Labour Standards, and Workers' Health in Burma and Malaya, 1900–1940." *Modern Asian Studies* 40 (2006): 425–475.

Keefe, James F. and Lynn Morrow, eds. *A Connecticut Yankee on the Frontier Ozarks: The Writings of Theodore Pease Russell*. Columbia: University of Missouri Press, 1988.

In *The Health of the Country: How American Settlers Understood Themselves and Their Land* by Conevery Bolton Valencius, 83. New York: Basic Books, 2002.

Keller, Richard C. *Colonial Madness: Psychiatry in French North Africa.* Chicago: University of Chicago Press, 2007.

Kennedy, R. H. *Notes on the Epidemic Cholera*, London, 1846, pp. ix–x. In *Colonizing the Body: State Medicine and Epidemic Disease in Nineteenth-Century India* by David Arnold, 173. Berkeley: University of California Press, 1993.

Khan, Hakim Hadi Husain. *Zakhirah-I-Khwarzmshahi* (*Thesaurus of the Shah of Khwarzm*), vol. 2. Lucknow, 1878. In *Islam and Healing: Loss and Recovery of an Indo-Muslim Medical Tradition 1600–1900* by Seema Alavi, 213. New York: Palgrave Macmillan, 2008.

Kiple, Kenneth F. *Plague, Pox and Pestilence: Disease in History.* London: Weidenfeld & Nicolson, 1997.

Knight, Ian. *The Anatomy of the Zulu Army from Shaka to Cetshwayo 1818–1879.* Mechanicsburg, PA: Stackpole Books, 1995.

The Lancet. Editorial. August 2, 1873, 159.

Lange, Raeburn. *May the People Live: A History of Maori Health Development 1900–1918.* Auckland: Auckland University Press, 1999.

Leavitt, Judith Walzer. *Brought to Bed: Childbearing in America, 1750 to 1950.* New York: Oxford University Press, 1986.

Leavitt, Judith Walzer, and Ronald L. Numbers, eds. *Sickness and Health in America: Readings in the History of Medicine and Public Health.* Madison: University of Wisconsin Press, 1978.

Leung, Angela Ki Che. "Organized Medicine in Ming-Qing China: State and Private Medical Institutions in the Lower Yangzi Region." *Late Imperial China* 8 (1987): 134–166.

Leung, Angela Ki Che. "'Variolation' and Vaccination in Late Imperial China, ca. 1570–1911." In *Vaccinia, Vaccination, Vaccinology: Jenner, Pasteur and Their Successors*, edited by Stanley A. Plotkin and Bernardino Fantini, 65–71. Paris: Elsevier, 1996.

Leung, Angela Ki Che, and Charlotte Furth, eds. *Health and Hygiene in Chinese East Asia: Policies and Publics in the long Twentieth Century.* Durham, NC: Duke University Press, 2010.

Li, Shang-Jen. "Discovering 'The Secrets of a Long and Healthy Life': John Dudgeon on Chinese Hygiene." *Social History of Medicine* 23 (2009) 21–37.

Lomax, Elizabeth M. R. *Small and Special: The Development of Hospitals for Children in Victorian Britain.* London: Wellcome Institute for the History of Medicine, 1996.

Lossio, Jorge. "British Medicine in the Peruvian Andes: The Travels of Archibald Smith M.D. (1820–1870)." *História, Ciências, Saúde-Manguinhos* 13 (2006): 833–850.

Low-Beer, Daniel, Matthew Smallman-Raynor, and Andrew Cliff. "Disease and Death in the South African War: Changing Disease Patterns from Soldiers to Refugees." *Social History of Medicine* 17 (2004): 223–245.

Lux, Maureen K. *Medicine That Walks: Disease, Medicine and Canadian Plains Native People, 1880–1940.* Toronto: University of Toronto Press, 2001.

MacLeod, Roy, and Milton Lewis, eds. *Disease, Medicine and Empire: Perspectives on Western Medicine and the Experience of European Expansion.* New York: Routledge, 1988.

Macpherson, Kerrie L. *A Wilderness of Marshes: The Origins of Public Health in Shanghai, 1843–1893.* New York: Oxford University Press, 1987.

Marland, Hilary. "The Medical Activities of Mid-Nineteenth-Century Chemists and Druggists, with Special Reference to Wakefield and Huddersfield." *Medical History* 31 (1987): 415–439.

Marmier, X. *Lettres sur l'Algérie*, Brussels, 1852. In Marie-Cecile Thoral, "Colonial Medical Encounters in the Nineteenth Century: The French Campaigns in Egypt, Saint Domingue and Algeria," *Social History of Medicine* 25 (2012): 621.

Martin, James. *The Influence of Tropical Climates on European Constitutions*. London, 1856. In *Colonizing the Body: State Medicine and Epidemic Disease in Nineteenth-Century India* by David Arnold, 27. Berkeley: University of California Press, 1993.

Matthee, Rudi. *The Pursuit of Pleasure: Drugs and Stimulants in Iranian History, 1500–1900*. Princeton, NJ: Princeton University Press, 2005.

Mazars, Guy. *A Concise Introduction to Indian Medicine*. Translated by T. K. Gopalan. Delhi: Motilal Bandarsidass Publishers Private Ltd., 2006.

McCandless, Peter. *Slavery, Disease, and Suffering in the Southern Lowcountry*. Cambridge: Cambridge University Press, 2011.

McCrea, Heather L. "Diseased Relations. Epidemics, Public Health and State Formation in Nineteenth-Century Yucatan, Mexico." PhD thesis, State University of New York, Stony Brook, 2002.

McIvor, Arthur J., and Ronald Johnston, eds. *Miners' Lung: A History of Dust Disease in British Coal Mining*. Aldershot, UK: Ashgate, 2007.

McKeown, Thomas. *The Modern Rise of Population*. London: Edward Arnold, 1976.

McNeill, William H. *Plagues and Peoples*. New York: Penguin Books, 1979.

Mead, Karen. "Beneficent Maternalism: Argentine Motherhood in Comparative Perspective, 1880–1920." *Journal of Women's History* 12 (2000): 120–145.

Mearns, Andrew. "The Bitter Cry of Outcast London." 1883. In *The Greatest Benefit to Mankind: A Medical History of Humanity from Antiquity to the Present* by Roy Porter, 400. London: Fontana, 1999.

"Medical Education: Bibliographical Record," *Indian Annals of Medical Science*, vol. 2 (1855): 723. In Christian Hochmuth, "Patterns of Medical Culture in Colonial Bengal, 1835–1880." *Bulletin of the History of Medicine*, 80 (2006): 52.

Meegama, S. A. *Famine, Fevers and Fear: The State and Disease in British Colonial Sri Lanka*. Dehiwela: Sridevi, 2012.

Melling, Joseph, and Bill Forsythe, eds. *Insanity, Institutions and Society, 1800–1914*. New York: Routledge, 1999.

Mercier, Jacques. *Art That Heals: The Image as Medicine in Ethiopia*. New York: Museum for African Art, 1997.

Messner, Angelika C. "On 'Translating' Western Psychiatry into the Chinese Context in Republican China." In *Mapping Meanings: The Field of New Learning in Late Qing China*, edited by Michael Lackner and Natascha Vittinghoff, 639–658. Leiden: Brill, 2004.

Mills, James. "A History of Modern Psychiatry in India, 1858–1947." *History of Psychiatry* 12 (2001): 431–458.

Mooney, Graham, and Jonathan Reinarz, eds. *Permeable Walls: Historical Perspectives on Hospital and Asylum Visiting*. New York: Rodopi, 2009.

Morier, James. *A Second Journey through Persia, Armenia, and Asia Minor, to Constantinople, between 1810 and 1816*. London, 1818. In *Public Health in Qajar Iran* by Willem Floor, 97. Washington, DC: Mage Publishers, 2004.

Moscucci, Ornella. *The Science of Woman: Gynaecology and Gender in England, 1800–1929*. New York: Cambridge University Press, 1993.

Nash, Linda. *Inescapable Ecologies: A History of Environment, Disease, and Knowledge*. Berkeley: University of California Press, 2006.

Ng, Beng-Yeong. "Hysteria: A Cross-Cultural Comparison of Its Origins and History." *History of Psychiatry* 10 (1999): 287–301.

Ng, Vivien W. *Madness in late Imperial China: From Illness to Deviance.* Norman: University of Oklahoma Press, 1990.
Numbers, Ronald L., and Darrel W. Amundsen, eds. *Caring and Curing: Health and Medicine in the Western Religious Traditions.* New York: Macmillan Publishing Company, 1986.
Opp, James. *The Lord for the Body: Religion, Medicine, and Protestant Faith Healing in Canada, 1880–1930.* Montreal: McGill-Queen's University Press, 2005.
Overseers Manual (Demerara, 1896). In Juanita De Barros, "Dispensers, Obeah and Quackery: Medical Rivalries in Post-Slavery British Guiana," *Social History of Medicine* 20 (2007): 255.
Palmer, Steven. *From Popular Medicine to Medical Populism. Doctors, Healers and Public Power in Costa Rica.* Durham, NC: Duke University Press, 2003.
Parle, Julie. *States of Mind: Searching for Mental Health in Natal and Zululand, 1868–1918.* Scottsville, South Africa: University of KwaZulu-Natal Press, 2007.
Parle, Julie. "Witchcraft or Madness? The Amandiki of Zululand, 1894–1914." *Journal of Southern African Studies* 29 (2003): 105–132.
Pati, Biswamoy, and Mark Harrison, eds. *Health, Medicine and Empire Perspectives on Colonial India.* London: Sangam Books, 2001.
Peltier, Leonard F. *Orthopedics: A History and Iconography.* San Francisco: Norman Publishers, 1993.
Pernick, Martin S. *A Calculus of Suffering: Pain, Professionalism, and Anesthesia in Nineteenth-Century America.* New York: Columbia University Press, 1985.
Pooley, Siân. "'All We Want Is That Our Children's Health and Lives Should Be Regarded': Child Health and Parental Concern in England, c.1860–1910." *Social History of Medicine* 23 (2010): 528–548.
Porter, Roy, ed. *The Faber Book of Madness.* Boston: Faber and Faber, 1991.
Porter, Roy. *The Greatest Benefit to Mankind: A Medical History of Humanity from Antiquity to the Present.* London: Fontana Press, 1997.
Porter, Roy, and Mikulás Teich, eds. *Drugs and Narcotics in History.* New York: Cambridge University Press, 1995.
Porter, Roy, and David Wright, eds. *The Confinement of the Insane: International Perspectives, 1800–1965.* Cambridge: Cambridge University Press, 2003.
Post, Justus. Letter to John Post, August 23, 1816. In *The Health of the Country: How American Settlers Understood Themselves and Their Land* by Conevery Bolton Valencius, 32. New York: Basic Books, 2002.
Powell, Margaret, and Masahira Anesaki, eds. *Health Care in Japan.* New York: Routledge, 1989.
Rampton, David. "The Doctors' Plot: Some Classic Nineteenth-Century Novels Revisited." *Modern Language Studies* 22 (1992): 57–66.
Reid, Janice. *Sorcerers and Healing Spirits: Continuity and Change in an Aboriginal Medical System.* Canberra: Australian National University Press, 1983.
Rogaski, Ruth. "Beyond Benevolence: A Confucian Women's Shelter in Treaty-Port China." *Journal of Women's History* 8 (1997): 54–90.
Rogaski, Ruth. "From Protecting Life to Defending the Nation: Tianjin 1859–1953." PhD thesis, Yale University, 1996.
Rogaski, Ruth. *Hygienic Modernity: Meanings of Health and Disease in Treaty-Port China.* Berkeley: University of California Press, 2004.
Rush, Benjamin. *Medical Inquiries and Observations upon Diseases of the Mind,* 1812. In *The Faber Book of Madness,* edited by Roy Porter, 41. Boston: Faber and Faber, 1991.
Russett, Cynthia Eagle. *Sexual Science: The Victorian Construction of Womanhood.* Cambridge, MA: Harvard University Press, 1989.

Ruznameh-ye 'elmi, March 19, 1887. In *Medicine, Public Health and the Qajar State: Patterns of Medical Modernization in Nineteenth-Century Iran* by Hormoz Ebrahimnejad, 123. Boston: Brill, 2004.

Sackett, F. Colyer. *Vision and Venture: A Record of Fifty Years in Hyderabad 1879–1929*, London, n.d., p. 106. In Rosemary Fitzgerald, "'Clinical Christianity': The Emergence of Missionary Work as a Missionary Strategy in Colonial India, 1800–1914," in *Health, Medicine and Empire. Perspectives on Colonial India*, edited by Biswamoy Pati and Mark Harrison, 108. London: Sangam Books, 2001.

Sadowsky, Jonathan. *Imperial Bedlam: Institutions of Madness in Colonial Southwest Nigeria*. Berkeley: University of California Press, 1999.

Satya, Laxman D. *Medicine, Disease and Ecology in Colonial India: The Deccan Plateau in the 19th Century*. New Dehli: Manohar, 2009.

Scheid, Volker. *Currents of Tradition in Chinese Medicine, 1626–2006*. Seattle, WA: Eastland Press, 2007.

Schwieso, Joshua John. "'Religious Fanaticism' and Wrongful Confinement in Victorian England: The Affair of Louisa Nottidge." *Social History of Medicine* 9 (1996): 159–174.

Scull, Andrew. *Most Solitary of Afflictions: Madness and Society in Britain 1700–1900*. New Haven, CT: Yale University Press, 1993.

Selin, Helaine, ed. *Medicine across Cultures. History and Practice of Medicine in Non-Western Cultures*. Boston: Kluwer Academic Publishers, 2003.

Sellers, Christopher C. *Hazards of the Job: From Industrial Disease to Environmental Health Science*. Chapel Hill: University of North Carolina Press, 1997.

Sengoopta, Chandak. "The Modern Ovary: Constructions, Meanings, Uses." *History of Science* 38 (2000): 425–488.

Sheils, W. J., ed. *The Church and Healing: Papers Read at the Twentieth Summer Meeting and the Twenty-first Winter Meeting of the Ecclesiastical History Society*. Oxford: Blackwell, 1982.

Shixiong, Wang. *Huoluan lun*, 1838, part 1, 2b. In Ruth Rogaski, "From Protecting Life to Defending the Nation: Tianjin 1859–1953," 68. PhD thesis, Yale University, 1996.

Shorter, Edward. *History of Psychiatry: From the Era of the Asylum to the Age of Prozac*. New York: Wiley, 1997.

Showalter, Elaine. *The Female Malady. Women, Madness and English Culture, 1830–1980*. New York: Pantheon Books, 1985.

Shutoka, Kagawa. *Ippondo-Gyoyo-Igen* (*My Extra Medical Commentary*), 1807. In Hiruta Genshiro, "Japanese Psychiatry in the Edo Period," *History of Psychiatry* 13 (2002): 134.

Siddiqui, Tazim Uddin. "Nazim-e jehan Hakim Muhammad A'zam Khan." *Studies in History of Medicine* 4 (1980): 234. In *Refiguring Unani Tibb: Plural Healing in Late Colonial India* by Guy Attewell, 133. Hyderabad: Orient Longman, 2007.

Sivaramakrishnan, Kavita. *Old Potions, New Bottles: Recasting Indigenous Medicine in Colonial Punjab, 1850–1945*. New Perspectives in South Asian History. Hyderabad, India: Orient Longman, 2006.

Smith, George. *The Hyderabad Medical School: Its Past History and Its Present Condition*. Madras, 1859. In *Refiguring Unani Tibb: Plural Healing in Late Colonial India* by Guy Attewell, 102. Hyderabad: Orient Longman, 2007.

Smith, George H. *A Narrative of an Exploratory Visit to . . . the Consular Cities of China*. London, 1847, 183. In *Needles, Herbs, Gods and Ghosts. China, Healing and the West to 1848* by Linda L. Barnes, 341. Cambridge, MA: Harvard University Press, 2005.

Speziale, Fabrizio, ed. *Hospitals in Iran and India, 1500–1950s*. Boston: Brill, 2012.

Spurgeon, C. H. *Autobiography*, vol. 2. Edinburgh, 1973, 414. In Timothy P. Weber, "The Baptist Tradition," in *Caring and Curing Health and Medicine in the Western Religious Traditions*, edited by Ronald L. Numbers and Darrel W. Amundsen, 291. New York: Macmillan Publishing Company, 1986.

Stowe, Steven M. *Doctoring the South: Southern Physicians and Everyday Medicine in the Mid-Nineteenth Century*. Chapel Hill: University of North Carolina Press, 2004.

Sullivan, Lawrence E., ed. *Healing and Restoring: Health and Medicine in the World's Religious Traditions*. New York: Macmillan, 1989.

Summers, Ann. "Pride and Prejudice: Ladies and Nurses in the Crimean War." *History Workshop Journal* 16 (1983): 33–56.

Sun, Trenton, Illinois. December 1, 1905, p. 8, http://tsu.stparchive.com/Archive/TSU/TSU12011905P08.php

Szonyi, Michael. "The Illusion of Standardizing the Gods: The Cult of the Five Emperors in Late Imperial China." *Journal of Asian Studies* 56 (1997): 113–135.

Szreter, Simon. "The Importance of Social Intervention in Britain's Mortality Decline c. 1850–1914: A Re-interpretation of the Role of Public Health." *Social History of Medicine* 1 (1988): 1–37.

Taithe, Bertrand. *Defeated Flesh Welfare, Warfare and the Making of Modern France*. Manchester: Manchester University Press, 1999.

Thoral, Marie-Cecile. "Colonial Medical Encounters in the Nineteenth Century: The French Campaigns in Egypt, Saint Domingue and Algeria." *Social History of Medicine* 25 (2012): 608–624.

Tokaku, Wada. *Syosou Zatsuwa* (*Small Talks by a Window Facing a Japanese Banana Plant*). In Hiruta Genshiro, "Japanese Psychiatry in the Edo Period," *History of Psychiatry* 13 (2002): 136.

Tolstoy, Leo. *The Sebastopol Sketches*. London, 1986, 44, 47–48. In *Crimea: The Last Crusade* by Orlando Figes, 298. New York: Penguin Books, 2010.

Ueyama, Takahiro. *Health in the Marketplace: Professionalism, Therapeutic Desires, and Medical Commodification in Late-Victorian London*. Palo Alto, CA: Society for the Promotion of Science and Scholarship, 2010.

Unschuld, Paul U. *Medicine in China: Historical Artifacts and Images*. Translated by Sabine Wilms. New York: Prestel, 2000.

Unschuld, Paul U. *Medicine in China: A History of Ideas*. Berkeley: University of California Press, 2010.

Unschuld, Paul U. *Medicine in China: A History of Pharmaceutics*. Berkeley: University of California Press, 1985.

Valencius, Conevery Bolton. *The Health of the Country: How American Settlers Understood Themselves and Their Land*. New York: Basic Books, 2002.

Van Evrie, John H. *Negroes and Negro "Slavery."* New York, 1861. In Todd L. Savitt, "Black Health on the Plantation: Masters, Slaves, and Physicians," in *Sickness and Health in America: Readings in the History of Medicine and Public Health*, edited by Judith Walzer Leavitt and Ronald L. Numbers, 316. Madison: University of Wisconsin Press, 1978.

Virchow, Rudolf. *Gesammelte Abhandlunger zur wissenshaftlichen Medizin (Collected Essays on Medical Science)*. Frankfurt, 1856, 747. In Chandak Sengoopta, "The Modern Ovary: Constructions, Meanings, Uses." *History of Science* 38, 2000: 428.

Vogel, Virgil J. *American Indian Medicine*. Norman: University of Oklahoma Press, 1970.

Waddington, Keir. *An Introduction to the Social History of Medicine: Europe since 1500*. Basingstoke, Hampshire: Palgrave Macmillan, 2011.

Wakefield and Halifax Journal, November 16, 1832. In Hilary Marland, "The Medical Activities of Mid-Nineteenth-Century Chemists and Druggists, with Special Reference to Wakefield and Huddersfield." *Medical History* 31 (1987): 433.

Wang, Hsiu-yun. "Stranger Bodies: Women, Gender, and Missionary Medicine in China, 1870s–1930s." PhD thesis, University of Wisconsin–Madison, 2003.

Warren, Adam. *Medicine and Politics in Colonial Peru: Population Growth and the Bourbon Reforms.* Pittsburgh, PA: University of Pittsburgh Press, 2010.

Watts, Sheldon. *Epidemics and History: Disease, Power and Imperialism.* New Haven, CT: Yale University Press, 1997.

Weindling, Paul, ed. *The Social History of Occupational Health.* Dover, NH: Croom Helm, 1986.

Wilson, John. "On Chinese Pharmacy." *Pharmaceutical Journal and Transactions* 5, 1846. In *Needles, Herbs, Gods, and Ghosts: China, Healing and the West to 1848* by Linda Barnes, 267. Cambridge, MA: Harvard University Press, 2005.

Wohl, Anthony S. *Endangered Lives: Public Health in Victorian Britain.* Cambridge, MA: Harvard University Press, 1983.

Wolff, Norma H. "The Use of Human Images in Yoruba Medicines." *Ethnology* 39 (2000): 205–224.

Worboys, Michael. *Spreading Germs: Disease Theories and Medical Practice in Britain, 1865–1900.* New York: Cambridge University Press, 2000.

Wu, Yi-Li. *Reproducing Women: Medicine, Metaphor, and Childbirth in Late Imperial China.* Berkeley: University of California Press, 2010.

Wu, Yi-Li. "Transmitted Secrets: The Doctors of the lower Yangzi Region and Popular Gynecology in Late Imperial China." PhD thesis, Yale University, 1998.

Wujastyk, Dominik. *The Roots of Ayurveda: Selections from Sanskrit Medical Writings.* New York: Penguin Books, 2003.

Wynbrandt, James. *The Excruciating History of Dentistry: Toothsome Tales and Oral Oddities from Babylon to Braces.* New York: St. Martin's Press, 1998.

Young, Theron Kue-hing. "A Conflict of Professions: The Medical Missionary in China, 1835–1890." *Bulletin of the History of Medicine* 47 (1973): 250–272.

Zola, Émile. *Nana*, trans. George Holden. New York: Penguin, 1972.

PART 4

20th Century and Beyond

Ruth Clifford Engs

1

Key Factors in Health and Wellness

More advances in public health and medicine have occurred since the early 20th century compared to the rest of known history. Some beliefs, practices, and activities have gone in and out of fashion, or have been lost in dark ages as civilizations declined over the millennia but were rediscovered around the turn of the 20th century. For example, sanitation and flushing human wastes with water and access to clean water were found in the ancient civilizations of Mohenjo Daro and Harappa of the Indus Valley of India. These sanitation methods, which would have curtailed many diseases, were lost when these civilizations declined but were reinvented by the classical Greek and Roman civilizations, only to be lost again in the early Middle Ages of Western civilization. It was not until the late 19th century and early 20th century that flush toilets, adequate sewers, refuse collection, and clean water again emerged. Access to clean water and general sanitation were the major factors for the increase in longevity and health in the 20th century worldwide. Higher-income nations, compared to low- to middle-income nations, had longer life expectancies inasmuch as many developing nations still struggled with adequate sanitation and access to clean water, which contributed to disease and curtailed longevity. Another factor in health and longevity worldwide was globalization, particularly in the late 20th and early 21st centuries.

Globalization included not only the movement of ideas, medical and public health practices, and new technologies but also the transmission of diseases, poor lifestyle habits, and environmental issues. Increased tourism rapidly transmitted diseases such as Ebola and AIDS/HIV from one continent to another. Rapid urbanization around the world produced mixed results for health. In higher-income nations, city dwellers had better access to health care and better public health infrastructure, but in less developed nations, increased urbanization often led to sanitation, pollution, and disease issues.

LONGEVITY AND RELATIONSHIP TO HEALTH ADVANCES

A key to the health of a nation is longevity. The average life expectancy at birth worldwide in 1900 was 31, in 1950 about 48, and in 2016, it was 72 years of age.

By 2016, overall life expectancy in mainly English-speaking higher-income nations was as follows: about 83 years in Australia and Canada, 82 in New Zealand, 81 in the United Kingdom and Ireland, and 78 years in the United States. It was around 82 years in Western European nations and about 72 in Eastern European nations. Life expectancy was around 76 years in China, 75 years in Latin America, and about 70 in South Asia and Southeast Asia, and approximately 62 years in sub-Saharan Africa. The highest life expectancy in 2016 was found in Japan at 84 years.

The increase in longevity in all regions of the world since 1900 was mainly due to the reduction of infant mortality, largely a result of public health measures. Food- and waterborne gastrointestinal diseases such as salmonella, typhoid, and cholera were reduced along with tuberculosis (TB) not only by access to clean water and sanitation but also by hand washing, pasteurization, and refrigeration.

In the late 20th century, as people were living longer, the leading causes of death globally shifted to noncommunicable diseases including heart disease, strokes, cancers, and chronic obstructive lung disease (COPD). In 2016, the leading causes of death globally were heart disease, stroke, COPD, lower respiratory infections (such as TB and pneumonia), Alzheimer's disease and other forms of dementia, and respiratory system cancers. However, in low-income countries, particularly the tropical regions of Africa and Asia, the leading causes of death still included infectious diseases such as AIDS, lower respiratory infections, diarrhea, and malaria.

What people were dying from greatly altered the concept of health and disease to the point that in developed countries public health and medicine focused on morbidity (illness) rather than mortality (death). The emphasis changed from keeping people alive to keeping people healthy and fit. Primary prevention included the encouragement of lifestyle changes, exercise, good nutrition, and smoking cessation to reduce premature deaths from chronic conditions. Death rates from chronic diseases had declined by preventative efforts in most developed nations in the mid-2010s. For example, decline in deaths from coronary heart disease and stroke resulted from risk-factor modifications, such as smoking cessation and blood pressure control along with tests for early detection of diseases and better treatment options.

HEALTH AND BURDEN OF DISEASE

By mid-20th century, it was realized that measuring how many people died and why they died each year was one of the most important factors for assessing the effectiveness of a nation's health promotion efforts, its health system, and the overall health of the country. In the 1950s, the World Health Organization (WHO) defined health as a "state of complete physical, mental, and social well-being, and not merely the absence of disease or infirmity." By the 1980s, this expanded into a concept of "wellness," or a person living to his or her fullest potential in all dimensions of life.

Near the end of the 20th century, it was realized that different health conditions and diseases could have serious economic, social, and health consequences for a nation. Therefore, the World Bank in 1990 and later the Bill & Melinda Gates Foundation funded a consortium of researchers to conduct a comprehensive regional and global study that assessed morbidity, disability, and premature deaths from major diseases, injuries, and risk factors. The study is updated every few years. The Global Burden of Disease (GBD) studies have been instrumental in guiding global health policy development since the early 1990s. The project provided key information about the major causes of mortality. A new measure to calculate the Burden of Disease, Disability Adjusted Life Year (DALY) was developed to assess health conditions in a nation or region of the world to guide public health policies.

Along with the GBD was the creation in 2000 of the United Nations' Millennium Development Goals (MDG). These eight international goals for the year 2015 had been established following the Millennium Summit of the United Nations in 2000. All 191 UN members committed to work toward achieving these goals by 2015. They included the eradication of extreme poverty and hunger, achieving universal primary education, promoting gender equality, reducing infant and child mortality, improving maternal health, combating HIV/AIDS, malaria, and other diseases, ensuring environmental sustainability and developing global partnerships.

They were only partially met by many nations. Therefore, the Sustainable Development Goals (SDGs) were launched in 2015 when the MDGs expired and were expanded to 17 goals to be reached by 2030. The 17 Sustainable Development Goals of the 2030 integrated the three dimensions of sustainable development: economic, social, and environmental. These goals included good health and well-being, quality education, clean water and sanitation, affordable and clean energy, decent work and economic growth, industry, innovation and infrastructure, sustainable cities and communities, responsible consumption and production, climate action, life below water, and life on land and international partnerships to achieve the goals. Unlike the MDGs, the SDG structure did not distinguish between "developed" and "developing" nations. Instead, the goals applied to all nations and regions.

HEALTH AND MEDICAL ADVANCES

Besides sanitation, hygiene, and clean water, one of the greatest achievements for the reduction of morbidity and mortality was the development of vaccines against infectious disease. By the 1930s, immunizations had become common to prevent tetanus and childhood diseases such as diphtheria and whooping cough. In the 1950s and 1960s, polio vaccines were introduced, which essentially eliminated this scourge in most higher-income nations. The success of vaccination programs in North America and Europe by the 1970s inspired the concept of "disease eradication" in all human populations through global cooperation. A major advancement was the worldwide elimination of smallpox by vaccination in 1977. In the late 1900s and early 2010s, immunizations against other childhood diseases

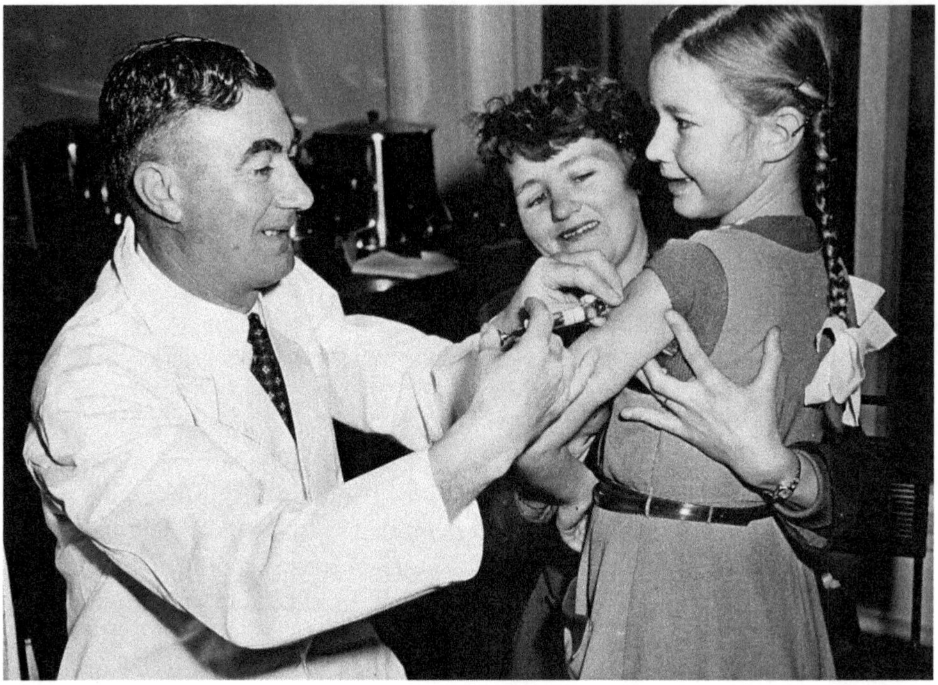

An Australian schoolgirl receives the Salk polio vaccine, ca. 1950. In the early 1960s, the injectable Salk immunization was replaced by the Sabin oral vaccine. (National Institutes of Health)

such as measles, rubella, and meningitis and diseases such as pneumonia, hepatitis, and shingles emerged. Public health efforts in the 21st century attempted to wipe out measles and polio but were curtailed by political, religious, and philosophical resistance in several nations. The rates of immunizations declined and offset some of the advances made during the 20th century to prevent infectious diseases.

Another major advancement in medicine and health were the antimicrobials. In the 1940s, antibiotics were introduced that cured many infections that had been leading killers in the early 20th century such as pneumonia and tuberculosis. In addition, sexually transmitted diseases (STDs) that could lead to sterility, birth defects, and dementia were also cured by antibiotics. However, due to widespread inappropriate global use of antibiotics, many diseases became resistant to them. In the 1940s and 1950s, the elimination of some diseases such as malaria in North America, parts of Latin America, and Europe were accomplished by draining swamps, using screens or mosquito netting, and utilizing new insecticides such as DDT. However, malaria and other vector-borne diseases were still prevalent in tropical developing nations, and some mosquitoes developed resistance to the insecticides. In addition these substances were found to cause environmental and pollution issues.

In higher-income nations at the beginning of the century, dental caries (cavities) were prevalent due to a diet of more refined and sugary foods and a lack of daily dental hygiene. A major advancement for dental health was fluoridation of the community water supply and education for more comprehensive dental hygiene during the second half of the 20th century in most higher-income nations. Advances were also made in eye care with the development of contact lenses and intricate surgery that could save sight.

Medical advances increased the ability to diagnose and monitor infectious diseases. For example, at the beginning of the century, serologic (blood) testing for antibodies to a disease allowed for the identification of syphilis. Tissue cultures identifying viral infections in the 1960s and molecular biology tools that examined DNA enhanced the ability to identify new diseases such as HIV/AIDS and to develop prevention and treatment methods in the last third of the 20th century. Another advance was evidence-based medical treatment and prevention programs derived from formal scientific research that became standard in Western medicine.

Medical education changed in most nations beginning in the early 20th century. Standards for teaching institutions and for student admittance became stricter, women were increasingly allowed into medical school by the 1980s, and the education of physicians and other health care professionals became more humanized. This humanization was often carried out through the vehicle of the arts and humanities. Over the latter part of the 20th century, treatment procedures from alternative medical and religious systems in Asia, South Asia, and other nations began to be integrated into Western medicine. Western medicine also became common, especially in urban areas, in many developing nations although native healing traditions were still used especially in rural areas.

Surgical techniques, treatment for trauma, and rehabilitation developed out of the battlefields of the many wars and conflicts of the 20th century and into the 21st century. Blood banking, transfusions, and better artificial limbs were developed. Out of the wars emerged ambulances, which saved lives because of rapid transportation of the sick and injured by helicopters to hospitals. Other advances in the late 20th and early 21st centuries included the transplantation of organs and the development of artificial hearts, kidneys, and other organs.

Early detection and screening tests for cervical, breast, and colon cancer evolved in the latter part of the century, which saved numerous lives by early treatment. Cancer treatment methods steadily advanced over the late 1990s and into the early 2000s. Besides surgery, these included radiation, chemotherapy, immunotherapy, targeted therapy, and by 2018, new substances that only killed cancerous cells. Likewise treatment of heart disease not only included various medications but also surgeries, valve replacements, stents, and implanted and external devices such as the automatic cardiac defibrillators (AEDs) to shock the heart back into normal sinus rhythm.

A major discovery of the 1950s was the identification of DNA—the cell's hereditary material—which is passed down from one generation to the next. It contains the instructions for growth, development, and reproduction and has the ability to switch an action of a gene on or off. Out of this discovery, a major advance in health and medicine, which has many future ramifications, occurred in the first decade of the 21st century. The Human Genome Project in the United

States sequenced and mapped the human genome—the blueprint of humans—in 2003. This advance created the ability for more medical discoveries along with potential prevention and treatment methods for numerous conditions and diseases.

TECHNOLOGICAL ADVANCES

Technological advances made in the post–World War II (WWII) era dramatically changed the face of medicine and health and medical practices with new diagnostic tools, treatments, surgeries, the computer, and digital medical record keeping. These new technologies had both positive and negative effects on the advancement of health and medicine.

X-ray technology, first introduced at the turn of the 20th century, enabled more advanced diagnosis and treatment. However, by the end of the century, this basic radiological technology evolved into major developments in diagnosis and treatment procedures such as CAT scans, PET scans, and digital mammogram diagnostic tools. Other tools including MRI, the electrocardiogram, and ultrasound technology also enabled quick diagnosis of various conditions and diseases. Advances in computer technology made it possible to obtain digital records of X-rays instead of the use of film for many diagnostic and treatment procedures, which could be instantly viewed. Digital images along with small cameras were used with minimally invasive surgical methods along with robotic surgery. Previously complex procedures with long hospital stays now were done as outpatient day surgery. For example, gall bladder surgery patients over most of the 20th century often stayed in the hospital for over a week with the standard surgical procedure, which produced a six- to eight-inch incision. By the early 21st century, minimally invasive surgery turned this operation into an outpatient procedure.

The Computer and Electronic Media

Many technological and medical advances in the late 20th century were based upon the computer, which profoundly changed all human activities, both positively and negatively. The development of the computer in the 1980s, the Internet and websites in the 1990s, social media in the 2000s, and inexpensive mobile smart phones in the 2010s led to the global spread of information and an increase in global communication. Up through the late 20th century, publications and conferences were the primary ways of communication among health care professionals and researchers. The development of computers and the electronic media rapidly increased the exchange of health and medical research. Not only was new information shared among health care and medical personnel but the impact of computers and mobile phones by 2010 made it possible for the layperson to find information about particular diseases and medical conditions along with their prevention and treatment. This information was available through health websites along with scholarly articles, information sheets, and reports by governmental agencies and nongovernmental organizations (NGOs). A negative side of this communication through the Internet and social media was that health and other information was not always accurate, and websites could be manipulated for political purposes. Some used the technology to psychologically abuse people, while others developed computer, Internet, and social-media addictive disorders.

Electronic Medical Records

One of the most important medical advancements that evolved in the late 20th century was the digitalization of patient records at all levels of care from individual primary care physicians and GPs to group practices and large hospitals. These records were integrated into increasingly complex health care systems, particularly in developed nations. As physician practices went from solo to large group practices under one system, digital records allowed health care professionals to keep all information in one place and to easily share records with other health care providers or state-controlled or private insurance entities.

By the mid-1990s, computers were being used in most medical offices for scheduling, printing reports, and for health care providers' clinical assessments. However, they were used only to a limited degree for record keeping. Electronic Medical Records (EMR) changed the way that traditional medical records were stored and managed. The EMRs were large data management systems. They included a range of data such as billing information, demographics and personal information, immunization status, medical history, allergies and medication, laboratory test results, radiology images, and vital signs. In isolated rural areas, local medical personnel could consult with larger medical centers about diagnosis and treatments.

To cut costs, some governmental entities worldwide began to require or suggest the adoption of EMRs. In the United States, for example, all public and private health care providers were required to adopt and demonstrate "meaningful use" of EMR by January 1, 2014, to maintain their existing Medicaid and Medicare reimbursement. By the late 2010s, many major medical systems in the developed world could communicate with each other via standardized EMRs. Medical records increasingly became paperless, although some private practices continued to use a combination of paper and computerized records while some developing nations did not have computerized records in rural areas.

However, this technology had negative aspects. For example, physicians taking notes or checking off boxes in the computer during patient assessments sometimes missed nonverbal cues as they were looking at their computer screens and not the patient. Concerns about privacy or hacking into computers to gain patient information also arose, and several health care systems at hospitals, workplaces, and institutions were accessed particularly in the United States in the 2010s. By the mid-2010s in developed nations, "patient portals" (which sometimes were difficult to access by older individuals) that gave patients the ability to view lab and radiology results, manage prescriptions, make appointments, pay bills, or communicate with their health provider on a website became common. This sometimes provided more rapid communication between patients and health care providers, but it also curtailed face-to-face or telephone interaction of the health care professional with the patient concerning the results of tests or medical findings. On the whole, maintaining patient medical records digitally for both health care providers and patients has shaped and will continue to shape medical practice and health care into the future.

LIFESTYLE AND THE ENVIRONMENT

Lifestyle issues of smoking, drinking, exercise, and diet have waxed and waned in importance or concern since the first decade of the 20th century. A progressive "clean-living movement," particularly in the United States, to clean up and eliminate the ills of society and improve health emerged. The use of tobacco, alcohol, drugs, sex outside marriage, and gluttony and sloth leading to obesity were considered immoral behaviors leading to many societal problems, so reformers attempted to ban or censure the behaviors. Out of this health and social reform movement, Prohibition, pure food and drug laws, and the banning of tobacco, and workplace safety and environmental preservations were instituted in the United States. An emphasis on exercise and fitness, sexual purity, eugenics (improvement and increased vitality of the human race), and a well-balanced diet in many Western cultures was also promoted. However, by WWII, the cycle of health and social concerns had ebbed, and smoking and prohibition laws were overturned and these issues were of little concern in many nations.

The cycle of health and social reform was on the upswing again by the 1970s in the United States. It emerged with campaigns against tobacco, alcohol and recreational drugs, lack of exercise and poor diets, and for cleaning up the environment. The roots of some of the campaigns were now grounded on more scientific evidence. By the 2010s, a decrease in life span and premature death due to smoking, obesity, poor nutrition, lack of exercise, and diabetes emerged globally and overshadowed the many advances in health and medicine that had evolved over the 20th century. Motor vehicle accidents increased while workplace hazards decreased in most nations. Concerns about environmental pollution and climate change causing global warming leading to deaths from disease and disasters increased. Although many of these behaviors, concerns, and conditions originated in higher-income nations, as developing nations adopted Western lifestyles, they were also affected by these issues.

Tobacco, Alcohol, and Other Drugs

Mental health treatment advanced since the early 20th century. Humane treatment and drugs enabled some individuals to lead near-normal lives. A major aspect of mental health is substance abuse. By 1921 in the post–World War I (WWI) era, smoking cigarettes was the most popular form of tobacco use. Smoking increased in many higher-income nations even further after WWII in the 1950s and 1960s. It had also become common in many developing nations by the end of the century—particularly, Asia. The United States' *Surgeon General's Reports on Smoking and*

Health (1964) suggested that chronic diseases such as lung and throat cancers, heart disease, COPD, and strokes were associated with smoking, and these conditions were increasing. The results of this study were accepted by other nations leading to antismoking campaigns in many countries in the late 1990s. The WHO *Framework Convention on Tobacco Control* (WHO FCTC), a 2003 global treaty against smoking, had been adopted by 168 countries by 2010 to reduce smoking. Globally, smoking had reached a peak in 2009. The primary means to control tobacco use were laws banning smoking in enclosed public places. However, the laws were not always enforced in some nations. Successful public health efforts resulted in a decrease in the prevalence of smoking among adults in many nations and a decrease in cancers beginning around 2005. A major advance over the 20th century in lifestyle choices was the recognition that using tobacco and exposure to environmental tobacco smoke were health hazards.

Due to the association of smoking with heart disease and cancer, the U.S. Department of Defense issued posters like this one that promoted smoking cessation, 1988–2000. This and other successful public health campaigns reduced smoking and smoking-related diseases worldwide. (U.S. Department of Defense)

Drinking alcohol in various forms such as wine and beer for centuries has been acceptable in most cultures. On the other hand, its harmful effects when overconsumed have also been observed. Due to conflicting opinions as to whether or not people should drink, only a few advances in reducing harm from alcohol abuse have been seen since 1900. To prevent health, social, and economic problems, some nations have attempted to prohibit all alcoholic beverages. In the United States, for instance, drinking was condemned by reformers in the early 20th century, which led to national Prohibition; however, most other nations did not follow suit as drinking was more culturally ingrained and considered part of the diet. Prohibition in the United States was soon repealed as being unworkable. In 1935, Alcoholic Anonymous (AA) was founded in the United States to help alcoholics recover, and the AA fellowship soon spread globally, which over the years has helped millions of members.

Beginning in the 1970s, damage to the fetus among pregnant women who frequently abused alcohol, called the fetal alcohol syndrome (FAS), was "discovered." This was despite the fact that the syndrome had been described for centuries among the children of heavily drinking women. By the 1990s, FAS had been transformed into a major public health campaign in the United States. However, a small amount of alcohol consumed during pregnancy causing harm was rejected by other studies and nations and still remains a contentious issue. Likewise, in 2018, a study reported that even low-alcohol intake by adults could pose health problems. The results of this study have also remained contentious as other research has shown decreases in heart disease and other chronic conditions from consuming small amounts of alcohol.

On the other hand, alcohol abuse disorder and excessive consumption is seen as a global health issue.

> The harmful use of alcohol is a worldwide problem resulting in millions of deaths, including hundreds of thousands of young lives lost. It is not only a causal factor in many diseases, but also a precursor to injury and violence. Furthermore, its negative impacts can spread throughout a community or a country, and beyond, by influencing levels and patterns of alcohol consumption across borders. (WHO, v, 2011)

In 2011, the WHO World Health Assembly resolution urged countries to plan various programs and public polices to reduce harm from alcohol abuse. By this date, the heaviest drinking nations were found in Eastern Europe and Russia.

Other psychoactive drugs have also produced waves of addiction or concern about addictive disorders. In the early 20th century, opiates and cocaine were prevalent in patent medicine. They were also used in raw form among "night people" in some Western cultures. National and international laws were passed against these and other recreational drugs. In post-WWII Japan, an epidemic of amphetamines abuse rose and fell. Western cultures were plagued by tranquilizer abuse in the 1960s and 1970s. Concern about possible permanent damage to infants from pregnant women using crack cocaine arose in the 1990s, but the extreme harm was found to be rare. In the 2000s, synthetic drugs such as methamphetamine plagued Western nations, in particular the United States in rural areas, as did increased deaths from opiates in the mid- and late 2010s. Countermeasures against recreational drug use included making them illegal and arresting and imprisoning sellers and users; these were not successful. Some European nations and Canada found that harm-reduction techniques such as allowing drug-dependent people to use drugs in a controlled environment with needle exchanges, offering housing, methadone maintenance for opiate users, or decriminalizing the drug reduced not only drug use but also death from drug overdose. On the whole, few advances in terms of prevention or treatment of drug abuse have been found.

Diet and Obesity

In the post-WWII years, vast changes in the diet of higher-income nations emerged that slowly spread around the world. In the 21st century, these dietary changes were found in most urban areas. They included an increase in the consumption of refined sugar and flour, more red meat consumption—particularly in North America and Europe—and the emergence of inexpensive fast food restaurants that primarily served meals high in fat and sugar. This trend resulted from the industrialization of agriculture and mass production of highly processed cheap foodstuff. Although these developments were initially thought to be a major advance for global food supply and health, by 2000 they were seen to have negative impacts on health including obesity, which is associated with heart disease, stroke, high blood pressure, diabetes, and some cancers.

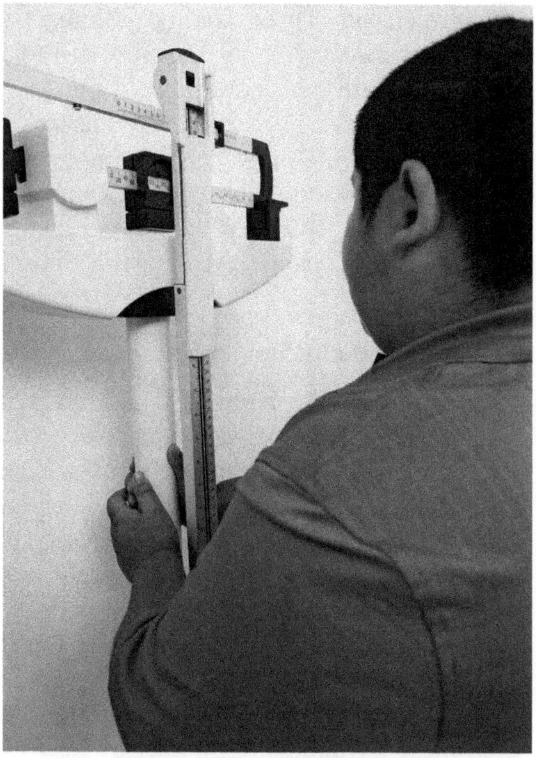

Childhood obesity increased globally beginning in the late 1900s. To determine obesity in children their weight is compared to height, which gives a body mass index (BMI). A BMI over 25 is considered overweight, and a BMI of 30 and above is classified as obese. (Photographerlondon/Dreamstime.com)

The obesity rate, which has continued to increase worldwide, was also associated with less physical activity as more people used motorized vehicles and mass transit and had a more sedentary work and recreational lifestyle. Although childhood obesity was higher in North America, Europe, and higher-income Asian nations, it also increased in lower-income nations as people moved from rural to urban areas and changed diet. Concern about the lack of physical activity in many developed nations by the 1970s resulted in the promotion of fitness programs by various governmental and NGO health-promotion organizations. Increased physical activity has primarily been embraced by higher socioeconomic status (SES) groups. On the other hand, smoking and poor nutrition tended into the 2010s to be found among lower SES groups.

Family Planning and Reproductive Technology

Access to family planning and contraceptive services altered social and economic roles of women globally. In North America and the UK, in particular, in the 1910s, agitation for women's right to vote and also to receive information and methods to control fertility arose. Family planning into the 21st century globally has provided health and economic benefits such as smaller family size and longer intervals between the births of children. It has also contributed to fewer infant, child, and maternal deaths. Barrier methods of contraceptives to prevent pregnancy and the transmission of HIV/AIDS and other STDs have been particularly effective globally, especially in developing nations. Reproductive technology such as the invention of the birth control pill to prevent pregnancies in the 1960s or methods to help with infertility such as in vitro fertilization by the 1980s aided family life. However, family planning like vaccinations and other sexual issues sometimes ran into resistance from religious or philosophical beliefs that in some cases prevented desired health care. Family planning and reproductive technology were important factors in the advancement of women, women's health and the improvement of maternal health worldwide since the early 20th century.

Safety and the Environment

As nations increased the use of motor vehicles and developed better highway systems, engineering advances made improvements in motor vehicle and highway safety. A decrease in driving-related accidents and fatalities in the late 20th century was because of improved roads, safer cars, and airbags. Improved safety also resulted from successful efforts to change personal behaviors such as increased use of safety belts, child safety seats, and educational efforts that decreased impaired driving. All these health promotion efforts contributed to a large reduction in motor vehicle related deaths in the 1980s and 1990s. In 2001, the WHO launched a five-year plan to improve global road safety. From 2001 to 2009, the number of annual traffic-related fatalities in the European Union declined. However, these advances were offset by new technology when inexpensive mobile phones and computers in vehicles began to be commonly used by the early 2010s. Accident rates increased worldwide because of distracted driving by people texting, talking on mobile phones, or using a navigation system. About 90 percent of global traffic fatalities occurred in low-and middle-income countries, while these nations only had less than half of the world's vehicles. Due to these increases in accidents, a number of nations started to take action to stop distracted driving. Measures included laws banning phone use while driving and public education and awareness campaigns about the dangers of this behavior.

In addition to the decrease in road accidents, workplace health problems and mishaps globally have also decreased since the 20th century. Deadly work-related illnesses such as black lung and silicosis, which were common at the beginning of the century, were reduced by the late 20th century. Severe injuries and deaths related to agriculture, mining, manufacturing, construction, and transportation also decreased through education and legislation that required safer workplaces.

Environmental issues such as water, air, and soil pollution became a concern by the late 20th century. Air pollution, in particular, appeared to cause an increase in global temperature due to greenhouse gasses. The global temperature surge led to a rise in ocean water level, record flooding, heat, fires, and fierce storms. It also caused tropical disease insect vectors to migrate into formerly cooler areas. Most large developed and developing nations were attempting to reduce pollution and conditions that contributed to global warming by 2010. Although there have been some setbacks, beginning in the late 20th century, on the whole, more advances in worldwide health, public health, and medicine have occurred compared to any other time in history.

2

Education and Training

During the early 20th century, conflicts developed between the orthodox, scientifically based and the unorthodox, traditional medical practices in some Western nations. The American Flexner Report profoundly changed medical education in most English-speaking nations and brought medical training and licensing under the control of the mainstream medical establishment. In light of this report, dentistry and nursing education also advanced. By 2000, orthodox medical education had integrated the humanities into its strictly biomedical curriculum, and Western alternative medical systems had integrated biosciences into their curriculum. Non-Western medical traditions were still used by indigenous peoples around the world into the 21st century although most had adopted Western medicine. Some of the old healing traditions entered Western medical practices as complementary medicine. The Internet changed the way people learned about disease, and medical tourism became rampant by 2000.

CONFLICTS BETWEEN MEDICAL SYSTEMS AND THE FLEXNER REPORT (1910)

In the early 20th century in North America, a struggle for control over medicine emerged between orthodox, or "regular," physicians who believed in a biomedical approach to treatment, and "irregular" physicians who considered medicine a healing art. These latter practitioners included osteopathic, chiropractic, homoeopathic, and eclectic schools of thought. However, these methods generally had little scientific basis. Both osteopathic and chiropractic systems had been developed in the United States in the 19th century. Homeopathic medicine was European based, and the American medical establishment considered them all quackery.

At the turn of the 20th century, many medical schools were proprietary colleges that operated primarily for profit and had poor medical training. Due to concern over the poor quality of medical education and as a way to gain control over all medical education and treatment, the American Medical Association

(AMA) in 1904 established a Council on Medical Education to rate medical schools. By that year, the number of medical schools had reached 166.

This concern over quality education prompted the Carnegie Foundation for the Advancement of Teaching in 1908 to commission American educator Abraham Flexner (1866–1959) to conduct an independent study of all North American medical schools. Flexner's 1910 report, *Medical Education in the United States and Canada*, revealed the discrepancies between academic catalogue descriptions of courses and clinical experiences and the realities of medical training in schools throughout North America. Flexner was most impressed with Johns Hopkins University, whose curriculum was based upon biomedical science and similar to German medical schools known for their rigorous scientific base. Based upon his study, Flexner recommended fewer and better schools, the placement of medical education within universities, higher standards of admissions to medical schools including at least two years of biosciences, and a two-phase curriculum of medical education consisting of medical science courses followed by clinical training in hospital-based academic departments for four years of medical school.

Based on studies of the physician-to-population ratio in Germany, Flexner recommended that the existing North American medical schools should be reduced. The guiding philosophy was to produce fewer but better doctors and that philosophy is still found in most English-speaking nations today.

Another important factor in the support of mainstream medicine was the evolution of statistics during the first two decades of the century. This development was fostered by such figures as British mathematician Karl Pearson (1857–1936), the founder of biometry. His techniques, which are widely used today, include the chi-squared test and correlation and regression coefficients. This advancement in statistical procedures enabled clinical trials with experimental and control groups to see if a treatment or practice was effective based upon statistics. This was in opposition to healers who believed that a treatment was successful based upon tradition. By 2010, "evidence-based" practices and treatment were the norm in many nations for a variety of fields.

The Flexner Report ultimately upgraded the standard of medical education and allowed for the control of medicine in North America by orthodox physicians in conjunction with state medical societies and the American and Canadian Medical Associations.

MEDICAL TRAINING IN NORTH AMERICA

After the Flexner Report, medical schools in the United States and Canada established a standard four-year curriculum that consisted of two years of classroom bioscience education, followed by two years of clinical experience for an MD degree. Training after World War I generally required three to four years of undergraduate studies preferably in the sciences and an internship after medical school to practice medicine. To be admitted to medical school in the post WWII years, besides having an undergraduate degree, one had to pass an entrance test,

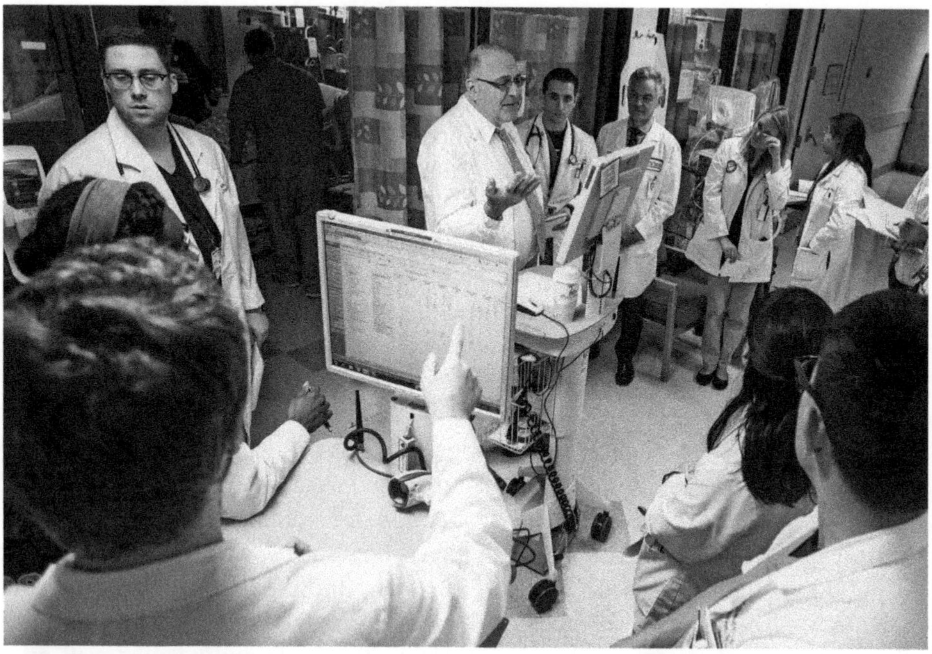

A physician educator discusses patient care with medical students and resident physicians during morning rounds at a Norfolk, Virginia, hospital in 2014. Hospital morning rounds became standard practice for all medical education institutions in North America in 2010. (Jay Westcott/For The Washington Post via Getty Images)

the MCAT; write an essay on why the person wanted to be a physician; be interviewed; and submit recommendations. However, admittance was, and is still, highly competitive. By the late 20th century it had become increasingly common for physicians to specialize. Few established practices after just an internship year. Residency programs ranged from three to seven years depending upon the specialty.

In 1959, the *Bane Report*, sponsored by the Office of the Surgeon General, concluded that there was an impending physician shortage. As a result of this report, the number of physicians trained doubled during 1965—1980; it has remained about the same since that time. However, Canada and the United States increasingly imported International Medical Graduates (IMG) to make up for an inadequate supply of physicians as the population increased in North America. By 2016, IMGs were about 23 percent of all physicians in North America—most were from Indian and Caribbean schools. Many graduates from Caribbean schools were North Americans who could not find admittance in their home nations because of the difficulty of getting into medical school.

Up to 1972 few women were admitted to medical schools until the United States federal government's Title IX law was passed that stipulated equal opportunity in education. By 2017 in the United States, 51 percent of medical students were women, and in Canada women outnumber men at most medical schools.

EDUCATIONAL REFORMS AND THE HUMANIZATION OF MEDICINE

In the late 20th century, a backlash against Flexner and the rigid medical education system that had been in place for decades emerged in nations following the North American and British systems. This led to the humanization of medicine and advances in the educational curricula where a patient was seen as a whole person rather than a disease. In Western nations, physicians have traditionally been taught that interactions with patients should be strictly objective and detached. This view began to be challenged especially in North America and the UK—initially by medical students—and a new model emerged. Engagement with patients, both emotional and intellectual, was valued and encouraged. It was realized that understanding the context in which illness occurs and the meaning of sickness in the person's life as an individual and as a member of a family and community were necessary for accurate diagnosis and successful treatment.

This new awareness resulted in changes in the medical curricula. In North America, "medical humanities," or compassionate care, was introduced by the late 1990s in medical schools to provide insight into the human condition. This included learning about interpersonal relationships, poverty, social concerns, different cultural groups, and seeing patients as people and not just sick body parts.

Humanistic medicine was an interdisciplinary field of the humanities, social sciences, and the arts and their application to medical education and practice. The humanities and social sciences helped medical professionals to understand how bioscience and medicine took place within cultural and social contexts and how culture interacted with the individual experience of illness and the way medicine is practiced. Literature and the arts helped to develop and nurture skills of observation, analysis, empathy, and self-reflection. In 1994, the New York University School of Medicine established *The Literature, Arts, and Medicine Database*, which contained various reviews of the visual, literary, and performing arts as an important source to aid in humanizing medical professionals. By 2000, medical-related literature had entered community hospitals through reading and discussion programs for hospital staff (see chapter 13 for literature and the arts concerning medical professionals and patients).

In addition, by 2000, profound advances in communication and educational technology precipitated further reforms in medical education. In 2010, 100 years after the Flexner Report was published, the Carnegie Foundation for the Advancement of Teaching in the United States again issued a report—sometimes called the "Second Flexnerian Report"—for further reform of medical schools and residency training. These included standardizing learning outcomes and individualizing the learning process such as promoting different forms of integration and collaborative learning; incorporating habits of inquiry and improvement; and strengthening the identity formation of the physician as a professional.

To meet these goals, the report called for medical educators and education systems to develop objectively measurable performance standards for learners at all levels. In addition, these standards needed to be met before the student completed the formal educational programs, which were recommended to be a competency-based advancement system rather than a time-based one where students passed from one year to the next. These recommendations are being instituted.

MEDICAL TRAINING IN THE BRITISH AND EUROPEAN TRADITIONS

Worldwide in most nations, other than the United States and Canada, students studying medicine enter medical training after secondary school. In the UK, and the many nations around the world that follow the British tradition, medical education is organized generally as a 6-year undergraduate program plus a year or two of clinical rotation. The student is awarded an MBBS degree, which is the first professional degree. However, it usually takes 3 to 7 more years to become a specialist or General Practitioner (GP). The right to the use of the title "Doctor" is conferred on medical graduates only when they are registered by their professional organization. In the British tradition, after students complete graduate education as a specialist or earning a PhD, many revert to "Mr.," "Ms.," "Mrs." Additionally, continuing education is mandatory for all physicians in the UK.

The British system is found in many nations worldwide. These include Asian and Southeast Asian nations such as China, Indonesia, and Singapore; South Asian nations such as India and Bangladesh; and a few Caribbean islands such as Jamaica. It is also found in African nations including Ghana, South Africa, and Zambia and Middle Eastern countries including Egypt, Saudi Arabia, and United Arab Emirates.

In the early 20th century, Britain also began to focus upon biomedical sciences followed by clinical experience based upon the Flexner Report. However, there was no standardization of training until the *Report of the Inter-Departmental Committee of Medical School* (1944). The report recommended that medical schools be based in universities and that teaching hospitals have academic departments of the medical specialties. These recommendations were slowly instituted.

In the UK from the 1950s to the 1990s, medical schools began integrating humanistic education, particularly in the GP curricula, along with a focus on the doctor-patient relationships. A more holistic model of care was advocated as the core of medical education and practice. But the dehumanization of patients was still seen as problematic in the UK by 2010. A study called the *Francis Report,* conducted between 2005 and 2009 in a National Health Service region, found that patients were still often treated as numbers. More patient-centered curriculum was advocated. However, as found in other nations, in view of rapidly advancing medical technology, contentious debates emerged about what classic core courses should be eliminated and what new courses should replace them to address all these new needs and trends in the medical curricula.

In Australia and New Zealand, six years of schooling had been the norm since Flexner's days. Postgraduate study to become a general practitioner or specialist was three to five additional years. However, in 1973, the *Report of the Committee on Medical Schools to the Australian Universities Commission* led to many reforms in medical training. More medical schools and rural clinic schools were created because of the need for additional doctors. It was also found that the apprenticeship as junior doctors in various clinic settings around the nation led to fragmented skills. In the 1990s, the North American system of having an undergraduate education was introduced in some schools resulting in several ways to enter medical schools. A continuing education program was mandated for all doctors in 2009. By 2010, a standardized Australian curriculum for junior doctors was developed for all medical schools. In addition a shift away from knowledge-based examinations at the end of training to continuous workplace assessment of performance was implemented as also recommended by the American "Second Flexnerian" report in 2010. New Zealand followed a similar course as Australia. The humanistic aspect of medicine was introduced around the late 1980s.

In contrast, India, firmly based in the British medical system, has struggled to achieve adequate medical education. Exams in India are based on memorization rather than knowledge and would-be physicians are not evaluated for clinical skills until they start practicing. A change in the law in the 1990s made it easy to open private schools resulting in the emergence of many new medical training institutions to serve rural areas. However, this allowed anyone who had money to enter these private schools even if they did not have the qualifications to become doctors. In some cases, individuals were granted degrees without much education. Moreover, many new physicians went abroad rather than going to rural areas. Since the late 20th century, India has been a great exporter of physicians to North America and the UK. In these and other Western nations, they generally have to pass exams and serve several years in a residency program to receive a license to practice medicine. Some Indian physicians have returned to India after advance education in North America or other European nations to staff large centers often for medical tourists.

On the Continent in France, Germany, Italy, for example, and most Central and South American nations, medical schooling generally begins after secondary school and is generally six years in length. Some nations require a year of medical sciences post secondary school. As in other countries, to become a specialist, a number of additional years of education and clinical experience are required. Western medicine by the mid-20th century was based on scientific research, and by 2000, most countries had subscribed to the World Federation for Medical Education (WFME) standards.

The WFME was founded in 1972 to improve the quality of basic, postgraduate, and continuing education knowledge and skills globally. The guidelines for these standards were developed between 1997 and 2003. Various nations were given authority to accredit schools in a region. For example, the Australian Medical Council (AMC) now accredits medical schools not only in Australia but also in the Western Pacific region including New Zealand and China. By 2000, China used Australia as a benchmark for its medical reforms and based their accreditation system on the AMC policies and procedures.

DENTISTRY AND NURSING EDUCATION

Besides the education of physicians, the education of dentists, nurses, and other health professionals greatly advanced from 1900. They followed the trends of medical education for further training, licensing, and continuing education.

Dentistry Education

By the turn of the 20th century in the United States, dental licensure requirements were adopted by all states. Dentistry focused on infections, extractions, and restorations. However, some of the freestanding for-profit schools did not provide adequate education. After the Flexner Report, dental schools sought affiliation with a major research university. In addition, the prerequisite for dental-school admission was graduation from secondary school. By 1917, a three-year dental curriculum was advocated. During 1933–1934, the first written National Dental Board Exam was introduced for candidates to be licensed to practice dentistry.

In the 1940s, four years of undergraduate work with a focus on sciences was required for admittance, and by the 1950s, dental education was increased to four years. In that decade, specialization in fields such as orthodontics and oral surgery developed with additional education. Dentists were now encouraged to save teeth and not extract them and to encourage prevention of tooth decay and periodontal diseases. In the 1950s, fluoridation of the water helped to reduce tooth decay. By the 1970s, continuing education courses were required to maintain a license, but this varied by state. In the 1990s, cosmetic dentistry evolved to make teeth more attractive, and by 2010, these procedures had become less inexpensive.

In Europe, formal dental education was diverse. Some nations by the late 1930s had adopted the North American model with separate dental schools, while in other countries dental education was placed within a medical school, and graduates received both a medical and dentistry degree. When the European Economic Community was formed in 1993, which included the UK, standardization of education and competences were needed for health professionals to have freedom of movement around the European Union (EU). Dental school was generally five years of post-secondary education and additional years for specialization. By the late 1990s, most countries had adopted the separated dental school model associated with a university, but problems still existed in the mid-2010s with curricula. Britain voted to leave EU in 2016, and ramifications of this move are still in development.

A similar process of dental education is found in British-based systems around the world. As an example, in Australia, a Bachelor of Dental Surgery (BDS) is a five-year post-secondary education course of study. However, after completing a bachelor degree in a related field, students may be admitted for a postgraduate degree in advanced fields. As with medicine, standardized exams for licensing and continued education is required.

Nursing Education

In 1900, "nurses training" schools were hospital based and run by physicians and the hospital. While in these hospital diploma programs, students carried out the majority of patient care and received only a little classroom education. Programs were not standardized and ranged from six months to two years in length. Each hospital sets its own curriculum and requirements, and training was essentially an apprentice program. After graduation, the majority of these "diploma" or "trained" nurses worked as private duty or "visiting" nurses in North America and "district nurses" in the United Kingdom and Europe. They aided new mothers and babies and cared for the sick in the home. Nursing associations in both Canada and the United States were created to attain nurse registration in each state and province and reform education. By 1921, laws had been enacted in all states to provide licensure as a "registered nurse" (RN) and in 1924 to all provinces in Canada. However, mandatory licensing laws with state or provincial examinations were not passed until the late 1940s.

In 1943, during WWII, due to a shortage of nurses, the Bolton Act—Nurses Training Act—was passed by the U.S. Congress. All ethnic groups were enrolled in this Cadet Nurse Corps program which lasted from 1943 to 1948. It had an accelerated curriculum and was required to provide students with clinical experiences in medical, surgical, obstetric, and pediatric nursing. In its wake, the Carnegie Foundations studied nursing education and published the *Brown Report* (1948). Like previous reports, it recommended that nursing schools be in academic settings rather than hospitals. However, hospital-based diploma programs continued, and these nurses increasingly worked in hospitals as staff nurses. Some worked in physicians' offices, schools, industries, or as public health nurses.

Due to a further shortage of nurses, in 1952, a two-year associate degree nursing (ADN) program was first implemented. The curriculum was composed of half nursing and half general-education classes that included biosciences such as anatomy and physiology, microbiology, nutrition, and pharmacology. Clinical practice was at different hospitals in the community to gain a wide variety of experiences. The nursing faculty was employed by the college rather than a hospital. All graduates were required to take and pass state nursing-licensing exams. This program created "technical nurses" who were proficient at delivering care.

Between 1960 and 1975, the old hospital diploma programs rapidly declined and were replaced by the ADN programs at two-year junior or community colleges; men also were admitted to these programs. Many states also implemented continuing education courses as a requirement to maintain a license to practice nursing. By 1960, approximately 172 four-year college-based nursing education programs awarded Bachelors of Science in Nursing (BSN) degrees of three to four years for "professional nurses" who had more education in clinical judgment skills. By the end of the 1970s, the number of graduates of ADN programs exceeded that of BSN and diploma programs.

In the 1970s, graduate programs offering a master's degree in nursing (MSN) emerged. These programs trained "nurse practitioners" or "advanced practice nurses" where students received education and clinical experience in various fields, in particular, primary care. These nurse practitioners were found to deliver more efficient, less costly, and safer health care services. By the late 1990s, there was a growing focus on evidence-based nursing practice. By 2010, more BSN graduates were entering master's programs. Some were earning doctoral degrees for teaching, research, hospital administration, and other positions as the need for higher education in nursing was growing. In 2010, the Institute of Medicine issued a landmark report called *The Future of Nursing.* Based upon extensive research in patient care and safety, it recommended that all nurses attain higher levels of education and that 80 percent of the nursing workforce hold a BSN degree by 2020.

The UK and nations following the British health care traditions had a path similar to North America from 1900 through the 2010s. Nursing education with hospital-based training was generally replaced by education in colleges in the post-WWII era. By the late 20th century, two paths for registered nurses existed—a two- to three-year diploma and a three- to four-year baccalaureate nursing degree. In the UK, the University of Edinburgh, in the 1960s, offered the first baccalaureate degree in nursing.

However, unlike most of North America, midwives in the British system had been able to practice on their own without supervision of a physician. In 1902, in the UK, for example, the Midwives Registration Act established the state regulation of midwives. World War I provided the final impetus for the establishment of nursing regulation for all nurses and midwives in 1919. This General Nursing Council survived intact until the legislative changes in 1979 created what was to become the National Boards of Nursing.

In 1983, to monitor the quality of nursing and midwifery education, a new regulatory body, the United Kingdom Central Council for Nursing, Midwifery and Health Visiting (UKCC), was formed, and in the 1990s, post-registration education was mandated. By 2001, nearly half of the newly registered nurses were immigrants, especially from Australia, India, Nigeria, Philippines, and South Africa with similar nurse education systems as the UK. In EU countries, the nursing course is three years with practical training in different hospital settings. The bachelor's, master's, and doctoral degrees in nursing are found in 60 percent of EU countries.

TRAINING IN WESTERN ALTERNATIVE MEDICINE

Several alternative medical systems had developed in North America, Germany, and other Western nations by the early 20th century. Some became accepted by, or even integrated, into mainstream orthodox medicine by the late 20th century. However, many of them in the early 20th century were considered quackery, particularly in North America.

In 1900, osteopathic medical training, for example, had minimal biomedical science courses and focused on manual manipulation of the spine for healing. The philosophy of osteopathy at this point in time suggested that disease was caused by malfunction of the body's muscular, skeletal, and nervous systems and that manual manipulation could help the body heal itself. Orthodox physicians (MDs) considered this system pseudoscience as it had little scientific support. Graduates of this program received a Doctor of Osteopathic Medicine (DO) degree.

In light of the Flexner Report, to be accredited, some osteopathic institutions fought to continue their traditional focus but incorporated a biomedical base into their educational curriculum. After 1915, the training programs were increased to four years, and osteopaths increasingly received accreditation in North American states and provinces acting as general practice or primary-care physicians. During World War II, when many MDs were serving in the military, DOs began to treat their patients. Because regular medical hospitals would not grant osteopaths staff privileges, they established their own hospitals.

Therefore, in 1967, the American Osteopathic Association (AOA) was recognized by the Council for Education Accreditation as the accrediting agency for osteopathic medical education. During the last two decades of the 20th century, the training of MDs and DOs became almost identical in North America. Most DOs acted as primary-care physicians, and very few practiced manipulation of the spine. In 2015, all DO and MD programs became accredited by the Accreditation Council for Graduate Medical Education. Thus any legal or licensing distinction between the two systems was eliminated, and they are now considered equivalent degrees. Some DOs go into specialties, but many still specialize in general and family medicine. About 8 percent of all physicians in North America are osteopathic physicians, and it is no longer considered an alternative medical system.

In the UK and nations that follow British health care system, a person with a DO from an accredited American school is accepted as equivalent to the MBBS (equivalent to an MD). However, osteopathic training in some nations, including the UK, may not be seen as equivalent. In Germany, osteopathic medicine, for example, is an additional qualification after the completion of medical school and specialty training.

Another Western system is chiropractic care. It is a learned alternative system and used most often to treat neuro-muscular-skeletal complaints such as pain in the back and neck. Early chiropractors believed that all disease was caused by interruptions in the flow of "innate intelligence," or a vital energy or life force similar to eastern medical philosophies (qi). Proponents claimed that mechanical disorders of the spine affect general health via the nervous system, but there is no scientific evidence for these claims. Some studies by 2000, on the other hand, have found that chiropractic manipulation may be effective for chronic lower back pain.

From 1900 to the late 20th century, chiropractic medicine was considered quackery by the American Medical Association (AMA), which for decades continuously fought against the practice. This resulted in chiropractors having problems getting state accreditation.

In the early years, the education of chiropractors was limited. After the Flexner Report, some schools offered a 12-month course with anatomy, physiology, and other sciences.

In the first 30 years of the 20th century, chiropractors were even arrested for practicing medicine without a license in the United States. By the 1930s, chiropractic medicine was the largest alternative healing profession in the United States. It was often used by poorer people who could not afford regular medical care. In its continuing attack on chiropractors, the AMA in 1966 called the practice an "unscientific cult," and it was not until 1974 that the profession was legal in all 50 states. In 1987, the AMA was barred by law from public criticism of chiropractic treatment.

By the 1990s, prerequisites for admission into a chiropractic program included at least three years of undergraduate education in life, physical, and social sciences along with humanities. To become a Doctor of Chiropractic medicine (DC), four years of studies were required at an accredited college. As with regular medical practitioners, students needed to pass national board exams before obtaining a license to practice, along with annual continuing education. By 2000, chiropractic had become accepted—along with other modalities such as therapeutic massage, exercise, and rehabilitation and sports medicine—by many MDs as part of the health care system in North America. Chiropractic was also well established in Australia. In other nations such as Belgium, Denmark, Finland, Sweden and the United Kingdom, chiropractors practice by specific legislation.

Another alternative system is homeopathy, which has been popular among European royalty for decades. It was developed in Germany, and its philosophy is "the law of similar" and "like cures like," along with dilution of a medicine to increase potency. The belief is that extreme dilutions of a substance that causes symptoms similar to the disease will cure it. However, numerous research studies have shown that homeopathic preparations tend not to be effective for treating illnesses. By the late 20th century, the UK and Commonwealth nations announced a policy of not funding homeopathic medicine because it was "a misuse of resources." However, homeopathic medicine was still practiced in Europe, and it was popular in Asia, especially India, Pakistan, and Sri Lanka. In the United States in 2015, the FDA allowed homeopathic medicines to be sold as over-the-counter preparations. Training to be a homeopath is varied and ranges from coursework or several years of education along with credentialing and is a major aspect of naturopathic practice.

Naturopathic medicine is an eclectic alternative medical system. Licensed naturopathic physicians (NDs) attend a four-year graduate-level naturopathic medical school and are educated in the same basic sciences as an MD. In addition, they have courses in homeopathic medicine, nutrition, and mind and body movement practices from diverse healing systems such as Chinese herbal and acupuncture techniques. Some individuals claiming to be naturopaths are self-taught and are not licensed. Most European countries, in particular Germany, consider naturopathic medicine as a system of health care. In North America, most schools of naturopathic medicine are accredited; however, not all states and provinces recognize NDs as part of health care.

Nonlearned treatment in Western nations include "home doctoring" based upon folk medicine, over-the-counter treatment often fostered by media advertisements, and nonaccredited nutritional or exercise consultants. Folk medicine is practiced by most individuals around the world. It includes various family remedies passed down from one generation to the next. These include treatments such as hot tea with honey and lemon for colds, herbs and botanicals collected to treat various conditions, or even placing mud on an insect bite. A wide variety of practitioners offering nutritional or exercise advice have little formal education, or even apprenticeships, and are often self-taught. These have led to misdiagnosis, nonreferral to regular medical practices, and harm to the patient. On the other hand, complementary treatment practices by licensed nonmainstream physicians such as osteopathic, chiropractic and naturopathic doctors increasingly became integrated into Western medicine by the late 20th century.

TRAINING IN NON-WESTERN TRADITIONAL MEDICINE

Although Western medicine and medical training is found in most nations today, many non-Western populations still rely on traditional healing for much of their populace. Several medical systems including Chinese, Ayurveda, and Unani are grounded in text-based classical knowledge, literature, and apprenticeships. Students learn this material under a master or teacher often in a school, and the training is usually considered an academic discipline within the culture. A commonality in most non-Western traditional systems of healing is the belief that illness is caused by an imbalance of life forces. Treatment techniques are designed to bring these forces back into balance. In 2009, United Nations' resolution WHA62.13 urged member states to consider, where appropriate, inclusion of traditional medicine in their national health systems and to establish systems for the qualification, accreditation, or licensing of practitioners of traditional medicine.

Traditional Chinese medicine (TCM) is the largest non-Western learned medical system. It originated in ancient China and has evolved over thousands of years. TCM practitioners use herbal medicines and various mind and body practices, such as acupuncture and tai chi, along with dietary therapy, coordinated breathing, and therapeutic massage to treat or prevent health problems. Similar systems of medicine also exist in other Eastern and South Asian countries, including Japan and Korea. These systems have been influenced by TCM, but each has developed its own distinctive features. In Western nations, TCM is used as a complementary treatment.

The basic philosophy of the eastern systems is as follows:

- The human body is a miniature version of the larger, surrounding universe.
- Harmony between two opposing yet complementary forces, called *yin* and *yang*, supports health, and disease results from an imbalance between these forces.
- Five elements—fire, earth, wood, metal, and water—symbolically represent all phenomena, including the stages of human life, and explain the functioning of the body and how it changes during disease.
- Qi, a vital energy that flows through the body, performs multiple functions in maintaining health (National Center for Complementary and Integrative Health, 2017).

In China in the late 1960s, because of a lack of medical personnel who wished to work in rural areas, peasant farmers were trained as "barefoot doctors" (they generally went barefoot) to treat common medical conditions and worked in rural villages. They were graduates of secondary school and received about six months of paramedical training and promoted basic hygiene, preventative health care, and family planning and treated common illnesses. Their training included both Western and Chinese medicine.

In 1982, the Chinese government promoted the integration of traditional and Western medicine in Article 21 of the Constitution of the People's Republic of China. It required examinations and allowed individuals who studied under the former apprenticeship system—training before the 1960s when formal examinations were not required—to take required examinations leading to qualification as a traditional medical physician. Today a physician of TCM generally needs to complete five years of study after secondary education; however, variations exist on the prerequisites and length of education in China.

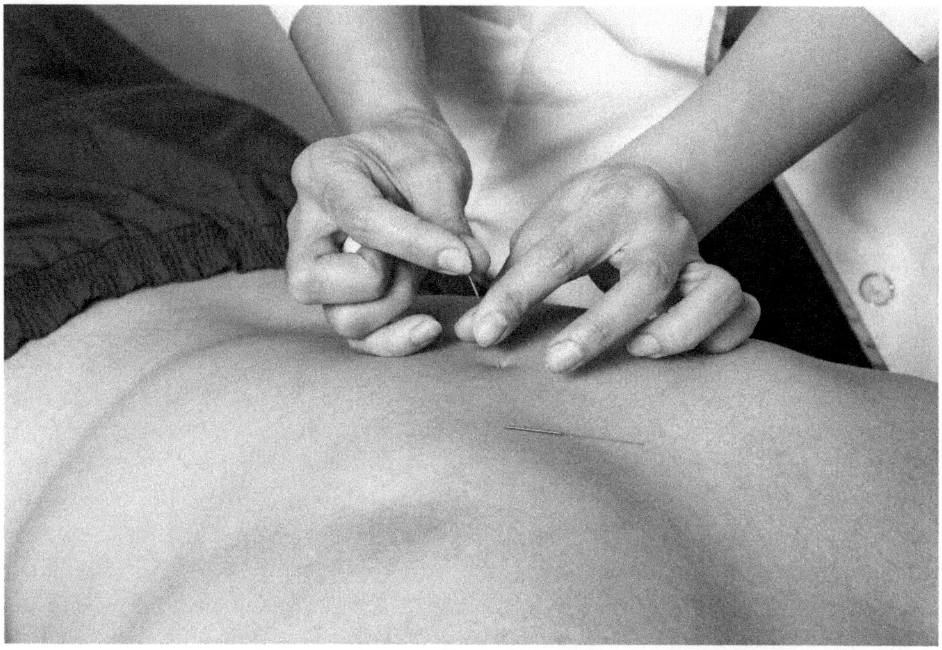

In complementary medicine, various techniques are used. One example from traditional Chinese medicine (TCM) is acupuncture, where a thin needle is inserted through the skin to stimulate specific points of the body. (Gleb Semenov/Dreamstime.com)

By the late 1990s, in North America, Europe, and other Western nations, accredited TCM training programs emerged. Most were four or five year post-secondary schools. Basic Western sciences along with eastern philosophy and treatment modalities were generally taught. Graduates usually needed to pass accreditation exams to be certified to practice. However, accreditation and practice were sometimes opposed by mainstream physicians.

Ayurvedic or Ayurveda (the "science of life") medicine is a traditional healing system native to the Indian subcontinent (see also chapter 3). Much of India's population uses Ayurvedic medicine exclusively, in particular the Hindus, or combines it with conventional Western medicine. The system promotes the use of herbal compounds, special diets, and cleansing techniques for achieving physical, mental, and spiritual health and well-being. Ayurveda emphasizes prevention, and in the Western world, it is practiced as a form of complementary and alternative medicine (CAM) where several of its methods including herbs, massage, and yoga became popular in the late 20th century. Personal hygiene is important along with tooth brushing, washing, physical exercise, and massaging the skin with oils.

Three ancient books known as the "Great Trilogy" were written in Sanskrit more than 2,000 years ago and are considered the main texts on Ayurvedic medicine: *Caraka Samhita*, *Sushruta Samhita*, and *Astanga Hridaya*. Key concepts of this system include universal interconnectedness (among people, their health, and the universe), the body's constitution *(prakriti)*, and life forces *(dosha)*. Training as an Ayurvedic physician now requires several years of formal schooling.

Students often are required to memorize classic texts along with apprenticeships with a master. In some nations, practitioners need to be licensed, and in others they do not. In 2015, the World Health Organization recommended certain criteria for certification in Ayurvedic and Unani medicine.

Unani medicine originated in Greek antiquity and became common in Islamic cultures in Arabic nations, India, and South Asia. Unani medicine teaches that disease is a natural process and that symptoms are the reactions of the body to disease. It presupposes the presence of four humors in the body, which include blood, phlegm, and yellow and black bile. If the four humors and the four temperaments (hot, cold, dry, moist) are not in a state of equilibrium, the person becomes sick.

Unani medicine has three levels of education based on prior training and clinical experience of the trainees. The Type I program is for those who have completed secondary school but have no prior health care education or experience. The Type II program is designed to enable those with prior medical or other health professional training to become qualified to practice Unani medicine in addition to their existing skills. At least a bachelor's degree in medical or other health sciences is required. The Type III is for existing practitioners who have learned Unani medicine through a recognized family tradition but who may have had little or no formal training.

Nonlearned indigenous practices, sometimes called "folk medicine," are generally passed down over generations by oral tradition and sometimes apprenticeships. The practices normally are not learned in text-based classical knowledge, but their healers may be skilled in therapies using regional medicinal plants. Traditional nonlearned healing varies from culture to culture and from region to region and is most common in Latin America, Africa, south Asia and Southeastern Asian cultures. For patients, these practitioners are less expensive than learned traditional healers such as Chinese, Ayurvedic, and Unani traditional medicine.

For example, more than 80 percent of people in rural African communities still rely on indigenous medicine as a primary source of health care. Traditional African medicines like many other indigenous systems believe humans have physical, spiritual, moral, and social aspects. When these function together harmoniously, a person will be in good health. On the other hand, when they are out of balance, a person will become physically, or even spiritually, sick. The traditional healer offers inexpensive remedies for treating common illnesses in the African regions such as malaria, stomach infections, bone fractures, and midwifery services. Training is based on the accumulated knowledge handed down by their ancestors and an apprenticeship with a respected healer.

Complementary, Alternative, and Integrative Medicine

By the mid-1970s, many non-Western, along with Western medical alternative regimes, were increasingly used in health care and defined in three different ways. "Alternative" medicine is a practice used in place of conventional medicine. "Complementary" medicine includes the use of natural products or mind and body methods along with conventional medicine. In "integrative" health care, both conventional and complementary treatment is coordinated between practitioners.

These complementary and alternative medicine (CAM) practices include food, vitamin and herbal supplements, and dietary regimes in addition to mind and body practices. Mind and body methods, for example, include meditation, progressive relaxation and hypnosis; yoga, tai chi, or qigong; and acupuncture, hydrotherapy, chiropractic manipulation, and massage therapy. Movement therapies include Feldenkrais, Alexander technique, along with Pilates and other exercises. Some of these practices require the practitioner to have a certain number of years of education and accreditation in many nations, and some do not.

CAM in the 1980s in Western cultures was mass marketed as effective "natural" treatments as opposed to science-based biomedicine, which tended to be more expensive. In addition, practitioners of these alternative treatments generally spent more time with a patient as the Western health care systems became more regulated, particularly in North America. By 2000, a more holistic approach to medicine had emerged resulting in increased acceptance of both traditional non-Western treatments and Western treatments.

By 2010, homeopathic remedies were the leading alternative treatments used in Europe. Herbal, vitamin, and mineral supplements or dietary regimes were commonly used in North America and nations that followed the traditional British medical system. Much of this change was the result of mass marketing through the media and Internet leading to self-diagnosis.

SELF-DIAGNOSIS AND NEW TECHNOLOGY

In Western cultures since the early 20th century, advertisements in newspapers and magazines for various over-the-counter nostrums have been common including such items as trusses for hernias and concoctions and cures for different conditions (see chapter 10). Advances in technology, including radio in the 1930s and television in the 1950s, contained advertisements for over-the-counter products to treat many common illnesses. This often led to self-diagnosis and self-medication. In the late 1990s, the development of the Internet—one of the greatest inventions in history for communication and information—allowed free access in most nations to information on almost any topic throughout the world. Self-diagnosis became common as it was easy for anyone to put in symptoms they were experiencing and to come up with a possible diagnosis. Along with diagnosis, treatment was often suggested, such as antihistamines for a stuffy nose or different supplements to cure a host of complaints. Many of these websites, however, were not based upon scientific evidence and are an aspect of folk medicine.

On the other hand, professional sites based upon the latest medical knowledge emerged. For example, a popular site WebMD began in 1996 and the Mayo Clinic website, which had an online presence by 2000, gave factual information based upon research. These and similar websites also provided contact information where an individual could talk to a health professional about particular symptoms or even make an appointment at the medical facility. Many sites also put out electronic newsletters or patient educational material on a variety of medical conditions.

By 2010, numerous medical-related organizations had established websites. Medical journals, some with public access, and health organizations such as the American Heart Association and professional organizations such as the American Academy of Family Physicians had a presence on the Internet. Other advancements by 2010 included "patient portals," which allowed patients to interact and communicate with their health care providers often with live video stream. Patients could also get prescriptions filled or access their laboratory and other test at clinics and hospitals on these portals. A popular use of the Internet was the rise in patient support groups by 2000. These allowed patients to exchange information about a specific disease or recovery information. Other advances in technology included the possibility of drones delivering prescription medications directly to the patient's house.

MEDICAL TOURISM

Medical, or "circumvention," tourism is not new and has been popular in many cultures for centuries. In the early 20th century, middle-class patients in Western nations with conditions including mental breakdowns, depression, alcoholism, obesity, cancer, or arthritis would go to sanitariums or spas to "take the waters" for a cure away from the area in which they lived. These cures were often based upon water therapy along with diet and exercise regimes. A number of centers existed in North America, the most famous being the Battle Creek Sanitarium. In Europe, "baths" and "spas" were even more popular. Middle-class Europeans and wealthy international patients would congregate at spas in Europe. If a person had TB, they would generally travel to sanitariums such as the ones found in the Swiss Alps, dry areas of Africa, or the Southwest United States.

By the 1960s, medical tourism generally meant traveling to another country to obtain medical treatment. International patients were generally wealthy individuals who traveled from less-developed countries to major medical centers in highly developed nations for complex treatments and surgery unavailable at home. However, by the late 20th century, those from developed countries began to travel to less developed countries for lower-priced medical treatments, shorter waiting time for some elective procedures, or medical services unavailable at home.

Medical tourism often supplied treatments that were illegal or not approved in the home country. For example, before abortion was legal in the United States in 1973, middle-class women would travel to Mexico for abortions, and the rich would often travel to the UK or Japan. By the turn of the 21st century, travelers were going to some nations for fertility treatments, organ transplants, cosmetic and dental surgery, sex-change operations, or doctor-assisted suicide. Poland and Ireland still had severely restrictive abortion laws and tourism from these nations to the UK and other European nations was common.

To assure good medical care and to attract medical tourists, the Joint Commission International (JCI) was established in 1951. Its mission was to improve patient safety and quality of health care in the international community by offering education, publications, advisory services, and international accreditation and certification in more than 100 countries. This not-for-profit organization now accredits hospitals in Asia, Europe, the Middle East, Africa, and South America.

Major nations for medical tourism by 2010 included Canada, Costa Rica, Ecuador, India, Israel, Hong Kong, Mexico, South Korea, Singapore, Taiwan, Thailand, Turkey, and the United States. To help potential medical tourists find hospitals and clinics in other nations, health tourism providers emerged. In some cases, health personnel in developing nations have received postgraduate specialty training in North America or Europe and had gone back to their home country to open clinics to treat international patients.

In summary, the American Flexner Report profoundly changed education for health care professionals in North America in the early 20th century and in most nations that followed the British medical educational systems. Non-Western medical traditions, some learned and some nonlearned, were still used by indigenous peoples around the world into the 21st century although most had adopted Western medicine. A few of the traditional practices were integrated into Western medicine and new educational reforms in the training of health professionals emerged.

3

Religion and Medicine

Religious beliefs have played an important role in how individuals, cultures, and governments have responded to the medical advances of the 20th century and early 21st century. Since 1900, developments in medicine such as vaccinations, contraception, blood and organ transplantations, pregnancy termination, and reproduction technology have often conflicted with, or have been rejected by, various religious traditions. The questions some religious groups have posed concerning medical advancement have been "When does life begin and when does it end?" and "Is medical science playing God?" Some religions were concerned that health and medical developments were a threat to the moral order of society. Moreover, religious traditions and cultural values are often interlinked with each other along with health beliefs. From 1900, some activities and medical procedures became accepted by the majority of a culture, while others based upon religious beliefs were not.

Different faiths, or sects, within a major religious tradition often have different views of health care and medicine. In addition, "official" religious doctrines are not necessarily followed by all adherents, so there can be a discrepancy between what a religion says and what its practitioners actually do. In much of the world, in particular, developed Christian nations, a trend toward secularization or separation of church and state has evolved since the mid-20th century. This has led to conflicts between those who advocate the use of new medical advances and those who oppose new technologies based upon their religious, spiritual, or philosophical beliefs.

FAMILY PLANNING, CONTRACEPTION, AND ABORTION

Family-planning information in many Western Christian nations in the early 20th century was illegal or difficult to obtain even for married couples. Christianity has been the largest religious group globally for decades. It has about 32 percent of the world's religious adherent. Christians are divided into Roman Catholics, Protestants, and Orthodox denominations. Of all Christians, about 50 percent were

Roman Catholics by the mid-2010s, and it is the predominant Christian group in Latin America, Ireland, East Central and Southern Europe. "Catholics are expected by church authorities to follow the church's teachings on moral matters. In reality, however, many Catholics find themselves at variance with some teachings, particularly those having to do with procreation and sexuality" (Hamel, 2002).

The pope is the head of the Catholic Church worldwide. Pope Pius XI in a 1930 encyclical *Casti Connubii* banned all artificial means of contraception, sterilization, and abortion. The Vatican believed that birth control violated the law of God and nature, and only abstinence was allowed to control pregnancy.

During the post-WWII era—although it was the height of the "baby boom"—middle-class Catholic women in many Western cultures started to use some form of birth control. In 1960, the contraceptive pill was developed by an American Catholic gynecologist John Rock (1890–1984). Since it was more natural, many Catholics around the world expected the Church to allow this method. But an encyclical released by Pope Paul VI in 1968, *Humanae Vitae*, reinforced abstinence only. Due to these doctrines, in poorer Catholic Latin American cultures, contraception devises and medications were, and still are, difficult to obtain. As to a possible change in position concerning contraception, Pope Francis in 2016 implied in *The Joy of Love* that an individual's own conscience should be the guiding principle in regards to sexuality.

Eastern Orthodox Christians are found in Eastern Europe, Russia, and the Middle East. In many beliefs and practices, they are similar to the Roman Catholic Church including their position on contraception.

As part of the feminist suffrage movement of the early 20th century in the United States, the UK, and British Commonwealth nations, a demand for access to birth-control information and devices emerged. It was largely undertaken by middle-class women from mainstream Protestant religions such as Episcopal, Congregationalists, Presbyterians, and many Lutherans and Methodists. Margaret Sanger (1879–1966), who had broken from the Catholic church, was the primary leader of the birth control (a word she coined) movement in the United States, but it was not until 1936 that contraceptive devices could be sent through the mail and women could more easily obtain them. However, many states continued to outlaw birth control clinics as they were opposed by the Catholic and some conservative Protestant churches. It was not until 1965 when the U.S. Supreme Court in *Griswold v. Connecticut* upheld an individual's private right to use birth control. But many states still did not allow single women access to contraception based upon religious principles that sex should only be within marriage. It was not until 1972 when the Supreme Court in *Baird v. Eisenstadt* legalized birth control for all citizens irrespective of marital status.

In the UK during the early 20th century, Marie Stopes (1880–1958), a feminist leader, championed the right for women to have birth control in Britain. At this time, the Church of England was against contraception. However, its view changed from concern about increased use of birth control to official acceptance of it by 1930. In that year, the Anglican Church at a Lambeth Conference of all Anglican/Episcopal churches worldwide allowed the use of contraception within marriage and did not consider its use a sin or against God's purpose.

Early in the 20th century, some American Protestant–derived religions, for example, the Church of Jesus Christ Latter-Day Saints (LDS or Mormons), were also opposed to birth control but considered contraception acceptable for certain medical or "inherited" conditions. By the end of the century, although contraception was not forbidden, couples were encouraged to bring many "spirit children" into the world. Other Protestant groups such as Church of Christ and Scientists (Christian Scientists) do not have a doctrine on contraception or reproduction technology. These are a matter of personal prayer.

Religions, other than Christianity, have various beliefs on family planning. Islam, the second largest religion in the world with roughly 24 percent of the global population, emphasizes that procreation within the family is a religious duty. Because contraception is not expressly prohibited in the Quran, many Muslim scholars approve the practice of family planning. The only stipulation is that the birth control method should be used with the consent of both husband and wife.

Hinduism is the third largest religious group in the world with about 16 percent of the world's population. The majority of Hindus live in India and Nepal. There are no specific religious beliefs on contraception, and all forms are accepted. India has a large population, so discussion about family planning focuses on overpopulation and is encouraged.

Buddhists, who are about 10 percent of the world's population, primarily reside in South, Southeast, and East Asia. Family planning that prevents conception is acceptable and is practiced widely. Taoism and Confucianism are found in China. Taoism is focused on the individual, and Confucianism on the collective; however, both of these religions/philosophies emphasize the importance of balance and harmony—in the individual, in the family, and in society generally. Having too many children by the late 20th century was seen as upsetting the balance of harmony of both the individual and society because of increased famine in China, so family planning was valued. In the People's Republic of China, contraception was mandated during the "one child era" (1979–2016). There was no religious opposition to any contraceptive method in either religion/philosophy. But natural methods of contraception were more acceptable among the traditional Chinese people.

Judaism is primarily found in the United States and Israel. Orthodox Jews have the most restrictive beliefs concerning contraception. Active prevention of pregnancy is in violation of the commandment "be fruitful and multiply." Therefore, most birth control is frowned upon, and more natural methods, such as "the pill," are preferred. Conservative and Reformed Jews accept most forms of birth control.

A major issue of reproductive medicine that intersects with religion is when a human life begins or has a soul. Depending upon the beliefs of the religion, the beginning of the human life is thought to be from conception (the egg and sperm are united); implantation of the fertilized egg into the lining of the uterus about seven days after conception; or 40 or even 120 days after conception—the time of quickening when the fetus is first felt by the pregnant woman.

Until the late 1960s, elective pregnancy termination, or abortion, was illegal in most predominantly Christian and Muslim nations and among Jews. The exceptions included the Soviet Union (1922–1991) and later Russia. But the availability of legal abortion has waxed and waned in Russia. For decades, Russia has had the highest abortion rate in the world followed by Latin American nations.

Abortion in the early 20th century was a dangerous procedure often resulting in infections and death. As antiseptics, new surgery techniques, antibiotics, and medication (such as RU483, which causes a miscarriage) were developed over the century, medical procedure to terminate a pregnancy became safer than childbirth. In predominantly Christian nations, particularly the United States and the UK and its former colonies, as part of the Women's Liberation Movement of the 1960s, elective pregnancy termination as an aspect of reproduction rights was advocated. However, this caused deep divisions between religious and secular forces.

In the UK, the Church of England and the Roman Catholic Church opposed legalizing abortion. However, the Abortion Act of 1967 was passed to permit pregnancy termination for a variety of reasons if certified by two physicians. Canada had passed a similar law by 1969, but in 1988, the Supreme Court of Canada ruled that abortion was legal for any reason at any stage of pregnancy.

In the United States, the Supreme Court decision (*Roe v. Wade*) in 1973 affirmed the legality of a woman's right to have an abortion under the Fourteenth Amendment to the Constitution. However, states were allowed to regulate abortion during the second and third trimesters. *Roe v. Wade* was, and is still, fiercely opposed by Roman Catholic, Eastern Orthodox, and conservative Protestants churches. Since the 1970s, these groups have attempted to overturn the ruling and to severely restrict or to make abortion illegal again other than to save the life of the mother. By 2018, many states had passed, or were attempting to pass, restrictive laws that were challenged by those from liberal churches or secular groups. Additionally, in some states, such as Indiana, OBGYN practices ceased any pregnancy terminations and referred patients to Planned Parenthood.

As part of a backlash against *Roe v. Wade* in the United States, by the late 20th century, an upsurge of anti-birth-control sentiments also arose among some conservative Protestants in addition to the Roman Catholic Church. Some denominations opposed all forms of contraception short of abstinence while others allowed some new medical methods but opposed others. For example, the Southern Baptists and the Lutheran Church–Missouri Synod supported all forms of birth control that prevented conception. However, they were against any method that kept a fertilized egg from implanting in the uterus such as Intrauterine Devices (IUDs) and the "morning after pill" as they believed this was killing a human life.

In the United States by the mid-2010s, conservative Protestant and Catholic groups fought against mandatory employee contraceptive coverage as stipulated in Affordable Care Act (see chapter 12). In 2014, the Supreme Court decision in *Burwell v. Hobby Lobby* allowed privately owned and religious organization to deny their employees birth-control coverage. In 2017, the Trump administration allowed any business or nonprofit group to exclude coverage for contraception for religious beliefs or moral convictions.

In Islam, it is believed that an embryo only has a soul at 120 days. However, some Muslims argue that destroying an embryo at any stage of pregnancy is not permissible. Abortion laws are often determined by the beliefs within various Islamic cultures but can be performed in all cultures to save the life of the mother.

A belief among Hindus is that all living things have a soul, which passes through successive cycles of birth and rebirth. In 1971, abortion was legalized in India. Since male children are preferable, some women resorted to abortion if they carried a female fetus. In 1994, to combat this practice, the Indian government outlawed prenatal testing to reveal the sex of the child. However, such abortions are still widely practiced and rarely prosecuted.

Among Buddhists, abortion is often bound by cultural factors though is acceptable in most Buddhist traditions in certain situations. China under its one-child policy mandated an abortion if a woman was pregnant with a second child. If the fetus was female, it was often aborted as male babies are desired. Both Taoism and Confucianism view abortion as a necessary evil, and there are no ethical codes that forbid the practice. Japan since the 1950s has had liberal abortion laws.

Judaism believes that the soul does not enter the fetus until 40 days after conception. Among Orthodox Jews, abortion is allowed only to save the life of the mother. Conservative Judaism allow abortion when a fetus has severe abnormalities or in case of incest and rape. Reform Judaism is the most liberal with few constraints. In Israel, abortion is allowed but with a few constraints.

ASSISTED REPRODUCTION TECHNOLOGY

Assisted reproduction technology (ART) includes many techniques that have been developed and used from the 1940s to the present time. As with other reproductive issues, many of these advances were opposed by some religious groups but accepted by others. In some cases, due to political pressures from religious denominations, procedures were made illegal or strictly controlled. The first medical ART technique to emerge—which had been used for decades on farm animals—was artificial insemination (AI), also called intrauterine insemination (IUI) where sperm is placed directly into the vagina or uterus. AI was first publicized in England in the early 1940s; however, it was condemned by various religious bodies when it was first announced. It only became legal in the United States in the mid-1960s.

Further condemnation of AI in several Christian cultures occurred in the 1950s when frozen sperm by third-party donors began to be used. The Catholic Church, in 1956, denounced AI as immoral and illegal as it separated the "unitive act of marriage (sex) from the procreative act (fertilization)." Masturbation for collecting the semen was considered a sin, and the use of third-party semen was adultery, and thus the procedure was forbidden. However, the Eastern Orthodox Church accepted AI. Mainstream Protestant religions believed the choice of using AI was up to the individual. Conservative Protestants had mixed feelings about AI especially third-party sperm donations.

On the other hand, Muslims believe that a husband and wife have the right to become parents and see no differences if pregnancy results through sexual intercourse or medical means. However, the use of sperm from another man is prohibited. Hinduism has no prohibitions on AI. In Orthodox Judaism, insemination with the husband's sperm only is permissible if the wife cannot become pregnant in any other way. Both the husband's and donor sperm are permissible in the other Jewish denomination. Buddhism and other eastern religions/philosophies support all forms of AI.

In the late 1970s, in vitro fertilization (IVF), resulting in a "test tube baby" was developed. In this process, eggs and sperm are mixed together in a petri dish. After several days of successful cellular development, a few healthy embryos are implanted into the uterus. Unused embryos are discarded, frozen for future use, given to other women, or used in research. The first child produced through IVF was Louise Brown in England in 1978. Later, egg donation became available, and the first child born of a third-party donated egg was in Australia in 1983. In some cases if a woman is unable to carry a pregnancy or if a single man wants a child, a gestational surrogate ("surrogate mother") is used, and embryos are implanted in her per a mutual agreement.

These medical advancements allowed many women worldwide to have healthy babies as embryos are screened for genetic and other problems before implantation. However, pre-implantation diagnosis and screening and destruction of defective or unused embryos were condemned by several Christian groups as the fertilized egg was seen as a person with human rights and its destruction viewed as murder.

The Vatican, in March 1987, issued *Instruction on Respect for Human Life in its Origin and on the Dignity of Procreation*. This publication was aimed at influencing the decisions of Roman Catholics and also to influence national legislation worldwide on biomedical issues. The Church opposed all reproduction technologies in particular IVF, embryo transfer, and surrogate motherhood under all circumstances. It also opposed experimentation on embryos and procedures to detect defects in embryos and fetuses when it was done for the purpose of deciding whether or not to implant the embryo or abort the fetus. Due to these condemnations, some Catholic nations instituted strict measures in regards to ART, including Italy and Austria. The Eastern Orthodox Church only allows treatment of infertility using the husband's sperm.

Most mainstream Protestant denominations accept all forms of ART including gamete donation by third parties. They also accept research on embryos, embryo reduction in the uterus, and therapeutic cloning to investigate life-saving treatment and have few qualms about single women also using ART techniques. However, there are some exceptions. The Church of England, for example, frowns upon fertility treatment for single women and gay couples. Although legislation was introduced to restrict single women in the UK from receiving fertility treatment, it did not pass. The Episcopal Church in the United States has no restrictions on any form of ART.

Conservative Protestants, who support IVF, generally limit its use to married couples. For example, the Lutheran Church–Missouri Synod requires that all embryos of a married couple be implanted in the wife. No experimentation, destruction, or storage of unneeded or defective fertilized eggs is allowed. The Church of Jesus Christ of Latter-Day Saints strongly discourages IVF fertilization from third parties. However, this is considered a personal matter left to the judgment of the husband and wife. Christian Science frowns upon ART as it involves medical techniques. In contrast to restrictions in many European nations, the United States, Australia, Brazil and Canada have relatively few restrictions with ART leading to medical tourism to these nations for infertility treatment from more restrictive cultures.

Islam allows assisted reproduction with a few restrictions. Egypt's Al-Azhar University religious scholars around 1980 issued a fatwa (religious legal opinion) regarding reproductive advances for Muslims. It judged that IFV and all ART procedures were permissible, with the exception of reproductive cloning, as long as only the gametes of a married couple were used. This was because family lineage is important in Muslim cultures. Although Muslims do not believe that the fetus has a soul until late in the pregnancy, some Muslim clergy have suggested that research be done only on embryos under 14 days old.

However, differences in opinion over third-party donation in the late 1990s developed between Sunni (about 80% of Muslims) and Shia (about 10% of Muslims) denominations. Some Shia authorities in Iran—the major Islamic religion in that nation—permitted third-party gamete donation under certain conditions. Sperm selection for gender was not allowed for the first child. But by 2015 a fatwa by Al-Azhar allowed it for family balancing if the couple already has two children of the same sex.

In many other religions, most assisted reproductive techniques and research with embryos are accepted. Although Reformed and Conservative Jews accept any techniques, Orthodox Jews generally refuse third-party involvement. In India and the Far East, Hinduism and Buddhism accepts almost all forms of ART including surrogacy. Buddhists believe ART is a compassionate act that alleviates the human suffering of distress of not being able to have children. Chinese culture, strongly influenced by Confucianism, accepts all forms of ART. By 2015, China had accomplished much research on embryos and cloning for therapeutic investigations because of more liberal attitudes about ART compared to most Christian nations. In 1918, one Chinese scientist genetically altered the embryos of twin girls to the condemnation of many worldwide. Although gender selection was not sanctioned in China, selection for more desirable boys was common during the one-child policy years. In Japan, where many follow Shinto traditions, egg donation and surrogacy are forbidden by law due to concerns of purity. In all religions other than Catholic, Orthodox, and some conservative Protestant denominations, fetal reduction due to the implantation of several embryos is allowed.

STEM-CELL RESEARCH AND BIOENGINEERING

Those religious groups opposed to elective pregnancy termination are also opposed to human therapeutic cloning, embryonic stem cell, and most other forms of bioengineering research. Therapeutic cloning involves creating an embryo with the same DNA as the donor cell to produce embryonic stem cells. Embryonic stem cells found in three- to five-day-old embryos can be made to transform into any

Demonstrators protest stem-cell research in San Diego, California, in 2002. In the United States, the use of therapeutic embryonic stem cells for research continues to be condemned by some religious groups. (David McNew/Getty Images)

other type of cell in the body and can be used for developing new treatments for disease. Extra embryos from IVF are generally used. Reproductive cloning is producing a new organism through birth. The first mammal cloned was Dolly the Sheep in the UK in 1996. This development created moral outrage by various religious groups. Although few groups supported human cloning, therapeutic stem-cell research was accepted or rejected depending upon a religious/philosophical view of either "sanctity of life" or a "quality of life" ethics. Other controversial areas are "designer babies" and "savior siblings" where certain desirable traits are selected or the tissue is compatible with a sick sibling.

Due to these different ethical and religious viewpoints, in the United States the use of therapeutic embryonic stem for research was condemned by Roman Catholics, Conservative Protestants, and the Eastern Orthodox denominations. Mainline Protestant churches such as Episcopal, United Methodist, Presbyterian (USA), Evangelical Lutheran Church of America (ELCA), United Church of Christ, and Disciples' of Christ, on the other hand, either had no explicit policy on embryonic stem-cell research or approved the techniques if the stem cells were to be used for research or medical or therapeutic purposes.

Pressure from religious groups, and organizations sponsored by them, opposed to this new technology convinced U.S. President George W. Bush (1946–) during 2006–2007 to veto a Congressional bill to allow the U.S. federal government to fund embryonic stem-cell research using extra embryos from fertility clinics. Without this federal funding, research in this field declined. Since this time the United States has vacillated between allowing and not allowing public funding for therapeutic cloning and stem-cell research depending upon the political party in power.

In the European nations, various actions were taken often depending upon pressure from dominant religious groups in their culture. In 2005, an ethical declaration was signed by Austria, Germany, Italy, Luxembourg, Malta, Poland, and Slovakia. These primarily Catholic nations, except Germany, called for the exclusion of any kind of stem-cell research from European public funding. However, Denmark, Greece, Finland, France, the Netherlands, and Spain, had more liberal regulations that allowed stem-cell research from extra embryos not used for IVF. Belgium, Sweden, and the UK legalized the creation of human embryos for therapeutic embryonic stem-cell research. Canada, legalized stem-cell research in 2004 on unused embryos from fertility clinics, but banned therapeutic cloning and the creation of embryos for research.

Likewise in Islamic nations, several opinions regarding embryonic stem-cell research emerged. Some Muslim leaders allowed for stem-cell research on the ground that, according to Islam, an embryo only has a soul in later stage of pregnancy, while others argued that destroying an embryo at any stage of pregnancy is not permissible. By 2002, government funding in Iran, Qatar, and Saudi Arabia supported research in human embryonic and adult stem cells. By 2003, Iran had developed a line of embryonic stem cells. Other Muslim groups and nations also supported embryonic stem-cell research and therapeutic cloning.

Several other major religious traditions worldwide were also more or less in favor of stem-cell research. The main Jewish denominations (Reform, Conservative, Orthodox, and Reconstructionist) supported embryonic stem-cell research as long as it is for medical or therapeutic purposes. Many, but not all, Buddhists subgroups in India, Southeast, and East Asian cultures contended that embryonic stem-cell research is in accordance with the Buddhist teaching of seeking knowledge and ending human suffering.

Hinduism, primarily found in India, has no official position on this type of research. Confucianism and Taoism philosophy/religions found in China, Korea, and Japan have no restrictions on the use of embryonic stem cells and received funding from their governments for research in this area. Consequently, they advanced medical research in the field. By 2010, researchers in these nations were able to reprogram somatic (body) cells into embryonic-like stem cells called induced pluripotent stem cells (IPSCs). This technique has many difficulties, and embryonic stem cells appear to be the easiest to manipulate. However, it is possible that adult stem cells in the future will likely reduce the need to use human embryonic stem cells for research and medical therapies.

Consequently in 2011, Pope Benedict XVI announced that the Catholic Church supported the use of adult stem-cell research. Lutheran Church–Missouri Synod affirmed that if there is no risk to the life of the donor, the Synod was very much in favor of the research and usefulness of adult stem cells to treat various diseases. Other conservative Protestant groups in the United States and Europe also support the use of adult stem cells.

VACCINATIONS AND IMMUNIZATIONS

The intersection of religion and medicine can have serious public health consequences in terms of infectious diseases. Individuals who do not accept immunization for religious reasons can not only become sick but can also spread an infectious disease to others. When vaccinations were being developed in the early 20th century, all major religious groups worldwide welcomed immunizations that would prevent epidemics. However, some conservative Protestant religious sects were against vaccinations as they felt immunizing people against diseases was playing God. It was in God's hands as to who survived and who did not from diseases (see chapter 5 for more information on immunizations). This resulted in protests against vaccination in several developed nations.

In the United States, for example, the Supreme Court in 1905 ruled that a state could enact compulsory laws to protect the public in the event of a communicable disease. In 1944, the Supreme Court stated, "The right to practice religion freely does not include liberty to expose the community or the child to communicable disease or the latter to ill health or death" (JUSTIA U.S. Supreme Court, 1944).

By the 1960s, about half the states had mandatory vaccination laws that increased over the century. Most states dictated mandatory DPT (diphtheria, pertussis, and tetanus) and by 1980, MMR (mumps, measles, and rubella) vaccinations for children to enter school, although exemptions for medical and religious reasons could be obtained.

Those who opposed mandatory immunizations were the Protestant-derived Jehovah Witnesses and Christian Scientists. During the 1920s through the late 1940s, Jehovah Witnesses were opposed to vaccination based on their doctrine against the use of human blood. However, by the early 1950s, the church took a neutral stand until the 1990s when it began to acknowledge the value of vaccinations for preventing epidemics. By the late 1990s, some Christian Scientists also began to accept immunization as there were no specific doctrines against it in their scriptures.

In the mid-1970s, an international antivaccination crusade erupted in Asia, Australia, Europe, and North America over the safety of the DTP vaccination. This was after some British children supposedly suffered neurological problems following DPT immunization. This surge increased in developed nations when, a later discredited, 1998 British study, linked the MMR vaccine to autism. Due to this flawed study, anti-vaxxers (vaccine hesitators) argued that the dangers of vaccinations far outweighed their benefits, and they began to ignore recommendations for immunizations.

Although by the late 1990s vaccines had been developed to prevent many infectious diseases, refusal to vaccinate for religious or philosophical reasons resulted in a global upsurge of childhood disease epidemics by 2005. For example, in Europe, the Dutch Orthodox Reformed Church, found mostly in the Netherlands, refused vaccination as they believed that God has predestined the fate of all human beings, including their health and diseases. Immunizations were seen as meddling in the work of God. During 2013–2014, a rubella epidemic emerged in schools run by the sect leading to some serious medical issues. The Dutch

National Vaccination Program began in 1976, so other than for medical reasons most other children in the nation were immunized and the diseases did not spread to them.

Among the Old-order Amish in the United States, there has been a low rate of vaccination against childhood disease, which has resulted in several epidemics of whooping cough and measles. In 2014, as an example, Amish members visiting the Philippines contracted measles and brought the disease back, which spawned an epidemic in their Ohio community. A major reason for lack of immunization among the Amish has been the lack of easy access to immunization and because the Amish do not carry medical insurance. A few very conservative communities prefer traditional remedies and are against immunizations and any modern medical care because of cost and distrust of clinics.

In the United States by the late 20th century, parents were able to get exemptions for childhood immunizations for medical, religious, personal, or moral beliefs in most states. A collective amnesia emerged concerning the danger of childhood diseases that could permanently damage a developing fetus, cause blindness, deafness, cognitive problems, permanent paralysis, or even death. The increase in exemptions for religious and philosophical reasons in the United States led to fewer children being vaccinated even those from mainstream religions as they feared immunizations could cause autism.

Although the UK has no requirement for mandatory vaccinations before a child attends school, many parents also asked for exceptions for religious or philosophical reasons. A global decline in immunization rates for many childhood diseases led to a surge of epidemics in many nations in the first two decades of the 21st century. For example, after a large multistate measles outbreak originated in Disneyland during 2014–2015, the state of California passed a law that only allowed medical exemptions for immunizations and not for religious and philosophical reasons. This increased compliance in inoculations before school entry, but conversely medical exemptions went up. Some Australian states by 2017 instituted fines for parents not immunizing their children and did not allow unvaccinated children into daycare or school. Italy, Romania, and Ukraine had wide spread measles epidemics in 2017 and were discussing fines for vaccine-hesitant parents.

A vaccine to prevent transmission of human papilloma virus (HPV), which can cause cervical and penile cancer, had been developed by 2008. However, conservative Protestant groups in the United States and some Roman Catholic diocese in Canada, the United States, and African nations were against this vaccine as they feared that immunization would undermine the abstinence messages of their belief system.

In addition, by 2010, a vocal antivaccination movement was active on websites where it conveyed misinformation on the negative effects of immunizations. The movement has several factions. It includes those with spiritual, philosophical, or holistic beliefs against vaccination and often mainstream medical science. The intersection of these beliefs with medicine has a potential to impact global public health with increased epidemics of disease that are easily prevented through immunization.

BLOOD TRANSFUSION AND ORGAN DONATIONS

Blood transfusions since the late 1930s have saved countless lives around the world, and the procedure is accepted by all major religions. However, two American-derived Protestant denominations denounce transfusions. First of all, the Jehovah's Witnesses (Watchtower Bible and Tract Society) refuse blood transfusions based upon their interpretation of biblical passages. This policy was introduced by the group's legislative body in 1945. The denomination believes that the Bible prohibits ingesting blood, and this includes blood transfusions and donation or storage of their own blood for transfusion. However, the three major Western religions believe that the biblical passages refer to dietary laws and consumption of blood. These scriptures are from the Old Testament in Christianity, the Quran in Islam, and the Torah in Judaism. In 2002, Witnesses amended their rules on transfusions and allowed fractions of blood such as albumin, immunoglobulins, and hemophiliac preparations to be used in certain medical procedures. "Bloodless surgery," or procedures that use a patient's own blood during the course of a medical treatment, were also considered a matter of personal choice.

Concerning organ transplants, Jehovah's Witnesses find no scripture against it. In the earlier part of the 20th century, it was not allowed but by the late century, donation or receiving cornea, kidney, bone, and other tissue transplants were up to the individual as long as the blood was removed. The second group to refuse blood, in addition to organ donations, is Christian Science. They believe that these material procedures are against their reliance on spiritual means of healing alone.

Most of the major religious traditions accept and encourage organ donations. Organ and tissue donation is considered an act of charity, love, and compassion given to help a fellow human being. Several Protestant denominations take no stand on donations but leave it up to the individual, including Mennonites, Pentecostals, and Southern Baptist. Some conservative Amish groups do not accept heart transplantations as they feel this is where the soul resides. Buddhism also leaves a decision for organ donation up to the individual.

A few religious practices, however, tend to be against organ donation. The ethnic group called the Roma, as part of their religious system, believe that for one year after a person dies the soul retraces its steps and that all parts of the body must remain intact because the soul maintains a physical shape. The Japanese Shinto religious philosophy views a dead body as impure and dangerous. Injuring a dead body is seen as a crime as it causes problems with the relationship between the dead and living family members. In Japan, it is difficult to obtain consent from family members for tissue or organ donation for treatment or medical education. A few ultra conservative Orthodox Jewish rabbis and Asian Muslims also opposed organ donations.

"FAITH HEALING," OR TREATMENT SOLELY BY PRAYER

All the major world religions have advocated medical technology as it has advanced since 1900 along with praying for the sick. However, a few groups use "faith healing" prayer or ritual as the only treatment. These include Christian

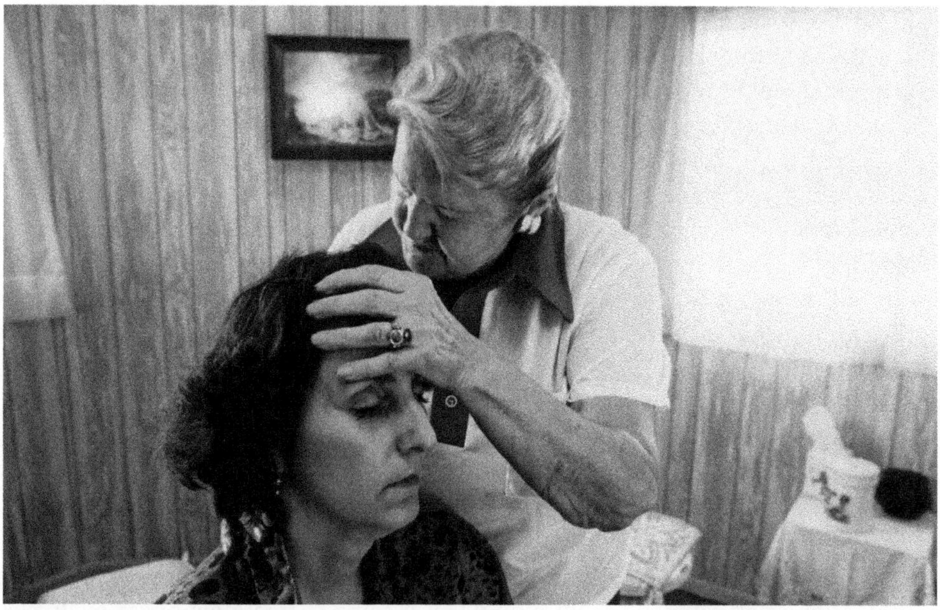
The world's major religions have accepted medical science as a means of healing the sick, but a few smaller religious groups still view prayer as the only effective medical treatment. Here, a faith healer treats a woman in Florida in 2008. (H. Christoph/ullstein bild via Getty Images)

Science, a few splinter Holiness/Pentecostal sects, and some Hindu sects in South Asia and indigenous groups in the Americas, Africa, Australia, and New Zealand (see also chapter 9).

Christian faith traditions that rely only on prayer have based their beliefs on their interpretations of the Bible and other scriptures. In Christian Science, for example, a Christian Science practitioner helps a person to accept that his/her disease is nonexistent. Although they generally do not seek treatment from traditional medical practitioners, Christian Scientists will generally use dentists, optometrists, obstetricians, and physicians for broken bones. The Holiness/Pentecostal sects will pray and often anoint a person with oil for a cure. Many adherents of these small sects also believe that if a person is sick or dies, the death was God's will.

Indigenous groups often prefer their traditional native healing practices although biomedicine has generally been available since the 20th century for many tribal groups. These healing traditions involve prayer, ritual, and/or herbs. Followers of tribal religions sometimes believe that some diseases cannot be treated by Western medicine as spiritual healing is needed. If Western medicine does not work, the person goes to their traditional healer and vice versa. Although belief systems differ, most indigenous religions see supernatural causes for illness or the body systems being out of balance.

The primary issue of religious beliefs that rely on prayer and spiritual practices is that children have died because their parents have refused blood transfusions, antibiotics, surgery, or other medical treatment to save their lives. Although adults have the right to refuse treatment based upon their religious beliefs, refusing life-saving treatment for children was seen as child abuse and neglect in the late 20th century in several nations.

Therefore, by 2000, to prevent these childhood deaths, Canada, the UK, Australia, Japan and some other nations passed laws where a parent or guardian's refusal to allow biomedical treatment for religious reasons could be legally overridden by medical personnel if a child's life was in danger. However, exceptions were still being made. For example, in Canada, a child of a First Nations tribe was allowed to receive alternative treatment even though it meant death from leukemia.

In the United States by the mid-2010s, many states still had religious exemption laws. In states that had no exemptions, some parents were charged with child abuse and second-degree murder for not obtaining medical care for their sick child. However, by 2016, more states eliminated religious exemptions for seriously sick children and allowed child welfare departments to gain guardianship of the child to get treatment. The American Academy of Pediatrics also called for the elimination of all religious exemption when it came to treatment of seriously sick children. Because of court cases and legal changes, Jehovah's Witnesses now comply with court orders requiring their children to receive life-saving transfusions. The church reasons that in such cases, the parents did not make the decision so they do not lose their religious standing as good members. Due to legal changes, Christian Scientists, if required by law, will also allow medical treatment for their minor children.

DEATH WITH DIGNITY, ASSISTED SUICIDE, AND EUTHANASIA

Most of the major religious traditions oppose medical-assisted suicide (physician providing the means) and euthanasia (physician taking action). However, within various denominations, there are different opinions on how far medical technology should keep a person alive or if a physician should help a terminally ill patient to die. Because of advances in medical treatment from the mid-20th century, individuals can be kept alive much longer than in the past. This has resulted in changes in the definition of death. Earlier in the century, death was considered to have occurred when breathing stopped or the heart stopped beating. However, the development of Cardio Pulmonary Resuscitation (CPR) and defibrillation made this definition of death obsolete as breathing and heartbeat could sometimes be restarted. Late in the century, lack of brain-wave activity was now considered the time of death. But an individual could be kept in a vegetative state on life support systems for years with little or no brain activity. Therefore, the issue of when death occurs became contentious and complicated due to various religious beliefs.

Another issue in end-of-life matters is death with dignity or physician-assisted suicide. Suicide and euthanasia have different interpretations in different societies due to spiritual, cultural, and religious beliefs. For example, in Japan, Shinto philosophy allowed for an individual to end his life with honor and to save face for the family by seppuku, or hara-kiri, a ritualized form of suicide. This type of suicide was considered a desirable and honorable death. However, this action according to most Christian, Islamic, and Jewish religions was viewed as a sin and against God's will.

With advancements in medical science that could keep a person alive on life support indefinitely, a physician-assisted suicide or "death with dignity" movement arose late in the century in some Christian nations. Support for this movement emerged from two contentious legal cases in the United States when some family members wanted to withdraw a brain dead loved one from life support while other members, or even hospitals, did not. Conflicts concerning end-of-life care changed medicine worldwide. For example, in 1990, the United States Congress passed the Patient Self-Determination Act (PSDA). This federal law acknowledges that a patient had the right to either refuse or accept medical treatment and it also protects physicians from litigation in end-of-life decision making. By 1992, all 50 states had passed some legislation on the legality of patients' advance directives or "living wills." By 2005, many European nations recommended legally binding advanced directives; however, they still are not legally binding in some nations.

As part of the death-with-dignity movement, the choice of physician-assisted suicide or euthanasia became a controversial religious, spiritual, legal, and cultural issue. Some faith traditions embraced death with dignity as an ultimate act of compassion, while others rejected it as murder and an immoral practice. Major Christian faith traditions that are opposed to medically assisted suicide or euthanasia include Roman Catholics, Eastern Orthodox, Assembles of God and most other Evangelicals, most Methodists, Latter-Day Saints, some Lutherans, Southern Baptists, the Anglican Church in the UK and former British colonies, and European Orthodox Protestants. They argue that death is a choice that only God can make. They believe that the practice of people with an incurable disease choosing to be painlessly put to death is against Biblical scripture and morality. As legislation in some Christian nations promoted laws legalizing death with dignity, these and other Christian denominations put out official statements against legalizing these end-of-life procedures. As an example, in the United States the Lutheran Church–Missouri Synod in 1993 asserted

> Advocates of euthanasia, as well as of assisted suicide, have sought to justify the taking of human life on moral grounds by describing it as a truly compassionate act aimed at the relief of human suffering. In light of what the Scriptures say about the kind of care God wills that we provide to those who suffer and are facing death, we reject such claims as neither compassionate nor caring. Christians aim always to care, never to kill. (Lutheran Church–Missouri Synod, 1993, 3)

However, these groups also believe that life need not be sustained at all costs with extraordinary technological means when there is no hope for recovery. Palliative care and pain relief is acceptable even if it hastens death. But Christian Scientist suggests that assisted dying or even palliative medication is not a genuine expression of their faith and is a denial of God's presence and power to heal.

A few Christian denominations have mixed feelings on physician-assisted suicide and euthanasia. In the United States, among Christians, some Episcopalians (as opposed to the British Anglican Church) believe it is morally wrong to take human life to relieve suffering caused by terminal illness. However, others Episcopalians approve assisted suicide in rare cases. The Presbyterian Church (USA) has not taken specific positions or provided guidance on assisted suicide or euthanasia. The American Baptists Churches and Southern Baptist Convention differ in their beliefs regarding assisted dying. The American Baptists have adopted the policy of asking the medical community to preserve the dignity and minimize the suffering of patients and respect personal choice for end-of-life care. However, Southern Baptists feel that assisted suicide violates the sanctity of human life.

On the other hand, liberal Christian churches feel that assisted dying should be a personal choice even if it hastens death and is based upon compassion and that a person has the right to die with dignity. These denominations include the Evangelical Lutheran Church, the Methodist Church on the U.S. West Coast, United Church of Christ (UCC), Unitarian Universalist, and some Amish and Quakers. The UCC supports the right of terminally ill patients to make their own decisions about when to die. The church also supports the right of families to discontinue treatment for incapacitated loved ones who are near death or in a vegetative state. Most Amish see life-prolonging care as excessive and unjustified when a person is terminal and often refuse extraordinary treatment and let a life expire naturally with dignity.

One of the most vocal denominations in favor of changing state laws and allowing personal choice in regards to assisted suicide or euthanasia in the United States has been the Unitarian Universalist church. In 1988, their Association of Congregations passed a resolution advocating "the right to self-determination in dying and to die with dignity due to the fact that 'medical knowledge and technology make possible the mechanical prolongation of life; and. . . such prolongation may cause unnecessary suffering and/or loss of dignity while providing little or nothing of benefit to the individual.'" As a result, the church has supported laws in several states that enabled terminally ill patients, under carefully defined circumstances, to seek the physician's assistance in hastening their own death.

However, religious traditions that considered active euthanasia and assisted suicide immoral fought against proposed laws to legalize them in several nations. For example, Dutch Orthodox Reformed and Catholic leaders, along with Muslim and Orthodox Jewish religious leaders in the Netherlands, fought against a bill introduced to legalize physician-assisted suicide. However, the bill was passed in 2001, and the Netherlands became the first nation to allow legal euthanasia and physician-assisted suicide. However, it had several stipulations. The patient had to have continual suffering and unbearable pain. They repeatedly had to have asked for help to die, and a second medical opinion was required.

Traditions other than Christianity are also against any type of physician-assisted suicide or euthanasia. In Islam, for example, all human life is considered sacred because it is given by Allah (God), and Allah chooses how long each person will live. Human beings should not interfere with the will of Allah. Thus end-of-life options such as assisted dying are forbidden. Islam also believes that suffering and other difficulties might be beneficial to test one's faith and purify previous sins. However, medications to relieve pain are perfectly acceptable.

In Hinduism, several points of view on medically assisted dying are found. Most Hindus believe that a patient's request for death assisted by a physician could cause the soul and body to be separated at an unnatural time. This in turn could damage the karma of both doctor and patient. However, other Hindus believe that helping to end a painful life is performing a good deed and fulfilling a moral obligation.

Buddhism does not address the topic. Buddha himself showed tolerance of suicide by monks, and Buddhist monks committed suicide as a protest during the Vietnam War in the 1960s and 1970s. Japanese Buddhist tradition includes stories of suicide by monks, and in Shinto spirituality, as discussed, the taking of one's life to save face has been accepted and practiced, especially during WWII.

In Judaism under Jewish law, preserving human life generally outweighs other considerations including extreme pain. Any form of euthanasia, including passive euthanasia, suicide and physician-assisted suicide is against the teachings of God. Palliative care to relieve pain is allowed. Since the 1970s, Jewish medical ethics have become divided over euthanasia and end-of-life treatment. Conservative and Reform leaders have called for increased discussion of end-of-life issues, but leaders have not issued official positions on assisted dying.

By 2019, a few nations had passed laws that allowed assisted suicide or active euthanasia. The Netherlands, Belgium, Colombia, Luxembourg, Canada, India, and South Korea allowed active euthanasia and assisted suicide. Assisted suicide was legal in Switzerland, Germany, Japan, several states in the United States, and one state in Australia. But other nations such as the UK rejected these procedures. Still other nations are grappling with how to legislate this difficult issue.

In summary, religious beliefs intersected with medical advances in many health areas from 1900 to the present. Medical issues, in nations where beliefs of different religious traditions were in opposition, became embroiled in political and legal disputes. These involved the right of personal choice versus public policy and the rights of society versus individual religious beliefs. These clashes of religion and medicine are continuing in the 21st century.

4

Women's Health

Advances in public health and medicine shifted mortality from infectious to chronic diseases among women, particularly in high- to mid-income nations, from the beginning of the 20th century to the early 21st century. An estimate of the health of a nation is its maternal and infant mortality rates. In Europe, mortality rates have been collected since the late 19th century, but it was only in the late 20th century that data have been gathered in developing low-income nations. In general, low-income nations have higher maternal mortality rates compared to high-income nations. Screening techniques for diseases such as breast and cervical cancer and earlier treatment emerged to lower mortality for women. The major advances, since the early 20th century for most women around the world, have included higher standards of living, better pre- and postnatal care, safer delivery and pregnancy terminations, the accessibility of family planning, contraception, and sexuality education for women. Conditions for working women—particularly in industrialized nations—improved, and suffrage and education for women emerged in many nations.

GLOBAL TRENDS IN WOMEN'S MORBIDITY AND MORTALITY

At the beginning of the 20th century, the major causes of death and disability for women in higher-income developed nations were influenza/pneumonia, tuberculosis, diarrhea/enteritis, and complications surrounding pregnancy. These conditions—along with malaria—were the major causes of death in lower-income developing nations. By the end of the 20th century, the major causes of death had shifted to chronic illnesses including cardiovascular disease, cancer, stroke, and diabetes in higher-income nations. On the other hand, in lower-income nations, infectious diseases along with AIDS (primarily in east and southern Africa) by 2000 were the major causes of death among younger women. Lung cancer became the leading cause of cancer-related death for older women, followed by breast, colorectal, and reproductive cancers in developed nations. In addition, women in higher-income nations were more likely to die from breast cancer while those in developing nations were more likely to die from cervical cancer due to lack of early detection.

ADVANCES IN SCREENING TESTS

Because of public health advances over the 20th century, the life-span of women increased in most nations. In addition to better sanitation, immunizations, and maternal care, screening tests were developed to detect some illnesses that could then be treated. In higher-income nations, pregnant women are routinely tested for Sexually Transmitted Diseases (STDs) as part of prenatal examinations and are treated if they are positive. STD's are still a concern in developing nations and among the poor who often do not seek prenatal care. As technology advanced over the 20th century, screening for cancers found in women emerged. The Pap smear was developed in the 1940s by Greek American Georgios Papanikolaou (1883–1962). This test has saved uncountable lives from cervical cancer, particularly in high-income nations. Self-breast examinations in the late 1940s and by 1970 mammograms have been recommended to reduce death from breast cancer. However, whether or not early detection of breast cancer saves lives is controversial. Most of these tests are routinely recommended in high-income cultures. In developing nations, prevention efforts are sometimes difficult to obtain, in particular, for poorer women or those living in regions with humanitarian crises. Although these advances over the 20th century have saved lives, the most important advance in women's health has been the reduction of maternal mortality on a global level.

MATERNAL MORTALITY

The *International Statistical Classification of Diseases and Related Health Problems* (ICD-10) defines maternal mortality as "the death of a woman while pregnant or within 42 days of termination of pregnancy irrespective of the duration and the site of the pregnancy, from any cause related to or aggravated by the pregnancy or its management but not from accidental or incidental causes" (WHO, 2014, 4). At the turn of the 20th century, it is estimated that the Maternal Mortality Ratio (MMR)—maternal deaths per 100,000 live births—was about 500 to 1,000 from complications of pregnancy in Western cultures. In developing lower-income nations such as in Africa, the Middle East, Latin America, and Asia, it is estimated that even higher death rates were found although this information was generally not recorded.

Reliable records only began in the mid-19th century in some Western European nations and not until around 1915 in the United States and the late 20th century in lower-income countries. The major causes of maternal deaths were infection (childbed fever), hemorrhage, preeclampsia or toxemia of pregnancy (pregnancy induced high blood pressure, often accompanied by seizures), and unsafe abortions usually carried out by untrained individuals. Although more aseptic conditions and hand washing—where it was practiced—by those assisting in childbirth had slightly lowered the death rate by the turn of the 20th century, a high death rate continued through the late 1930s. In addition, wide differences between rich and poor women in the West and also between Western nations were found. For example, Sweden had a lower MMR than the United States and the UK at the beginning of the 20th century as hand washing was commonly used by midwives in Sweden and not necessarily in other nations.

After 1937 through the late 20th century, the maternal mortality rate rapidly declined and leveled off in high-income nations. In developing low-income nations, the decline was less. Worldwide the MMR declined by around 44 percent between 1990 and 2015. However, this was less than half of the target for the 2015 Millennium Development Goal 5 of the United Nations. This goal was developed in 2000 by member states of the United Nations to reduce the MMR three-quarters from 1990 to 2015 and to achieve universal access to reproductive health to improve maternal health.

In 2016, in a continuing effort to improve women's health globally, the United Nations International Children's Emergency Fund (UNICEF) developed The Global Strategy for Women's, Children's and Adolescents' Health. Its aim is to achieve the highest attainable standard of health for all women, children, and adolescents and to help them thrive between the target dates of 2016 and 2030. The World Health Organization considers "One of the most easily preventable causes of maternal death and ill-health is unsafe abortion, which causes approximately 13% of all maternal deaths" (Mahler, 2007). Death results from hemorrhage, infection, sepsis, and reproductive and internal organ injury.

International health professionals consider the primary methods for preventing unsafe abortion are greater contraceptive accessibility and less restrictive abortion laws in addition to trained health care providers. However, these approaches are often curtailed by social, religious, economic, and political factors. This is particularly true in developing nations where 97 percent of unsafe abortions occur. Women who have a lack of access, or knowledge, of contraception undergo unsafe abortions due to social stigma and the financial burden of an unintended pregnancy. Most women globally who seek induced abortions already have children. In industrialized nations, only 3 percent of abortions are unsafe, whereas in developing nations 55 percent are unsafe. The highest rates of unsafe abortions are found in Latin America, Africa, and Southeast Asia. The more restrictive the abortion laws, the more frequent are illegal induced abortion-related deaths. In addition, less restrictive abortion laws do not appear to lead to more abortions. For example, in the developed world, abortion rates declined from 46 to 27 per 1,000 from 1990 to 2014 but remained at around 38 per 1,000 for developing nations over this time period.

Maternal Mortality in High-Income Developed Nations

Since the late 19th century, poor women in higher-income Western nations generally had higher MMR due to inadequate nutrition, illnesses, unsanitary environments, and other factors. On the other hand, richer women began to experience higher rates compared to poorer women in the 1920s. Poor women used midwives at home, while richer women began to go to "lying in" hospitals or special maternity units in hospitals. Delivery was increasingly done by male physicians in hospitals who induced labor, used episiotomies (cutting the pelvic floor during delivery), forceps, more frequent Cesarean sections, and anesthesia. These often caused blood loss, fatal infections, and other complications.

A steep decline in MMR after 1937 was the result of the use of antibiotics and blood transfusions and more rigorous aseptic conditions. By 1950, the rates in all Western countries were similar. In addition, after the mid-1940s, most women delivered in hospital units devoted to maternity care under strict aseptic conditions. Other factors for a dramatic decrease in maternal mortality in developed nations over the century was better educated women, higher standard of living, use of the contraceptive pill and other family planning methods to space children, smaller families, and prenatal care.

The United Kingdom (UK) is an example of the trends in the developed world. In the UK from 1900 to 1937, the annual MMR was a bit over 400. The rigorous use of face masks, gloves and strict aseptic conditions reduced it by 1970 to fewer than 20 and in 2015 to 9 per 100,000. In England and Wales, hospital births increased to about two-thirds from the late 1940s to the mid-1960s. By 1975, home births had fallen to below 5 percent and still remains at this level. In 1948, Britain instituted the National Health Service, which enabled all women to have pre- and postnatal care. In 1967, England liberalized its abortion law to permit any woman to have an abortion up to 24 weeks with the written consent of two physicians and at any point to save her life. This law reduced maternal mortality rates.

In Northern America, at the turn of the 20th century, almost all births occurred outside a hospital with the assistance of a midwife. In the United States, because of lobbying by the medical profession and improved care, a shift from home to hospital deliveries occurred between 1938 and 1948. In 1938, about a half of United States' births were taking place in hospitals, and this rose to 99 percent by 1955. However, out-of-hospital births or "home births" began to increase in the late 20th century—mainly among the middle class—and by 2012 had increased to over 2 percent among non-Hispanic white women and less than 1 percent among other women.

The overall decrease in maternal mortality in the United States has declined due to several factors. The use of antibiotics, blood transfusions, and treatment of preeclampsia to prevent convulsions evolved in the mid-20th century. This resulted in a decrease of maternal deaths by 71 percent from 1939 to 1948. Medicaid in 1965 helped disadvantaged women obtain better and safer medical care. In addition, in the 1960s, states began reforming their strict anti-abortion laws, so when the Supreme Court made abortion legal nationwide, legal abortions were already available in 17 states. The legalization of pregnancy terminations in the late 1960s and early 1970s contributed to an 89 percent decline in deaths from infections from unsafe illegal abortions even before *Roe v. Wade*. By 2014, the abortion rate was 14.6 down from 29.3 per 1,000 women at its peak in 1981. This reduction is likely due to more education concerning family planning and easier access to contraceptives.

However, in terms of maternal death, a difference has been found between women of color and white women. In the beginning of the 20th century, black women were twice as likely to die from pregnancy-related complications compared to white women. This had risen to about three times as likely by the second decade of the 21st century. Possible factors include a lack of prenatal care, low standard of living, poor nutrition, and obesity, which is particularly high among poor black and Mexican American women. More troubling, in the United States between 1990 and 2013, the MMR more than doubled from an estimated 12 to 28 per 100,000 births. It is the highest in any high-income nation. When only non-Hispanic white women are considered, the MMR is still higher compared to other industrialized nations. It is estimated that about half of all deaths are preventable. Some explanations for this increased trend in the United States have been put forth. One factor is that older women are now given birth. A major factor is that since the 1960s, obesity among adults 20 years of age and older more than doubled. This obesity has led to chronic conditions, such as hypertension, diabetes, and heart disease, which have contributed to pregnancy-related complications. Lack of a standard of care for pregnancy-related emergencies across the nation and inconsistent obstetric practices along with few review boards, data collection, and state forums to discuss issues are also thought to be factors in an increased MMR.

On the other hand, Canada, like the United States, is also a nation of immigrants with various minority groups. Its dramatic decrease in MMR over the 20th century into the 21st century reflected other high-income cultures with very low MMR. The MMR in Canada has remained stable from 1990 to 2015 at around 7 per 100,000. A factor for a lowered MMR after 1969 was easy accesses to contraception and safe medical abortions. Unsafe abortions by untrained illegal practitioners were mostly eliminated with a 1969 law that legalized abortions in medical facilities. In 1988, the courts eliminated laws concerning the procedure and allowed provinces to establish their own regulations.

Maternal Mortality in Developing Low-Income Countries

In contrast to high-income developed nations, low- and middle-income nations have had a slower decline in maternal death rates over the last century, and even by 2015 great differences were still seen. Over 99 percent of maternal deaths are found in developing nations, which had an MMR of 237 as opposed to an average of 10 per 100,000 births in high-income nations. The poorest countries also have the poorest data sets on all health factors. Poor women in remote areas are the least likely to receive adequate health care. This is especially true for regions with low numbers of skilled health workers, such as sub-Saharan Africa and South Asia. Many developing countries also do not have adequate registry systems. In addition, MMR from unsafe illegal abortion are often covered up due to religious/cultural/political reasons, or the mother may die in an isolated village and her death not be reported. Therefore, MMR for many low-income nations are often difficult to determine. Progress in these nations has only been determined since the late 20th century.

Some other factors that cause high MMR in low-income nations include child marriages, lack of knowledge to prevent an unintended pregnancy, untrained midwives at home births, misclassification of causes of death, and the ability to recognize a medical emergency in childbirth. Malaria and AIDS are often factors in the high death rate in sub-Saharan Africa. In high-income countries, virtually all women have at least four prenatal visits, are attended by a skilled health worker during childbirth, and receive postpartum care. In 2015, only 40 percent of all pregnant women in low-income countries had the recommended prenatal care visits. A new goal under *Global Strategy for Women's, Children's and Adolescents' Health, 2016–2030* is to reduce the global MMR to less than 70 per 100,000 births, with no country having a maternal mortality rate of more than twice the global average.

It is estimated that the sub-Saharan African region accounted for 62 percent of the global MMR in 2014. However, the MMR in sub-Saharan Africa dropped from 987 in 1990 to 546 per 100,000 in 2015. Most of these deaths could have been prevented by education and access to adequate health care. On the other hand, most African nations are attempting to give all women access to prenatal care during pregnancy along with skilled health care during and after childbirth. But this is often difficult due to distance, poverty, lack of information, civil wars, and conflict, and a weak health care system. Most African nations were committed to the Millennium Development Goal (MDG) 5 and in 2016 to The Global Strategy for Women's, Children's and Adolescents' Health or Countdown to 2030. Moreover, by 2014 African First Ladies began to spearhead efforts to improve maternal policy as they were concerned about child wives, early pregnancy, unsafe abortions, and the risk of HIV.

South Asia—which was British India under the British Empire—including Afghanistan, Bangladesh, India, Pakistan, and others nations had the second highest maternal mortality after sub-Saharan Africa. Only about half of all births were attended by a skilled health person, and about 25 percent of pregnancies ended in abortion. India, with the second largest population in the world after China, had 19 percent of the global MMR although there was a decline from 558 to 182 per 100,000 during the 1990–2015 time periods. This high death ratio is found in particular among the tribal and marginalized populations of the country. The Medical Termination of Pregnancy Act of 1971 allowed for safe abortions up to 20 weeks for various reasons, which helped to reduce the maternal death rate.

To further decrease maternal deaths, India by 2015 had developed a plan of action among its rural and poor populations. These include physicians and health care workers ensuring that women know their blood group and Rh factor and not having abortions unless these are known, informing the head of household that girls should be over 20 years of age before marriage, and more family planning and health care services. In India, about 80 percent of deliveries do not take place in hospitals, particularly in rural areas. However, since 1990—as in all other nations—a decrease was seen in the MMR because of earlier detection of problems, reduced infection, and control of bleeding. The MMR went from 556 to 174 per 100,000 by 2015.

The Middle East and North African region had the third highest maternal deaths rates after sub-Saharan Africa and South Asia. There was some progress as the maternal mortality risk declined from 221 to 110 per 100,000 between 1990 and 2015. Many of these nations wish to improve infant and maternal health. However, by the second decade of the 21st century, civil wars, refugees, extreme terrorist threats, and natural crises have made this difficult for some nations.

The fourth highest region for maternal mortality is found in Latin America and the Caribbean region. Nonetheless, the MMR declined from 135 to 68 per 100,000 from 1990 to 2015. Since 1990 every country in the region has attempted to increase overall and maternal health care. However, there has been a lack of adequate public health strategies. As with many other nations, maternal mortality rates are worse in indigenous and rural populations compared to urban and high-income citizens. Like most developing regions of the world, these nations also have instituted steps over the last part of the 20th century to improve maternal mortality.

The greatest improvement of any region in maternal mortality was found in East Asia, where the MMR fell from approximately 95 to 27 per 100,000, or a reduction of 72 percent, between 1990 and 2015. Only 9 countries achieved the MDG 5 target of reducing the MMR by at least 75 percent between 1990 and 2015, and this included four from East Asia (Cambodia, Lao PDR, Mongolia, and Timor-Leste). However, the MMR in some of these countries remained higher than the global average.

In the People's Republic of China, maternal mortality fell by 98 percent in urban areas from 1949 to 1983, but it was still high among the rural population and the economically disadvantaged. This lowering rate was accomplished by training traditional birth attendants in better hygiene and recognizing problems of pregnancy. In 1979, with unrestricted legal abortion in China—except for sex selection—maternal deaths further declined. From 1990 to 2015, the MMR decreased from 97 to 32 per 100,000 in China.

FAMILY PLANNING

The major method to reduce maternal mortality since the early 20th century has been family-planning programs. Family planning includes the reducing of the number, and the spacing, of pregnancies. Each pregnancy carries a risk of morbidity and mortality, particularly for women already in poor health. Rubber condoms, pessaries (cervical caps), and diaphragms were used by the middle-class and educated in Europe—in particular Holland and Germany—to prevent conception in the early 20th century. The rhythm method and coitus interruptus (withdrawal) were also used around the world but the rhythm method is the only methods sanctioned by the Roman Catholic Church and some other faith groups but has limited effectiveness. Over the 20th century, an increasing number of women used modern birth control, particularly in higher-income nations.

Family planning activist Margaret Sanger published information about contraceptive methods in *Birth Control Review*, a magazine she founded in 1917. At the time, under the Comstock laws, it was illegal to send information on contraception through the U.S. Postal Service. (New York Public Library)

Family Planning in High-Income Nations

In the United States, contraception had been legal throughout most of the 19th century, but the 1873 Comstock Law prohibited information about safe sex, sexuality, STDs, and contraception device being sent through the postal service. Because of this law, it was also illegal for physicians to dispense contraception devices in charity clinics. However, during the early 20th century, educated and well-to-do women were able to obtain contraception secretly from their private physicians. Poor women often bore children they did not want or died from unsafe illegal abortions.

Health and family-planning advocate Margaret Sanger (1879–1966) challenged the Comstock laws by not only publishing material on contraception methods, which she called "birth control," but by also by setting up a birth control clinic in 1916 in Brooklyn, NY, for which she was arrested. Numerous challenges by American pioneers in family planning, including Sanger, in addition to woman suffrage advocate Mary Ware Dennett (1872–1947) and various health and medical organizations, advocated sex education to prevent sexually transmitted diseases, unplanned pregnancies, and the use of birth control in the 1920s and 1930s. Contraceptive devices and sexuality information were finally legalized in the United States in 1936 and accepted by the American Medical Association a year later as a regular part of medical practice.

By the early 1940s, several hundred birth control centers were established in the United States. In 1942, various birth control organizations merged to form Planned Parenthood of America to offer family planning services to all women. However, some states continued to outlaw birth control clinics until the late 1960s. The contraceptive pill was developed in the late 1950s, and by the early 1960s, it was widely used not only in the United States but in many other nations. "The pill" was developed by Jewish American biologist Gregory G. Pincus (1903–1967) and Catholic American gynecologist John Rock (1890–1984). The pill is considered by some as the most important invention ever for women as it gave them control to avoid an unintentional pregnancy. More importantly, it allowed women to space their children for better health. Some religious faiths, such as Catholic Church, however, were against the pill and wanted it banned. Other contraceptives were developed such as intrauterine devices over the late 20th century. By the turn of the 21st century, the top methods for contraception were the pill and female sterilization in the United States, and by 2011 around 74 percent of married or in-union (cohabitating or regular partner) women used some type of contraceptive method.

In Canada, a federal law deemed contraception information illegal in 1892. However, physician Elizabeth Bagshaw (1881–1982)—one of the first female physicians in Canada—established the first family planning clinic in Canada in Hamilton, Ontario, in 1932. She believed women should have the right to prevent pregnancy. Contentious debate and a trial brought public support for the birth control movement. The pill was first available in 1957 to regulate menstrual periods but was illegal for contraceptive purposes until 1969; therapeutic abortions were also made legal in Canada that year. Around 85 percent of married or cohabitating women used some type of contraception by 2011.

In Britain, by the early 20th century, many middle-class women were educated about contraception and how to avoid pregnancy using the rhythm method, condoms, and diaphragms. In 1921, British women's rights crusader and family planning advocate Marie Stopes (1880–1958) established the first permanent birth control clinic in Britain, which was run by midwives and visiting physicians. She also influenced the establishment of clinics in British colonies in the Middle East, Asia, Africa, and other regions. After a birth control conference in April 1930, the Ministry of Health allowed birth control advice to be given at welfare centers.

In the early 1960s when the pill was available, the National Health Service allowed it to be prescribed to married women only who already had children and did not want any more. After campaigning by women's rights advocates, in 1974, family planning clinics were allowed to prescribe the pill to single women. This was highly controversial as some felt it would promote immorality. By 2000, about 80 percent of married or in-union women were using some type of contraception.

On the Continent, by 2000, most women who were married, or had regular partners, were using some type of contraception including Germany (85%), Norway (80%), and Finland (84%). In Catholic countries, it ranged from about 92 percent in Hungary to 66 percent in Lithuania and about a third in Poland. They generally used the rhythm method or withdrawal. In France, the ban against birth control was lifted in 1965, and by the turn of the 21st century, 95 percent of women were using contraception. In Italy, women gained the right to access birth control information in 1970, and 1980 in Ireland.

Family Planning in Low-Income Nations

Little information on family planning in developing nations was available until the late 20th century. A fear by the 1960s in developed nations was the worldwide population explosion, particularly in developing nations with high fertility rates.

It was feared this dramatic population increase could lead to more famine, wars, and disease in these nations. Women had five to six children, on average, in some Asian and African nations, and population growth was outstripping economic growth. The replacement fertility rate is roughly 2.0 births per woman for higher-income countries but ranged from 2.5 to 3.3 in developing countries because of higher infant mortality rates. To determine family planning needs, a series of national surveys began to be carried out in less developed countries beginning in the 1970s.

These surveys found that high fertility rates in these nations were the result of patriarchal concepts of women's roles within the family, lack of access to family planning services, a preference for male offspring, early marriage and frequent pregnancies spaced too closely together, and a lack of human rights, all of which had health consequences—sometimes fatal. Lack of education for girls and lack of sexuality information also contributed to the problem. Information gathered from the studies led to major health interventions for low and middle income countries to reduce maternal morbidly and mortality and decrease the number of pregnancies per women. These were outlined in the 1994 International Conference on Population and Development and the 1995 Fourth World Conference on Women, which addressed family planning, birth control, forced female circumcision, and a right for a woman to control her own body. Some nations embraced these programs, and some still struggled in the early 21st century.

Family planning was, and is still, woefully inadequate in sub-Saharan Africa. In many African nations, religious, social, or cultural reasons have resulted in resistance to modern contraception. This has led to the highest population growth rate compared to any other region of the world threatening further economic, social, and political crisis due to decreased death rates from immunization and improvements in health care. In addition, the decline in the birth rate slowed in the 21st century and fertility remained high. In sub-Saharan Africa, as a whole, in 2015, only 28 percent of married or in-union women were using contraceptives. Only a few nations including South Africa, Zimbabwe, Botswana, and Kenya, have had successful family planning programs with around 50 percent using contraception. By the second decade of the 21st century, more education to address negative attitudes toward family planning, education for girls, and more family planning services have been recommended to meet international health goals. However, wars and a refugee crisis in several African nations resulted in a humanitarian catastrophe in the second decade of the century that made these goals difficult to meet.

In India around 1927, family planning was suggested by British health reformers. However, India's independence leader, Mahatma Gandhi (1869–1948), was opposed to any family planning as he felt that self-control was the best form of birth control. After Gandhi's death, a national family planning program was launched in 1951, which was only marginally successful. In the 1970s, in an effort to curb rapid population growth, poverty, and food shortages, it was mandated that all men with two or more children be sterilized. This most unpopular law failed and created an aversion to any family planning for several decades. However, programs aimed at women in both urban and rural areas have resulted in increased practice of contraception use. In 1970, 13 percent, and by 2011, 54 percent of married or in-union women used contraception. IUDs, the pill, and condoms were the most common methods. But contraception use is very low among women with either no surviving or only one surviving child. However, it is generally used among women with at least two surviving children resulting in India approaching the international goals of reducing fertility.

North Africa and Middle Eastern nations have spotty practices of family planning. One of the reasons is various interpretations by different Muslim clerics on its practice. However, "Islam is considerate of FP [Family Planning] as spacing pregnancies and curtailing the number of pregnancies makes mothers more physically fit and fathers more financially at ease" (Shaikh, Azmat, and Mazhar, 2013, S-70). Some Islamic sects only allow coitus interruptus while others allow modern contraception. In Egypt, for example, a religious decree was issued in the mid-1930s permitting modern contraception. Family planning clinics were then established in urban areas. As found in many nations, rural and isolated populations are less likely to have access to many health services. Other barriers by the early 21st century to access to contraception were civil wars and large refugee populations. In some of these nations, educating the mother-in-law, who is often the main decision makers in terms of contraceptive use, is important. By 2015, about 53–58 percent of married or in-union women were using contraceptives in this region of the world.

In the Latin American and Caribbean region, family planning services and modern birth control were not widely available in the early 20th century in many of the nations that make up this region. This was primarily due to conflict between pro- and anti-birth-control factions. Promodern contraception is encouraged by businesses, middle- and working-class women, physicians, and mainstream Protestants. It is generally opposed by Roman Catholic and evangelical Protestant clergy and groups, some Amerindian communities, and peasants. In these primarily Catholic nations, the use of modern methods of contraception in the first decade of the 21st century ranged from around 35 percent in Bolivia to 77 percent in Brazil with an average of 73 percent for the region. Most nations, however, have had increased use of contraception since the latter half of the 20th century although more than a half of all pregnancies were unintended. Beginning around 2015, a major concern in this region was the Zika virus epidemic—carried by the *Aedes* mosquito—that caused some infected mothers to bear infants with microcephaly (small brain and skull) and various neurological disorders. Basic contraception, such as birth control pills and IUDs, were in short supply even for middle-class women. This epidemic resulted in the United Nations in 2016 pressuring governments to make birth control more available and loosening abortion laws.

The nation with the largest population changed its policies on family planning in the mid-20th century. After the formation of the People's Republic of China in 1949, the central government initially encouraged people to have more children. It provided material incentives and severely limited the use of sterilization and elective abortions. However, this program caused a dramatic population increase with resulting famine in several areas of the country. As a result, the Regulation of Contraception and Induced Abortion action by the Ministry of Health in

August 1953 promoted contraception and abortion services that were also extended into the rural areas. The program promoted later marriage, longer intervals between births, and smaller families. To further decrease its burgeoning population, a one-child policy was introduced in 1979, which reduced the fertility rate. Under this policy, the central government advocated family planning, contraception use, sterilization, and induced abortions. This was a successful but contentious program that brought economic stability and growth to China. After this policy—since boys were preferred—female infanticide increased, and after ultrasound tests were developed, abortions for sex selection became common; screening for gender was banned in 1994. By 2014, 85 percent of married or in-union women were using contraceptives—one of the highest rates in the world. In addition, an aging and decreasing population led the central government to end the controversial one-child policy law in October 2015.

WOMEN'S RIGHTS, WORK, AND HEALTH CARE

Women gained considerable rights over the 20th century and into the 21st century, particular in high-income developed nations, but in low-income nations they were still disadvantaged in social and economic power, which restricted their access to well-paid employment and good health care. Women's health goes hand in hand with women's rights, education, and work. As women gained more rights, their health improved. Secretary General of the United Nations, Ban Ki-Moon (UN Women, 2015, 2), notes that "A quality education, a decent job, access to health care and a life free from violence and discrimination are necessary foundations for women and girls to be equal partners with men and boys in every aspect of life."

Over the 20th century, women gained suffrage—the right to vote—in most nations. By the first decade of the century, New Zealand, Australia, and Finland granted suffrage to women. However, indigenous populations were often excluded. Women in many higher-income nations gained suffrage rights at the end of WWI, including Canada, Austria, Germany, and Poland in 1918; the United States in 1920; and Britain in 1928. However, it was not until the 1940s and 1950s that women in some higher- and lower-income nations gained suffrage, including in France, Italy, Japan, Mexico, Argentina, Columbia, Pakistan, China, India, Nicaragua, and Egypt. The right was gained in both higher- and lower-income nations between 1970 and 1999 in Switzerland, Bangladesh, Portugal, South Africa, and in some Arab nations in the early 21st century including Kuwait, United Arab Emirates, and Saudi Arabia in 2011.

In addition to suffrage, in the United States and the UK, a women's health movement that campaigned for birth control as previously mentioned occurred in the early part of the 20th century. A second women's health movement emerged in the 1960s and 1970s to improve the health of all women. It championed a woman's right to control her own body, which eventually resulted in more liberal birth control and abortion laws. It pushed to change childbirth practices to become less medicalized and more humanized in the United States as found in other developed nations that used midwifes. "Natural childbirth," without medical intervention, and with husbands and significant others present during the birth process emerged in the 1970s in free standing birth centers. These were, and are, generally staffed by midwives or advanced-degreed nurse practitioners who have arrangements with an obstetrician in case of birthing issues; the centers generally only accept low risk births. By the beginning of the 21st century, hospitals also began more family centered care along with childbirth classes. Lamaze (a breathing method) introduced to the West around 1950 reduced discomfort during childbirth. In most developed nations, breastfeeding, which had become unfashionable by the late 19th century, was again advocated beginning around 1970. However, this practice decreased again in the early 21st century.

In developed nations, opportunities for women working for pay outside of the home and more education advanced over the 20th century. Working-class women in the early 20th century in higher-income countries worked in factories, domestic service for richer households, or in family businesses. In Britain, for example, in 1911, domestic services employed 28 percent of all working women. Poorer women worked at home doing laundry, repairing and making clothing, and other crafts—the destitute sold themselves as prostitutes. These jobs were in addition to housework and childrearing. Among middle-class women, nursing, teaching, secretarial, and other business careers became common over the century.

However, in the pre-WWII years, upon marriage women in some professions, such as teaching, were often required to quit their jobs—this was particularly true if they became pregnant. These "marriage bars" did not affect women's employment in very low paid jobs. In the 1960s, in the United States, antidiscriminatory laws were passed, and more married women entered the workforce. Upper middle-class women until the latter third of the century were generally expected to do charity work and to stay home. However, by 2014, about 57 percent of women in North America worked for wages. Many of them were now engaged in full-time professional careers. In the UK, 56 percent of the women worked for wages; in Europe, 50 percent; in Latin America and the Caribbean, 54 percent; in the Arab world, 24 percent; in sub-Saharan Africa, 64 percent; in South Asia, 31 percent; and in China, 64 percent.

As more women worked outside the home, better health and safety conditions including laws in the early part of the 20th century, such as the number of hours a day women could do factory work, were passed in developed countries. Workplace safety for women also increased. In 1911, the Triangle Shirtwaist Fire in New York City left 146 dead, mostly teenage and immigrant young women. Doors had been locked by the management, so they could not escape. The fire and deaths led to legislation requiring improved factory safety standards.

Women in the nations involved in WWII worked in factories and war-related jobs, but when the men returned home, they often lost their employment. At the turn of the 21st century, concerns about working women's health resurfaced. The Maternity Protection Convention of 2000 of the International Labour Organization Convention recommended that women have health protection, maternity leave (more than 14 week), leave in case of illness, employment protection, non-discrimination, and accommodation for breastfeeding mothers. However, by 2017 this convention had only been signed by a few nations.

Until the Flexner Report of medical education in 1910, women were freely admitted into medical schools. This changed in the 1920s when, until late 1970s, few women were allowed into medical school or other postgraduate education so as to enter occupations historically considered male such as engineering, human and veterinarian medicine, dentistry, academia, and law in many developed nations. For example, in medical schools in 1965, only 8 percent were women compared to 47 percent in 2013 in the United States. However, women in these traditional male fields were, and are still, often paid less for the same position and are less likely to be in leadership positions.

By the end of the 20th century, the middle-class female workforce was still heavily represented in the health care industry, teaching, social work, and office careers. Working class-women increasingly moved to jobs that did not require heavy labor ranging from light factory and ancillary health care to food and other service jobs in developed nations. In addition, these jobs were still generally low-paid positions. Most importantly, women also acquired advanced education that led to higher wages and long-term careers. By the second decade of the 21st century, a similar, or even a higher, proportion of women were attending colleges and universities compared to men in many developed nations. By 2014, for example, women accounted for 55 percent of undergraduates enrolled at four-year colleges in the United States, 58 percent by 2009 in Canada, and 55 percent in the UK in 2011.

For women in developing low-income nations, a living wage represented a pathway out of poverty. In Asia, during the late 20th century, women migrated from small farm villages to urban areas and were about 80 percent of the workforce in the garment and textile industry. However, they had low wages, long hours, and workplace safety issues. In 2012, a fire at a textile factory in Bangladesh killed at least 117—mostly women. Similar to the Triangle Fire in New York City, a hundred years earlier, exits were blocked, and women jumped to their death. In the aftermath of the fire, better safety standards were imposed on Asian factories manufacturing goods for developed nations. Advances in some African nations have occurred in terms of work. Farm women by the 21st century, in some African nations, were allowed to own land with their husbands. In Latin America, many women worked in garment factories and other manufacturing jobs along with farming and as migrant laborers.

On a global scale although there are still many gaps in employment, wages, and health services for women, by the early 21st century, many advances in women's health were made since the early 20th century. The reduction in maternal mortality, the availability of family-planning services, the right to vote, the right to work outside of the home in meaningful careers, and the availability of better health care reduced overall death rates and enabled many women to reach their highest potential.

5

Infant and Children's Health

Globally, at the turn of the 20th century, most deaths and disabilities in infancy and childhood were from birth complications, infectious diseases, and malnutrition. In low-income tropical regions, malaria was also a killer. By the 21st century in developing low-income nations, these conditions, in addition to HIV, were still the major causes of mortality among infants and children under five years of age. In higher-income nations, birth defects, preterm birth, and low birth weight were the major causes of morbidity and mortality. Factors that advanced infant and children's health from the early 20th century included immunizations against—and the prevention of—childhood and other illnesses, identifying issues that led to congenital birth defects, and laws curtailing child labor in developed and most developing nations. The consequences of advanced technological developments, generational differences and parenting styles, bullying and child abuse, which caused emotional harm, emerged. In addition, eugenic concerns at the beginning of the 20th century and assisted reproduction techniques and genetic manipulation to produce healthier babies by the late 20th century evolved.

GLOBAL TRENDS IN INFANT AND CHILD MORTALITY

The infant mortality rate, like the maternal mortality rate, is a major indicator of the health of a society over time. It also indicates the differences between populations both within, and between, nations. As with maternal mortality, adequate data were not collected from many low-income nations, especially in sub-Saharan Africa, until 1990.

Mortality in Developed Higher-Income Nations

The infant and child mortality rates dramatically decreased over the 20th century in Western nations. The French, in the late 19th century, were the first to become concerned about high mortality rates among infants and young children. Worries about these high death rates led European nations, and northern America, to enact measures that reduced these mortality rates. The interventions included better sanitation, clean water, and pasteurized milk, which reduced common infections such as "summer diarrhea," a major killer of infants in the early 20th century. Better hygiene among the population, in particular hand washing and frequent bathing, helped to prevent infection. Rising standards of living, especially better nutrition, reduction of poverty and crowding, central heating, and cheaper clothing to keep infants warm in cooler climates, led to healthier infants and mothers. Well-baby clinics and postnatal clinics caught early health problems, and spacing of pregnancies and education for mothers assisted in reducing the death rate.

During the first three decades of the century, public health, social welfare, and clinical medicine—in particular pediatrics and obstetrics—professionals collaborated to combat infant mortality in Western nations. These groups joined forces to assure legislation requiring pasteurized milk and other public health issues. Trained midwives using aseptic techniques prevented the spread of disease to newborns. However, as more women delivered in hospitals, the death rate of infants from birth injuries actually increased from around 1915 through the late 1930s due to inadequately skilled physicians performing techniques such as using forceps to extract the infant during childbirth. In the post-WWII years, more babies were born in hospitals in higher-income nations. A decreased usage of some surgical interventions and better aseptic techniques lowered mortality along with antibiotics.

In the United States, for example, from 1915 through 1997, the infant mortality rate declined greater than 90 percent from about 165 to 7.2 per 1,000 live births. After this time, it essentially plateaued. In 1900 in some cities, up to 30 percent of infants died before reaching their first birthday. To cope with this high mortality rate, the Children's Bureau was formed and became the primary federal agency to work toward improving maternal and infant welfare. By 2016, overall advancements had reduced the under-five-years-of-age mortality rate to 6.5 per 1,000 live births in the United States. But compared to similar high-income nations, the United States had the highest rate. Countries with lower rates included Australia at 2.2, Canada 4.9, Finland 2.3, France 4.3, Germany 3.7, Israel 4.4, Japan 2.7, Sweden 3.0, and the UK at 4.2 per 1,000 live births.

Reasons for higher rates in the United States included an increase in preterm multiple births due to assisted reproduction and differences due to ethnicity and poverty. Infant mortality (up to one year of age) has been the highest among non-Hispanic African Americans since records had been kept beginning around 1915. By 2001, the death rate among this group was about 14 compared to 6 per 1,000 live births for both Hispanic and non-Hispanic Caucasian Americans, 5 for Asian and Pacific islanders, and 9 per 1,000 live births for Native American Indians. Poverty, lack of prenatal care, inadequate nutrition, and other lifestyle factors were thought to contribute to these differences.

However, differences due to ethnicity have also been found in Canada, Australia, and New Zealand. High infant mortality rates were found among indigenous peoples in these nations. These higher rates were caused by low birth weight, stillbirth, preterm birth, environmental factors, and among older infants, sudden infant death syndrome (SIDS) and respiratory-tract infections.

Mortality in Developing Lower-Income Nations

In developing nations, throughout the 20th century and into the 21st century, conditions such as preterm birth complications and infections, such as diarrhea and pneumonia, were still the major killers of infants due to inadequate nutrition and poverty. In Southeast Asia and sub-Saharan Africa, less than half of infants younger than 12 months had their birth registered leading to probable underreporting of deaths. The major risk factors for children dying before the age of five were poverty, being born in rural areas in low-income nations, and having mothers without basic education.

To address the needs of infant and child mortality in developing nations, the World Health Organization (WHO), through the UN Millennium Declaration, developed various goals for nations to achieve to attain basic human rights including health. The Millennium Development Goal (MDG) 4—to reduce child mortality—encouraged nations to decrease by two-thirds, between 1990 and 2015, the mortality rate of those under five years of age. Although global mortality rates dropped from 91 per 1,000 live births in 1990 to 43 in 2015, the rate was not adequate to reach the target MDG.

This was particularly true in WHO's African region. In 2016, the highest under-five-years-of-age mortality rate was 81 compared to the lowest rate found in the European region of 11 per 1,000 live births. The neonatal mortality (first month of life) rate for these two regions was 28 and 6 per 1,000 live births, respectively. Under five-years-of-age mortality rates were 52 per 1,000 live births in the Eastern Mediterranean region, 43 in Southeast Asia, 15 in the region of the Americas, and 14 per 1,000 live births in the Western Pacific region.

To further decrease the high death rates of developing regions, WHO developed the 2030 WHO Sustainable Development Goal (SDG) Target 3.2, to assure healthy lives for all ages. To meet this target, a number of countries would need to accelerate prevention programs to reduce neonatal mortality to at least 12 per 1,000 and under-five-year-old mortality to at least 25 per 1,000 live births by 2030. More than half of the deaths of infants and young children were preventable and treatable through simple interventions. These included strengthening health systems, better hygiene education, sanitation and clean water, and more trained birth attendants. Prevention and treatment of pneumonia and diarrhea, vaccination to prevent childhood diseases, and reducing various diseases including HIV, tuberculosis, cholera, malaria and emerging tropical diseases such as Ebola needed to be addressed. Methods to increase both agriculture techniques and food aid to prevent malnutrition in areas prone to draught and conflict also needed to be implemented to achieve the SDG.

GLOBAL CHILDHOOD MALNUTRITION

Throughout history, malnutrition has been a major underlying factor in infant and childhood morbidity and mortality. Although advances had been made over the 20th century in agriculture and food distribution worldwide, large scale famine still occurred in the early 21st century in some developing nations due to

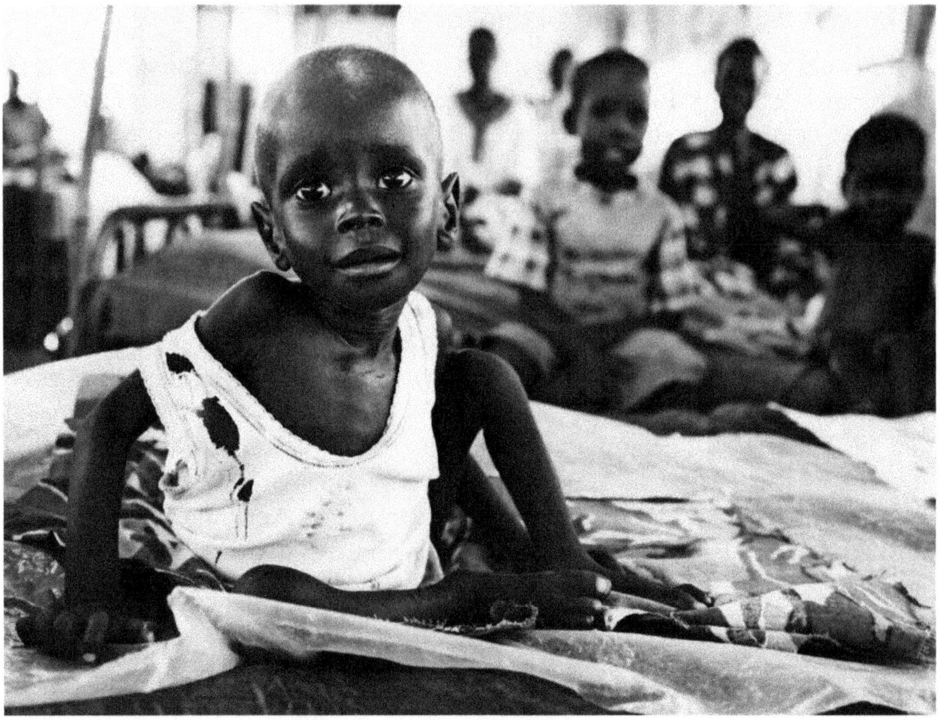

A child at a mission hospital in South Sudan suffers severe malnutrition, August 2016. Malnutrition throughout history has been a major causal factor in infant and childhood morbidity. (Albert Gonzalez Farran/AFP/Getty Images)

natural disasters, climate change, political conflicts, and war, leading to childhood malnourishment and death. Malnutrition in children and infants came in three forms—stunting, wasting, and childhood obesity.

Childhood stunting, according to WHO, is a "height for age" value defined as less than two standard deviations below the WHO Child Growth Standards median scale. Wasting is a "weight for height" value and is considered less than two standard deviations below the WHO Growth Standards median for children (WHO, 2017a). Stunting results from the cumulative effects of both undernutrition and infections before and after birth. Children suffering from stunting may never grow to their full height and may have a lack of brain growth that can reduce their maximum cognitive potential. They often have learning disabilities, difficulties in school, are discriminated against by their communities, and earn less compared to adults, which perpetuates a poverty cycle.

In wasting, children are both stunted and underweight. Wasting is a symptom of acute malnutrition, resulting from inadequate food intake and/or infectious diseases. Children suffering from wasting have weakened immunity, are susceptible to long-term developmental delays, and face an increased risk of death. Stunting and wasting were found in some African nations, North Korea, and China in the late 20th century and in portions of Central Asia, South Asia and Africa in the early 21st century.

In contrast to a lack of food, by the early 21st century, an emerging aspect of childhood malnutrition was an overweight and obesity epidemic. These conditions increased in urban areas in developing nations and throughout high-income nations. The epidemic resulted from rapid socioeconomic changes beginning in the late 20th century. These changes included increased availability of food and cheaper food high in fat, sugar, and salt being fed to infants and children along with increased global urbanization, sedentary lifestyles due to electronic devices, and decreased physical activity leading to excess weight gain. Overweight and obese children were likely to stay obese into adulthood and be more likely to develop chronic conditions such as diabetes and cardiovascular diseases at younger ages. This worldwide obesity epidemic among children had the potential of negating many health advances that had led to increased longevity since the early 20th century. Although childhood obesity is higher in North American, European, and other higher-income nations, childhood obesity is also found in lower-income nations where people have moved to cities from rural agricultural areas.

To tackle this worldwide problem, the Commission on Ending Childhood Obesity was established in 2014. This commission recommended national health programs to promote the intake of healthy food, weight management, preconception and pregnancy care, early childhood diet, and physical activity. Breast feeding up to two years of age and solid foods at 6 months were recommended along with adequate nutrition for pregnant women for optimal fetal development.

PRENATAL INFLUENCES AND CONGENITAL CONDITIONS

In addition to nutrition, other environmental and genetic factors can lead to abnormal fetal development, mental and physical congenital deformities, and preterm births. Preterm babies are small for gestational age and have low birth weight, which is a major factor in 60–80 percent of all neonatal deaths. Prenatal examinations to determine potential problems with in utero development are essential to help prevent low birth weight. Advances in medicine and health knowledge by the late 20th century led to prevention and treatment interventions for some causes of death from low birth weight. These included adequate feeding, keeping the infant warm, hygienic umbilical cord and skin care, and early detection and treatment of infections. Preterm births occur globally but are higher among the poor and in low-income nations without adequate prenatal care.

One of the factors in low birth weight is smoking. Smoking was not common among women in most countries in the early 20th century. After WWI, smoking began to increase in many Western nations among women. Smoking peaked in the 1960s and 1970s and decreased to less than 20 percent by the 2010s in most high-income nations. As smoking decreased in developed nations, it increased in lower-income developing nations. By the second decade of the 21st century, developing countries accounted for nearly 70 percent of tobacco use worldwide with one in 10 women who was a smoker or living in a home environment with second hand smoke. Women who smoked during pregnancy were also more likely than other women to have a miscarriage, early separation of the placenta from the womb, and babies with cleft lip or cleft palate. Smoking during pregnancy was also a risk factor of Sudden Unexpected Infant Deaths (SUID).

SUID, also called Crib Death or Sudden Infant Death Syndrome (SIDS), has been a killer of infants for centuries. A caregiver checks on the infant and finds it has stopped breathing and is dead for no apparent reason. Sometimes death was attributed to accidental suffocation, strangulation in bed, or infanticide. The exact cause of these deaths in many cases was still unknown in the early 21st century. However, by the turn of this century, the SUID rate declined significantly in most higher-income nations when a "Back to Sleep Campaign" was introduced in the mid-1990s recommending that infants be placed on their back for sleep without blankets.

Infectious diseases transmitted to the developing fetus can cause congenital problems for the newborn. In the early 20th century, syphilis transmitted by an infected mother to her fetus often resulted in mental retardation, facial deformities, deafness, heart conditions, and early death. In 1906, German physician and bacteriologist August von Wassermann (1866–1925) developed a test for syphilis. The disease was then treated with the sulfonamide—Salvarsan—discovered in 1908 and first used in 1910, which reduced the incidence of the disease. Once antibiotics were developed in the late 1930s, they generally cured syphilis in pregnant women, so congenital syphilis became rare by the late 20th century in developed nations but was still found in sub-Saharan Africa or other areas that lacked adequate prenatal care.

Other infectious diseases cause congenital deformations. An emerging infectious disease, the Zika virus, brought fear to pregnant women by 2016 in Mexico, Central and South America, the Caribbean, and south Florida and Texas in the United States. It was transmitted by the bite of the daytime-active *Aedes* mosquito and sexual activity with an infected person. The disease is endemic in Southeast Asia, some areas of Africa, and Uganda, where it was first identified in 1947. From 2007 to 2015, the virus spread across the Pacific Ocean to the Americas, leading to a Zika epidemic during 2015–2016. Roughly 5 percent of infants born to infected mothers have microcephaly (small brain) and/or neurological damage, along with mental and physical disabilities. Pregnant women were advised to avoid unprotect sex with a person who has traveled in the area, and if they lived in the epidemic area, use mosquito repellant, cover exposed skin, and get tested for the infection if they believe they had been exposed. Avoiding pregnancy was also recommended. As of 2019, there is no known treatment but a vaccine against the scourge is in clinical trial.

A lack of folic acid or B complex vitamins also has consequences for the developing fetus. The connection between lack of folic acid and neural-tube defects—specifically anencephaly and spina bifida—was first suggested in the 1960s. In this condition, the spinal cord may not adequately close and can cause paralysis. In the worst case, the infant is lacking most of its brain. However, it was not until the 1990s that pregnant women, along with all women of child bearing age, were advised to take supplemental folic acid in an effort to reduce this condition. By the second decade of the 21st century, neuro-tube defects had decreased in developed nations where supplements were taken. However, they had not declined in impoverished low- and middle-income countries with lack of adequate nutrition and poor maternal care such as sub-Saharan Africa and parts of Asia.

On the other hand, too much of another substance could cause congenital defects. Heavy alcohol consumption by pregnant women could lead to Fetal Alcohol Syndrome Disorder (FASD). This condition is characterized by growth retardation, facial abnormalities, decreased mental capacities, and other serious issues among infants and children. However, it was not until 1973 that this syndrome was "discovered" in the United States. This was despite the fact that drinking and drunkenness during pregnancy had occurred for centuries in many cultures. Although the amount of alcohol consumed by a pregnant woman that could harm a developing fetus was debated, several nations by the end of the century recommend that women not consume more than one drink per day or abstain from alcohol during pregnancy. However, by 2017, alcohol use during pregnancy had increased globally to around 10 percent. The estimated prevalence of FASD in the general population was 1.5 per 1,000 people. The five countries with the highest alcohol use in pregnancy were in Europe and included Russia, the United Kingdom, Denmark, Belarus, and Ireland. The lowest levels of drinking and FASD were found in the Eastern Mediterranean and Southeast Asia regions because of high rates of abstinence for religious reasons. High rates of FASD were found among the indigenous people in Australia, North America, and South Africa. Screening mothers for alcohol abuse along with education to help prevent FASD was recommended.

CHILDHOOD DISEASES AND THEIR PREVENTION

In 1900, childhood diseases and other infectious diseases often maimed or killed infants and children. Advances over the 20th century, such as clean water, immunizations, and antibiotics, had eliminated or reduced the scourge of many of these diseases by the end of the century. They were called childhood diseases because an infection during childhood generally gave immunity for life. A major cause of death among children in the early 20th century was diphtheria, and in England and Wales in the 1930s, it was the third leading cause of death in children. Diphtheria is caused by a bacterium (*Corynebacterium diphtheria*) that secretes a powerful toxin. The toxin often causes a pseudo membrane to appear in the throat that prevents breathing. An antitoxin was discovered in 1890s by German physician Emil von Behring (1854–1917) that neutralized the toxic effects. However, the antitoxin, along with a vaccine against the disease developed in the 1920s, was not widely used until the early 1930s in many developed nations. Antibiotics to treat diphtheria were not available until after WWII. By the late 20th century, it was a rare disease in industrialized nations and was primarily found in sub-Saharan African nations in the 2010s.

Another disease, pertussis (whooping cough) is an extremely contagious disease caused by the bacterium *Bordetella pertussis.* These bacteria produce toxins that lead to inflammation in the respiratory tract. An infant or young child experiences bouts of rapid coughing followed by a "whooping" sound; adults often just have a lingering cough. Pertussis can be deadly for infants. In the 2010s, whooping cough was still found in higher-income nations—although they had high vaccination rates—and it remained a major factor for infant mortality in the developing world where about 95 percent of cases were found. In higher-income nations, a dramatic decline in pertussis was found after 1943 with the development of a vaccine against it. However, a rise in incidence occurred at the end of the century, with an epidemic in Australia in the late 1990s and also during 2008–2012 and in North America and Europe around 2012. China began national immunization in the 1960s and saw a decrease in the disease. However, between 2013 and 2016, China also had an epidemic of pertussis, and the disease remained endemic in most nations.

Besides pertussis, another disease, tetanus, sometimes called "lockjaw," could lead to infant deaths. The disease is contracted by spores of the bacterium *Clostridium tetani*, which produces a toxin. The disease can occur in a newborn infant whose mother was not immune to the disease and thus had not received passive immunity. By the late 20th century, it was rare in developed nations but was common in some developing countries due to the use of dirty instruments in post-birth rituals to cut the umbilical cord or circumcision. For example, in the south Eastern Cape of Africa, the umbilical cord was cut by a piece of thatch and smeared with various substances. Older individuals contracted the spores in cuts and puncture wounds particularly when working with soil or animals. The disease is characterized by convulsive muscle spasms starting in the jaw and neck. Although the tetanus toxoid vaccination was developed in 1924, it was not widely used until World War II.

While diphtheria, pertussis, and tetanus immunizations were developed in the 1920s, they did not see widespread use in industrialized nations until around 1940, when they were combined as the DPT vaccine given to infants in a series of injections. By the 1980s, it was recommended that adults receive a booster immunization of tetanus and diphtheria (Td) vaccine every 10 years and a single dose of the combined formula Tdap (tetanus-diphtheria-acellular pertussis) for one of those years. By 2004, most WHO regions had 90 percent or more children vaccinated. The exception was the African, Eastern Mediterranean, and Southeast Asian region where fewer than 70 percent of children had been vaccinated with DPT although these regions had made substantial improvements since the late 1990s.

Another group of childhood diseases in which vaccines were combined included rubella (German, or three-day, measles), measles (rubeola), and mumps. A vaccine to prevent measles first became available in 1963, and an improved one in 1968. Vaccines for mumps and rubella became available in 1967 and 1969, respectively. The three vaccines were combined in 1971 to become the measles-mumps-rubella (MMR) vaccine, which became widely used in higher-income nations. However, these three diseases caused health issues around the world into the 2010s despite the availability of safe and effective vaccines. The rubella virus could produce serious congenital malformations. Pregnant women infected with the virus during the first trimester could transmit the virus to the fetus resulting in miscarriage or an infant born with Congenital Rubella Syndrome discovered in 1941. This syndrome included severe brain damage, blindness, deafness, heart conditions, and low weight births. There was a pandemic of rubella between 1962 and 1965, starting in Europe and spreading to northern America. As a result, these nations began a concerted effort to vaccinate not only infants but young women. By 2015, the WHO Americas region had essentially eradicated the disease although it was still prevalent in other areas of the world, in particular Africa and Southeast Asia. However, in 2017, Bhutan and the Maldives both had eliminated Rubella because of the WHO vaccination program.

However, rubeola measles, a highly contagious viral disease, still contributed to the death of infants and young children into the 2010s globally. Severe measles was more likely to be found among poorly nourished children with a vitamin A deficiency and HIV infections in lower-income nations. Measles can lead to blindness, deafness, and inflammation of the brain and death. Up through the mid-20th century, children with measles in Western cultures were kept in darkened rooms as this was thought to reduce the potential threat of blindness. By 2000, measles had almost been eliminated in the United States and some Western European nations. However, by 2011, it was increasingly found in Europe and was a major problem in some African nations, India, China, and Southeast Asia due to low vaccination rates. In 2014, two measles outbreaks occurred in the United States. One outbreak emerged in an unvaccinated Amish community in Ohio, transmitted by a missionary who had traveled to the Philippines. The other originated out of Disneyland where unvaccinated children became sick and spread it to others around the nation.

This outbreak occurred because some parents in North America, and also England and Wales, feared that vaccines might cause autism, based upon a 1990s fraudulent study. Measles outbreaks also occurred on college campuses in the 2010s in North America, and an epidemic erupted in Europe in the winter of 2017 as vaccination rates had declined. To prevent the spread of communicable diseases, the "herd immunity"—when enough people are immune—needs to be high. In the case of measles, it is at least 90 percent of the population.

The other highly contagious childhood disease—mumps—which is part of the MMR vaccine, is caused by a virus from the genus *Rubulavirus.* Its major symptom is swelling of the salivary glands below the ear. However, it can cause inflammation of the testes in males who have reached puberty and permanent deafness and meningitis. Other infectious diseases that can affect infants and children are discussed in chapter 6.

To eradicate dangerous childhood diseases, the World Health Organization's Global Vaccine Action Plan of May 2012 targeted measles and rubella for elimination in five WHO regions by 2020 and to achieve vaccination coverage of at least 90 percent nationally around the world. An earlier global campaign had dramatically reduced the dreaded disease poliomyelitis, polio or "infantile paralysis"—the term used through the mid-20th century. This disease was not common in industrialized nations until the early part of the century. Polio mainly affected children under five years of age. About one in 200 infections led to irreversible paralysis of legs or arms, and from 5 to 10 percent died when their diaphragms also become paralyzed even though they were placed in "iron lungs" that breathed for the patient.

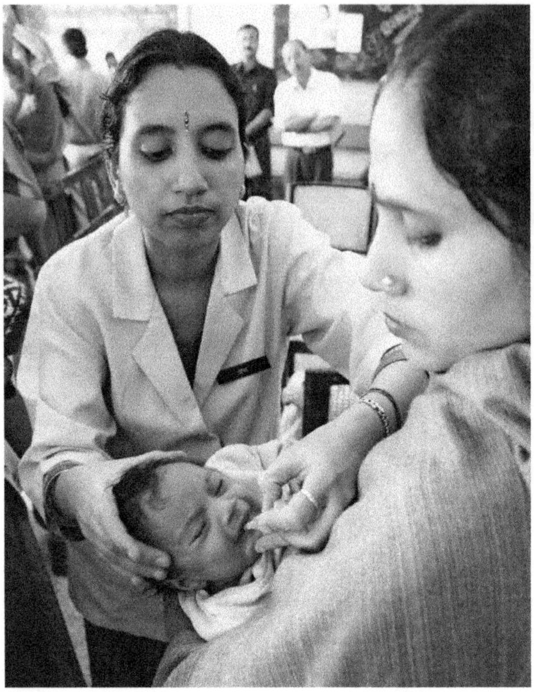

A World Health Organization (WHO) worker in India vaccinates a child against polio as part of a worldwide campaign to eradicate the disease, 2005. Another WHO initiative has targeted measles and rubella for worldwide elimination by 2020. (WHO/Pallava Bagla)

By 1910, frequent epidemics regularly occurred throughout the developed world, primarily in cities during the summer months. The disease often struck middle-class children. A cause for more frequent epidemics was the growth of indoor plumbing and cleanliness resulting in children not being exposed to the virus as babies. The disease reached a peak in the 1940s and 1950s. The only partially successful treatment was developed by a controversial Australian nurse, Elizabeth Kenney (1880–1952), who used hot packs and physical therapy to move paralyzed limbs, contrary to medical practice of the time, which immobilized the limbs.

The development of an injectable inactivated virus vaccine in 1955 and a live oral vaccine in 1962 dramatically reduced polio in higher-income nations. In 1988, the 41st World Health Assembly adopted a resolution for the worldwide eradication of polio called the Global Polio Eradication Initiative (GPEI). It was sponsored by national governments, WHO, the American CDC, UNICEF, and nongovernment organizations such as the Bill & Melinda Gates Foundation and Rotary International. Due to its efforts, in 1994, the WHO region of the Americas was certified polio-free, followed in 2000 by the Western Pacific region, in 2002 the European region, and in 2014, the Southeast Asian region, which includes India. Polio cases decreased by over 99 percent from an estimated 350,000 cases in 1988 to 37 reported cases in 2016. Because it was still endemic in Afghanistan, Nigeria and Pakistan, the WHO Polio Eradication and Endgame Strategic Plan 2013–2019 was developed with the aim of eradicating the disease globally (WHO, 2017).

GENERATIONAL CHANGES AND PARENTING IN WESTERN NATIONS

Since 1900, particularly in Western and industrialized nations, cultural developments have resulted in changes in parenting styles and the characteristics of children and the generations they represent. In many developed nations, families evolved from the extended multigenerational family to the nuclear family of parents and children only in the post-WWII years. At the beginning of the 20th century, parents were often strict disciplinarians raising children to be well mannered and independent. This generation born from 1901 to the mid-1920s—called the "greatest generation"—went through WWI and the worldwide Depression. They matured early and fought in WWII on all sides of the conflicts. Marriage was for life, while divorce and having children out of wedlock were not acceptable.

The next cohort (group) was the "silent generation" (born during 1928–1945), who grew up in an era of conformity during the end of the depression and postwar happiness where there was peace, job opportunities, and prosperity. Middle-class women stayed home to raise children, or if they worked, it was in traditional jobs. People generally kept their employment for life. Marriage was also for life while divorce and having children out of wedlock was not accepted. "Baby boomers" were born between 1946 and 1964 in the postwar period. They were brought up on Dr. Benjamin Spock's (1903–1998) philosophy that suggested parents should be flexible, which was interpreted as permissiveness leading to this generation becoming self-centered. One group, the "hippies," changed sexual norms, used drugs, protested against the Vietnam War, and advocated for civil and women's rights. The other group, "the yuppies," worked to achieve high-paying jobs. Women of this generation with children began working outside the home and entered nontraditional fields in the late 1970s. Divorce began to be accepted, and it was the first generation where many children were raised in a two-income or single parent household.

"Gen X" were born between 1965 and 1980. They often grew up with divorced or career-driven parents. As children, they saw the advent of computers. They often cohabitated, were late to marry, and had a high divorce rate. It was not normal to work for a company for life, unlike previous generations. Generation Y, also known as "millennials," were born between 1981 to about 2000. Their boomer parents were over protective, and this generation learned as children that the world was not a safe place. Younger members of this generation tended to play indoors on video games and later computers rather than outdoors, experienced knowledge transitioning from written to digital form, and their parents scheduled many of their activities as children. They had a sense of entitlement as parents gave into their wants and showered them with undue praise. Many young adults in the 2010s were still dependent upon their parents and moved back with them after college. Out of wedlock births were the norm, and many never married but cohabitated or became single parents. Middle-class millennials often delayed plans to start a family to establish their careers, and many were obsessed by success while in secondary school. The youngest group along with the next generation was viewed as being less resilient and more prone to taking offence than previous generations. Increased suicides, reports of bullying, depression, and heroin deaths among this group were frequent topics in the media during the 2010s.

Generation Z—or "boomlets"—were born after 2001. Most of the Z generations were children or teenagers by the late 2010s. Computers and cell phones had always been a part of their lives, and they spent much of their time socializing with these devices. They perceived the world as an endlessly scary place and were constantly made aware of potential dangers and abuse from their peers and adults. Rather than playing with the neighborhood children, they were often scheduled for "play dates," particularly in the United States. Their Generation X overprotective parents attempted to eliminate all risk from their lives leaving them ill prepared for adult responsibilities. In several Western nations, an upsurge of opiate use was found in the older members of this generation, particularly in rural areas of the United States.

Although these much generalized characteristics and parenting styles tended to be found in Western cultures, some parenting activities common in one nation were not acceptable in other nations by the early 21st century. For example, in Norway, childhood was institutionalized as most children enter state-sponsored daycare at one year of age because most parents worked. In Denmark parents, would leave their children sleeping in a stroller outdoors next to an establishment while they ate or shopped. In Spain and some South American cultures, children would go to bed at the same time as their parents.

PARENTING IN NON-WESTERN OR DEVELOPING NATIONS

In non-Western nations, Japanese parenting, for example, supported close physical contact between mother and child. The mother would co-sleep and bathe with her child. Parents encouraged mature behavior and self-sufficiency. In the early 21st century, they allowed their children as young as six or seven to ride the subway and sent them on errands alone. In Korea, along with other Asian nations, parenting from an early age focused on academics and college acceptance among the middle class. Within the family, obedience was important. The Confucian philosophy of filial piety, showing reverence and respect for elders, continuing the family name and honor was common in all Asian nations.

In urban areas of the People's Republic of China, the nuclear family became increasingly common by the first decade of the 21st century. The one-child generation born between 1979 and the early 1990s resulted in many more male children as males were desired over females to provide for their elders. These children received doting attention from their parents and often became self-centered. Parenting styles of shaming, overprotectiveness, and encouragement of modesty were found. Children of this era were optimistic for the future and of transforming China into a worldwide economic and political power.

In India, the extended family still played a significant part in the upbringing of children. Children were taught respect for elders, the importance of religious worship, and depended on their families for life decisions such as marriage and jobs. Marriages were still often arranged. In Africa—for example Ghana—mothers were oriented toward a permissive style of parenting, whereas fathers used an authoritarian style. Some parents accepted corporal punishment as a method of disciplining children, while others frowned on its usage. Throughout the Congo, children were seen as the responsibility of the whole community and taught to respect their elders. All adults were expected to discipline children.

TECHNOLOGY, PSYCHOLOGICAL WELL-BEING, AND CHILD MALTREATMENT

Parenting has been made easier, and more difficult, by new technology since the early 20th century, particularly in industrialized nations. Moreover, every new method of electronic and other technology resulted in fears and concerns of damaged youth. This included radio and film in the early 20th century, television in the mid-20th century, computers and arcade games in the late 20th century, and the Internet and mobile devices in the early 21st century. The early 21st century saw rapid technological advances, especially the almost universal use of computers, the Internet, and smart phones, which were the major and constant communication tool for both parents and children in most developed and high-income cultures by the 2010s. Rather than playing outside with other children, children relied on these devices for the majority of their play and entertainment. This limited their physical activity important for sensory and motor development.

Being overly connected to the Internet and social media was found to have psychological health issues. Overstimulation by rapid information affected brain development of young children, including speech delays. The more screen time for children under 18 months old, the more delay in development was found. Among older youth, constant use of smart phones—and even addiction to the Internet and social media—and lack of face-to-face interaction led to psychological issues such as underdevelopment of social skills, distraction, depression, narcissism, and the need for instant gratification. Impact on physical health included vision problems, hearing loss, obesity from sitting too much, and neck strain. Negative behavior such as cyber bullying became a widely discussed topic in the media by the second decade of the 21st century due to misuse of these devices.

Bullying has always been found among warm-blooded animals where the alpha member of the group sometimes bullies weaker ones. By the turn of the 21st century, bullying (physical, verbal, or online) was considered a leading mental health issue among children and adolescents in many Western cultures. However, whether or not it had increased is unclear. However, in Australia in terms of mental health issues in the schools, a research group found that

> Psychological and emotional distress manifests in internalising behaviours (such as anxiety and depression) and externalising behaviours (such as aggressive, violent or disruptive behaviour), and has an impact on the child's successful learning at school. (Urbis, 2011, iv)

Moreover, anyone involved with bullying—those who bully others and those who are bullied—are at an increased risk for depression. Children and adolescents who are bullies are at increased risk for substance use, academic problems, and violence to others later in life. Victims of cyberbullying are at a higher risk for depression than cyberbullies or non-cyberbully victims. Suicide-related behavior has been blamed on bullying. LGBT and disabled children and youth are most likely to be bullied.

Bullying, along with increased awareness of childhood abuse and depression, elicited concern about the psychological well-being of children by the end of the

20th century. Child abuse takes the form of emotional, physical, or sexual maltreatment. Through the late 20th century, the way a family disciplined a child was considered the family's business and not society's. It was common for parents to spank or whip children for misdeeds in many cultures. Corporal punishment was also carried out in schools in Western cultures. Teachers would "crack a ruler" over the hands of unruly children, or principals would paddle them. Corporal punishment in schools had historically been justified by the common-law doctrine where teachers were considered authority figures and had the same rights as parents to discipline children in their care. However, concerns that physically disciplining children could lead to aggressive behavior and psychological problems led most developed countries, by 2016, to abolish the practice. Although, it is still found in a few states in the United States, Australia, and in some developing nations.

The effects of child maltreatment, whether physical or emotional abuse, may last a lifetime and can include emotional, behavioral, and learning problems along with depression. In the late 1980s, sexual abuse on the part of Roman Catholic clergy came to the surface in well publicized cases throughout Australia, Canada, Ireland, the United Kingdom, and the United States, and later in other nations. This led to further reports of abuse by entertainment and sports personalities, teachers, coaches, and others into the 2010s. This abuse led to various psychological problems among many of its victims.

Another form of abuse was child labor. Employment of children interfered with their ability to attend school, was often physically dangerous, or mentally, socially, and morally harmful. During the early 20th century, poor children—even in Western nations—often worked in mills, factories, mines, or on the farm. Over the century, legislation was passed by most developed nations to eliminate this type of labor and to ensure children attended school. By the 2010s, child labor was mostly found in rural areas of developing nations with a high degree of poverty and few opportunities to attend school. The percentage of children as part of the workforce was the highest in sub-Saharan Africa (30%), followed by Asia (16%), Latin America (13%) and the Middle East and North Africa (12%). Children were less than 1 percent of the workforce in Western and wealthy nations. Concerns about unhealthy working children also emerged as a factor in the eugenics movement in the early 20th century.

FROM EUGENICS TO GENETIC ENGINEERING

The eugenics movement in the early 20th century evolved out of the hereditarian movement of the 19th century, which deemed that human characteristics such as intelligence, health, alcoholism, tuberculosis, disabilities, and poverty were passed from generation to generation. Although the movement waned after WWII as it was associated with the holocaust in Nazi Germany, it morphed into new forms such as assisted reproduction technology and genetic engineering in search for the perfect baby by the early 21st century. The eugenics movement of the early 20th century was a social and public health movement to improve the health and well-being of society and was intertwined with other health movements of the day in Western cultures. Most middle-class individuals and professionals in many nations around the world accepted eugenics as a matter of course. As defined by the founder of eugenics, Francis Galton (1822–1911) in 1904, eugenics was "the science which deals with all influences that improve the inborn qualities of the [human] race; also with those that develop them to the utmost advantage." (1904, 1) Eugenicists advocated that the "fit"—healthy, intelligent and strong—reproduce (positive eugenics) and that the "unfit"—the mentally and physically ill or disabled—not reproduce (negative eugenics) to create healthier children and nations. They believed this program would also reduce disease and welfare costs.

A law was first passed in 1907 for eugenic sterilization of the mentally and physically "unfit" in the state of Indiana in the United States to achieve this end. The overall movement was largely an aspect of the American Progressive Era's clean-living movement (1890–1925). Reformers advocated exercise, fresh air, good nutrition, chastity before marriage, and well-baby clinics to improve health. Antituberculosis, social hygiene (antisexually transmitted disease) and antismoking programs to reduce disease and improve health were also championed. "Better babies" and "fitter families" contests in the 1910s and 1920s at state fairs promoted the health of children and families. Young adults were encouraged to be physically and morally fit. Public policies were implemented such as Prohibition, immunizations against communicable diseases, and a physical exam to diagnose possible syphilis before a marriage license was issued. These reforms along with clean water and milk, pure food, and drugs were employed as part of eugenics and public health campaigns. Public playgrounds and national parks were also created to encourage exercise and recreation for better health and improvement of the human race.

In the UK, unlike the United States and some other nations, few eugenics laws were passed, and eugenics did not become institutionalized. In the UK, the only major eugenics legislation passed was the Deficiency Act of 1913, which allowed for the segregation of mentally disabled and ill individuals in state-run institutions. The British movement focused on positive eugenics and encouraged the fit to reproduce. The Scandinavian, some South American and Eastern European nations, and Japan embraced eugenics. In Germany, before National Socialism, legislators rejected negative eugenics. They promoted positive eugenics to increase national vitality. However, under Nazi rule, in 1932, they passed eugenic sterilization laws. Several hundred thousand "unfit" ethnic Germans were sterilized or euthanized in addition to the execution of about 20 million others including Jews, the ethnic group called the Roma, Poles, and peoples in occupied lands. Although these atrocities were not eugenics, this genocide, called the holocaust, became associated with eugenics, and in the aftermath of World War II the idea was condemned.

However, eugenics arose again in the late 20th century and early 21st century under the guise of "assisted reproduction," "genetic engineering," and genomics. New technologies such as amniocentesis in 1956, ultrasound in 1972, and chorionic villus sampling in 1983 were used to identify numerous genetic and other abnormalities along with the gender of the fetus. By 1980, pregnant woman could obtain pregnancy termination for fetal deformities in many nations. Advances also included artificial insemination in the 1950s, in vitro fertilization (IVF) in the 1980s, and "third-party assisted" techniques where genetic material is used from a third person. Preimplantation genetic diagnosis (PGD) of an embryo to determine a genetic disorder was possible by the mid-1990s. This "new eugenics" was driven by personal desire to have healthy, intelligent, and fit children. The technology also enabled gender selection for "family balancing" (having a child of a desired gender) practiced in India and in China under its one-child policy. Although illegal in both nations, these practices resulted in more boys than girls by the early 21st century.

With the advent of genomics and genetic engineering, by the mid-2010s, the sequencing of an embryo's DNA became possible so as to detect potential abnormalities of chronic diseases such as cancer or diabetes. Genetic engineering to manipulate genes, to cure or prevent genetic diseases, or introduce desirable traits in developing human embryos became promising. On the other hand, these techniques were fraught with controversy in many cultures for the potentiality of changing humankind on the genetic level.

In developing nations, among the well off, assisted reproduction was desired. Infertility in these countries was often caused by gonorrhea and chlamydia infections in the reproductive tract. Islam as a religion, for example, not only accepted but endorsed and encouraged the seeking of treatment for infertility. The development of IVF clinics in the Middle East, with large Islamic populations, was faster than in Europe and North American. Sub-Saharan Africa lags behind due to few clinics for this purpose.

In summary, over the 20th century and into the 21st century, a dramatic reduction in infant and childhood morbidity and mortality have occurred globally. For those regions that still had problems, the WHO and other groups were attempting to address these issues. Advances in technology have allowed for cures and prevention of many health issues of infancy and childhood.

6

Diseases

Many infectious diseases that were the major causes of death at the turn of the 20th century had been eliminated or controlled through clean water, sanitation, vaccinations, and antimicrobials by the latter part of the century. The deadly smallpox was eradicated worldwide in the 1970s. Some infectious diseases that were endemic (prevalent), but rare, resurfaced and resulted in epidemics later in the century. Increased travel and climate change were factors in new diseases emerging out of developing areas of the world and being carried to other nations by travelers, birds, transportation vehicles, or imported goods in the latter part of the century. Some bacterial diseases developed resistance to antibiotics by the end of the century, and one infectious disease (AIDS) became a chronic condition. As death from infectious diseases declined, noncommunicable conditions such as heart diseases, cancers, diabetes, and accidents evolved as major killers in both developed and developing nations over the 20th century and into the 21st century.

AIRBORNE DISEASES

Numerous bacterial and viral infections are transmitted through the air by aerosols (tiny droplets) from coughs and sneezes. Many of these diseases have been described since antiquity. Exploration, travel, and wars introduced them from one region of the world to other areas, and by the early 21st century, they were found globally. However, by the late 20th century, many childhood diseases, which are discussed in chapter 5, were prevented by immunizations. Other diseases, such as pneumococcal pneumonia, were cured by antimicrobial drugs. Two major airborne respiratory diseases—still found in the early 21st century—that tend to come in cycles of virulence (severity) are tuberculosis (TB) and influenza.

At the beginning of the 20th century, TB, also known as the "white plague," "phthisis," and "consumption," was the major cause of death in many nations. It is an ancient disease as evidence has been found in both ancient Peruvian and

Egyptian mummies. The illness, caused by *Mycobacterium tuberculosis* was generally contracted by close contact with an infected person or drinking unpasteurized milk. Like many infectious diseases, TB has waxed and waned in severity. The tuberculosis cycle is believed to be about 200 years. Poverty, overcrowding, poor diets, lack of fresh air, and unsanitary surroundings are thought to lead to increased susceptibility and incidence (occurrence) of the disease. For generations, it had been noted that tuberculosis tended to "run in families" and was thought to be inherited. At the beginning of the 20th century, tuberculosis's familial occurrence was found to be a household member who was passing the disease on to other family members by close contact.

Mortality rates for TB began to fall in the late 19th century throughout Europe and North America, likely from isolation of patients and treatment at sanatoria, higher standard of living, and better nutrition and hygiene. French physician Albert Calmette (1863–1933) and veterinarian Camille Guérin (1872–1961) in 1906 developed the BCG vaccine, which was first used on humans in 1921 in France. After WWII (post 1945), it received widespread acceptance in Great Britain and Germany. Active TB was determined by X-ray and sputum examinations and inactive form of the disease by the tuberculin test. In the post–World War II years, antibiotics were introduced. The BCG vaccine and antibiotic only slightly reduced mortality as TB mortality rates had already declined by 90–95 percent before these substances were widely available.

Over the 20th century, a decrease, or stabilization, of the disease was also found in many developing nations until the 1980s when the incidence of TB increased especially in Asia and southern Africa. The emerging HIV epidemic and drug-resistant TB strains were factors in this increase. Although TB had slightly increased in the 1980s in high-income nations due to these issues, it became a major cause of morbidity and mortality in many developing regions by the early 21st century.

In response to the resurgence of tuberculosis, the World Health Organization issued a declaration of a global health emergency in 1993, and the World Health Assembly in 2014 developed the End TB Strategy. The program aimed to reduce TB mortality by 90 percent and morbidity by 80 percent between 2015 and 2030. India, Indonesia, China, Nigeria, Pakistan, and South Africa accounted for 60 percent of the new cases in 2015. Over 95 percent of TB deaths occurred in low- and middle-income countries. To accomplish the WHO goals, early screening for the disease, health education, patient and family support, preventative vaccination, and treatment with various anti-TB drugs needed to be carried out.

WHO, in an earlier initiative in 1959, aimed to eliminate smallpox worldwide, which was one of the most deadly afflictions known to humanity. The disease is caused by the variola virus. Sporadic outbreaks were found in industrialized nations through the first half of the 20th century, and it was wide ranging in poorer nations. After WWII, mandatory vaccination programs eliminated smallpox in North America (1952) and Europe (1953). By 1971, WHO's international program had eradicated smallpox from South America, followed by Asia (1975), and finally Africa (1977). WHO declared the world free of smallpox in 1980, and it is the only disease that has been completely eradicated.

In addition to tuberculosis and smallpox, influenza, often followed by pneumonia, has been a major cause of mortality. Worldwide, lower respiratory disease (influenza/pneumonia) was the leading cause of death in 1900 and the third leading cause of death in 2016. In low-income nations, it was still the leading cause of death. The influenza virus is seasonal and most prevalent during the winter months. The virus is subject to mutations and can be a combination of swine, avian, and human DNA, resulting in different types and subtypes. A pandemic is when a new subtype of influenza A spreads worldwide.

Over the 20th century and into the 21st century, four influenza pandemics have emerged. The 1918–1919 "Spanish flu" (H1N1 virus) likely originated in the United States and primarily attacked young adults. It had an extremely high mortality rate worldwide—from 20 to 40 million were killed. It likely originated in a Midwestern pig in the United States that infected a World War I recruit, who infected others, who in turn carried it to Europe on troop ships. The second pandemic—the "Asian flu" (H2N2 virus) in 1957—originated in China. The third pandemic was the "Hong Kong flu" (H3N2 virus) in 1968. In 2009, the "swine flu" (H1N1 virus) first appeared in North America and swept the globe as a result of airline travel. It mostly affected children and young adults. Over the century, mortality declined in each succeeding pandemic due to antibiotics, influenza vaccination, and antiviral drugs particularly in developed nations. By 2010, immunizations were recommended for most people. This "flu shot" needed to be done on a yearly basis due to mutations of the virus. However, vaccination was often difficult in low-income developing nations resulting in high death rates from influenza complications.

WATER- AND FOOD-BORNE DISEASES

Diseases such as cholera, typhoid fever, and other enteric (gastrointestinal) diseases, and polio, are transmitted through contaminated water and food. Polio that was common in children causes muscle damage and paralysis and is discussed in chapter 5. *Streptococcus*, *E. coli*, and *Salmonella* bacteria are sometimes found in contaminated food products and can cause "food poisoning," which generally is not fatal. Cholera is caused by the *Vibrio cholerae* bacterium resulting in severe diarrhea, vomiting, and dehydration. About 50 percent die without treatment. Cholera was a local disease around the Bay of Bengal in India until the early 19th century. Worldwide travel brought this deadly scourge to Europe and North America in the early part of that century. Epidemics in more recent times have occurred after war, civil unrest, or natural disasters when water and food supplies become contaminated with the bacterium in areas with crowded living conditions and poor sanitation.

By the early 20th century, clean water supplies prevented cholera's spread throughout developed nations based upon British physician John Snow's (1813–1858) discovery that drinking water contaminated with sewage transmitted the disease. During the 6th pandemic (1899–1923), the disease spread and caused major epidemics in Eastern Europe, Turkey, the Middle East, and North Africa. In the mid-20th century, local epidemics occurred in China, Burma, India, and other

Asian nations. Between 1965 and 1975, widespread epidemics were also found in these areas. The 7th pandemic beginning in the 1960s and 1970s originated in Indonesia and extended to India, Russia, and North Africa. In Latin America, the first cholera epidemic of the 20th century originated along the coastline of Peru in 1991. It rapidly spread though Latin America via transportation of contaminated crabmeat from the coastal area and eating unwashed fruits and vegetables. Almost a million cases were reported between January 1991 and December 1993.

From 1991 onward, sporadic epidemics of cholera have also broken out in Asia and several sub-Saharan African nations. In the aftermath of the Haiti earthquake in 2010, a cholera epidemic emerged, which was thought to have been imported by Nepalese United Nations peacekeepers. In 2017, an epidemic broke out in war torn Yemen. However, due to medical care including intravenous hydration, the disease caused fewer fatalities by the second decade of the 21st century compared to the past.

Another ancient enteric disease is typhoid fever caused by the bacterium *Salmonella Typhi.* It—along with similar gastrointestinal diseases—was endemic worldwide at the beginning of the 20th century. The disease was transmitted by food and water contaminated with fecal material of typhoid-fever patients. Epidemics of the disease would run through communities resulting in 10–30 percent of patients dying before antibiotic therapy was developed in the late 1940s. Some individuals became carriers of the disease and could transmit it to others through poor hygiene. One of the most infamous known cases in an industrialized nation was Mary Mallon (1869–1938)—called Typhoid Mary—a cook in New York City, who infected 46 individuals resulting in four deaths during the first decade of the century.

The incidence of typhoid declined in higher-income nations by mid-20th century in parallel with the introduction of better hygiene practices, treatment of municipal water supplies, and pasteurization of dairy products. The first effective vaccine for typhoid was developed by British bacteriologist Almroth Edward Wright (1861–1947) in 1896 and was used by the 1920s to prevent the disease. It was generally used by individuals in high-income nations who were traveling to regions with a high prevalence of typhoid. By the late 20th century and into the early 21st century, typhoid infections were brought by travelers from infected areas into developed regions of the world. However, because of clean drinking water, it rarely spread. On the other hand, the typhoid bacterium had developed resistance to many antibiotics making it more difficult to treat.

Beginning in the late 1990s, Asian nations with high typhoid rates, including China, India, Vietnam, and Fiji, undertook typhoid vaccination programs, especially for children. This, along with cleaner water and better sanitation, reduced the incidence of the disease in this region. By 2005, improvement in the quality of drinking water was found to be more important for the prevention of enteric infections compared to sanitation measures. In Haiti, for example, after the 2010 destructive earthquake, an increase in typhoid occurred in one village due to structural damaged of the water source. The water was treated and cases subsided.

The 2010 Global Burden of Disease study estimated that the Indian subcontinent had the largest number of outbreaks and death from typhoid globally. Africa also has a high rate of outbreaks. Typhoid fever was the highest for children in Pakistan, followed by India and Indonesia. China, which had a high rate of typhoid throughout the 20th century had, by the second decade of the 21st century, one of the lower rates in Asia due to vaccination and better water supplies. In Latin America, typhoid fever outbreaks have declined with an increased standard of living and better water and sanitation that were introduced to control cholera during the early 1990s pandemic.

INSECT-BORNE DISEASES

Mosquitoes, lice, ticks, fleas, and other insects are vectors (carriers) for many diseases. Fleas transmit the bubonic plague (*Yesenia pestis* bacterium) also called the Black Death. Lymph nodes swell—called buboes—and become black, thus giving the name to the disease. The bacterium infects rodents and about 200 wild and domestic species, along with humans. In 1894, two bacteriologists, French Alexandre Yersin (1863–1943) and Japanese Kitasato Shibasaburō (1853–1931) independently identified the bacillus that caused bubonic plague, but its transmission was still unknown. It was not until 1905 that it was established by the Plague Research Commission in Bombay, India, that the bacillus, which they named *Pasteurella pestis*, usually was transmitted by the bite of a flea that had fed on infected rats, the primary host. In 1970, the bacillus was renamed *Yersinia pestis* in honor of Yersin. Usually the fleas bite an infected rodent and transmit the disease to humans and other mammals. The second most common route of transmission is by handling diseased animals. Sometimes it can be transmitted by an infected person coughing, leading to the pneumonic form of the disease. The plague is thought to have originated out of central Asia and since antiquity has caused three known pandemics.

The third pandemic, beginning in 1894, originated in Yunnan, China. It spread to Hong Kong and India and then to the rest of the world where it waxed and waned until 1959. Poor sanitation breeds rats in crowded conditions, which is the likely etiology (cause) of these pandemics. In 1901, plague arrived in San Francisco's Chinatown on rat infested immigrant ships. However, it was contained due to enforced sanitation practices. Although the epidemic ended in 1904, the disease spread to wild rodents in the western region of the United States where it is still endemic and by the 1970s had resulted in a few cases each year.

In the late 20th century, outbreaks occurred in China and India. Some cases have occurred in other parts of Asia and South America, but most human cases since the 1990s have been found in Africa among people living in rural agricultural areas. Plague was treated with antibiotics, but by the late 1990s a multidrug restraint strain had developed. The World Health Organization considers plague a reemerging disease that could erupt in conflict-torn regions and refugee camps with poor sanitation.

Mosquito-transmitted diseases are responsible for several million deaths and hundreds of millions of cases of various diseases annually. The two major mosquito-borne diseases are malaria and yellow fever. Both have been scourges since ancient times in warm climates. Malaria (meaning "bad air") is caused by several species of the *Plasmodium* parasite. Until the turn of the 20th century, it was thought to be caused by bad or foul air from swamps. In antiquity, malaria originated in Africa and spread to Eurasia and later to the Americas. It is transmitted to humans through the bite of an infected female *Anopheles* mosquito. A strain of malaria became established in Europe as a seasonal disease, called the "Ague" in Britain. By the late 20th century, due to advances in mosquito control and newly developed drugs, the disease was essentially eliminated in mid-latitude developed nations. However, in the 2010s, it was still a major cause of morbidity and mortality in Africa particularly among children. In 2015, the WHO African region had 90 percent of the world's malaria cases and 92 percent of malaria deaths. Other regions with malaria were the Southeast Asia region, Eastern Mediterranean region, and Latin America.

Traditional medicine and medicinal plants have been used in malaria-prone areas to prevent and treat the disease for centuries. For example, native healers in South and Central America used the extracts of the bark of the cinchona tree, which contains quinine. This substance when purified became the classic treatment for malaria. The plant was imported to India, and it is still used by traditional healers. In China and parts of Africa, a tea from sweet wormwood (*Artemisia annua*), also called *qinghaosu*, had been used to prevent severe malaria. From this herb in the 1980s, Chinese researcher You you Tu (1930–) derived artemisinin as an effective cure for malaria. In addition, various other antimalarial were developed. German chemist Hans Andersag (1902–1955) had synthesized chloroquine in 1932, which became the most effective treatment for malaria for a number of decades. However, the malaria parasite developed resistance to it in many regions. Therefore, by the 1990s, the standard treatment for malaria became artemisinin combined with other antimalarial drugs.

Efforts to reduce malaria first came with the construction of the Panama Canal. In 1900, both malaria and yellow fever were shown to be carried by mosquitoes (see chapter 11 for more information about malaria and yellow fever control by the military in the Canal Zone). Both of these diseases sickened or killed numerous canal workers in the first decade of the century. To reduce the spread of the diseases, mosquito control and the use of "mosquito bars" (net over bedding) were implemented with success. In the mid-1940s—when malaria was still endemic in the southern states—the United States began to eliminate mosquitoes by draining swamps, oiling standing water, spraying areas with heavy mosquito infestation, placing screens on windows, and spraying inside houses. DDT and other insecticides were used and malaria was eliminated. This led to the nation being malaria free by 1951. Due to this success, the World Health Organization in the mid-1950s established recommendations for elimination of malaria worldwide. Europe was malaria free by 1975. Reduction of the disease was also was found in the Mediterranean, Middle Eastern, and Asian nations. However, in the 1990s, local transmissions had been reintroduced in the Caucuses, Turkey, and Russian federation due to refugees, conflicts and other crisis.

Continued initiatives by WHO in low- and middle-income nations supported the use of insecticide-treated mosquito nets (ITNs) and indoor residual spraying (IRS) resulting in a decrease in new malaria cases between 2010 and 2015. Malaria was also reduced by 21 percent both globally and in the WHO African region. Since 2010, the malaria mortality rate also declined in all other regions. WHO in May 2015 developed the Global Technical Strategy for Malaria 2016–2030 (GTS). The program provides technical assistance to poorer nations with endemic malaria as they work toward malaria control and elimination.

Some of the same strategies to eliminate malaria—in particular mosquito control—have also been used in the fight against yellow fever, dengue, and other mosquito-borne diseases. Virus infections transmitted by insects are known as arboviruses (arthropod-borne virus). Both yellow fever and dengue fever are part of the *Flaviviridae* viral family and are spread by an infected female *Aedes aegypti* mosquito. Yellow fever originated in West Africa and was imported to the Americas by early explorers and the slave trade. It is an acute viral hemorrhagic disease that results in joint pain, fever, vomiting, and in the severe form, jaundice (yellowing of skin). Around 50 percent die within a week with the severe form.

Yellow fever was seasonal in temperate climates when mosquitoes died in cold winter months. Although it had caused deadly epidemics in the United States in the previous century, by 1910, yellow fever had been eradicated. The production of an effective vaccine in the 1930s led to a change of emphasis from vector control to vaccination to manage yellow fever. Travelers from developed nations going to endemic areas by the mid-20th century were advised to be immunized against it. By the 1980s, WHO recommend immunization against the disease where it was endemic, which was only partially successful. Yellow fever by the 2010s was still endemic in Africa and South America and more than 200,000 people a year were thought to be affected. For unexplained reasons, the disease is mostly absent in Asia. Although by the 2010s, concerns about Chinese workers in Angola bringing the disease back home after working in Africa were raised.

Similar to yellow fever, but with milder symptoms, dengue, or "break bone," fever is found throughout the tropical and subtropical regions of the world. A rise in dengue cases in the mid-20th century resulted from population movement during WWII into endemic areas. By the end of the century, due to travel and global warming, dengue had establishes itself throughout tropical and subtropical regions of the world and was a growing concern by 2010. An experimental vaccine against the disease was under research by 2017.

Several mosquito-borne infections can cause encephalitis (brain inflammation), which can lead to permanent brain damage or death. Japanese encephalitis, also of the *Flaviviridae* family, is primarily found in Asia and the west coast of North America. Western and Eastern equine, St. Louis, and other viral encephalitis infections are endemic in the United States. Murray Valley encephalitis is endemic to northern Australia and Papua New Guinea. As with many of the viral mosquito-borne diseases, the only treatment is supportive care.

Numerous other diseases caused by biting insects are found around the world. Lice transmit a *Rickettsia* that causes typhus with up to 20 percent of those infected dying from the disease without treatment by antibiotics. It was found among soldiers and refugees in both world wars of the 20th century. By the late century and beyond, it has been found primarily in Africa in crowded unhygienic living conditions. Disease carrying ticks are found in most regions of the world.

Some tick species, for example, in North America, Europe, and Asia carry the *Borrelia burgdorferi rickettsia* (Lyme disease), which was first identified in the 1970s but has been endemic since antiquity. It, along with many tick-borne diseases, can cause weakness, fever, joint pain, and sometimes encephalitis and death. Prevention for tick-borne disease includes wearing long pants and sleeves when walking in woodsy grassy areas and using insecticide. Many of these diseases can be treated successfully with antibiotics.

EMERGING INFECTIOUS DISEASES

Global travel and trade in the late 20th century transported "new" diseases from developing to developed nations. Many were endemic in the country of origin and caused only small isolated outbreaks. Clearing forests, mining, building roads, and faster transportation allowed travel between villages and urban areas, which resulted in diseases spreading around the world. Global warming and climate change, in some cases, allowed these diseases to spread to these other areas.

Mutations of the influenza virus emerged in the late 20th century. In Hong Kong, the most common form of bird, or avian, flu (H5N1) was first identified in humans in 1997. It was transmitted by breathing infected bird droppings or by handling dead birds and infected poultry. Although water fowl are the primary host, it was readily transmitted between birds and is deadly to both birds and humans. Antivirals are used for treatment but are not always successful as about 60 percent of infected people die. Another deadly infection is Severe Acute Respiratory Syndrome (SARS) caused by a coronavirus that causes a life threatening pneumonia. It infects both humans and animals. Two self-limiting SARS outbreaks originated in China during 2002 and 2004 and spread to other Asian nations, the UK, and Canada.

Several emerging diseases are caused by the bite of infected mosquitoes. West Nile virus, which can cause neurological damage and death, is now found in most regions globally. It was originally identified in the western Nile district of Uganda in birds—its host—in 1953. Outbreaks by 2000 were occurring on major bird migratory routes around the world. In 1999, the virus was imported to New York City area and by 2010 was established from Canada to Venezuela. Another mosquito-borne illness, the Zika fever, was also first isolated in Uganda in 1947. The disease spread to tropical and subtropical areas of the world and by 2015 to the Americas. Zika struck terror in pregnant women in the Americas by 2016 (further discussed in chapter 5). Other emerging mosquito-borne diseases transported to the Americas include chikungunya, which causes joint pain. As of this writing, no vaccines have been developed to prevent zika and chikungunya. Prevention is still largely mosquito control and repellant.

Person to person contact of two deadly diseases emerged in the late 20th century and early 21st century. The HIV virus, which causes Acquired Immune Deficiency Disease (AIDS), was first identified in 1982 among men who had sex with men and resulted in a high death rate from opportunistic infections. But since their lifestyle was blamed for the disease, only minimal research was initially focused on this "gay plague." However, by 1990, AIDS had emerged among heterosexuals who had acquired the disease via sexual contact, IV drug use, or blood-transfusion products. Those with hemophilia were in particular danger until the blood supply was screened. In many cultures, fear of the disease bred stigma toward those infected with HIV. However, intensive research increased to determine the nature of the infection, its prevention and treatment.

This AIDS awareness poster from 1991 was part of a health promotion effort to alert the public that AIDS/HIV was not restricted to the "gay community." (Wellcome Collection)

The HIV virus had originally been transferred to humans from African monkeys in the 1930s and 1940s, later leading to a condition called "slim disease" in isolated sub-Saharan African villages first seen in the 1950s. Better transportation allowed infected individuals to carry the disease to urban areas where sex workers were infected and in turn passed the disease to tourists. Different strains spread to Southeast Asia and Haiti. The European and North American pandemic likely originated from infected Haitians. By 1997, HIV was considered a chronic condition as drugs for its treatment were developed.

In 1996, UNAIDS was established to take responsibility for coordinating international action against the epidemic. In that year, an effective combination therapy known as HAART became available for those living with HIV in high-income nations. This resulted in an AIDS death rate decline of 84 percent over the next four years. By 2001, inexpensive generic versions of these drugs were manufactured and used in low-income developing nations. By 2013, AIDS-related deaths had fallen 30 percent since their peak in 2005. Besides treatment, prevention efforts for HIV continue to be promoted in most nations. However, by 2017, sub-Saharan Africa remained the most severely affected WHO region, with nearly 1 in every 25 adults living with HIV.

Even more fearful than AIDS was the Ebola hemorrhagic fever caused by a virus that also emerged out of Africa. It was transmitted from slaughtering or eating infected meat of wild indigenous animals and from human to human through physical contact with body fluids. Local outbreaks were first recognized in the late 20th century, and it had a high case fatality rate. A massive outbreak in Guinea, Liberia, and Sierra Leone occurred in 2016, which caused a major loss of life.

Western health workers in Africa imported the disease to Spain, the UK, and United States when they returned home. This led to secondary infections of a few medical workers. However, the disease did not spread further because of strict quarantine and isolation. Diseases such as Ebola could emerge in the future causing pandemics.

NONCOMMUNICABLE OR CHRONIC DISEASES

As advances over the 20th century reduced morbidity and mortality from communicable diseases, noncommunicable diseases (NCD) became the major causes of mortality worldwide. These included cardiovascular diseases (heart attacks and stroke), cancers, chronic respiratory diseases, and diabetes. NCDs tended to be of long duration, or chronic. The World Health Organization at the beginning of the 21st century remarked that

> The chronic disease problem is far from being limited to the developed regions of the world. Contrary to widely held beliefs, developing countries are increasingly suffering from high levels of public health problems related to chronic diseases. In five out of the six regions of WHO, deaths caused by chronic diseases dominate the mortality statistics. Although human immunodeficiency virus/acquired immunodeficiency syndrome (HIV/AIDS), malaria and tuberculosis, along with other infectious diseases, still predominate in sub-Saharan Africa and will do so for the foreseeable future. (WHO, ca. 2002)

Globally, by 2000, NCDs accounted for more deaths than all infectious diseases combined. By 2007, chronic diseases were responsible for 50 percent of the total disease burden in most developing countries, and by the 2010s represented 63 percent of all annual deaths worldwide. These diseases are largely preventable and are associated with tobacco use, poor diets, lack of physical activity, alcohol abuse, and obesity. On the other hand, since the late 1980s, death from some chronic conditions such as cardiovascular diseases and some cancers had decreased or plateaued by the 2010s in higher-income nations.

Obesity

Although obesity and being overweight are not considered chronic diseases, they contribute to the major causes of NCD deaths. Sporadic food shortage and malnutrition had been common throughout the 20th century in developing nations and in conflict torn areas of Europe, Asia, and Africa. However, by the beginning of the 21st century, an obesity epidemic had emerged that was associated with an increase in heart disease, hypertension, stroke, diabetes, and some cancers. The epidemic was also found among children (discussed in chapter 5). Not only was obesity prevalent in high-income nations, it became a serious problem throughout Asia, Latin America, and parts of Africa despite the widespread presence of undernutrition. By 2006, in many lower-income nations malnutrition, along with communicable diseases, created a "double burden" of disease that threatened to overwhelm the health services of many poorer nations.

The obesity epidemic in higher-income nations began between 1950 and 1970 but was not noticed until the 1980s. Many factors appear to have been involved for this epidemic, including a decrease in physical activity and manual labor, the advent of affordable mechanized transportation, TV and later personal computers, inexpensive processed food products high in fat and sugar, microwave ovens, and increased eating at food establishments outside of the home. These factors led to leisure time passive activities and the convenience of eating anytime, anywhere. In low- and middle-income nations, obesity began to surge after increased migration into urban areas with a less active lifestyle that included a lack of traditional foods, more refined food products, and reduced physical activity.

Cardiovascular Diseases

By 2010, heart disease and stroke emerged as the two leading causes of premature death (under age 70) in all WHO regions with the exception of sub-Saharan Africa. The most important risk factors of these NCDs were an unhealthy diet, physical inactivity, tobacco use, and high alcohol intake. These lifestyle risk factors can lead to hypertension (high blood pressure), increased blood glucose, high cholesterol, being overweight, and obesity. Over time, these risk factors can cause damage to the heart and blood vessels leading to atherosclerosis (hardening and narrowing of the arteries). In atherosclerosis, there is a buildup of a fatty substance (plaque) on the arteries' wall, which narrows them. This constriction can result in hypertension. A buildup of plaque can create a complete blockage resulting in a heart attack or cerebral vascular accident (stroke). Sometimes a piece of plaque will break off and block arteries in the brain, also resulting in a stroke. Congestive heart failure, when the heart is unable to maintain adequate circulation of blood, from weakened heart muscles can also occur.

Primary prevention efforts in most nations for cardiovascular diseases include interventions aimed at smoking cessation, increased physical activity, and weight control. Secondary prevention, or treatment, can include drugs to lower blood pressure and cholesterol. Low-dose aspirin is also often recommended. Although heart disease and stroke do have a genetic component, lifestyle changes and reducing the risk factors are most important in reducing mortality from cardiovascular diseases.

Diabetes Mellitus

A major risk factor for heart disease is diabetes. The condition is caused by the lack of insulin, which is produced by certain cells on the pancreas, or insulin resistance (cells are unable to use insulin effectively), resulting in high levels of glucose (sugar) in the blood and urine. High glucose levels can damage blood vessels and nerves causing various problems such as the inability of wounds to heal properly sometimes leading to amputations, neuropathy (numbness or tingling in the extremities), and blindness unless diabetes is controlled.

Type II adult onset diabetes mellitus is precipitated by poor nutrition choices, inactivity, being overweight, and obesity. It tends to run in families so some genetic, or even epigenetic (gene function being switched on or off), factors are likely involved. Type II diabetes by the early 21st century accounted for around 90 percent of all diabetes cases worldwide. Type I, formerly called juvenile diabetes, generally occurs in childhood or early adulthood. Type I was a fatal condition until 1921 when Canadian medical researchers Frederic Banting (1891–1941) and Charles Best (1899–1978) isolated the hormone insulin. It revolutionized the treatment of diabetes and transformed Type I diabetes from a fatal disease to a long-term chronic condition. Insulin through the early 1980s was extracted from livestock. In 1982, the first commercially available biosynthetic human insulin was available. About 40 percent of diabetics need insulin injections to prevent health problem; others can rely on diet alone, or in the case of type II diabetes, oral medication is available. Gestational diabetes during pregnancy can cause the infant's birth weight to be over 9 pounds and complicate pregnancy. Gestational diabetes is usually controlled with diet.

The prevalence of diabetes increased worldwide beginning in the 1970s in tangent with other NCDs and in particular with the rise in obesity. It also increased more rapidly in middle- and low-income countries due to more affluence and westernization. By 2015, the worldwide prevalence of diabetes was about 8 percent. It was 10 percent in the Americas and Europe and 12 percent in the Middle East. Asia accounted for about 60 percent of the world's diabetic population. The prevalence in China was about 10 percent while in urban areas of south India, it had reached nearly 20 percent. In rural areas of developing nations and sub-Saharan Africa, it was around 5 percent of the population.

The classification of diabetes along with diagnosis and treatment were designed by the National Diabetes Data Group of the United States and the second World Health Organization Expert Committee on Diabetes Mellitus in 1979 and 1980. Other than minor modifications by WHO over the years, their guidelines are still the basis of testing, prevention, and treatment. By the 2010s, studies had shown that moderate reduction in weight and only a half-hour of daily walking reduces the incidence of diabetes by more than one half.

Malignant Neoplasms (Cancer)

Another condition often associated with unhealthy lifestyles is cancer. Cancer is a generic term for a large group of diseases that can affect any part of the body. Some are likely heredity, some environmental, and others a combination of both.

For centuries, cancer was stigmatized as it was considered a death sentence in most cultures. At the turn of the 20th century in Western cultures, this fatalistic attitude was accepted by both the physician and the family. The diagnosis generally was not revealed to the patient, and cancer was a taboo subject of conversation. However, in 1913, in the United States, for example, the American Cancer Society formed to fight this fatalism and to educate the public that early treatment by surgery and radiation could increase survival rates. In 1937, the National Cancer Institute formed to seek a cure for cancer. Combined surgery and radiation and advances in treatment such as chemotherapy first used in the 1940s—along with screening tests for early detection—increased survival (screen tests are discussed in chapters 5 and 8). This led to attitudinal changes, and physicians began to reveal cancer diagnosis to their patients in the 1960s and 1970s. A major champion of changing attitudes toward cancer and reducing its stigma was Betty Ford (1918–2011), wife of President Gerald Ford, who gave public awareness to breast cancer after a mastectomy in 1974.

By the late 1970s, public education about lifestyle changes to reduce cancer risks such as tobacco use, lack of exercise, and poor diets were put in place by governmental and nongovernmental organizations (NGO) in higher-income nations, which have continued into the present time. In many developing nations, however, cancer in the 2010s continued to have stigma, myths, and taboos.

Tobacco use is the most important risk factor for cancer and by 2015 was responsible for approximately 22 percent of all cancer deaths worldwide. In addition, cancer was the second leading global cause of death. By 2015, nearly 1 in 6 deaths worldwide was due to cancer, and the most common cancer deaths were from lung, liver, colorectal, stomach, and breast cancers. Higher-income regions such as North America, Europe, and Australia and New Zealand saw a plateauing effect or reduction in some cancer deaths due to decreased smoking and early detection, screening, and treatment. Cancer was the leading cause of death in Europe and Canada as opposed to cardiovascular disease in the United States. On the other hand, many low- and middle-income regions experienced a surge in some cancers. For example, lung cancer has dramatically increased since the 1990s in Asia, in particular China, due to smoking and was the leading cause of cancer deaths throughout the region as it was in the Latin American and Caribbean region. In sub-Saharan Africa, about one-third of all cancers are estimated to be related to infections of HIV/AIDS, human papillomavirus, and hepatitis B virus. This region along with some other developing nations often do not have necessary health centers for prevention programs, screening, diagnosis, and treatment of cancers.

Other Noncommunicable Conditions

Some other conditions among the top causes of global mortality include lower respiratory problems. This category consists of chronic obstructive pulmonary disease (COPD), chronic bronchitis, emphysema, and asthma. COPD is a chronic lung disease that causes the airways in the lung to inflame and thicken resulting in shortness of breath. It is generally associated with smoking along with indoor and workplace air pollution. Accidents (unintended injuries) in the mid-2010s were the leading global cause of death among 15 to 29 year olds. The mortality rate was highest in low- and middle-income nations. The African region had the highest accident fatalities at 27 per 100,000 people, while the European region had the lowest rate at 9.3 per 100,000 people. In most developed nations, vehicle accidents had decreased since the 1980s because of seatbelts, airbags, child restraints, motorcycle helmets, drink-driving laws, and safer roads.

In summary, as mortality decreased due to infectious diseases, mortality from chronic conditions became the leading causes of death in most nations by the 2010s. To reduce chronic diseases, in 2013, WHO launched the Global Action Plan for the Prevention and Control of Noncommunicable Diseases 2013–2020. This program purposed to reduce by 2025 premature mortality from cancer, cardiovascular diseases, diabetes, and chronic respiratory diseases by 25 percent.

7

Environmental and Occupational Hazards

Over the 20th century and into the 21st century, concerns about human-made environmental hazards in the home, workplace, community, region, and the planet evolved. These included the prevention and elimination of toxic and hazardous materials that could affect health and contribute to the burden of disease on a global level. In developed nations, the focus was on occupational hazards by the 1940s, radiation and toxic materials in the 1950s, population pressures, and air and water pollution by the 1960s, and climate changes by the 1990s. Occupational health and safety became a worldwide issue by the 2000s. Various groups warned about hazards and worked to mitigate them through legal activity, individual education, and international activities and treaties. In developing areas of the world, advancement of environmental and occupational concerns was more difficult.

ENVIRONMENTAL HAZARDS

An environmental hazard is a natural (earthquakes, volcanoes, tornados, forest fires, etc.) or anthropogenic (human made) condition, substance, or event that has the potential to threaten the surrounding natural environment and/or adversely affect people's health. Environmental hazards include biological, chemical, physical and mechanical, and psychosocial agents. These hazards in the workplace are occupational hazards. Most environmental hazards have been created by human activities.

The basic requirements for a healthy environment include clean air, safe drinking water, safe and adequate food, efficient sanitation, safe working environments and communities, and global peace and stability. Advancements in public and environmental health and the reductions of hazards often emerged from disasters.

To determine the effect of a health hazard, the World Health Organization (WHO) in 2016 reported on the Global Burden of Disease for environmental issues. They report that "23% of global deaths and 26% of deaths among children under five [were] due to modifiable environmental factors. Heading this list are stroke, ischaemic heart disease, diarrhoea and cancers." (Prüss-Ustün, 2016, x). Although the two most important environmental hazards that affect health are chemical and physical agents, biological hazards are endemic in developing regions of the world.

BIOLOGICAL HAZARDS, SANITATION, AND CLEAN WATER

Biological hazards include air-, food-, and waterborne diseases in addition to insect and other vectors that transmit diseases. In the early 20th century, prevention of disease from biological hazards through sanitation, hygiene, clean water and food, immunizations, and the elimination of vectors was a primary public health effort in higher-income nations. Control of biological hazards had eliminated many infectious diseases by midcentury. By the 21st century, biological hazards included the reemergence of some old diseases such as cholera and the emergence of new diseases such as Ebola. However, numerous developing nations still had poor sanitation, a lack of clean water, and little vector control resulting in millions still suffering illnesses such as dysentery and malaria. (Diseases are discussed in detail in chapter 6 along with prevention efforts.)

To address these continued biological hazards on a global level, the United Nations in 2005 introduced the Millennial Development Goals 2015. By 2015, although over 90 percent of the world's population used improved drinking water sources and two-thirds had improved sanitation facilities, the lack of clean water and sanitation still resulted in millions of people worldwide becoming sick. This was particularly found in the rural areas of Central and Southern Asia, Eastern and Southeastern Asia, and sub-Saharan Africa.

In China, for example, over half of all rivers in the country were unsafe for human contact due to contamination from the dumping of industrial chemicals, agricultural waste, and urban sewage. In Beijing, the city water by the mid-2010s was not safe to drink without boiling due to rapid urbanization along with antiquated water lines and treatment facilities. By 2015, a global water crisis was looming. It was caused by several factors including a warming climate, population growth, urbanization, more frequent droughts, and increased water pollution. In addition, incidences of serious water shortages were increasing in several urban areas of the world including Bangalore, Cairo, Cape Town, Jakarta, Mexico City, Rome, and Los Angeles among others.

An indication of the challenge in managing water and sanitation issues, particularly in low-income nations, was reflected in the difficulty of most Africa nations to meet the Millennium Development Goals. A key issue was the ability of both rural and urban Africans to access a clean water supply as there were limited sources of water available on the African continent. Sanitation is another area of concern in Africa. Few rural areas have privies, and open defecation is common. Efforts to improve sanitation and clean water in urban slums have been outpaced by rapid population growth and urbanization. To improve conditions, in 2015 the United Nations established new development goals for 2030. For this new program, Sustainable Development Goal (SDG) 6 was to "Ensure availability and sustainable management of water and sanitation for all." A major sanitation issue is open defecation found in several developing nations.

One nation is attempting to tackle this problem in a unique way. In India, about half of the population does not use toilets to defecate as they do not have a nearby toilet or because of traditional cultural practices. In an effort to meet the 2030 SDG sanitation goals, combat the problems of open defecation in the streets, and reduce disease, India introduced a public education program called "Take the Poo to the Loo." This ongoing social media campaign sponsored by UNICEF began in 2014. It included a silly song, amusing animated music video, and posters that encouraged people to defecate in a toilet.

CHEMICAL HAZARDS IN WATER POLLUTION AND FOOD

Besides poor sanitation leading to food and water contaminated with biological hazards, chemical pollutants also contaminate water and food supplies. Chemical agents are responsible for causing the majority of environmental hazards and are the chief factors in air, soil and water pollution. Sometimes these hazards have resulted from industrial disasters and sometimes from slow accumulation of chemicals in the water, soil, or atmosphere. Disasters helped to advance regulations to prevent and control chemical hazards by the late 20th and early 21st centuries.

Several heavy metals including mercury and lead have been known for years to cause various health issues including neurological and multiple organ damage. Although heavy metals are naturally occurring in the Earth's crust, most environmental contamination and consequent human exposure results from human activities such as mining, refineries, fossil fuel combustion, industrial manufacturing, and power-plant emissions.

For example, when mercury is released into the environment from various industrial activities, it can be transformed by bacteria into methylmercury, an organic compound, which gets into water and contaminates the food chain. Methylmercury is a persistent organic pollutant (POP) that does not break down and accumulates in living organisms. It causes increasing levels of harm in higher order species such as predatory fish through a process known as biomagnification. People are mainly exposed to methylmercury when they eat fish and shellfish that contain the compound.

In May 1956, the worst mass disaster in history from mercury poisoning occurred in Minamata, Japan. A chemical plant dumped a waste product that contained mercury into Minamata Bay, contaminating the entire ecosystem. More than 1,000 people died by eating contaminated fish, and developing fetuses were harmed. Politics kept the cause of these health problems from immediately being divulged. The results of this disaster ultimately led to advising the population to limit the intake of fish and for pregnant women to avoid fish likely to be contaminated. Laws were also introduced to curtail mercury and other toxic waste dumping. By the end of the century, mercury was increasingly found in fish around the world in both fresh and salt water.

Lead is also a toxic heavy metal that is especially dangerous to children and pregnant women. It was used in toys, water pipes, glazes, ceramic plates, and paint in the early through late 20th century. In 1912, chronic lead poisoning was found in Australian children with high blood lead levels who exhibited neurological problems. It originated from lead-based paint. In 1922, the League of Nations suggested banning indoor lead paint because of health concerns, but many nations did not adopt the recommendations as it was fought by paint manufactures. Also in that decade, tetraethylene lead (TEL) was added to gasoline to prevent knocking in the more powerful engines and caused further environmental pollution. After increasing concern about its toxicity in air pollution, by the late 1990s most nations had restricted the use of lead in gasoline. By 2010, children's blood lead levels had declined globally largely due to the elimination of leaded gasoline. However, some African nations still used leaded gasoline resulting in lead hazards in local areas.

Most lead was limited in indoor paints in higher-income nations by 2009. In that year, the Global Alliance to Eliminate Lead in Paint was formed by the United Nations and joined the United Nations Environment Programme as a worldwide partnership to ban the use of lead in paint. China, Singapore, and South Africa soon had limits on the lead content of household paints. The Alliance in 2015 announced plans to phase out lead in paint by 2020 but only 34 percent of countries had confirmed that they have legally binding controls on the production, import, sale, and use of lead paints. Lead paint was still being sold to other African and developing nations by companies in higher-income nations who manufactured it in lower-income nations. It was used to paint homes, schools, toys, and even playgrounds exposing children to this environmental hazard.

Many communities around the world still use lead water pipes, especially in older cities. This has resulted in lead leeching into the water system. A lead disaster in the United States, for example, occurred from early 2014 to late 2015 in the economically depressed city of Flint, Michigan. In 2014, the domestic water service was reconnected to a cheaper but polluted river water source. However, city officials failed to carry out sufficient water treatment resulting in the water being contaminated with elevated levels of lead. This resulted in over 100,000 residents being exposed to this hazard. In October 2015, Flint's water supply was switched back to its previous water systems and adequate treatment was initiated, which decreased the lead hazard by 2017. However, a conclusion from this disaster found that Flint's lead poisoning catastrophe could have been prevented if the Clean Water Act (1972) for regulating water systems and discharging of pollutants into the waters of United States had been followed.

Pesticides are also a major chemical environmental hazard. Dichlorodiphenyltrichloroethane (DDT), one of a group of chemicals, was discovered to have insecticidal properties in 1939 by Swiss chemist Paul Müller (1899–1965). In 1942, during WWII, DDT was used to eliminate typhus-carrying lice and malaria-carrying mosquitoes, and its use was initially encouraged by WHO. However, DDT was found to be toxic to other insects, such as butterflies, and led to the decline of birds due to thin eggshells that easily broke. As DDT was a persistent substance that did not easily break down, it stayed in the food chain and harmed

The city of Flint, Michigan, experienced an environmental disaster when lead contaminated the public water supply in 2014 and 2015. Here, the National Guard distributes bottled water to Flint residents who were still without clean water in 2016. (Linda Parton/Dreamstime.com)

wildlife and led to cancers and other health problems in humans. American nature writer, Rachel Carson's (1907–1964) *Silent Spring* (1962), warned of the worldwide environmental dangers from the misuse of DDT and initiated the contemporary environmental movement. In early 1970, WHO recommended limiting DDT, and many higher-income nations in the 1970s and 1980s banned its use for agriculture. Exemptions were allowed in African, the Eastern Mediterranean and Central Asian nations for killing disease-carrying mosquitoes. However, some mosquitoes became resistant to DDT.

Due to increased concerns about this environmental hazard, in 2004, the Stockholm Convention on Persistent Organic Pollutants, an international environmental treaty, was signed by 151 nations, and by 2017 there were 181 parties to the convention—an exception being the United States. The purpose of this treaty was to eliminate the "dirty dozen"—a group of twelve toxic persistent organic pollutants (POPs)—from the environment. The convention restricted the use of DDT to emergency insect control such as an outbreak of malaria or plague. In 2009, the United Nations established a program to eliminated DDT use by 2020. But exemptions were again given to some African, Eastern Mediterranean and Central Asian nations to spray homes to fight malaria-spreading mosquitoes. To regulate the manufacture and sale of chemicals in the United States, the Toxic Substances Control Act of 1976 mandated the EPA to protect the public from "unreasonable risk of injury to health or the environment"; it was amended in 2016. Between

2001 and 2014, global productions of DDT had declined by 32 percent with India, followed by sub-Saharan Africa, still having the highest production and use.

Another highly toxic hazard is a chemical group commonly called dioxins. They are a family of chemically related polychlorinateds dioxins and furans. They are formed as a by-product in many industrial processes involving chlorine such as waste incineration, pesticide manufacturing, and pulp and paper bleaching. Some dioxin-like polychlorinated biphenyls (PCBs) with similar toxic properties are also included with this group. Once in the environment, they enter the food chain and do not easily break down. By the turn of the 20th century, dioxin was known to cause painful, oozing skin lesions known as chloracne. By the late century, these chemicals were found to cause cancers, reproductive and developmental problems, and damage to the immune system. Dioxin was the primary toxic component of the herbicide Agent Orange, used by the United States from 1961 to 1971 in the Vietnam War.

An environmental disaster with dioxin occurred in 1976 in Seveso, Italy. A chemical explosion in a pesticide-manufacturing plant released a thick, white cloud of dioxin that exposed residents to this hazard. Long-term health problems emerged. However, the Seveso disaster led to the creation of tighter environmental regulations to prevent and control such accidents and to protect health throughout Europe. This agreement, called the Seveso-Directive (Directive 82/501/EEC), was later amended in 1996 in view of the lessons learned from later accidents such as the Bhopal Disaster, which was one of the largest chemical industrial disasters in history. A large amount of toxic methyl isocyanate was vented into the atmosphere and settled over the surrounding shanty towns. This toxic material killed 4,000 immediately and up to 20,000 over the next several years. The directive was again amended in 2012 as Seveso-III (Directive 2012/18/EU) due to changes in the EU's classification of chemicals.

Solid Waste and the International Waste Trade

Solid wastes include discarded or abandoned materials such as household garbage, construction debris, industrial waste, mining residues, electronics, sewage sludge, medical wastes, and other materials. They often contain hazardous chemicals and can be solid, liquid, or semisolid. Up through the mid-20th century, solid wastes of higher-income nations in rural areas were often burned in back yards, thrown into ravines, rivers or the ocean, dumped along the road side, or burned or buried in town dumps. In large urban areas, solid wastes were incinerated or buried in municipal landfills. In developing regions, burning, landfills, and open dumps were, and still are, common. Waste is also illegally dumped in oceans or in isolated rural areas. To counteract the growing waste, recycling of plastic, paper, and aluminum became established by the 1990s in many nations along with stricter governmental and waste-management regulations in higher-income nations. However, in some lower-income nations no coordinated waste-management system had been established by the late 2010s.

From the early to the late 20th century, glass bottles containing drinks such as milk, beer, or soda pop were often recycled in many nations. Beginning in the

1980s, plastic containers—because they were inexpensive—replaced glass, and they cost less to ship. These cheap plastics were discarded. However, they were not biodegradable and disintegrated into small particles. Most ended up in landfills or were dumped into oceans. The microscopic particles were later found in agricultural and even composting soil and in water runoff. Microbeads in cosmetics were also washed into water.

Larger pieces of plastic debris became increasingly common along beaches in many nations, especially developing ones, in the wide expanse of the oceans. In 2003, the "Great Pacific Garbage Patch" was discovered, which was largely made up of microscopic plastic particles along with some larger items such as fishing gear and plastic bags and bottles. Many larger items are thought to have sunk below the surface. Two huge patches were found in the northern Pacific. One vortex is located near Japan and the other between California and Hawaii. The one between California and Hawaii by 2018 was estimated to be about the size of France, although, the size and composition was still being debated. Some of the debris was from the 2011 Japanese tsunami. In addition, these debris vortexes have also been found in the north and south Atlantic, Indian, and south Pacific oceans. These collections of hazardous debris have endangered or killed wildlife, and the microscopic particles have entered the food chain. In the late 2010s, it was unknown what health effect microplastics have on humans.

By 2015, China followed by Indonesia, the Philippines, Thailand, and Vietnam were the primary ocean polluters due to mismanagement of plastic wastes. However, by 2018, China, India, Bangladesh, Californian in the United States, France, Italy, much of Australia, and some African nations had banned the use of lightweight plastic shopping bags. Partial tax or bans in some municipal areas were found in most EU nations, some American states, Canada provinces, and South Africa; interventions were seriously lacking in Latin America.

Due to the massive increase in solid wastes from the late 20th century in higher-income nations, an international waste trade emerged for the treatment, disposal, or recycling of wastes. Toxic or hazardous wastes from municipal dumps were often exported to lower-income countries. For example, although it is often illegal, electronic wastes were sent from North America, Europe, and higher-income East Asian nations to poorer nations in south Asia, Africa, or Latin America. The material is transferred to dumps where waste pickers, often children and young men, scavenge amid material containing heavy metals and other toxic chemicals. Many of these nations do not have safe recycling processes or facilities. Electronics are stripped of their raw metals, often with bare hands. Toxic chemicals from these dumps have polluted the immediate environment leading to deaths of humans, domestic animals, and wildlife.

To regulate this waste trade and prevent toxic materials from being dumped, in 1989, the international Basel Convention on the Control of Transboundary Movements of Hazardous Wastes and their Disposal was agreed upon. Its aim was to regulate the hazardous waste trade; to prevent transportation and dumping of hazardous material into lower-income nations; to promote environmentally sound management of hazardous wastes, wherever the place of disposal; and to protect human health and the environment against the adverse effects of hazardous wastes. Over 180 nations and the EU were parties to the convention. The United States signed it but has not ratified it. This convention is in line with WHO's Sustainable Development Goal (SDG) 3 (target 3.9): "By 2030, substantially reduce the number of deaths and illnesses from hazardous chemicals and air, water and soil pollution and contamination."

CHEMICAL HAZARDS IN AIR POLLUTION

Several hazardous chemicals and gases contribute to air pollution. Most air pollution is caused from burning fossil fuels, such as coal, oil, natural gas, and gasoline, to produce electricity and power vehicles. One chemical group contributing to pollution is the polycyclic aromatic hydrocarbon (PAH). In nature, PAHs are commonly found in tar, oil, and coal, and can result from the incomplete combustion of organic matter. They are found along major highways from vehicle exhaust. They also arise from electric-power generating plants, industrial processes, major oil spills, massive forest fires, and even cooking fires—particularly in India and China where biofuels such as dung are burned. The highest outdoor air, soil, and water concentrations of PAHs have been found in Africa, Asia, and Latin America. The lowest have been found in Europe, Australia, and North America due to stricter pollution controls, cleaner sources of cooking, and prohibitions of public smoking. PAHs have been linked to various cancers.

Another component of air pollution is particulate matter (PM), which is associated with lung cancer. PM is a mixture of solid particles and liquid droplets such as combustion particles, metals including lead, and organic substances including PAHs. Ozone is found in the upper atmosphere and protects the Earth against ultraviolet rays. However, ground-level ozone is a major component of air pollution. It is created by chemical reactions between oxides of nitrogen and volatile organic compounds (VOCs) in the presence of sunlight and heat. These chemicals come from vehicle emissions and some industrial operations. Ozone pollution contributes to acute heart attacks and breathing problems among the very young and elderly and those with respiratory conditions. Other components of air pollution include carbon monoxide, nitrogen oxides, and sulfur dioxide. Although these substances are individually toxic, when they are combined they can form a photochemical smog that is a poisonous and deadly environmental hazard.

In the early 1940s and 1950s, photochemical smog had deteriorated air quality in many major cities of the world. For example, in 1943 during the middle of World War II, Los Angeles residents believed the thick smog was a Japanese chemical attack as their eyes stung and some had breathing difficulties. This smog was later found to be caused by ozone and other pollutants derived from automobiles and industrial emissions. In December 1966, a deadly smog in New York City caused the public to pressure the government to take action. This resulted in the Air Quality Act (1967).

In 1970, the formation of the Environmental Protection Agency (EPA) to monitor and regulate environment pollution and consolidate many environmental responsibilities of the federal government under one agency was created. Because of resistance from the automotive industry, it was not until the mid-1970s, under the Clean Air Act, that vehicles, first in California, and then the rest of the states, were required to have catalytic converters to remove pollutants and improve air quality. The act was amended in 1990 and required the EPA to set National Ambient Air Quality Standards for pollutants considered harmful to public health and the environment—particulate matter (PM) 2.5 micrometers and smaller. Two standards were established. Primary standards provided public health protection for children, the elderly, and those with respiratory and heart conditions. Secondary standards provided protection from damage to animals, crops, vegetation, and buildings. From 2000 to 2016, a 42 percent decrease was found in PM in the United States. However, Los Angeles and other major cities were still struggling with smog problems.

The UK also enacted legislation to reduce hazardous air pollution. In December 1952, in London, a smog disaster from coal burning killed roughly 4,000 Londoners. This led Parliament to enact the Clean Air Act of 1956, which reduced the burning of coal. In the 1960s, Japan was among the most polluted places on earth with toxic levels of air, water, and ground contamination. Its hazardous smog originated from power plants, chemical factories, and other manufacturing units as the nation became an industrial power in the post-World War II era. A combination of public protests, lawsuits, local government action, use of nuclear energy, and upgrading of industries and technology reduced emissions from coal and oil-burning plants. By the early 1970s, the country possessed some of the strictest regulatory standards in the world, and many of these pollution problems decreased.

On the other hand, the rapid urban and industrial growth of the People's Republic of China beginning in the 1980s resulted in serious environmental hazards that had not abated by the late 2010s.

> China's environmental crisis is one of the most pressing challenges to emerge from the country's rapid industrialization. Its economic rise, in which GDP grew on average 10 percent each year for more than a decade, has come at the expense of its environment and public health. China is the world's largest source of carbon emissions, and the air quality of many of its major cities fails to meet international health standards. (Albert and Xu, 2016)

Since the 1980s, China has been the world's largest coal producer and accounts for about half of global consumption. In 2014, a record 17 million new vehicles were being driven in China, which further added to air pollution. Although China's industrialization pattern is similar to the industrialization of other modernizing nations, such as the European nations in the early 19th century, China's adverse environmental impact was more widespread than other countries. In January 2013, major North China cities experienced smog so thick that highways, factories, businesses and schools were closed, and flights canceled until the air quality was better. The pollution drifted over Korea, Japan, and Taiwan. After this record-high air pollution, an Action Plan for the Prevention and Control of Air Pollution was revealed by the country in September 2013. This ambitious plan aimed to reduce PM2.5 by over 10 percent from 2012 to 2017. Beijing, in particular, was attempting to decrease its air pollution. However, in December 2015, the government declared

A cyclist wears a mask to protect against pollution as she rides along a busy street in Beijing in early 2017. China's dramatic increase in coal use since the 1980s has resulted in a serious air pollution problem. (Fotokon/Dreamstime.com)

its first "red alert" in Beijing that was part of a new emergency plan to warn people about hazardous air pollution in an effort to decrease health problems. The poor air quality had caused significant health complications, including respiratory, cardiovascular, and cerebrovascular diseases. Other nations have cleaned up massive air pollution and China plans to upgrade its coal-fired power plants to reduce the discharge of pollutants by 60 percent before 2020. The main problem with China's environmental control system has been one of enforcement.

Other nations also struggle with air pollution. For example, India's major cities have high levels of pollution from various sources ranging from coal burning, wood for cooking, and dust storms and forest fires from rural areas that waft into the cities. India does have antipollution laws, but they are not well enforced. This is due to the politics of coordinating across city and provincial boundaries. In Africa, the Middle East, and Latin America, differences in air quality are also found between scantly populated and overpopulated areas. In areas where there is little industrial development and few people, air quality is high. However, in densely populated and industrialized regions, there is poor air quality leading to health issues.

Population Pressure, Carbon Dioxide, and Climate Change

A major gas produced from burning fossil fuels is carbon dioxide (CO_2), which is also a good indicator of how much fossil fuel has been burned and the quantity of other pollutants emitted. CO_2 is a greenhouse gas as it traps heat from the sun and warms the planet's surface, air, and oceans. Other greenhouse gasses include methane, nitrous oxide, and ozone. The warming effect of CO_2 on the planet was first suggested in 1938 by English steam engineer Stewart Callendar (1898–1964). This association of increased CO_2 levels with rising temperature was later called the Callendar effect. Other researchers expanded Callendar's work in the 1950s and 1960s.

Also, in the 1960s, the "population explosion" was seen as a major cause of all types of pollution and human suffering. American biologist Paul R. Ehrlich's (1932–) 1968 book, *The Population Bomb*, predicted that the rapid increase in population worldwide would lead to famine, disease, and death for millions. However, high-yielding, disease-resistant crops led to an agricultural "Green Revolution," which provided plenty to eat in developed nations and reduced population concerns. Regional famines, particularly in Asia and Africa in the late century, were still found. By the 2010s, famine was largely due to political discord, corruption or civil unrest, wars, and decreased agriculture due to drought in some developing nations. However, birthrates globally were now below replacement levels not only in high-income nations but also in India, China, much of Southeast Asia, and Latin America; several regions in Africa were the exception. By the early 21st century, the fear of an overpopulated planet had declined on the international level. On the other hand, a higher standard of living and the excessive demands for resources produced more carbon dioxide and other wastes that led to further climate change, which became a major international concern.

During the 1970s, scientific opinion increasingly accepted the burning of fossil fuel as the most probable cause of climate change and global warming rather than just a natural climate cycle. By the 1990s, the greenhouse effect was accepted by scientists in multiple disciplines and by most educated citizens around the world. One major exception was that in the United States, due to partisan politics, some political factions rejected climate change as being caused by humans.

Between 1998 and 2019, 10 of the hottest years on record had occurred, which paralleled the increase in CO_2 in the atmosphere. Glaciers melted faster than expected, and erratic weather became more common. Eastern China, the southwest United States, and eastern Australia in 2017 had the warmest years on record. NASA and National Oceanic and Atmospheric Administration (NOAA) indicated that the average global temperature was 2.02°F (1.12°C) above the 1881 to 1910 baseline when heavy industry was beginning to expand. Carbon dioxide levels accelerated in the 1990s and averaged more than 410 parts per million by the spring of 2018—the highest level in 800,000 years, which was also the hottest year on record.

In 2008, WHO suggested that "the warming of the planet will be gradual but the frequency and severity of extreme weather events, such as intense storms, heat waves, droughts and floods could be abrupt—the consequences for health will be dramatic" (WHO, 2008). By 2017, these events were occurring.

Human health has always been influenced by climate and weather, but the rapid changes in the early 21st century increasingly threatened human health and well-being. The health consequences from warming temperatures were global in

Firefighters in California watch a hillside go up in flames, November 2018. Extreme heat and dry conditions caused by climate change have led to wildfires and severe drought across the globe. (Erin Donalson/Dreamstime.com)

nature, but each region struggled with different issues. In warmer climates, extreme heat waves in India, Indonesia, parts of South America and Africa, and northern Australia by the mid-2010s killed thousands each summer especially the very young and very old. Extreme heat hazards were also occurring more frequently in Europe and North America, and climatologists predicted more intense, frequent, and longer lasting heat could increase illness and death from dehydration and cardiovascular events. Widespread wildfires that destroyed life and property had increased in frequency in the western part of the United States, South America, and most semiarid regions, including the Sahel region across central Africa, central Australia, Central Asia, and southern Africa. Due to drought in some regions in Africa, declining agriculture, increased malnutrition and dehydration—especially among children—lack of clean drinking water, and more displaced populations were also seen.

In temperate climates, warmer weather and higher concentrations of carbon dioxide in the atmosphere stimulated some plants to grow faster, mature earlier, and/or produce more potent allergens causing increased allergic reactions and poor air quality. Higher temperatures and a longer warm season in sub-Arctic and Arctic regions melted the permafrost with the release of potential pathogens such as smallpox, anthrax, and influenza from decomposing animal and human corpses. In addition, global warming increased the geographic range of disease-carrying ticks and mosquitoes into cooler climates where winter had once killed them. By the mid-2010s, malaria cases were on the upswing in some developed nations from travelers returning from—or immigrants from—malaria-ridden regions of the world. Health workers were concerned that this disease, eliminated decades ago in higher-income nations, could reoccur in addition to rare tropical diseases such as Zika, chickungunya, dengue, and West Nile fever. It was feared that as malaria-carrying mosquitoes continued to migrate to once cooler climates, the disease could again become endemic in currently malaria-free nations (see also chapter 6).

Other effects of the warming climate included more rainfall and flooding. These hazards led to increased toxic algae blooms, polluted water, gastrointestinal illness, and mold inside houses in regions where they had been rare. Algae blooms are precipitated by agriculture run off of fertilizers into warmer waters. Ingesting, breathing, or touching this toxic alga causes sickness. Warmer oceans and other surface waters could increase cholera outbreaks and harmful bacteria in shellfish.

Extreme weather hazards can result in more displaced people who crowd into developed nations leading to political controversies. Higher-income nations are more likely to be able to adapt to projected climate changes. However, those in lower-income nations, and the less economically fortunate in wealthier nations, are more vulnerable because they have fewer resources to escape danger and are less likely to have air conditioning and well-insulated homes. In addition, water and food scarcity are also likely to increase.

International Agreements to Control Greenhouse Gases

Due to worldwide concern on the global increase in temperature, international agreements instituted efforts to mitigate the greenhouse gases. A UN report in 1990 resulted in an international consensus that climate change was human induced. This led to a worldwide convention to address the issue. In 1992, the United Nations Framework Convention on Climate Change (UNFCCC) was signed by over 150 countries at the Rio Earth Summit to level greenhouse gases that were found in air conditioners and other equipment. At that time, the 1987 Montreal Protocol had already started reducing the ozone hole, but greenhouse emissions continued to increase. To reduce these gases, other United Nations agreements were established. The Kyoto Protocol of 1997 set emission reduction targets for a handful of developed countries, but the United States pulled out of the agreement and others failed to comply.

The next major accord was the Paris Agreement of 2016 (*Accord de Paris*). It dealt with greenhouse gas emission reduction and finance for developing nations beginning in 2020. The goal of the agreement was to limit the global temperature increase to less than 2°C. Every nation by 2017, other than the United States, had signed the pact for a joint effort to cut back greenhouse gas emissions and stave off human-influenced climate change. The United States under the Obama administration had entered into the accord. However, the new Trump administration in 2017 pulled out of the agreement although the United States was the second highest greenhouse gas emitter in the world—China was the highest and India the third highest. America's withdrawal from the Paris Agreement gave the Chinese government the opportunity to take the lead in the global fight against climate change.

PHYSICAL AND OCCUPATIONAL HAZARDS

Physical hazards are often associated with occupations. These hazards include dust, radiation, heat and cold stress, dangerous equipment, unsafe working conditions, vibration and noise, and repetitive motion. A major global environmental hazard is dust. The inhalation of dust particles from working in mines, agriculture, foundries, and other industries over time can scar lung tissue leading to respiratory illnesses. Coal dust causes black lung disease, silica particles silicosis, and asbestos fibers cancers; smoking exacerbates the lung damage. Silicosis is the most common occupational lung disease worldwide, especially in low-income nations.

Advancement in technology, such as wearing respirators, brought a steady decline in death rates in higher-income nations from these dusts beginning in the late 20th century. However, in less-developed countries, the lack of respirator use and poor working conditions continue to contribute to high morbidity and mortality rates from this occupational hazard. In addition to dusts causing physical health problems, some dusts under the right condition can cause explosions, particularly in enclosed spaces and mines.

Mine safety was one of the first occupational health hazards to be addressed in higher-income nations. The United States in December 1907 saw a series of coal mine explosions from gas and dust due to miners carrying open flame lamps. These explosions killed more than 600 miners, many of them young boys. As a response to these tragedies, Congress passed an act creating the United States Bureau of Mines (1908) to investigate the causes of mine explosions and to promote safety and efficiency in the mines; child labor laws were also passed. Similarly, Britain passed the Coal Mines Regulation Act (1911).

These acts and organizations were amended over the century to make mines and other workplaces safer and to reduce health consequences in higher-income nations. For example, in the United States the Occupational Safety and Health Act (1970) became the primary federal law that governed occupational health and safety in all workplaces in the nation. Its main goal was to ensure that employers provided employees with an environment free from known health hazards. To reduce workplace hazards, such as temperature extremes, noise and eye threats, dangerous or heavy equipment, or repetitive injury risks, the Personal Protective Equipment (1992) at work regulations required an employer to provide protective clothing, safety glasses, ear protectors, safety footwear, hard hats, respirators and other devices to guard against a hazard. Many lower-income nations do not have these requirements in place, and if they exist, they are not enforced.

Another physical hazard is radiation, which is both found in nature and produced by humans. Two kinds of radiation exist. Nonionizing low-energy radiation includes electromagnetic and infrared radiation, sunlight (UV rays), and lasers. They can cause burns, eye damage, cancers, or even death among power-plant workers. This type of radiation is found in agriculture, welding, electrical work, and the military.

The other kind, ionizing high-energy radiation includes X-rays and gamma rays along with other nuclear particles. They can cause death at high doses in a short period of time or cancers at lower dosages over longer periods of time. This type of radiation is found in occupations that use X-ray machines, nuclear medicine, nuclear reactors in ships and submarines, nuclear energy plants and bombs, and from cosmic radiation at high altitudes or space.

Early users of X-rays were unaware that large radiation doses were a serious hazard. American dentist and physician, William Herbert Rollins (1852–1929), was one of the first to understand the dangers of the newly discovered X-rays and ionizing radiation after he suffered radiation burns to his hand while experimenting with them. In 1901, he advised that anyone working with X-rays should shield themselves and cover the patient in radiopaque material other than what was being radiographed. However, this advice was ignored until the mid-1920s.

In the mid-1920s, a widespread practice highlighted the hazards of ionizing radiation in radium. From around 1910, luminescent radium was used by several nations in paint for watch, clock, and instrument dials and to make glowing cosmetics and even clothing. Women who painted these instrument dials became sick as they licked their brushes to make them pointed. In the United States, these dying "Radium Girls" sued their companies and won; the use of radium declined. By the mid-1960s, radium and other isotopes were increasingly being used in nuclear medicine for diagnosis and treatment, which decreased death rates. Many lower-income nations in Africa, Latin America, and Asia could not afford advanced nuclear technological equipment for medical use by 2010 other than in large urban areas.

To measure the amount of radiation a worker received, in the early 1940s, film badge dosimeters were introduced. Concerns about radiation exposure in the workplace in developed nations increased in the 1950s. Observation of Japanese survivors of the Hiroshima and Nagasaki nuclear bombings showed higher rates of leukemia and other cancers. There was also a fear of mutations of genetic material (by the mid-2010s, negative effects to DNA had not been found). The deadly consequences of ionizing radiation led to the International Commission on Radiation Protection (ICRP) in 1953. In 1957, the commission recommended an annual occupational dose limit of 5 rem per year. However, by 1990, they lowered this to 10 rem over any five-year period. In 1960, the Radiation Protection Convention, an International Labour Organization Convention, was established to restrict workers from exposure to ionizing radiation. All workers around radiation wore devises to measure the amount of radiation they received. These occupations included dentistry, medicine, academic research, power plants, and certain military occupations.

Since the early 1940s, with the increased use of radioactive materials, there have been numerous accidents in power plants, submarines, industry, and medical situations where workers and others have been injured or killed. Several have occurred in developed nations. The most serious include the Japanese Fukushima Daiichi disaster (2011) and the Russian Federation Chernobyl disaster (1986), which contaminated the environment with radioactive material around the world and endangered thousands. Out of these severe disasters have come stricter regulations and international agreements. For example, within four months of the Chernobyl accident, the Convention on Early Notification of a Nuclear Accident (1986) was established. It was an International Atomic Energy Agency (IAEA) treaty where nations agreed to provide notification of a nuclear accident that could affect other states. In addition, with the Convention on Assistance in the case of a Nuclear Accident or Radiological Emergency (1986), nations also agreed to provide any assistance that they could offer to another nation with a nuclear accident.

PSYCHOSOCIAL AND OTHER OCCUPATIONAL HAZARDS

Psychosocial threats are occupational hazards that can include poor and unsafe working conditions, long hours, feeling of job insecurity, sexual harassment, or bullying. A relationship exists between a hazardous psychosocial work environment and its negative effect on employees' physical and mental health. These include increased hypertension and heart disease, musculoskeletal disorders, gastrointestinal ailments and excessive alcohol and drug consumption.

Many psychosocial occupational threats have emerged since 2000 due to new forms of employment contracts and new and emerging jobs, particularly in the information-technology sector. Many jobs in higher-income nations are now temporary with few benefits. In addition, companies are increasingly outsourcing their manufacturing to lower-income countries leading to job-insecurity stress among workers in the developed nations. In higher-income nations by the mid-2010s, women were beginning to bring charges of sexual harassment against their employers, especially in the entertainment, business, and political spheres.

Unsafe working conditions are a major occupational hazard that embodies many dangers in the workplace. For example, in the first decade of the 20th century, American author Upton Sinclair's *The Jungle* (1906) described horrific conditions in the meat-packing industry. These included bizarre accidents, threats of being fired, long working hours, and early deaths for poor immigrant workers. Due to unsanitary meat processing techniques, this book was the tipping point for the Pure Food and Drug Laws to be enacted (see chapter 10). In 1911, a disastrous fire at the Triangle Shirtwaist factory in New York City left 146 dead—mostly teenage and young immigrant women. Doors had been locked by management, so they could not escape. The fire and deaths led to legislation requiring improved factory safety standards in the United States. Other industrialized nations also adopted safer and better working conditions.

However, many developing nations by the end of the century still did not have adequate or safe working conditions. By the late 20th century, the number of fatal work related accidents was much higher in low-income nations than in higher-income ones. This can be attributed to better first-aid and medical facilities and health and safety regulations in higher-income nations. Industries with the highest risk of accidents globally are mining, logging, agriculture, and construction.

Factories in developing nations making apparel for the Western market have had disasters. As an example, in May 1993, a fire emerged at the Kader Toy Factory in Thailand. Like the Triangle Shirtwaist fire, the exit doors were locked, which resulted in 188 young women being killed and over 500 injured. The fire helped to tighten building codes and safety regulations in Thailand. In Bangladesh, during 2013, numerous factory fires and a collapsed building killed several thousand, mostly young female garment workers. Although better safety had been discussed, improvements have been slow.

Only a small proportion of the global workforce has access to occupational health and safety programs to protect workers from various environmental hazards. Most of these are in higher-income nations. To improve conditions, in 2007, the 60th World Health Assembly endorsed a Global Plan of Action on Workers' Health for 2008–2017. They urged WHO member states to devise national policies and plans to implement occupational health and safety to prevent work-related accidents, disasters, and diseases. The global action was intended to stimulate development of policies, infrastructure, technologies, and partnerships to improve the health of all workers and workplaces around the world.

In summary, from the early 20th century, advancements in mitigating environmental hazards that affect human health have been attempted. Although there has been some success, not all nations have fully joined the effort, and the effects of a warming climate may cause increased health issues.

8

Surgery and Medical Procedures

At the turn of the 20th century, maintaining a sterile environment for surgery gained prominence and set the stage for advances in surgical procedures into the 21st century. Developments of safer anesthesia worked hand in hand with sterile environments enabling more complex procedures. In the post-WWI era, surgical specialties arose. Various surgeons also developed techniques and inventions during the late 20th century and early 21st century that could only have been dreamed of as science fiction in earlier years. Surgeons developed instruments and equipment, such as the heart lung machine, that made open heart surgery possible. Better diagnostic tools were also invented. By 2000, minimally invasive techniques such as laparoscopic surgery and computer-assisted and robotic surgery evolved, and joint-replacement surgeries had become routine. The transplantation of organs, limbs, eye lenses, and faces also emerged. By 2000, eye surgeons improved vision and prevented blindness, and dental surgeons implanted screws for artificial teeth. Many of the advances in surgery allowed most routine surgical procedures being done on an outpatient basis. By 2015, practical artificial hearts, the growing of livers, kidneys, and other organs from stem cells along with 3D printing to make artificial bones and organs were being perfected.

GENERAL SURGERY

Almost all surgical innovations have come from Western higher-income nations beginning in the early 20th century. New types and safer surgeries evolved not only because of antiseptic conditions but also improved understanding of the causes of shock and its treatment, the development of antibiotics to control infection, and analgesics to control pain. Knowledge of blood-group typing, blood clotting, and transfusion techniques was also important along with new procedures and instruments.

> [General surgery] began to progress through an increasingly important process of refinement and professionalization. William Halsted [*1852–1922*] introduced and popularized the use of rubber gloves to help prevent infection. Care of burns and

> other wounds was made radically simpler and less traumatizing. Anesthetic techniques and apparatus were being made more reliable and sophisticated. . . . [and] the role of hospitals [shifted] from serving primarily as a place for the convalescence of the sick poor to providing safe and effective care for patients undergoing surgery. (Atul Gawande, 2012)

Refined surgical instruments also developed. Electrically powered implements were devised for cautery. Surgical stapling instruments, first developed in the Soviet Union, could join blood vessels or other tissues more quickly than hand suturing. Medical glues, surgical tapes, and even zippers were developed to close some wounds without stitches.

Diagnostic equipment, used before and during surgery, was developed often by teams of researchers. The conventional X-ray of the early 20th century had, by the end of the century, evolved into sophisticated medical imaging devices that led to improvements in the diagnosis and treatment of numerous conditions. Fluoroscopy, a continuous X-ray image, is displayed on a monitor and often used in surgery. Computed tomography (CT) took "slices" of internal organs and tissues, and by the 1980s, it was widely used in developed nations. Positron emission tomography (PET) scans took images of radioactive material in an organ to determine function or abnormalities.

One of the greatest advancements in imaging was the invention of the digital X-ray, which produced filmless images and was introduced in the mid-1980s. Since it used less ionizing radiation, had the advantage of the image being kept digitally on computers, and could be easily stored in electronic patient record, it had replaced film by 2010 in higher-income nations.

Nonradiation imaging was also developed. Ultrasound, first used in medicine in 1956, uses high frequency sound waves to produce images such as a fetus in utero or to break up kidney stones. Magnetic resonance imaging (MRI) was developed late in the century. This scan uses a strong magnetic field and radio waves to generate images of parts of the body that can't be seen as well with X-rays, CT scans, or ultrasound, such as inside joints, the heart, and other soft tissues. Holograms can be created using data from the MRI to give surgeons a three-dimensional image of the area being operated upon. Supercooled, or cryogenic, probe beams were developed to precisely remove tissues and abnormal growths.

Surgical procedures also advanced. In the early 20th century, as surgeons developed more skill and instruments, there was a rise of exploratory laparotomies (cutting into the abdomen) for the purpose of diagnosis. Into the late 20th century, however, most of these surgeries, along with the removal of diseased organs, were accomplished with large incisions that resulted in a week or so of hospitalization and a long convalescence. Postsurgical procedures also changed as new knowledge was gained. During the earlier part of the century, patients after surgery were often kept on bed rest for one or two weeks. By the 1980s, it was found that early ambulation after surgery helped to prevent deep vein thrombosis (DVT), blood clots, and pneumonia, which were often fatal.

Two trends evolved in the late 20th century. With the advent of chemotherapeutics, molecular medicine, and other developing technologies, surgery was no longer the driving force behind medical breakthroughs. In addition, a trend toward less invasive surgery and shorter hospital stays began. By 2000, more than a half of all surgical procedures, in most higher-income nations, were done on an outpatient basis without an overnight stay in a hospital because of one of the greatest advances in surgical equipment in recent times—the development of the flexible fiber-optic endoscope. This instrument not only could be inserted through the skin (percutaneous) and abdominal wall to view organs, take images, or conduct surgical procedures, it could also be used for diagnosis, screening, and treatment in the colon, stomach, and lungs. In the 1980s, German surgeon and engineer Kurt Semm (1927–2003), German surgeon Erich Mühe (1938–2005), and French surgeon Philippe Mouret (1938–2008) accomplished the first laparoscopy gallbladder surgeries with an endoscope. The use of this instrument accelerated with the invention of a small computer-chip television camera that magnified the view. This minimally invasive laparoscopic surgery turned incisions into small puncture wounds.

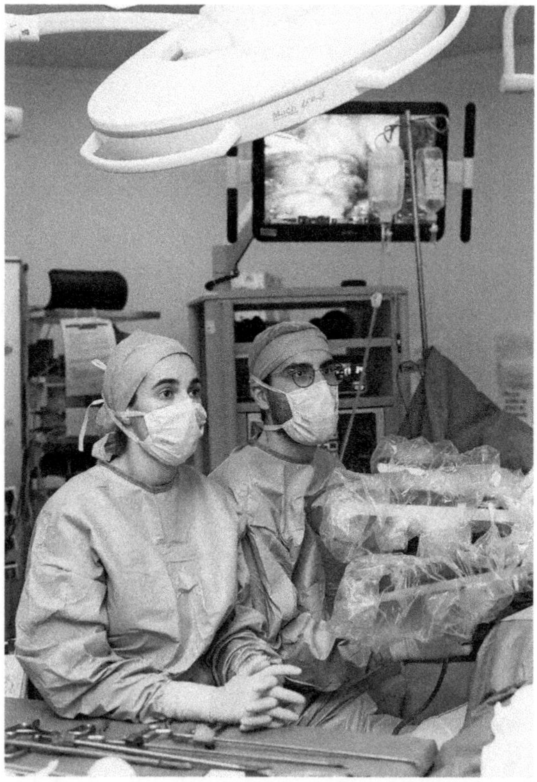

Doctors remove a kidney from a living donor using the da Vinci robot in Nice, France, April 2018. Robotic or robotic-assisted surgery was developed in the 2000s. (BSIP/UIG via Getty Images)

Developing nations also started using this "Band-Aid" surgery. For example, China performed its first laparoscopic surgery in 1991. This surgical method was in agreement with deep-rooted Chinese cultural and medical beliefs regarding preserving the integrity of the body and treating disease internally. In the mid-2015, due to high costs, minimally invasive surgery was uncommon in sub-Saharan Africa, except in the larger cities. On the other hand, in Latin American nations, laparoscopic surgery was growing in popularity especially in Brazil and Mexico.

In the 21st century, robotic or robotic-assisted surgery evolved augmented by minimally invasive surgery. Italian physician Pier Cristoforo Giulianotti (1953–) at the University of Illinois at Chicago developed methods of robotic-assisted surgery. This procedure offered the potential for surgeons to operate on patients remotely. On the other hand, this surgical technique is expensive and may not have significant benefits that justify its cost. In the 2010s, techniques for combining noninvasive ways of seeing into the body through the insertion of small-scale devices using nanotechnology that can be injected or swallowed were developed. At some point in the future, this may make most invasive surgeries obsolete or even fully automated.

BONE, OR ORTHOPEDIC, SURGERY

Many orthopedic surgical advances evolved out of the wars of the 20th and 21st centuries (discussed in chapter 11). In the early 20th century, the newly introduced X-ray machine gave the ability to diagnose orthopedic conditions ranging from fractures to osteoarthritis. From 1900 through the 1940s, orthopedics was primarily concerned with the care of "crippled children" and treating fractures. However, by the end of the century, it specialized into many areas including degenerative arthritis, congenital deformities, athletic injuries, and a growing industry of joint replacements. Orthopedic surgery now occupies a prominent role in all modern hospitals globally.

A major advance in the treatment of fractures was "internal fixation" of bone with the use of metal plates, rods, nails, screws, wires, and the like. In 1931, Norwegian-born American physician Marius Nygaard Smith-Petersen (1886–1953) developed a three-pronged nail to treat fractures of the neck of the femur (thigh bone). In 1939, German surgeon Gerhard Küntscher (1900–1972) used intramedullary (inside the bone) rods to treat fractures of the femur and tibia during WWII, which shortened recovery time. A metal rod was forced into the inner cavity of a long bone to act as an internal splint. Until the late 1970s, traction and/or plaster of Paris casts were the main techniques of treating thigh-bone fractures. However, intramedullary locking long nails became the more popular method by the late 20th century. A patient with a fracture treated with these nails was often allowed weight bearing soon after surgery before bone union (healed fracture). This early ambulation decreases some negative consequences of surgery, and new walking casts that allow a patient to walk are still used.

Spinal surgery developed rapidly with American surgeon Russell A. Hibbs (1869–1932). In the early 20th century, he devised a method of lengthening the Achilles tendon that had shortened as the result of polio and developed early methods of surgical spinal fusion. American surgeon Paul Randall Harrington (1911–1980) invented the Harrington Rod in 1953 to help straighten the spine and keep it immobilized, which helped those with scoliosis. The rod was used with spinal fusion from the 1960s until the late 1990s when newer techniques to fuse the spinal column together were developed. In the mid-1950s, Soviet physician Gavriil Abramovich Ilizarov (1921–1992) invented an apparatus and surgical technique for lengthening limbs. A bone is separated by a small amount and the apparatus holds the severed bone in place allowing bone to grow in the gap. This procedure is useful in lengthening uneven limb growth and serious fractures.

A major advancement in orthopedic surgery since the 1940s has been hip, knee, and other joint replacements. In 1940, American surgeon Austin Moore (1899–1963) performed the first metal hip arthroplasty (hip replacement). Joint replacement was subsequently advanced by the work of British surgeon John Charnley

(1911–1982) in the 1960s, who replaced the head of the femur with a small metallic prosthesis used in combination with a low friction plastic socket to reduce frictional force. Until the mid-1990s, the procedure was generally preformed on the elderly. However, continued improved surgical techniques along with bioengineering resulted in total hip replacement becoming common among active younger individuals in developed nations for the treatment of osteoarthritis of the hip. Various substances including metal, ceramic, and high-density plastic by 2005 were used for the prosthesis. In the 2010s, some all-metal and other prosthesis were recalled due to complications. Hip, along with knee replacements, have now become one of the most common surgeries in the world. New developments including restructuring arthritic joints by biotechnology are now in the process of being researched.

BRAIN AND NEUROSURGERY

Neurosurgery involves the brain, spinal column, peripheral nerves, and cerebrovascular system. As antiseptic surgical conditions evolved in the early 20th century, so did successful brain surgery. In addition, many subspecialties of neurosurgery developed along with numerous advances in techniques and procedures. In 1907, for example, Austrian surgeon Hermann Schloffer (1868–1937) became the first to successfully remove a pituitary tumor in the brain by the transsphenoidal method (going through the nose), which laid the foundation for future development and refinement of brain surgery.

American surgeon Harvey Cushing (1869–1939), one of the founders of neurosurgery, made important contribution to head-injury surgery during WWI. He also developed techniques to remove cerebral tumors and devised many basic surgical techniques. Cushing syndrome caused by abnormal growth of the pituitary gland that results in abnormal secretions from the adrenal gland was also discovered by him. As discussed in chapter 10, lobotomies—cutting into the prefrontal cortex of the brain—were performed to remove some mental illness symptoms during 1930s–1960s but fell out of favor by the 1980s.

Although the stereotactic frame (which had three planes) for brain surgery was first pioneered in the early 20th century, it did not mature until the post-WWII era. Advances were developed simultaneously in several nations. For example, Japanese neurosurgeon Hirotaro Narabayashi (1922–2001) used stereotactic surgery for the treatment of Parkinson's disease. In 1952, an injection of a small amount of oil wax into a certain area of the brain stopped the tremors of a patient with Parkinson's disease.

In the 1950s, Swedish neurosurgeon Lars Leksell (1907–1986) at the Karolinska Institute devised radiosurgery. A stereotactic device allowed a beam of radiation coming from several directions to be aimed at a precise point in the brain to destroy a tumor or other anomaly. This noninvasive method of destroying a small region in the brain without damaging surrounding tissues was commonly used by 2005. Advances such as 3-D imaging including intra-operative MRI and techniques involving smaller openings with the aid of microscopes and endoscopes were developed. A major contributor to modern neurosurgery was the development of microneurosurgery devised by Turkish born Gazi Yasargil (1925–) at the University of Zurich. By the 1990s, his methods allowed previously inoperable brain and neurological conditions to be performed by a team of skilled surgeons.

In the latter part of the century, an important new technique was brain-stimulation surgery, which treated many neurological conditions. Spanish born physician Jose Rodríguez Delgado (1915–2011) at Yale University invented the first electrode that was implanted in an animal's brain in the 1950s. This early radio controlled device could control behavior including reduction of epileptic seizures in humans. By 2010, advanced versions of deep-brain-stimulation implants (brain pacemakers) were used to control tremors of Parkinson's disease, essential tremors, and other conditions. Electrodes in the brain were connected to wires and a battery electric generator, which delivered a mild shock to the brain. These small devices were buried just below the skin and have aided numerous patients.

HEART, OR CARDIOVASCULAR, SURGERY

In cardiac surgery, numerous advances in procedures and devices now save millions of lives worldwide. A few of the most important ones that evolved to advance cardiac surgery and care will be discussed. Dutch physician Willem Einthoven (1860–1927) invented the first practical electrocardiogram (ECG or EKG) in 1903 for which he won the Nobel Prize in 1924. Over the century, the equipment became more refined and portable. It is now used worldwide to monitor the heart in many areas of medicine and surgery.

German physician Werner Theodor Otto Fossmann (1904–1979) published an experiment on cardiac catheterization in 1929 and shared the 1956 Nobel Prize for the procedure. Fossmann, against the advice of his professors to attempt the technique on either animals or patients, performed it safely on himself. This procedure allowed for direct delivery of drugs or radiopaque dyes to diagnose heart issues, which advanced cardiology.

Other developments saved lives in the latter 20th century. In the 1940s, African American surgical technician Vivien Theodore Thomas (1910–1985) helped develop a procedure to treat "blue baby syndrome" (cyanotic heart disease) caused by a hole between the two ventricles of the heart. He was the assistant to surgeon Alfred Blalock (1899–1964) at Vanderbilt University in Nashville, TN, and also worked with Helen Brooke Taussig (1898–1986), the founder of pediatric cardiology at Johns Hopkins University in Baltimore, Maryland. Although Thomas was not given credit, the three developed the Blalock-Taussig shunt—a tube designed to deliver oxygen-rich blood from the lungs to the heart in babies with the syndrome. The procedure was first published in 1945.

Cardiac surgery was revolutionized by American surgeon John Heysham Gibbon (1903–1973) who invented the heart–lung machine that made open heart surgery possible. This cardiopulmonary-bypass machine took over the blood-pumping and breathing functions during heart surgery. Its first successful clinical application was in 1953 to repair a hole in the wall between the atriums in a young woman.

Due to this machine and other inventions, cardiac surgery rapidly advanced in the 1960s. The first successful coronary artery bypass surgery was performed in 1960 by a team led by German-born surgeon Robert H. Goetz (1910–2000) at Albert Einstein College of Medicine in New York. American surgeon Albert Starr (1926–) and coinventor engineer M. Lowell Edwards (1898–1982) began research on heart valves and used durable, rigid components. In 1960, Starr performed the first successful mitral valve replacement. Surgeon Dwight Harken (1910–1993) soon followed with an implantation of an aortic valve. In 1977, the first coronary angioplasty using a deflated balloon catheter threaded through a vein into a clogged artery was performed in Switzerland by German cardiologist Andreas Gruentzig (1939–1985). Once in the artery, the balloon was inflated to expand the vessel. Stents could also be placed to keep the vessel open. The procedure demonstrated that surgeons could work inside of the arteries safely reducing the need for open heart surgery. Angioplasty is frequently used to prevent or postpone the need for coronary artery bypass. By the 2010s, robotic surgery inside the blood vessels and heart had been used globally.

In 1967, South African surgeon Christiaan Barnard (1922–2001) performed the first human-to-human heart transplant. Although the patient only lived a few weeks, by 2000, various immunosuppressant drugs prevented rejection of the heart allowing about 75 percent of patients to live at least 5 years and 57 percent 10 years with a human heart transplant. During this decade, artificial hearts were also developed. American cardiac surgeon Denton A. Cooley (1920–2016) in 1969 implanted a totally artificial heart into a human patient. This surgery was unbeknown to his former mentor and colleague Michael E. DeBakey (1908–2008)—who had developed this artificial heart—and led to a falling out between the two men. The first totally artificial heart, originally intended for permanent use, was the Jarvik-7. It was first used in 1982 and designed by a team including Dutch-born surgeon Willem Johan Kolff (1911–2009), who also produced the first dialysis machine, and American medical scientist and inventor Robert Jarvik (1946–). Cardiac surgeon William DeVries (1943–) implanted the device in a patient at the University of Utah. However, after implantation on further patients, due to complications, the device is now used for patients waiting for a human heart transplant. By the mid-2010s, artificial hearts printed from stem cells were on the horizon.

Lifesaving cardiac devices were developed in the late 20th century, such as pacemakers to control abnormal heart rhythms and defibrillators to restart normal cardiac rhythm. An American engineer Wilson Greatbatch (1919–2011) devised the implantable pacemaker (cardiac resynchronization therapy, or CRT) in the 1960s. Also in the 1960s, the portable defibrillator (Automated External Defibrillator, or AED) was developed by Irish surgeon Frank Pantridge (1916–2004). An implantable cardioverter-defibrillator (ICD) was first researched in 1970 by Polish-born Israeli cardiologists Michel Mirowski (1939–1990), American Morton Mower (1933–) and others at Sinai Hospital, Baltimore, MD. Despite heavy objections of leading cardiologists of the time, in 1980, the ICD was first inserted into the chest of a woman who had survived a cardiac arrest. By the mid-1990s, the apparatus was accepted worldwide. Since 2003, both the CRT and ICD were combined to treat patients with both abnormal heart rhythms and heart failure. By 2009, these implantable devices had become quite small. In the early 2010s, telemonitoring of their functioning via phones or the Internet became available making it easier for the patient to lead a normal life.

"PLASTIC," RECONSTRUCTIVE, AND REGENERATIVE SURGERY

As discussed in chapter 11, facial and other reconstructive "plastic surgery" had its beginnings during WWI. It was usually done with autologous grafting where healthy tissue from one part of the body would be grafted onto the burned face or hands. During WWII, in the 1940s, New Zealand military surgeon Archibald McIndoe (1900–1960) repaired very deep burns and serious facial disfigurement of airmen in the Royal Air Force. Noticing that airmen landing in salt water had better outcomes compared to those who landed in land, he introduced saline soaks into his burn treatment. In the postwar period and into the 21st century, new methods of reconstructive and regenerative surgery were advanced with the development of antibiotics, better blood and tissue typing, and immune suppressant drugs—so that tissue from others would not be rejected—and the use of stem cells to create tissue and organs. New advances also led to cosmetic surgery of celebrities, and by the late century, many individuals in developed nations sought out plastic surgery to correct perceived facial and other defects.

Organ transplants, in particular kidneys, had been tried in the early 20th century but were not successful as there were mismatches in the donor and recipient blood groups and the donor kidney rarely functioned. However, new inventions allowed some patients with kidney failure to be kept alive. For example, in 1948 Dutch American surgeon Willem Kolff (1911–2009) first used his Kolff-Brigham "artificial kidney" on a human patient. This hemodialysis machine purified human blood of toxins and kept patients alive but was often done in an outpatient setting. By 2000, the use of home dialysis, particularly peritoneal dialysis, became more common. In this procedure, a cleaning solution is injected into the lining of the abdomen (peritoneum) to removed impurities. However, all dialysis procedures were cumbersome and could limit a patient's lifestyles, so interest in kidney transplants grew.

In 1954, American Nobel laureate Joseph E. Murray (1919–2012) and his colleagues at Peter Bent Brigham Hospital in Boston performed the first successful kidney transplant from one identical twin to another. Since the procedure was carried out between identical twins, rejection of the new kidney was less likely as they were genetically the same. In the 1950s, full-body irradiation was used to suppress the immune system in nonrelated individuals, which was highly toxic to the patient and often led to death in a few years due to cancers. However, new drugs, such as cortisone developed in the 1950s and cyclosporine developed in the late 1970s, decreased the rejection problem, but they also had issues.

Two major researchers who worked on immunosuppressive drug regimens and organ transplantations were American surgeon Thomas Earl Starzl (1926–2017) and British surgeon Roy Y. Calne (1930–). Their work made possible the successful transplant of organs, including the heart, pancreas, lungs, liver, and intestines. In 1964, Starzl directed the first extensive trial of tissue matching to increase survival of transplanted organ and in 1967 performed the first successful human liver transplant. By the late 1970s, the majority of liver-transplant patients were surviving longer than a year. Starzl used cortisone and newly developed immune suppressants in the early 1980s to prevent rejections of transplants. Calne preformed the world's first liver, heart, and, lung transplant in 1987. He also performed the first successful combined stomach, intestine, pancreas, liver, and kidney transplant in 1994 and developed successful liver transplant surgical techniques. Organ transplantation, considered impossible in the early 20th century, is now a standard surgical procedure. It is only limited by the number of organs available. However, the use of stem cells to produce organs and other techniques will likely make organ donors obsolete in the next few years.

Limb and hand transplantation also became possible by 2005. Since the early 1960s, limbs that had been severed in accidents have been able to be reattached with some success. French surgeon Jean-Michel Dubernard (1941–) was the first surgeon to successfully perform the transplant of a single human hand in 1998. About a year later he did a double transplant of human hands although it remained secret until mid-2004. In 2005, Dubernard was asked to assist with the first partial human face transplant led by French surgeon Bernard Devauchelle (1950–) in Amiens, France, on a woman mauled by a dog.

The world's first successful full face transplant was completed in Spain in 2010 on a man injured in a shooting accident. Soon afterward, China, Turkey, Poland, the UK, and the United States were performing the complex procedure. By the mid-2010s, France, the United States, and Spain were the leading countries researching face transplants. However, transplant patients must take immune-suppressant drugs for life so as not to reject the transplant, and they are more susceptible to cancers and other health issues, so the usefulness of transplantation is currently limited.

However, surgeons are working on other techniques. For example, American surgeon Anthony Atala (1958–) researches restoring damaged tissue to original healthy conditions so that the body can use it without the complications of transplantation. He and other researchers in Europe and North America are attempting to grow human cells and tissues along with printable organs derived from stem cells. These techniques include 3-D printing of either biological materials from stem cells or synthetic polymers that act as scaffolds for a body part. It also includes locating stem cells that can form any organ, using growth factors to enhance natural healing processes, and utilizing other regenerative medicine technologies.

EYE, OR OPHTHALMOLOGIC, SURGERY

In 1900, other than glasses that corrected vision, many eye conditions were untreatable and resulted in blindness. To correct common seeing issues, since

1900 corrective spectacles evolved from heavy glass lenses to lightweight plastic lenses, which reduced glare and UV light, and also contact lenses in the late century. One of the most common eye conditions requiring surgery was cataracts (clouding of the lens) in individuals over 60 years of age. Cataract surgery made great advances in the post-World War II era, and by 2010, it was a simple routine outpatient procedure. In the early 20th century, eye surgeons (ophthalmologists) would cut into the eye with a small blade and remove the cloudy lens; the patient could then see with thick glasses. This method was also used in developing nations, such as in India, by itinerate healers. Since native healers often did not use sterile procedures, infections could develop. In industrialized nations, even in sterile conditions, cataract surgery was only done on patients who were blind from the condition as the procedure could cause complete eye damage, and recovery time without moving the head was generally several days. However, advancements in medicine allowed this procedure to change by the late 1970s into a very short and relatively safe outpatient surgery. Cataract surgery is now performed when the effects of the cataract interferes with a person's ability to perform daily tasks (such as reading or driving).

In 1949, British ophthalmologist Harold Ridley (1906–2001) invented an artificial plastic mono-focus lens that could be inserted inside the eye following the removal of the patient's own clouded lens. By 2000, multifocal and accommodative lenses were developed that provided focus of both distance and near objects. During the late 1960s, American ophthalmologist Charles Kelman (1930–2004), developed an ultrasonic probe and aspiration machine that permitted a cataract removal through a smaller corneal incision. This phacoemulsification method breaks the lens inside the lens capsule and then removes the pieces. A new plastic intra-ocular lens (IOL) is then inserted into the capsule. However, the procedure was not widely used until the operating microscope was developed. This device was a major advancement for all eye surgeries developed by several researchers in the mid-1970s.

A major advancement in eye surgery was the invention of the laser, first devised by American physicist Theodore Maiman (1927–2007). A serious eye issue leading to blindness was retinal detachment for which there was no treatment in 1900. In this condition, the retina pulls away from the back of the eye. In 1920, Swiss ophthalmologist Jules Gonin (1870–1935) was the first to treat retinal detachments by piercing the sclera (white of the eye) and cauterizing the area of the tear on the retina; extreme cold (cryosurgery) was later also used. The argon laser, first used in 1969, welded a retinal tear back into place.

In the mid-1990s, researchers American Ronald Kurtz and Hungarian Tibor Juhasz (1958–) pioneered the femtosecond laser for medical applications. This computerized technique is often used for corneal procedures since it can be precisely focused to create a corneal flap at the precise depth and diameter desired by the surgeon, and it allowed bladeless eye surgery. By the mid-2010s, this laser was used in cataract and other eye surgery.

American ophthalmologist Stephen Trokel (1934–) and others in 1983 introduced the idea of using the laser to reshape or sculpt the cornea to correct refractive errors. Trokel in 1987 introduced photorefractive keratectomy (PRK). In this procedure, cells are removed from the cornea by the excimer laser. This "refractive surgery"—surgery to correct refractive errors such as myopia (nearsightedness) or hyperopia (far sightedness)—was based upon Russian ophthalmologist Svyatoslov N. Fyodorov's (1927–2000) radial keratotomy procedure (RKP). It was first performed in 1970, where radial incisions were made into the cornea, and the healing process of these incisions would "flatten" the cornea and thus correct nearsightedness. In 1990, Greek and Italian ophthalmologists Ioannis G. Pallikaris (1947–) and Lucio Burrato, respectively, enhanced PRK by developing what would become LASIK surgery. This technique became known as the "flap and zap" technique. Instead of working on the top cellular layers of the corneal surface, Pallikaris and Burrato used a blade to cut a thin flap in the cornea, removed the underlying corneal stromal cells and some tissue underneath, and then replaced the flap, which acted like a natural bandage. By 2000, this LASIK surgery for corrective vision became widely used in developed nations. This surgery allowed many patients to eliminate glasses. Augmenting this procedure was the development of 3-D imaging optical coherence tomography (OCT), which allowed the smallest structures of the inner eye to be viewed and precisely measured prior to surgery or to detect eye issues.

The most common cause of blindness in the developed world, and the third most common globally, is age-related macular degeneration for which there are limited treatment options that can slow down or stop further vision loss. However, potential advances include time-release implants with growth-factor inhibitors of the vascular system of the eye, stem cell therapy, and retinal pigment cell transplantation. For people with low vision and blindness issues, bionic eye technology is already in use in patients, with these devices being updated as technology advances.

DENTISTRY AND DENTAL SURGERY

Dental surgery from 1900 until the present time evolved from painful tooth extraction to prevention of tooth loss, implants, and cosmetic surgery with minimal pain. Dentistry and dental surgery had been subdivided into various specialties in many nations by 2010. In much of Europe including the UK and countries such as Australia, dental surgery is recognized as a specialty of medicine but in North America, India, and some South American nations, it is a specialty of dentistry. For example, between 1976 and 2003 in North America, dentistry became divided into several areas including oral surgery specialties. These included oral maxillofacial surgeons who treated a wide variety of dental problems such as the removal of impacted teeth, reconstructive facial surgery such as cleft palates, and implants. Endodontists focused on the pulp, or root of the tooth, such as "root canal" surgery. Prosthodontics focused on post-oral cancer reconstruction and dental prosthetics such as dentures, crowns, bridges, and periodontists were responsible for the care and prevention of gum-related diseases, bone regeneration, and dental implants. Many other nations also recognized these surgical specialties. General dentists often do all of these special surgeries in low-income nations.

The dentist's main activity at the turn of the 20th century was removing decayed teeth. The middle class in higher-income nations could have dental caries (cavities) drilled out of the tooth and replaced by gold, or other inlays, and later by amalgams of metal. However, dental procedures were usually painful. Although cocaine was used at the turn of the 20th century to numb pain, it had undesirable side effects. In the first decade of the 20th century, German chemist Alfred Einhorn (1856–1917) introduced procaine (Novocain), a local anesthetic. In the 1940s, it was mostly replaced by lidocaine for dental work and dental surgery.

In 1919, gum disease and its contribution to tooth loss was first discussed by Austrian physician and dentist Bernhard Gottlieb (1886–1950) who immigrated to the United States after the Nazis regime annexed Austria in 1938. Better prevention became emphasized, such as tooth brushing to prevent decay and save teeth. Boar bristles were used until 1938, when nylon bristles were introduced by Dupont de Nemours Company in the United States. The use of these new tooth brushes soon spread worldwide. In the post-WWII era, fluoride in water and toothpaste was recommended to reduce tooth decay and loss (see chapter 1). Flossing to remove particles of food was not commonly emphasized until the 1980s. An electric toothbrush was invented in 1939 in Switzerland but was not marketed until the

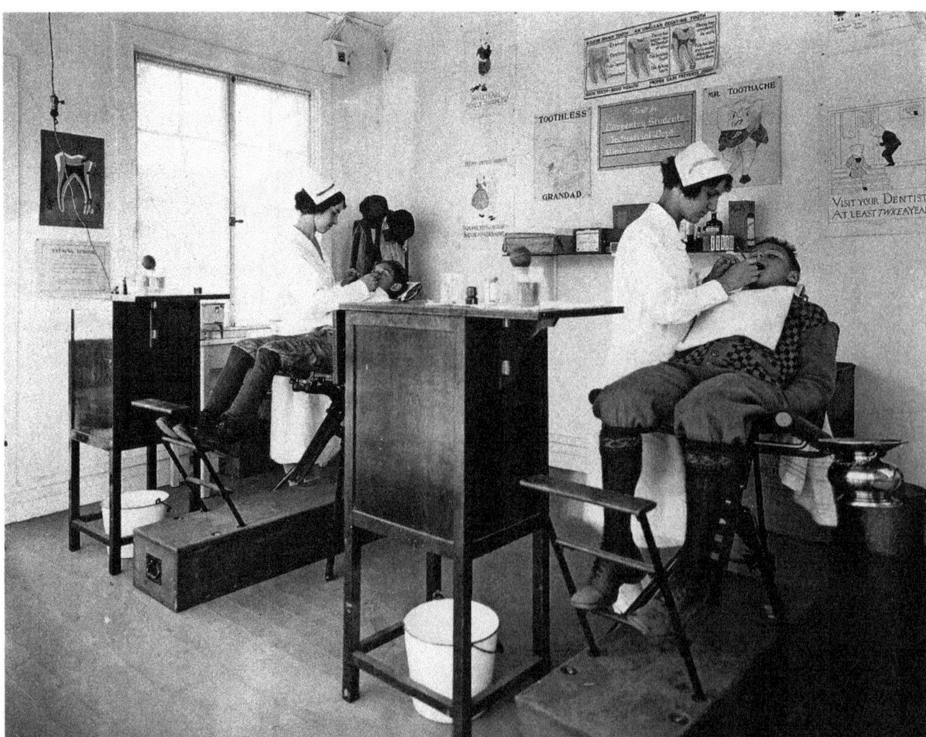

Dental hygienists examine and clean the teeth of two boys in an American clinic, ca. 1920. Hygienists educate patients about tooth brushing and other efforts to prevent tooth decay and loss. (Wellcome Collection)

1960s. Later in the century, water flossing picks were developed for cleaning of teeth and preservation of teeth was emphasized.

Many new instruments and techniques served to advance dentistry and dental surgery. For example, in higher-income nations, or areas with electrification, electric dental drills were introduced in the early 20th century. By 1920, electric dental drills had replaced drills operated by foot pedals. More developments occurred in the post-WWII era. In 1949, New Zealand dentist John Patrick Walsh (1911–2003) invented a high-speed compressed-air-driven handpiece drill that is still used today. In the 1990s, some alternative devises were developed including laser and air abrasion (miniature blaster) devices to remove cavities and repair gums.

Other inventions also advanced dentistry and dental surgery. The first dental X-ray machine was introduced in the 1920s, but by the late 1930s, it had been transformed to a flexible X-ray head that was easy to adjust. By 2010, digital computerized X-rays were used in many higher-income nations in most dental practices. This digital imaging was introduced to the dental profession in 1987 by French dentist Francis Mouyen. The technology allowed immediate visualization of the X-ray of the teeth and jaw on a computer screen and a reduction in radiation exposure as opposed to the older film. Along with digitalization, a small intraoral camera that took digital photos of the mouth, which also could be viewed immediately, was developed for diagnosis.

A major advancement in dental surgery was the dental implant to replace the root of a tooth to which an artificial tooth could be attached. Although this had been tried earlier in the century, it was not always successful. Beginning in the 1950s, American dental surgeon Leonard Linkow (1926–2017) pioneered the field of oral implantation. He developed various implants with different types of metals to be placed into the bones of the jaw. In 1980, Swedish physician Per-Ingvar Brånemark (1929–2014) describes techniques for osseointegration (new bone bonding with the implant). He used a pure titanium screw, which he termed a fixture. Advances were made in the 1990s in cosmetic dentistry as implants became smaller, stronger, and cheaper. By 2015, they were commonly being used by the middle class and in high-income nations. Dental implants are now considered the best solution for missing teeth and have long-term success.

Some changes in dental practices occurred in the 1960s that are still found today. The idea of "four hands," or the dentist and an assistant, was introduced. This shortened a patient's time in the chair. In addition, up until the 1960s, modified barber chairs were used by dentists. After this time, a fully reclining dental chair was introduced that made it easier on the patient, dentist, hygienist, or assistants. After the HIV crisis of the 1980s (see chapter 6), disposable latex or plastic gloves became widely used by dental personnel in most developed nations.

Although many advances in dentistry and dental surgery have been made since 1900, oral diseases are a major chronic public health problem among the disadvantaged across the globe. Those in isolated areas and in low socioeconomic groups are affected more than others due to the unavailability of dental care and surgery. For example, there is still little access to dental care in the remote villages of the world, especially in sub-Saharan Africa and some areas of the Americas. Losing teeth is still seen by many as a natural consequence of ageing. Since 2005, some NGOs have trained local health care workers to provide basic essential dental care, including extractions and control of infections. Prevention education programs for children are also offered.

In summary, great advances in all areas of surgery have occurred from 1900 into the late 2010s. The development of new techniques and inventions may result in noninvasive procedures in the future.

9

Mental Health

Mental disorders have always been part of the human condition. A mentally ill person generally fell outside the norms of acceptable behavior in a given time and place and was often stigmatized. In Western cultures from the early to the mid-20th century, mental disorders were referred to as "insanity" or "madness." Other terms included "lunatic," "crazy," "odd," and so on. Because of stigma, terms changed over the 20th century and into the 21st century. In the early part of the 20th century, those with mental and learning disorders were generally taken care of by their families, but if families were unable to do so, they were institutionalized. In Western cultures in the first few decades of the 20th century, a mental hygiene movement led to better treatment in institutions. Moreover, in the 1960s, new psychotropic (mind altering) medications such as Thorazine, discovered in 1950, allowed some patients to live more or less independently, and the concept of community mental health care evolved. However, the closing of mental hospitals and the new community care system by the 21st century was not viewed as entirely successful as many patients did not receive adequate treatment. This led to some mental health workers advocating building modern asylums.

Conflicting theories concerning the etiology (cause) of mental and substance-use disorders changed throughout the 20th century. Some theories went in and out of fashion, as did treatment techniques, as the result of scientific developments in addition to social or political influences. Mental health care generally reflected these theories as did diagnostic systems, which attempted to categorize mental disorders. Low-income and developing cultures often relied on traditional treatment into the 21st century as their governments attempted to establish Western type of mental health care. Substance-abuse disorders evolved over the 20th century from being considered a moral weakness to a criminal behavior to finally an illness. By the 2010s, all mental disorders were thought to be caused by, or a combination of, genetic, biological, psychological, environmental, and genomic influences.

THEORIES OF MENTAL DISORDERS

Since the turn of the 20th century and into the early 21st century, views as to the etiology of mental disorders have changed. In addition, by the late 20th century, the prevalence and global impact of these diseases worldwide have been able to be determined.

Changing Views of the Nature of Mental Disorders

From the beginning of the 20th century, three broad theories as to the etiology of mental disorders have been proposed, namely the supernatural, biological/heredity, and psychological/environmental concepts. Supernatural beliefs are still found in some non-Western or low-income cultures. Mental disorders are thought to be caused by being possessed by evil spirits, or the person is thought to have a special psychic ability to communicate with the gods. By the mid-20th century, professionals in most non-Western nations had adopted Western ideas in terms of mental disorders although supernatural beliefs were still found among the public. By the late 19th century, Western cultures had abandoned the supernatural theory as the medical and health fields became based on science. For centuries, all cultures had noticed that mental disorders tended to run in families, so they must be inherited. At the turn of the 20th century, the Lamarckian theory of the "inheritance of acquired characteristics" was accepted. However, after Austrian monk Gregor Mendel's (1822–1884) rules of heredity and genetics were rediscovered in 1901, along with Darwinian theories, many health workers adopted this genetic theory, which prevailed until the 1930s. When mental health professionals became aware that the Great Depression was causing psychological problems in formerly employed nonmentally ill individuals, the biological theories lost favor and psychological/environmental theories gained acceptance. However, the genetic and biological theories resurged in the late 20th century based upon new medical discoveries, suggesting that both heredity and the environment played a part in mental processes and behaviors.

A proponent of biological causes of mental disorders at the turn of the last century was German psychiatrist Emile Kraepelin (1856–1926), who is considered the founder of "scientific," or biological psychiatry. He studied drug effects on the nervous system. Psychosis had been thought to be one disorder, but in 1899, based upon his research, Kraepelin classified its symptoms into two categories: manic depression, or mood problems, and dementia praecox, or premature madness. In 1911, Swiss psychiatrist Eugen Bleuler (1857–1939) renamed dementia praecox to schizophrenia as he thought it better described the condition. Kraepelin was a strong proponent of the genetic theory of mental disorders and rejected the psychoanalytical theories of Sigmund Freud (1856–1939), a rising star at this time, as he felt they were not scientific.

Nonetheless, Freud's ideas became the dominant theory of mental illness through the 1950s and overshadowed the biological theories. Freud was an Austrian neurologist and is considered the founder of psychoanalysis, which is a method of treating patients through dialogue, or talking therapy. Freud developed a theory of the unconscious and a model of psychic structure. He believed that many mental disorders arose from poor childrearing and cold, distant mothers.

In the meantime, behavioral psychological theories to explain mental disorders emerged in the mid-1930s and ran concurrently with Freudian theories and were accepted by clinical psychologists. They proposed that abnormal behaviors had been shaped by being reinforced, or learned. American John B. Watson (1878–1958) established the psychological school of behaviorism. This was based upon Russian physiologist Ivan P. Pavlov (1849–1936), who discovered "classical conditioning" to change behavior. Watson rejected the theories of the mind as advanced by the psychoanalysts. Another American, psychologist Burrhus Frederic Skinner (1904–1990), expanded Watson and Pavlov's works and suggested "operant conditioning" (reward and punishment) shaped behaviors. This behaviorist school proposed that abnormal behaviors were learned behaviors. Therefore, if dysfunctional behaviors such as depression or serious phobia were learned, they could be unlearned.

Also in the 1930s, work by Hungarian-born endocrinologist Hans Selye (1907–1982) proposed that physiological stress was linked not only to physical illness but also mental illness. In the early 1950s, some psychiatrists embraced this biological approach to mental illness. When Hungarian American psychiatrist Thomas Szasz (1920–2012) wrote *The Myth of Mental Illness* (1960), an anti-psychiatry movement emerged along with a resurgence of biological theories. This resulted in conflict with the Freudians, who were losing power as their theories were considered unscientific. To avoid disputes between psychoanalytically, biologically, and behavioristic-oriented mental health professionals, American psychiatrist George Engel (1913–1999) around 1977 came up with the biopsychosocial theory, which integrated all theories.

By the early 1980s, biochemical, biological, and genetic explanations of mental illness were in their ascendency because advanced technology such as the fMRI, which took images of the brain while it was functioning, were developed. Describing mental illnesses as a brain or chemical malfunction, also, helped minimize the stigma against it. By the end of the century, genetic and environmental influences were thought to cause mental disorders. A gene that was associated with schizophrenia, for example, was discovered in 2002. By 2010, genetic, biological, psychological, epigenetic (changes to gene expression by environmental conditions), and social/environmental factors—or an interaction between all of these—appear to be the causes of various mental disorders.

PREVALENCE OF MENTAL DISORDERS

In terms of the prevalence of mental disorders, simple statistical methods in the early 20th century attempted to survey the number of mentally disabled. A British study in 1911, for instance, found that 79 percent of children in public schools were "feeble-minded" (learning disability). However, it was not until the beginnings of the computer age in the mid-1970s, when rapid calculations and advanced methods such as meta-analysis (the analysis of many studies) had evolved, that large global and trend studies could be undertaken. For example, one study in

2014 examining surveys from 1980 to 2013 showed that about 17 percent of people worldwide have experienced a common mental illness such as mood disorders, anxiety, or substance-abuse disorders during the preceding year, and about 30 percent have experienced one of these issues over their lifetime. English-speaking counties had the highest lifetime percentage while countries in north and Southeast Asia and sub-Saharan Africa had the lowest one-year and lifetime prevalence. Anxiety disorders were the most common form of mental issues worldwide.

For psychotic or more serious mental illnesses, the rates are generally similar from country to country as they are now considered to have a strong genetic component. Lifetime prevalence of schizophrenia worldwide is about 0.5–1 percent while bipolar spectrum disorders are found in about 0.4 percent of the population worldwide. For those with bipolar disorders, in the post-WWII years it was discovered that despite differences in the prevalence of substance abuse between cultures, those with bipolar conditions were also more likely to have a substance-abuse disorder; this is called dual, or co-occurring, diagnosis. These terms were first used in the 1980s as it increasingly became apparent that the two conditions were often found together.

Like the large prevalence rate studies for mental disorders, the international concept of Global Burden of Disease (GBD) was not developed until 1990. However, it is a useful measurement to determine where a worldwide and national focus for medical and health care should be placed. A 2007 article entitled "No Health without Mental Health" suggested about 14 percent of the GBD was attributed to mental health disorders. The Disability-Adjusted Life Years (DALYs), a measure of overall disease burden due to the number of years lost due to ill health, disability, or early death worldwide was 7.4 percent for chronic depression, psychoses, and substance abuse. Depressive disorders carried the heaviest burden. In terms of substance abuse, 5.1 percent of the GBD was attributable to alcohol consumption and 9 percent to tobacco use in 2015.

SYSTEMS FOR CATEGORIZING MENTAL DISORDERS

Two major manuals for classifying mental illness evolved over the 20th and into the 21st centuries. These were the American Psychiatric Association's *Diagnostic and Statistical Manual of Mental Disorders* (*DSM*) and the World Health Organization's *International Classification of Disease* (*ICD*).

Diagnostic and Statistical Manual of Mental Disorders (DSM)

Since Kraeplin's first classification, mental health professionals have attempted to standardize categories of mental disorder. In 1917, the United States Bureau of the Census collected health statistics from all mental hospitals, but it was not useful for health professionals. In 1933, the New York Academy of Medicine and, what would become the American Psychiatrist Association (APA), developed the *Statistical Manual for Mental Diseases.* In the aftermath of WWII, there were many "shell shocked" (now called PTSD) military personnel with the result that the Veteran's Administration and APA developed the *Diagnostic and Statistical Manual of Mental Disorders* (*DSM-I*) in 1952 to have a standard guide for mental disorders. In the *DSM-II* (1968), the APA coordinated the manual's entries with the WHO's *ICD* to develop a cross-cultural standard.

The *DSM* has undergone several revisions reflecting the theory of mental illness most prevalent at the time. In addition, political and social pressures resulted in disorders being added or eliminated, and offensive terms "updated." These alterations were made by a majority vote of committee members who often did not agree. This was particularly true for the *DSM-III* (1980) when the APA published a radical revision that reorganized and expanded the classification of mental illnesses and did away with the term neurosis. Symptoms for each mental illness now had to be met to diagnose a patient with the disorder. Rather than focusing on a specific problem, all aspects of the individual were taken into account. These changes were based upon politics, psychiatric drug trials, the decline of Freudian theory, and even a revision of Kraepelin's work. For this edition, the term "mental illness" was renamed "mental disorders" for political reasons.

The DSM has been revised several times since 1980. *DSM-IV* (1994) took six years to write and involved over 1,000 individuals and many professional organizations. The next two revisions closely involved the APA and WHO so that the systems would be similar. However, the *DSM-V* (2013) was the most contentious revision. It required that for a condition to be a mental disorder, the symptoms must involve problems in behavior, thoughts, or emotions; personal distress or impairment; and have biological and/or psychological origins. However, even before the manual was published, critics from around the world claimed that it categorized some normal behaviors as pathological, which would contribute to over-diagnosis and over-medication along with other issues. Although there have been changes since the turn of the 21st century in terms of classification of mental disorders, some conflict exists as to what is, and what is not, a mental disorder.

International Classification of Diseases (ICD)

Parallel to the development of the *DSM* was the *ICD*. In the 1940s, the WHO's *ICD* was framed. In the sixth edition of *ICD* (1949), a section, chapter V, on mental disorders was first included. This was expanded in *ICD-8*. WHO over the years has worked with American mental health professionals to have concordance between the two manuals as the world became more international.

The *ICD-10's* (1992; revised 2016) chapter V on mental disorders was influenced by the APA's *DSM-IV*, and there is much similarly between the two. In 2018, the 11th edition (*ICD-11*) was introduced and had changes in the classification of mental disorders. The *ICD* is accepted by the World Psychiatric Association as the international standard and other than in North America is used worldwide for diagnosis. However, insurance companies in North America now use the ICD-10 for reimbursement. Due to the evolution of the Internet in the 21st century, WHO maintains the *ICD* online for anyone to use. By 2010, critics considered it more accurate, reliable, and less politically influenced than the American *DSM-V*.

Since both the *DSM* and *ICD* are based upon Western culture norms and theories, some developing nations wanted manuals more suited to their cultures. Therefore, China in 1979, for example, developed the *Chinese Classification of Mental Disorders*, and in 2001, the *Latin American Guide for Psychiatric Diagnosis* to incorporate cultural variables in diagnosing mental disorders was created. Both are similar to the *DSM* and *ICD* and have helped change the field of mental health in these countries.

RENAMING MENTAL DISORDERS

The names for many mental disorders were changed from the early 20th century through the early 21st century when the term for the disorder became stigmatized or offensive. New disorders were also identified, and broad categories of mental disorders were redefined as separate conditions. Although some terms are still used by the general public, health professionals renamed the condition, often with pressure from families of patients. For example, in the early 20th century, "imbecilic," "idiot," "moron," and "feebleminded" (severe, moderate, and mild mental disability), and "Mongloid idiot" were considered scientific terms. When they became derogatory in the mid-20th century, the generic term "mental retardation" replaced these earlier terms. "Mongloid idiot" was changed to "Down syndrome" or "trisomy 21" in the 1960s. By 2010, when the word "mental retardation" became objectionable, to reduce stigma, it was renamed intellectual disability.

Neurosis, hysteria (found primarily among women), or shell shock (among soldiers returning from battlefields) were terms used from the early to the late 20th century. They were reclassified as anxiety disorders in 1980 in the *DSM-III* as the older terms were considered "outdated." Bipolar disorder—previously known as "manic depression"—is characterized by episodes of an extreme elevated mood and/or energy level (mania) often followed by depression. In the early 1950s, German psychiatrist Karl Leonhard (1904–1988) introduced the term bipolar to differentiate unipolar depression (a major depressive disorder) from bipolar and other depressive disorders. The term "mood disorder" for all these conditions was first used in the *DSM-III* as the terms "manic" and "mania" had become offensive to some.

The term "schizophrenia" used since 1911 for the serious psychotic mental illness characterized by auditory hallucinations, paranoia, and delusions is now under consideration for change. In 2013, international discussions emerged about whether or not to rename it to something less stigmatizing. Suggestions included "salience syndrome" or "psychosis susceptibility syndrome." At present, no changes have been made in the *ICD* or *DSM* manuals. The *DSM-5* (2013), however, changed "senility" and "dementia" to "major neurocognitive disorders" or "minor neurocognitive disorders," as the terms were now considered offensive by some.

Some "new" disorders came to the attention of the public in the mid- to late 20th century when they were separated out from the category of childhood schizophrenia or behavioral problems. These included Autism Spectrum Disorder (which included Asperger's syndrome) and Attention Deficit Hyperactivity Disorder (ADHD). Eating disorders, primarily found in high-income nations and among the wealthy, were first noticed in the 1930s although binge-eating behaviors were not described until 1959. These disorders reached public consciousness in Western cultures in the late 1970s. As new terms for various conditions become stigmatized over time, they will undoubtedly be replaced in the later 21st century.

SUBSTANCE-USE DISORDERS (DRUG ABUSE OR ADDICTION)

Psychotropic drugs, public policies, trafficking, and efforts to control drugs globally over the time period of this book will be discussed in chapter 10. Drugs such as alcohol, tobacco, cannabis, coca, mushrooms, opiates, and other substances have been used since prehistoric times for medicinal, religious, and recreational purposes, and many have been subject to abuse. Both natural occurring and synthetic drugs have been used from the early 20th century into the early 21st century. What was called "drug abuse" or "drug addiction" in the middle (the 1940s through the 1970s), or "addictive behaviors" in the latter 20th century, was renamed substance-use disorders in the *DSM-5* (2013) in an effort to reduce stigma as attitudes concerning the nature of addiction had changed.

The depressant drugs have been used to relieve pain, promote feelings of well-being, induce sleep, and cure mental illness. However, all of them can cause severe physical dependency, and abrupt withdrawal can sometimes produce life-threatening symptoms and psychotic behavior. The alcoholic, or "drunkard"—a term used in the early 20th century—was thought to have a lack of "will power" and was stigmatized. Alcoholics Anonymous (AA) was founded in 1935, in Akron, OH, as a self-help group. Up until that point, alcoholics were often treated in mental institutions and considered incurable. With the rise of AA's popularity, and success, the American Medical Association (AMA) in 1956 declared that alcoholism was a treatable disease or illness. In the 1960s, some researchers from around the world suggested that alcoholism and other drug addictions were obsessive compulsive disorders while others proposed it was a genetic condition. By the 1980s, many conflicting theories of the nature of alcoholism had arisen, which fostered different methods of treatment ranging from behavior modification, in- and outpatient, group therapy, and drug therapies along with self-help "12 step programs."

To reflect all the theories of this addictive disorder, in 1991, the *ICD-10* classified alcoholism under both the psychiatric and medical sections. To further reduce stigma, the term "alcohol use disorders" (AUD) was first used in the *DSM-V* in 2013. It combined alcohol abuse and alcohol dependence (mild, moderate, or severe) and is defined as follows:

> Problems controlling intake of alcohol, continued use of alcohol despite problems resulting from drinking, development of a tolerance, drinking that leads to risky situations, or the development of withdrawal symptoms. (SAMHSA, October 27, 2015)

Another depressant that can cause severe but generally not fatal withdrawal symptoms is opium and its derivatives. In the 19th century, morphine was purified from opium. Heroin was derived from morphine at the turn of the 20th century and was first claimed to be nonaddictive; however, this proved not to be the case. Until WWI in the West, many middle-class women were addicted to opiates in patent medicines and were looked at with sympathy. But this view changed in the post-WWI era when heroin began to be used recreationally as morphine was not readily available. Since heroin was now primarily used by "night people" and the criminal element, addicts, or "junkies," were stigmatized as criminal, arrested, and often imprisoned. The view that drug abuse is a criminal activity increased in the 1970s and is still found in many nations.

However, in the 1990s, new thinking about addictions emerged. Drug addiction began to be seen as a psychological or medical disorder and the concept of harm reduction emerged. HIV and other diseases were increasing among those who injected drugs so the UK, and then other Western nations, started needle exchange programs or supplied heroin under controlled situations to reduce the spread of disease. In some Asian cultures, such as China, opium use has been considered the "great shame" since its peak use in the early 20th century. In the late 1940s, under the new sanctions in the People's Republic of China, which arose in the aftermath of WWII, drug use decreased, and mandatory treatment in work camps or asylums was instituted. By 2010, addicts began to be seen as patients in China rather than criminals, and methadone treatment centers were instituted.

The opposite of depressant drugs are the stimulants, and like other natural psychoactive substances, they have been used for centuries. Mild stimulants, such as coffee and tea, with caffeine and other xanthines, are widely used around the world to increase alertness and work effort. For the most part, they have not been stigmatized as they are not perceived to cause social problems. Tobacco use increased after WWI in Western cultures and is highly addictive. But, when the dangers of smoking became apparent in the 1960s, smoking declined in the West but continued to increase in developing nations due to marketing. In 2016, around 20 percent of the population in Western nations smoked and up to 40 percent in Asia.

Another natural stimulant is the leaf of the coca plant, which has been chewed for energy by rural Andean mountain dwellers for centuries. When cocaine was derived from this plant in the 19th century, it entered Western cultures as part of patent medicine tonics, medications used by physicians, and was found in Coca-Cola. By the 1920s, like heroin, it was considered a "narcotic," later known as a Schedule II drug, and followed a similar trend as heroin over the century in terms of how users were perceived. A "crack cocaine" epidemic was thought to have led to more crime in the mid-1980s to mid-1990s, and cocaine users were further criminalized. Synthetic amphetamine type stimulants (ATS) were first prescribed in the 1930s for weight loss, asthma, and depression. In the post-WWII years, an epidemic of medical and nonmedical use of amphetamines emerged as the result of large war surplus supplies in Japan and the United States; many became psychologically dependent upon them. Physicians decreased prescribing ATS, leading to a decline in their use. In addition, by the 1960s new drugs had been discovered for depression and other medical conditions. On the other hand, more dangerous and easily manufactured ATS such as methamphetamine began to increase in the late 1980s leading to serious health problems, and psychotic behaviors among users are still found today.

Psychotic behaviors can also be elicited by some hallucinogens. This class of drugs includes a wide range of natural and synthetic substances. Most can cause out of body experiences, euphoria, hallucinations, delusions, or religious experiences. Peyote cactus for centuries has been, and is still, used by southwest Native American Indians for religious purposes. The mushroom fly agaric was used in Siberia for similar reasons. Since the early 20th century, who used a substance often determined how they, or the drug, were perceived. For example, artists such as British author Aldous Huxley (1894–1963), who used natural hallucinogens in the immediate post-WWII era, were largely ignored. However, when these substances, along with synthetic ones such as LSD or ecstasy, began to be used by youth in the West during the 1960s and 1970s, they were now seen as causing a medical and social problem, and many Western cultures banned them. Although illegal, people who use them are generally not stigmatized. However, they can trigger psychosis in susceptible people.

Another plant used for centuries in the Middle East, India, and Southeast Asia for various purposes is cannabis sativa (marijuana, hashish). Since the 1930s, most Western cultures considered it harmful, and it became "officially" illegal in most nations. During the turbulent 1960s, baby boomers began to use it with few harmful effects, and they were seen as criminals. Although a few people became psychologically dependent, because of its widespread use, public perception changed, and by 2015, it was decriminalized in a number of states in the United States and around the world.

TREATMENT PROCEDURES

Treatment of mental disorders in Western cultures since the turn of the early 20th century was often based upon the prevailing theory of mental illness, which resulted in specific techniques and procedures being developed. With the advent of new drugs to treat mental disorders, many older techniques in the 1960s were discarded as being dangerous or ineffective. In non-Western cultures, shamans or healers treated both mental and other disorders. Both were seen as stemming from the same factors.

At the turn of the 20th century, some traditions were carried over from earlier times, including asylums. Seriously ill patients were often cared for in these institutions for life. A common technique used in asylums was hydrotherapy. Patients were wrapped like mummies in towels soaked in ice water, placed in baths of ice water or under high-pressure cold-water showers. Restraints including straightjackets, mitts, and wristlets were used on violent patients who harmed themselves, others, or destroyed property. Violent patients were also put into padded locked cells. By the end of the century, restraints were still used for hospitalized psychiatric patients who were persistently suicidal or dangerous to others and confused patients who attempted to pull out IV tubing or tear off dressings.

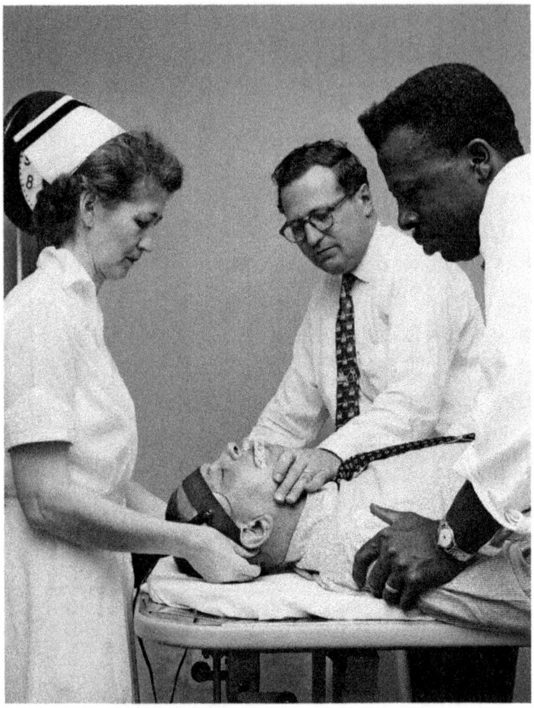
To treat depression and mental illness in the mid-20th century, electroconvulsive therapy (ECT) or "shock therapy" was commonly used. Here, a patient in an American hospital undergoes this treatment, ca. 1955. (Carl Purcell/Three Lions/Getty Images)

When mental disorders were thought to be biologically based, specific techniques were developed. This included insulin shock therapy, used in mental hospitals in the 1930s through the 1950s. It involved administering large doses of insulin to patients to cause a coma to treat schizophrenia. It was discontinued as it sometimes caused death and was rarely effective. However, it was still used in China and the Soviet Union into the 1970s. Another dangerous treatment was psychosurgery. It included such techniques as lobotomy or leucotomy, which cut the nerve pathways in the prefrontal cortex of the brain. This procedure evolved in 1935 and was widely preformed in the post-WWII era in the United States and other Western cultures due to overcrowding of mental hospitals. It was primarily used as a treatment for schizophrenia and bipolar and obsessive compulsive disorders. By the 1960s, it was considered controversial as it often changed the patient's personality and had other severe side effects including mental dullness, incontinence, and the inability for patients to function independently. Although Japan performed its first lobotomy in 1939, in the early 1950s it, along with Germany and the Soviet Union, outlawed the procedure as being inhuman. By the 1970s, the surgery fell into disrepute, and the procedure declined in developed nations. However, through the early part of the 21st century, India still practiced psychosurgery (now called stereotactic) for serious depression.

Other techniques based upon biological theory to change the brain also emerged. In the 1940s and 1950s, electroconvulsive therapy (ECT), commonly called "shock therapy," was widely used. It causes electrically induced seizures and short-term amnesia. It is still used today for serious depression, suicidal behavior, or acute mania when medication fails. In the mid-1980s, transcranial magnetic stimulation (TMS) was developed and is now used for serious depression, epileptic seizures, and Parkinson's disease. It creates magnetic fields to stimulate nerve cells in the brain to improve symptoms.

The most prevalent treatment beginning in the early 20th century continuing into the 21st century is talking therapy or psychotherapy based upon various psychological theories. Until the post-WWII years, Freudian psychoanalysis was the dominant treatment for mental illness. It fell out of favor as it was too expensive, and many psychiatrists did not consider it to be based on scientific evidence. But from this basic therapy, many schools of psychotherapy developed, which are still found today. Behavior modification and stress reduction therapy also emerged in the post-WWII years and competed with psychoanalysis. By the late 20th century, hundreds of different types of psychotherapies had evolved. Psychotherapy is practiced by psychiatrists, psychologists, social workers, counselors, and other professionals. Most importantly, by the mid-1960s, these psychotherapies were often augmented by psychopharmacological treatments.

The major advance in the treatment of mental disorders was the development of antipsychotic and antidepressant medications in the 1950s. The drug chlorpromazine (Thorazine), a phenothiazine, was synthesized in 1950 in France. This major tranquilizer underwent clinical trials at a French military hospital with remarkable improvement in psychiatric patients. Within a decade, a number of other phenothiazines were developed and became widely used beginning in the 1960s. Minor tranquilizers for anxiety were also synthesized. During the same time period, antidepressant medications such as the tricyclic amines were developed. Since then, dozens of other antidepressants have emerged. Because of the use of these psychotropic medications, along with psychotherapy and the concept of community-based care, many patients were discharged from mental hospitals beginning in the 1960s and 1970s.

MENTAL HEALTH CARE IN HIGH-INCOME OR WESTERN CULTURES

Mental health care in Western cultures became more humane over 20th and into the 21st centuries. This was largely the result of patients, family, and later professionals working together for change.

Mental Health Care in North America

In North America, a mental health movement emerged to ensure better treatment for the mentally ill in the first decade of the 20th century. In the United States, conditions in most "insane asylums" were deplorable. Clifford Beers (1876–1943), a Yale graduate and Wall Street financier, who had been in and out of mental institutions for bipolar disorder, wrote about his experiences in *A Mind that Found Itself.* He notes:

> Frequently it was so cold I could see my breath. And, though my canvas jacket served to protect part of that body which it was at the same time racking, I was seldom comfortably warm. For, once uncovered, my arms being pinioned, I had no way of rearranging the tangled blankets. What little sleep I managed to get I took lying on a filthy and hard mattress placed on the bare floor. . . . It seems to be the prevailing opinion that "anything is good enough for a crazy man" (Beers 1908, 134).

Beers's book had an immediate impact and launched a massive mental health reform movement not only the United States but also in other Western countries. Psychiatrist Adolf Meyers (1866–1950) encouraged Beers to use the term "mental hygiene" and helped him form the Connecticut Society for Mental Hygiene (1908), a voluntary health agency, or NGO. Its purpose was to promote legislation for better treatment of the mentally ill, to educate the public about mental illness, and to prevent mental illness. The following year the National Committee for Mental Hygiene (1909) was formed. It later joined other voluntary foundations and was renamed the National Association of Mental Health in 1950, the National Mental Health Association in 1979, and Mental Health America in 2006. In 1979, the National Alliance for Mental Health—another grassroots NGO—was formed to advocate for the mentally ill in the United States.

In terms of professional organizations, although the American Psychological Association was founded in 1892, the American Psychiatric Association was not established until 1921. However, as a result of advocacy on the part of these professional associations and the NGOs, the National Mental Health Act (1946) was passed, which created the National Institute of Mental Health (1949) and later the Department of Health and Human Services (1953). Further public policies were instituted after the widespread use of new medications for mental illness. The Community Mental Health Centers Act (1963) recommended deinstitutionalization and authorized construction grants for community mental health centers. Medicaid in 1965 provided health coverage for the low-income elderly, families, and children, pregnant women, and those with disabilities. In 1966, mental health coverage was included in Medicare for senior citizens.

In the 1970s, more federal funding led to community-based care with group homes, half-way houses, and sheltered workshops. This led to a 95 percent reduction in the population of state mental hospitals. Some private institutions changed their focus to substance abuse and dual diagnosis treatment. By the 1980s, some mental health care was provided through insurance at the workplace, private plans, or the federal government. The Mental Health Parity and Addiction Equity Act of 2008 prohibited insurance companies from imposing less favorable benefit limitations on mental health care than the benefits for medical/surgical services.

However, on the negative side, deinstitutionalization has been considered a failure by many mental health professionals inasmuch as it has led to increased numbers of seriously mentally ill people being housed in jails, prisons, nursing homes, or becoming homelessness due to underfunded community services. Since the beginning of the 21st century, more and more professionals have advocated the reinstitution of state mental hospitals.

Compared to the United States, Canada has experienced a similar trend in mental health care from the early 20th century. Clifford Beers, along with Canadian psychiatrist Charles K. Clarke (1857–1924) and physician Clarence M. Hincks (1885–1964), founded the Canadian National Committee for Mental Hygiene. In 1953, it was renamed the Canadian Mental Health Association. The Canadian Psychological Association was founded in 1938 and the Canadian Psychiatric Association in 1951. All these groups worked together for better treatment.

In the 1950s, Canada embraced the community mental health movement. Care is delivered through the Medical Care Act of 1984, which is a national publicly funded health care system, called Medicare. Additional government acts gave increased rights to the mentally ill, including the Mental Health Act (1990), which established criteria for voluntary, informal, and involuntary admissions and the Health Care Consent Act (2010). As with other Western cultures, community treatment and support replaced state mental hospitals with mixed results.

In North America, among First Nations and native peoples, traditional care, like many indigenous health belief systems, view mental and physical health the same. Mental disorders are regarded as a community, and not just an individual, problem. The individual and community are seen as being out of balance with the cosmos. So care and treatment often involved community ceremonies with a combination of natural and spiritual remedies.

Mental Health Care in Europe and Other Western Cultures

Mental health care also changed in other Western nations from the beginning of the 20th century along more or less similar lines to North America. Clifford Beers in 1919 formed an International Committee for Mental Health, and by 1930, mental health societies were found in 25 countries. In 1930, Beers fostered the First International Congress for Mental Hygiene. In 1948, the World Federation of Mental Health was formed. It provides consultants and interrelates with several United Nations agencies including WHO.

Similar to North America, most European nations established comparable agencies. For example, in the UK, the National Association for Mental Health (NAMH) was founded in 1946 to provided services for mentally ill or disabled individuals. It changed its name to MIND in 1972. The Royal College of Psychiatrists, in 1972, also helped in shaping patterns of care, treatment, and public policy. In the European Economic Community, mental health is often a shared responsibility of governmental organizations and NGOs.

Germany took an aberrant path in the mid-20th century under National Socialism. From 1934 until the beginning of the WWII, roughly 360,000 mentally ill or disabled were sterilized against their will, and later around 100,000 ethnic mentally disabled Germans were euthanized during the war to save food supplies for the troops. In the post-WWII era, former Nazis were found guilty for these crimes. By the 1970s, Germany had embraced the process of community-based mental health care. After the reunification of Germany in 1991, issues emerged in policy, different systems, and lack of funding. However, by 2014, Germany was a world leader in integrating people with mental health disorders into society and employment.

In Australia, reformers, like in the rest of the Western world, advocated for better care of the mentally ill in the early decades of the 20th century. Care has evolved to the point that state and territory governments provide care for people with mental illness. These include a range of mental health-related services funded by the Australian Government through the Medicare Benefits Schedule (MBS) and the Pharmaceutical Benefits Scheme (PBS). Other governmental support includes care in acute and psychiatric hospital settings, social and community support, disability services, workforce participation programs, and income and housing assistance. The nation is working to improve outcomes ranging from early detection to diagnosis to treatment to ongoing recovery.

MENTAL HEALTH CARE IN MEDIUM- TO LOW-INCOME OR NON-WESTERN CULTURES

In many developing and low-income countries, Western mental health treatment was carried out by missionaries in the early 20th century with the addition of intergovernmental aid programs, or United Nations agencies after WWII. In Latin America, Africa, and Asia, there is a shortage of trained staff and local sources of support leading to low treatment rates. Therefore, in 2012, the WHOs 66th World Health Assembly to Improve Mental Health Treatment established the Comprehensive Mental Health Action Plan 2013–2020 to improve mental health care in developing nations. One of their goals was by 2020 to increase service coverage for severe mental disorders by 20 percent. Pilot programs in a few countries around the world including Guinea-Bissau, India, Iran, Pakistan, and the United Republic of Tanzania have shown the feasibility of providing care to people with severe mental illness through the primary health care system rather than specialized clinics or hospitals.

However, even today the belief as to the cause of mental illness in many developing nations is often quite different to Western thinking, and families may not think a loved one needs Western medical care. Both mental and physical disorders are often thought to be caused by supernatural forces outside of the control of the afflicted person or an imbalance in vital life energies. Afflictions, therefore, are thought to be best treated by traditional healing practices to bring these vital energies back in balance.

In Latin America, for example, mental disorders are considered "shameful" in indigenous communities. Therefore, traditional medicine, *curanderismo,* is often sought. Its healers, *curanderos,* are respected within the community and practice a variety of treatments, including incantations, prayers, and herbs to cure mental, emotional, physical, and spiritual afflictions. In addition, the tropical forest areas in Latin America for centuries have produced various healing herbs, which were, and still are, used by traditional healers. Latin America has 10.5 percent of the world total Global Burden of Disease due to mental disorders, and few mental health services or providers exist in many of the countries. In the first decade of the 21st century, the Pan American Health Organization (founded in 1902) fostered increased multidisciplinary approach for the care of the mentally disabled, and improvements of care have been seen in some of the countries.

In Asia, 48 nations exist with numerous cultures, ethnic groups, languages, and religions that spread from the arctic to deserts and tropical jungles. China and India are the largest countries with over a billion inhabitants each. These two countries account for about 30 percent of the global burden of mental, neurological, and substance-use disorders. In addition, less than 1 percent of the national health care budget in either country is allocated to mental health care.

In China, among much of the uneducated population, mental disorders are seen as a punishment for misdeeds of the ancestors and are associated with weakness, guilt, and shame, so few seek treatment. The person is often hidden from view. The first psychiatric hospitals were founded by missionaries to China in the mid-19th century, and until the mid-1930s, other such hospitals were built in a few large cities. After WWII when the People's Republic of China emerged (1949), psychiatric hospitals were gradually built in every province. In 1958, the first National Mental Health Meeting mandated the establishment of community mental health centers and training of mental health care workers. However, many community programs were disbanded during the Cultural Revolution (1966–1976). In its aftermath, the National Mental Health Plan (2002–2010) was established to implement an effective system of mental health care, to educate citizens about mental disorders, and to train mental health care workers. But the hospitals or asylums (*Ankang*), besides treating those with mental disorders, also held political prisoners with the diagnosis of political mania—speaking out against the government or practicing banned religions. In 2012, the country adopted a new mental health law, which included the right of patients not to be hospitalized against their will; however, the effect of this law is not yet known.

Like other Asian cultures, mental disorders are stigmatized in Japan, although about 20 percent of the population will experience some type of depression in their lifetime. Japan, in addition, lags behind other high-income countries in terms of mental health care. The Mental Health Law of 1988 was supposed to establish community-based care and the development of rehabilitation programs. However, progress has been slow, and many people are still hospitalized for months rather than a few weeks.

Similarly, in India, mental illness is often seen as a stigma and is not reported, and the mentally ill are locked away. On the other hand, someone who claims he is a god, might be considered an incarnation of a Hindu god or be possessed by evil magic, but not mentally ill. People with severe psychic issues may go to a healing temple or shrine for treatment. This is considered a more socially acceptable way to cure mental disorders. As in other British colonies, Western medicine was instituted in urban areas in India during the 19th century, but it was primarily for the wealthy. India became independent in 1947, and mental health professionals emphasized improving conditions in existing hospitals and encouraging outpatient care. A few new mental hospitals were built in urban areas. The Indian government then launched a major reform, the National Mental Health Programme, in 1982. It required more training for all mental health workers, public education to increase awareness and reduce stigma, early detection and treatment, the integration of mental health and primary health care, and a decrease in custodial care. In 2002, other goals were added along with increased research and evaluation. By 2010, India still struggled to reach rural populations with mental illness but increased research in more urban modern health centers. Traditional practices such as meditation and yoga were sometimes integrated with Western medicine.

In sub-Saharan Africa, there are 48 countries, and many were former European colonies. Within each country, different tribal groups and traditions exist. The prevalence of epilepsy is high, largely due to inadequate care at childbirth, malnutrition, malaria, and parasitic diseases. Epilepsy is still highly stigmatized along with other mental disorders. In 2002, mental disorders accounted for 5 percent of the total Burden of Disease and 19 percent of all disability in Africa. Mental health issues are last on the list of priorities for health improvement in sub-Saharan Africa, as infectious diseases and malnutrition are still the major causes of death. In addition, health services are poorly developed, particularly in rural areas.

Widespread and frequent wars and internal strife in several African nations have disrupted society and left mental disorders in their wake, including PTSD and depression. However, mental illness is a taboo subject, and the mentally ill or disabled are stigmatized in most African countries. Many families with a mentally ill person hide them for fear of discrimination and ostracism from their communities. Inadequate public awareness of mental health and limited knowledge about the causes of mental illness exists. For example, a survey in Nigeria on the cause of mental illness showed that 34.3 percent of respondents cited drug misuse; 18.8 percent, divine wrath or will of God; and 11.7 percent, witchcraft/spiritual possession.

Some African countries, however, have attempted better mental health care since the early 20th century. For example, in South Africa, the Cape Province Committee for Mental Hygiene (1913) promoted mental hygiene care in the early 20th century. Now called Cape Mental Health, it is part of the South African Federation for Mental Health. It, along with professional organizations, fostered the Mental Health Care Act (2002), a major legislative reform, to improve care for the mentally ill. Although there are large gaps in service resulting from the long-term effect of apartheid, this legislation fostered reforms at the provincial and district level and increased care at the community level. Government agencies and NGOs in South Africa now promote public education and awareness campaigns targeting vulnerable groups. In Kenya, the Africa Mental Health Foundation, established in 2004, researches mental health and substance-abuse disorders. It also aids patients in finding appropriate treatment facilities.

In southern Africa, among indigenous Africans, traditional healers such as diviners (*sangoma*), herbalist (*inyanga*), and missionary groups provide much of the mental health care. However, in many African cultures, the community shows empathy for the sick person if they visit traditional healers but not if they chose to seek help from a Western mental hospital. However, in civil-war torn African countries, the mentally ill are often chained or imprisoned. In West Africa, fundamentalist Christian groups have established private "prayer camps" for treatment. Patients at these camps are generally chained against their will. Prayer is generally the only treatment. However, chaining people violates the 2006 United Nations' Disability Rights Convention, which most West African countries have ratified. Education about mental disorders in Africa is slowly gaining acceptances for Western medication and other treatment.

In summary, mental health care, although it became better from 1900 into the 21st century, still had much room for improvement in all nations. This was particularly true in low-income countries. Medical advances, further scientific evidence as to the causes of mental disorders, and the development of effective prevention and treatment methods are likely to evolve in this century.

10

Drugs and Remedies

Globally, over the 20th century and into the 21st century, many changes have occurred regarding the use, manufacturing, and control of drugs. More restrictions were placed on proprietary over-the-counter (OTC) medications, particularly those that contained psychoactive drugs, such as opiates and cocaine, and also prescription medications. Numerous pharmaceutical companies were established, and many new drugs were developed—some with serious side effects. In most nations, all medications needed to meet quality and safety and effectiveness standards, which became increasingly restrictive by the late 20th century. During this same time period, clinical trials for new drugs increased in developing or low-income nations with some negative consequences, and direct-to-consumer prescription drug marketing began in the United States and New Zealand. By the late 20th century, some common human conditions were classified as drug-treatable diseases. In a few Western countries, this led to the "diseasing" of the population and resulted in an increase in the amount of drugs prescribed and higher prices. International treaties to restrict illegal drug manufacturing, sales, and trafficking were instituted in the early 20th century. However, by the early 21st century, this war on drugs was seen as a failure by numerous nations. In addition, views on drug use and prevention slowly changed from being a criminal problem to a medical problem, which led to harm-reduction programs to reduce public health dangers in some nations.

PATENT MEDICINES AND DOMESTIC DRUG REGULATION

At the beginning of the 20th century, a nascent drug industry was emerging based upon 19th-century ideas. In 1847, the American Medical Association (AMA) had divided drugs into two categories: "ethical" and "unethical" preparations. Ethical, or pharmaceutical, drugs, were listed in the *United States Pharmacopoeia,* had a known ingredient, and were generally used for a specific illness or complaint such as digitalis for heart disease or morphine for pain. In Britain, a similar document, the *British Pharmacopoeia,* was first published in 1864. The

Medicines Act 1968 deemed the *British Pharmacopoeia* as the UK standard for medicinal products. Over 100 countries including Australia and Canada now used it as their standard.

"Unethical"—patent medicines, proprietary, OTC—drugs were protected by copyright or trademark. Common nostrums included tonics such as Lydia Pinkham's Vegetable Compound or Ayer's Cherry Pectoral. These proprietary drugs did not list their ingredients and often claimed to cure most ills. The primary ingredients of most of these tonics were water, alcohol, and "narcotics," which included opiates, cocaine, or cannabis.

North America

However, problems were seen with the sale and use of some medication, and various laws were passed to control both OTC and prescription medications over the 20th century. Near the turn of the 20th century, on the heels of the Woman's Christian Temperance Movement (WCTU), the Anti-Saloon League emerged in the United States to eliminate alcohol from society. This group became the major player in the prohibition movement—an aspect of the second clean-living movement during the Progressive Era—to improve and clean up American society and bring it back to a golden age. The anti-alcohol movement was opposed by various beverage manufactures pointing out an increase in drug use under local option laws. Reformers, on the other hand, pointed out that alcohol could lead to crime, poverty, and disease and that many patent medications contained alcohol and other drugs. The consumer was not aware of these ingredients as the nostrums were not labeled. Therefore, reformers were in favor of laws to force manufacturers to disclose the ingredients in proprietary drugs. This pressure resulted in passing of the Pure Food and Drug Act of 1906. The law required drug companies to accurately label contents and dosage of all their medications, particularly those containing alcohol, cannabis, cocaine, heroin, morphine, and opium, as these substances were included on a list of "addictive" and/or "dangerous" drugs. However, as long as they were truthfully labeled, they continued to be legally available without a prescription. After labeling, it is estimated that sales of nostrums containing opiates decreased by about a third, and cocaine was eliminated from Coca-Cola. This was the first of several laws to control addictive substances.

In 1914, the Harrison Narcotics Act was passed, which restricted the manufacture and sale of marijuana, cocaine, heroin, and morphine. However, it did allow physicians to prescribe opiates to patients for medical conditions but not for the treatment or maintenance of addiction. Small amounts of opiates such as paregoric for diarrhea and codeine for pain and cough were allowed without a prescription until the 1990s in the United States. The Harrison Act is the foundation of U.S. drug policy. An undercurrent for the promotion of these laws in the early 20th century was hostility and fear of immigrant and minority groups on the part of white rural Protestants. Cocaine became associated with "crazed N—o cocaine fiends," cannabis with the "Mexican menace," opium with the Chinese "yellow peril," and drinking with "undesirable" southern Europeans, Irish, and other

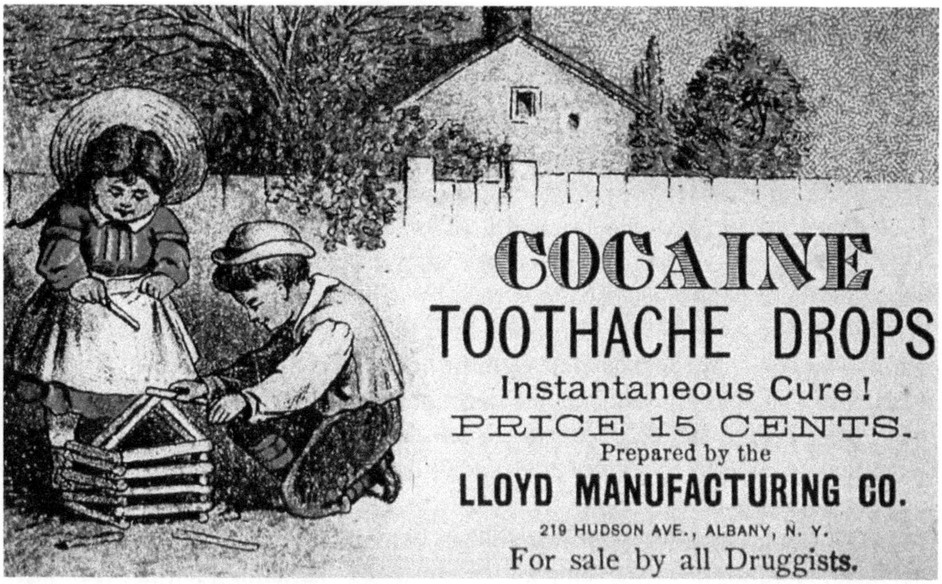

This American trading card advertises a toothache remedy whose active ingredient is cocaine, a dangerous drug. Although the Pure Food and Drug Act of 1906 required that all such ingredients be clearly labeled, products containing them continued to be legally available without a prescription. (National Library of Medicine)

immigrants. To control their perceived dangerous behaviors, drug laws and the Eighteenth Amendment (1919) to the Constitution, which prohibited the manufacturing, transportation, and sale of alcohol, were instituted. However, Prohibition resulted in increased criminal activity to supply alcohol to a thirsty public and deaths from methyl alcohol, and it was repealed by the Twenty-first Amendment in 1933.

In 1927, the Food and Drug Administration (FDA) was formed. Congress passed the 1938 Food, Drug, and Cosmetic Act after a prescription drug containing diethylene glycol (antifreeze) killed 100 people, mostly children. This act allowed various remedies to be sold directly to the consumer without seeking treatment from a health professional as long as they were proven safe and also tightened the control of prescription medication. In 1951, the Durham-Humphrey Amendment to this act was passed, which required certain drugs to be labeled "for sale by prescription only." When birth defects were reported in Europe and Canada after pregnant women used the antinausea medication thalidomide, Frances Oldham (1914–2015) of the FDA, and her committee did not approve it, and Congress, in 1962, passed the Kefauver-Harris Drug Amendments. Drug companies now had to prove not only safety but also evidence of effectiveness through well-controlled clinical trials and studies. In addition, the FDA was required to approve drug advertisement before marketing a new drug. After this time, other requirements were mandated including packaging inserts on side effects, clinical trials in children, quality control, and child-proof and antitampering caps among others. The drug review process in the United States became globally recognized as the most rigorous by the late 20th century.

Some new medications, which were originally prescription only, were later released for OTC sales in the late 20th century and early 21st century. These included topical antibiotic, antifungal, and antiallergy ointments and creams, antihistamines, antiheartburn medications, emergency contraceptives, and the like.

In Canada, the Food and Drug Act of 1920, revised in 1985, established the requirements for manufacturing and licensing drugs. It required that products be safe, their ingredients disclosed, and that drugs be effective. In 1923, Canada was one of the first nations to make marijuana illegal without any real explanation; heroin and codeine were also added to this law. However, lobbying on the part of health professionals allowed codeine in cough syrups and pain pills, which needed to be kept behind the counter and dispensed by a pharmacist who could limit quantities. Concern about codeine addiction resulted in codeine becoming a prescription-only medication in the province of Manitoba in 2016.

In 1951, all Canadian pharmaceutical companies were required to submit a detailed record for newly developed drugs prior to marketing their product. After the thalidomide disaster, manufacturers of OTC and prescription medications were required to have all drugs evaluated and approved for sale by the Therapeutic Products Directorate. After approval, they were issued a Drug Identification Number (DIN) indicating that they have been evaluated and authorized for sale in Canada. In 2008, an amendment to the Food and Drugs Act was tabled due to fear that various supplements and OTC drugs would be made illegal.

Other Nations

Britain became concerned about drug use from OTC medications in 1916 when opiates were used by servicemen. The 1920 Dangerous Drugs Act established that medical practitioners were allowed to prescribe morphine, cocaine, and heroin, and the *Rolleston Report* (1926) affirmed the right of doctors to prescribe these "controlled drugs" to addicts in some circumstances. This practice became known as the "British System" and lasted for about 40 years. However, the use and distribution of these substances without a prescription was illegal. The Food and Drugs Act (1938) prohibited the adulteration and mislabeling of drugs. In 1941, the Pharmacy and Medicines Act required manufacturers to list the active ingredients of their drugs on the packaging.

Due to international pressure, under the Drug Misuse Act (1964), restrictions on prescribing heroin and cocaine to treat addicts were mandated. Other substances, such as amphetamines and hallucinogens, were also added to the list of controlled drugs. Under the Medicines Act (1968) higher-strength codeine medications became prescription only. In addition, three categories of medicines, "general sale," "pharmacy" (dispensed by a pharmacist), and "prescription" were classified. As in some other countries, a few prescription-only medicines have been reclassified to "pharmacy" or "general sales" medications by the turn of the 21st century.

In Australia, some state governments, in 1938, required "quack" or OTC products to eliminate unproven claims for their effectiveness. In 1956 the Therapeutic Substances Regulation Act was passed, which established reforms including expiration dates on antibiotics and vaccines and the testing of new materials in several labs. After the thalidomide problem, however, a tighter federal act relating to medications or "therapeutic goods" was enacted in 1965. The National Biological Standards Laboratory was established to test drugs for quality. Drug regulation was the responsibility of individual states and territories and not the Australian Commonwealth, which limited its control to imported products. This Therapeutic Goods Act was changed in 1989 and mandated federal oversight over all drugs and medications. Under the terms of the act, Australia in 2018 required codeine products to be prescription-only due to concern about drug abuse. Australia also has the three classifications of medications similar to the UK.

Other commonwealth nations had controlled OTC and prescription drugs by the mid-20th century. As an example, India—before independence in 1947—passed the Drugs and Cosmetics Act (1940) and the Drug and Cosmetic Rules in 1945. A registered medical practitioner—a person having a degree in modern medicine—could prescribe narcotic and other drugs. However, prescription medicines were, and even today, are not affordable by many Indians. By the late 20th century, OTC medicines were available in shops and bazaars. More importantly, many of their ingredients have been used for centuries to cure common tropical illnesses. These include antimalarial extractions from the cinchona tree (quinine), the *ipecacunaha* root for amoebic dysentery, and the *ephedra vulgaris* plant for asthma and cardiac failure. These drugs are generally cheaper than the prescription forms. By the second decade of the 21st century, concerns of dependency resulted in codeine-containing cough medicine being banned in India in 2016. But other opiate preparations can be obtained with a physician's prescription, and laws have not always been enforced.

Due to concern about the misuse of OTC drugs, such as the decongestant pseudoephedrine to make methamphetamine, by the late 20th century, many nations required stricter controls over many nonprescription drugs. On the whole, over the 20th century and into the 21st century, stricter controls on all propriety and prescription drugs evolved in most countries.

RISE OF THE PHARMACOLOGICAL INDUSTRY

Although the origin of the pharmaceutical industry is found in the apothecaries of antiquity, the beginnings of modern drug companies go back to the mid- to late 19th century. Pharmaceutical companies emerged out of the synthetic-dye industry, which used organic materials from coal tar to create new drugs. As an example, in 1897, a stable form of acetylsalicylic acid was synthesized by German chemist Felix Hoffman (1868–1946). His employer, Freidrich Bayer, patented it as "Aspirin," marketed it to the public worldwide and established the first modern pharmaceutical company. By the second decade of the 20th century, drug companies were well established. Germany, Switzerland, Britain, the United States,

France, Canada, Russia, and other nations made proprietary and prescription medications along with cosmetics and other products. Most had subsidiaries in other nations, and this era is considered the dawn of globalization of the drug industry.

During the WWI, German pharmaceutical companies, including the Bayer subsidiaries, were confiscated by the allies along with Bayer's aspirin trademark (in 1994 the American rights to the Bayer name and trademarks were sold back to the German Bayer AG company). The United States and other countries began to market aspirin, which through the late 1960s became one of the most widely used drugs in the world. However, WWI disrupted Germany's position as the leader in pharmaceuticals. This resulted in the United States and Britain having an advantage in a growing and highly competitive drug industry. The interwar period (1918–1939) was also characterized by the discovery of several new drug classes including insulin, some vaccines, and antibiotics in North America and Britain.

During WWII, research into curing specific diseases and collaboration between pharmaceutical companies and the government emerged. After the war, American firms were in a leading position for research, development, and marketing. By the late 1940s, they produced over half of the world's pharmaceuticals and accounted for one-third of international trade in medicines. Other nations' pharmaceutical companies including those in Europe and Japan soon followed. In this period of rapid growth, companies also expanded more intensive collaborations and consulting relationships with academic researchers leading to the development of miracle drugs.

However, the development of socialized medicine in Europe and health insurance in the United States resulted in increased drug prices that neither patients nor physicians paid close attention to until the late 1980s. In addition, by the early 1980s, a number of small biotech companies emerged that focused on molecular biology, genetics, and later genomics in the United States. European firms established joint ventures with the American companies, and large pharmaceutical companies also became involved with them.

The next stage in the development of the pharmaceutical industry was the merger or acquisition of companies to form a few large global conglomerates. Between 1985 and 2005, nearly 40 major mergers produced gigantic pharmaceutical firms, and between 1995 and 2015, pharmaceutical firms decreased from 60 to just 10. In addition, North America and Western Europe produced the most pharmaceuticals although India and Singapore were now among the top 15 producers. These gigantean corporations formed a powerful influential group to shape policies on drug advertisement and research—they were first called "Big Pharma" in 1994. The industry through the early 21st century focused on mergers, advertisement to maintain market share, lobbying of politicians to protect commercial interests, filing legal claims on intellectual property rights, and higher prices. Suspicion of the industry increased when these activities were brought to the attention of the public. The high cost of drugs led some Americans to obtain prescription from international Internet pharmacies or fill them while traveling outside of the country.

In 2012, reflecting these concerns about the large pharmaceutical companies, British physician Ben Goldacre (1974–) published *Bad Pharma: How Drug Companies Mislead Doctors and Harm Patients*, which discussed the pharmaceutical industry's relationship with the medical profession, its influence on publishing, and even academic research. In addition, by 2015, some drug companies dramatically raised their prices, particularly in the United States. For example, in 2015, one company increased an old generic drug to treat toxoplasmosis—it can cause mental disability in the unborn—5,000 percent, and in 2016 another company dramatically increased the price of an epinephrine injection pen used to counter severe allergic reactions. This price gouging led to an outcry among consumers and health care professionals leading both companies to slightly lower the price. Other drug companies also raised prices leading to higher cost for consumers, medical insurance companies, and health services globally by 2017. An increasing complaint is that large pharmacy chains make contracts with drug companies for the cheapest generic drugs to meet insurance requirements and more profit. Some patients complain that other generic brands are not as effective compared to what they had been using but are unable to get their former generic medication, much less, the brand-name drug anymore.

Development of Miracle Drugs by the Pharmaceutical Industry

The golden age of drug advances came in the aftermath of WWII when numerous drugs were developed by various academic intuitions and pharmaceutical companies in industrialized nations. These included antibiotics, vaccines, chemotherapies for cancers, anti-high blood pressure, psychotropic, cardiac, contraception and hormonal compounds, and pain medications. Many of these new drugs went through a cycle of huge popularity for a couple of decades, followed by a decline, because of serious side effects, toxicity, expiration of their patent, or, if they were antibiotics, bacteria became resistant to them.

One of the most important classes of drugs to be developed over the 20th and into the 21st centuries, which dramatically reduced mortality rates from infectious disease, were the antibiotics or antimicrobials. At the turn of the 20th century, few drugs were available to treat infections. Various compounds containing mercury were often toxic to the patient. Around 1909, German physician Paul Ehrlich (1854–1915) developed Salvarsan, the "magic bullet," as a treatment for syphilis. Salvarsan was the most effective drug for treating syphilis until penicillin became available in the 1940s. The sulfanilamide (Prontosil) was synthesized by Bayer chemists from dyes in the 1930s, but bacteria soon developed resistance to it. However, other synthetic drugs were developed, including quinolones, that are still used today. The first major antibiotic or antibacterial used worldwide was penicillin, which was accidently discovered by Scottish bacteriologist Alexander Fleming (1881–1955) from a *Penicillium* mold in 1928. But it was not developed for mass use until near the end of WWII in 1945. The discovery of the first three antimicrobials, Salvarsan, Prontosil, and penicillin, set up the procedures for future antibiotic research.

After the war, various soils, plants, molds and other substances were tested for antimicrobial properties. Ampicillin, a broad spectrum derivative of penicillin, was developed in 1961, but overuse caused some bacteria to evolve resistance to it. In 1949, cephalosporin—a broad spectrum antibiotic—was developed and first became available for use in 1964. By the late 20th century, thousands of antibiotics had been found and were being tested and developed. On the other hand, penicillin, cephalosporin, tetracycline, and other infectious-disease fighting drugs were used indiscriminately in food producing animals and human populations, which led to more resistant bacteria. In Britain during 1961, a methicillin-resistant *Staphylococcus aureus* (MRSA) was found in a hospital and soon became a lethal problem internationally. By the turn of the 21st century, MRSA had become endemic (common) in many hospitals, gymnasiums, and urban regions of the world leading to death from often untreatable blood, lung, and wound infections. Although new antibiotics are being developed today, resistance to both old and new ones are likely to continue to emerge.

Another major lifesaving class of drugs was vaccines against childhood diseases. In the 1920s, diphtheria and tetanus immunizations were developed, which decreased the morbidity and mortality rates of these childhood disease. However, whooping cough immunizations were not perfected until 1948. During the immediate post-WWII period, polio maimed and killed many children. Fortunately, new methods of growing virus developed by 1950 and led to the development of two polio vaccines. American physician Jonas Salk (1914–1995) in 1955 developed an injectable inactivated virus vaccine against polio. Polish American Albert Sabin (1906–1993) developed the live oral vaccine in 1962. Mass polio immunizations eradicated the disease from most of the world by 2014. By the late 1970s, measles, mumps, and rubella vaccines were developed along with immunization against pneumonia and meningitis. Later in the century, vaccines against hepatitis B and other infectious diseases evolved and continue to this day.

Antipsychotic, antidepressant and anti-anxiety drugs—as mentioned in chapter 9—were developed in the 1950s. Barbiturates and then tranquilizers, such as Valium, were enormously popular from the late 1950s to 1970s as the "housewife's friend" but appeared more problematic by the middle of the 1970s as they began to be considered drugs of abuse. By 1980, their use had steeply declined due to these concerns and because their patents had expired. However, newly developed antidepressant drugs, such as selective serotonin reuptake inhibitors (SSRIs), were considered more effective and safer. By 2000 they were aggressively marketed, which resulted in increased use in many Western nations.

Treatment of chronic diseases by new drugs also developed. As an example, treatments for cancers—other than surgery and radiation—were not developed until the post-WWII years. It had been noticed that nitrogen mustard gas victims of WWI, and victims of an accident with the gas in WWII, had depressed white blood cells. In 1929, it was found that nitrogen mustard was anticarcinogenic, but it was not until the late 1940s that it was used as chemotherapy for cancers. Mustard agents were found to halt lymphoma in children. In the 1950s, some plant alkaloids were found to be beneficial for leukemia patients, and various derivatives were developed in the 1960s. Around 1949, American physician Sidney Farber (1903–1973) and his colleagues found that a chemical similar to folic acid, such as methotrexate, would slow the progress of cancer. This led to significant advances in chemotherapy in the 1960s and 1970s. By 1971, chemotherapy for solid tumor cancers such as breast and colon began. It was found that a combination of different chemotherapy drugs with different actions given simultaneously led to a further decline in mortality rates. From 1990 until now, mortality rate from most cancers have continued to decline by use of different chemotherapy drugs often along with surgery and radiation.

On the other hand, the development of many medications in the post-WWII era led to some serious problems due to inadequate testing. As previously mentioned, thalidomide caused severe limb and ear deformities in children born to mothers who took it during the first trimester of their pregnancies. This epidemic of malformations followed the sales figures of thalidomide about 8 months later. Thalidomide led to tougher testing and drug approval procedures in many countries.

Another drug with serious consequences was flecainide in the late 1980s. The Cardiac Arrhythmia Suppression Trial (CAST) found that after a heart attack, twice as many post-heart-attack patients with a heart arrhythmia died from sudden death compared to the controls who were receiving placebos. In 1997, the FDA withdrew the diet drugs fenfluramine and dexfenfluramine after evidence suggested about a third of the people tested showed some evidence of damage to their heart valves. The anti-arthritic drugs, rofecoxib and valdecoxib, which were heavily advertised, were withdrawn from the market in 2004 and 2005, respectively, because they excessively increased the risk of heart attacks and strokes with long-term use.

Direct-to-Consumer (DTC) Advertising of Drugs by the Pharmacological Industry

At the turn of the 20th century, in the United States, pharmaceutical drugs were theoretically available only with a prescription from a physician or dentist and were generally filled by a pharmacist. Because of the efforts of organized medicine, they were not advertised directly to consumers. On the other hand, advertisement of patent medicines containing opiates and cocaine was directed to the public in newspapers, magazines, billboards, and stores. Roughly half of a newspaper's advertising income came from patent medicines at this time.

However, medical societies in the United States were critical of the marketing of these nostrums as they felt it discouraged the sick from seeking legitimate treatments and took away potential patients. By 1941, due to various laws, Western nations banned direct advertising of pharmaceuticals to consumers. However, in the post-WWII years, increased marketing to physicians by drug companies' "sales reps," along with more advertisement in medical journals, dramatically increased prescription drug use.

During the 1980s, a change in the political and cultural climate in the United States emerged that led to direct-to-consumer (DTC) advertising. This allowed Merck in 1981 to run the first DTC print advertisement for its new antipneumococcal vaccine, which educated older individuals about how to prevent this disease. In 1985, the FDA ruled that DTC advertisements must also list the possible side effects of any medication and not make false claims. After several years of negotiation, in 1997, the FDA created guidelines for pharmaceutical companies to advertise on television. This led to drug companies aggressively marketing new drugs to cure many chronic conditions, which radically increased prescription sales. In addition, clever marketing to physicians between 1996 and 2001 vastly increased the use of the opiate painkiller OxyContin leading to an opiate-dependence epidemic by 2015.

By the turn of the 21st century, some companies suggested that hair loss, erectile dysfunction, or menopause were disorders that could be treated rather than portraying them as normal aging conditions. By 2016, physicians, politicians, and the public expressed unease about the safety of some drugs and felt that massive expenditures on advertising were creating higher drug prices. In addition, the FDA was increasingly criticized for weak enforcement of laws regulating advertising. This resulted in pressure for stricter limits on prescription-drug advertisement including a three year moratorium on DTC advertisement for new prescription drugs, which as of this writing is still in limbo.

In term of other nations, DTC advertisement is only allowed in New Zealand. However, pressure from the pharmaceutical industry to allow DTC advertisement is growing in Australia, Brazil, Canada, and the European Union. In addition, advertisement over the Internet is seen globally, and drug companies have been investing increased funds into marketing over this media, leading to uncertainty about the future trends of DTC advertisement worldwide.

Drug Testing in Developing Low-Income Nations by the Pharmaceutical Industry

As drug companies created more drugs, expanded, and combined in the late 20th century to form large conglomerates, more subjects were needed for clinical trials. Since patients are generally paid for their participation, they were often taken from the poorest groups in society. Although drug testing takes place worldwide, by the 1990s, developing countries in Asia—including India, Thailand, China—South America, and Africa—became cost-effective locations. Companies began to conduct, or outsource, their trials to low-income nations. To create basic standards for research, in 1964, the World Medical Association had developed the Declaration of Helsinki—last revised in 2008—which stipulated required procedures for medical testing. However, it was, and is, frequently ignored, and testing is difficult to monitor as trials are often subcontracted to clinical-research organizations, or CROs, which select the patients and conduct the testing.

By the turn of the 21st century, some physicians and medical researchers began to be troubled about clinical trials in developing nations. Concerns about standards of care, affordability of the new drugs to the population where the drug was tested, the quality of informed consent, and integrity of the data were voiced. In addition, language difficulties, unethical procedures, and whether or not the results of a clinical trials using one population could even be applied to others arose. For instance, in 1997, some unethical research by a few drug companies was uncovered. The drug AZT, to prevent HIV/AIDS, was tested in Asia, the Caribbean, and Africa. In 1994, one half of HIV-positive pregnant African women in a trial were given a placebo rather than another drug that was effective in preventing HIV. The other half were given the experiment drug. This resulted in about 1,000 babies contracting HIV in the placebo group. In another case, a clinical trial in 1996 of a new antibiotic against meningococcal meningitis during an epidemic was carried out in northern Nigeria. One half of the children were given the new drug. The other half was given a lower amount of another drug that was known to cure the disease. Children from both groups died, and the experimental drug had only limited effectiveness. These and other unethical drug trials resulted in lawsuits.

Nonetheless, these poor practices did not stop as corporations continued to compete with each other for new drugs and market shares into the 21st century. In 2012, a clinical trial was carried out in India for a drug to prevent serious diarrhea from a rotavirus that killed many children in Asia and Africa. A third of the children—the control group—were given a saltwater placebo instead of a drug known to be effective in preventing this illness. This procedure would not have been allowed in Western nations. Drug companies have also hidden their negative results, particularly ineffective or toxic effects. However, in 2013, this changed when GlaxoSmithKline, Britain's largest pharmaceutical company—who had been criticized for some of its practices—became the first drug company in the world to begin to publish all clinical trials since 2000 when the conglomerate was formed by the merger of several companies.

A CULTURE OF MEDICALIZATION OR THE "DISEASING OF THE WEST"

In conjunction with the rise in large pharmaceutical corporations and increased advertising of many new drugs in the late 20th century, the diseasing of high-income Western culture emerged. Christopher Lane (1966–) in *Shyness: How Normal Behavior Became a Sickness* (2007) describes that in the 1990s Westerners, particularly in the UK and the United States, began to use antidepressants for routine emotions and normal behaviors that medical experts now deemed medical conditions. For example, shyness was now considered a social disorder on a spectrum of social-anxiety disorders when numerous new disorders were entered into the *DSM-III* in 1980.

For these new disorders, drug companies pushed new antidepressants. In addition, insurance companies required *ICD* disease codes by the mid-1980s for reimbursement only of a definable medical condition. Common and normal human conditions were now considered diseases for which patients should be prescribed medications. These ills included premenstrual syndrome, mild post-partum and other mild depression, anger outbursts, hyperactivity, erectile dysfunction in older men, and even grieving. The consumer now considered prescription medication as harmless and developed an attitude that it was all right to take a pill for any complaint, in particular, if their doctor suggested it.

In the United States, prescription-drug use increased between the late 1990s and the 2010s. One out of five people took a drug to treat a psychological disorder. In addition, 8 of the 10 most commonly used drugs in 2011–2012 were used to treat metabolic syndrome related to obesity. Obesity in the United States tripled between 1960 and 2000; worldwide, from 1980 obesity more than doubled. These drugs include those for high blood pressure, high cholesterol, and diabetes. However, some prescription drugs declined, such as hormone replacement for menopausal women and some COX-2 inhibitors for pain due to concerns about adverse effects.

Of concern to some health professionals was the fact that sales of prescription opioids nearly quadrupled from 1999 to 2014 in the United States, but there had not been an overall change in the amount of pain. By 2012, Americans consumed twice as many prescription opiates per capita compared to Canada, the second ranking opiate-consuming nation, followed by Western Europe. The lowest consumption was found in developing nations. Moreover, during this time period, prescription-opioid overdose deaths increased due to the misuse of these drugs by those who had become addicted to it, leading to an opiate misuse epidemic by 2015.

In Western cultures, antidepressant prescriptions have risen since the late 1990s. The highest use of antidepressants is in North America, Iceland, Australia, and Western European nations. In the United States, for example, from 1999 to 2014, the percentage of Americans on antidepressants had nearly doubled along with an increase in suicide rates. Problem related to increased psychoactive prescription medications, in addition to life-threatening allergic reactions, toxic effects, and overdose due to the diseasing of the West concerned health professionals. Moreover, overmedicalization contributed to rising health costs. By 2010, many health professionals recommended a reduction in drug advertisement, patient and physician education, and early intervention programs to reduce prescription drug use.

THE RECREATIONAL DRUG MARKET

Besides prescription and over-the-counter medications, from the early 20th century, recreational nonmedical drug use has been common. For any given drug, use has waxed and waned depending upon the culture. After the two world wars of the 20th century, heroin and cocaine use increased, then declined, and then increased again in industrialized nations. Marijuana and other drugs surged from the mid-1960s, when cultural norms changed in the West.

At the turn of the 20th century, most opium was produced in Asia, and coca in South America, where they had been grown and used for centuries. Coca

(*Erythroxylum coca*) was transported from the Andes, to German, Dutch, Swiss and North American chemical companies that processed it into cocaine. Manufacturing also began in Peru—with the help of German scientists—and in Japan. As the worldwide market grew for cocaine, coca production expanded to a number of Asian territories, including Ceylon (a British colony, now Sri Lanka), Java (a Dutch colony, now part of Indonesia) and Formosa (a Japanese colony, now Taiwan). In the post-WWI years, through the late 1920s, Peru supplied North America, and the Asian countries tended to supply Europe with the substance. However, when health consequences from this drug, and also opiates, became apparent, various international laws were passed to curb drug abuse (discussed in the next section). Production decreased worldwide, but a large black market rose over the century to supply these drugs for recreational use. By the 21st century, most cocaine products came from the Americas to fuel global demand.

Like cocaine, opium was a popular recreational drug. By the turn of the 20th century, opium was transported from India to China, which also started to grow the opium poppy (*Papaver somniferum*) for domestic production. Iran and Turkey and other Middle Eastern countries had also grown and used the opium poppy for centuries. China, at this time, had become the largest consumer of opium in the world. To supply China and other nations, British, Dutch, and French colonies in Southeast and Southwest Asia also cultivated the poppy. After WWI, in the 1920s, heroin became the most produced derivative of opium for recreational use in the West, which continued into the 21st century. In the post-WWII era, the major supplier of heroin was from the "golden triangle," which included Burma (Myanmar), Laos, and Siam (Thailand) although other developing nations in the region cultivated the poppy. By the late 20th century, these countries along with the Middle East and southern Asian nations, grew poppies and manufactured heroin. Their primary markets were Europe and Oceania, while Mexico and Columbia and a few other Latin American countries mostly marketed heroin to North America. By 2016, the use of opiates grew while overall opiate use in Asia had remained stable.

The use of cannabis—from the Indian hemp plant—flowered over the 20th century and into the 21st century. Cannabis (*Cannabis sativa*) had been produced for centuries in the Middle East, Asia, and Africa. Only a limited amount was exported as most nations grew the plant for their own domestic consumption. Mexico and some areas of the North America had also grown it for domestic use for decades. Cannabis use increased in Western cultures in the 1960s with the postwar "baby boom" generation who rebelled against conventional societal norms. Its use continued to increase into the 21st century in many nations. By the 1980s, large drug cartels had developed in Columbia and Mexico to grow and supply cannabis and many illicit drugs. This led to massive crime, black-market activities, and serious social problems in these countries. Illicit drugs were mainly marketed to North America. In addition, cannabis in many forms by the 2010s had become the most illicitly trafficked drug worldwide. As other drugs became popular, such as amphetamines and hallucinogens, they were also produced and trafficked around the world.

INTERNATIONAL TREATIES AND THE GLOBAL WAR ON DRUGS

Global activities against opiates, coca, and other drugs began in the early years of the 20th century. Numerous international treaties were signed and expanded upon, which are still in effect in the 21st century. At a 1909 conference in Shanghai, concerns about international opium trafficking and its high use in China laid the groundwork for the first major global effort to control recreational drug use. Representatives to The Hague, in the Netherlands, from China, France, Germany, Italy, Persia (Iran), Japan, the Netherlands, Portugal, Russia, Siam (Thailand), the UK, and British territories including India signed the International Opium Convention on January 23, 1912, at The Hague Convention. Heroin and cocaine were also included. This treaty did not result in much change due to conflicting opinions, and WWI led to increased drug use among allied troops in France, which in turn resulted in increased control over the drugs as part of the wartime effort, particularly in Britain.

In 1919, immediately after the war, all countries signing the peace Treaty of Versailles became party to this convention. The treaty required signers to control manufacturing, importing, distributing, selling, or exporting opiates, cocaine, and their derivatives. However, a large proportion of manufactured drugs were still sold for nonmedicinal purposes in many countries. At Geneva in February 1925, cannabis was added to the drug list, but this new requirement was not accepted by all countries as the plant was used in indigenous traditional medicine. In addition, governmental authorities were required to control both the importing and exporting of drugs, but countries were not mandated to limit the production of opium and coca, which resulted in neither the U.S. nor Chinese delegations signing the convention. By the mid-1920s, close to 60 countries around the world had signed and ratified the agreement, and in 1949 this had risen to 67. In the 1931 convention, the concept of drug scheduling in terms of perceived harm was added to the treaty. The treaty did result in better control of legal drug manufacturing and sales, but illicit drugs sales and trafficking were now taken over by the underworld.

The WWII years resulted in decreased traffic. But in the postwar years, by 1961, nine international legal agreements on narcotic drugs caused confusion. In addition, many countries had not signed them; therefore, the Single Convention International Treaty of 1961 was implemented. It superseded all previous international conventions, protocols, and treaties and prohibited the production and supply of all narcotic drugs including synthetic ones except if licensed for medical treatment and research. The United Nations Office on Drugs and Crime (UNODC) was delegated to monitor each country and work with national authorities to ensure compliance with this treaty. The agreement was supplemented by the February, 21, 1971 Convention on Psychotropic Substances, which was designed to control all psychoactive drugs. But the enforcement of these treaties was difficult, and much illicit production and trafficking still remained. This was particularly true in the Middle East, Southeast Asia, and the Indian subcontinent where cannabis and opiates were grown and in the Andes of South America where coca has been used for centuries. Moreover, in 1971, President Richard Nixon (1913–1994) proclaimed a "War on Drugs," a slogan that was eventually adopted by United Nations' agencies along with curtailing both the "supply side" and "demand side" for nonmedical drug use.

Despite all these efforts, by the end of the 1970s, an increase in illegal drug use occurred in many countries. Therefore, other international meetings were convened. In 1988, the United Nations Convention against Illicit Traffic in Narcotic Drugs and Psychotropic Substances was implemented. It was now mandatory for signatory countries to establish manufacturing, distribution, and trafficking as criminal offences under its domestic law. The 1998 United Nations General Assembly Special Session on drugs reaffirmed this treaty with the motto "A drug-free world—we can do it!" Member countries were asked to completely eliminate illicit substances within 10 years. However, this effort was also a failure. In 2011, the Global Commission on Drug Policy (2011, 2) finally stated the following:

> The global war on drugs has failed, with devastating consequences for individuals and societies around the world. Fifty years after the initiation of the UN Single Convention on Narcotic Drugs, and 40 years after President Nixon launched the U.S. government's war on drugs, fundamental reforms in national and global drug control policies are urgently needed.

In the wake of this pronouncement, by 2016, the total elimination of drugs was seen as impracticable and that "simplistic 'just say no' messages and 'zero tolerance' policies" needed to be replaced by educational efforts based on credible information, more treatment services, and less focus on arrest and imprisonment of users and small-time producers such as farmers. In addition, some countries including Mexico, Colombia, and Guatemala, now fraught by corruption and extreme violence over drug production and trafficking by large cartels, have asked the UN to eliminate the war on drugs program as it was destroying their countries. Since the beginning of the 20th century, rather than eliminating a problem, various measures and treaties had actually increased the problem by the early 21st century.

CHANGING VIEWS ON DRUG USE

As noted previously, since the 20th century, opinions concerning drug use have waxed and waned. Over the century, harsher policies evolved on the global level for illegal drugs, particularly in the late 1960s, and were still enforced into the second decade of the 21st century. On the other hand, in the late 20th century, some health professionals saw these policies leading to public health issues. In the 1970s, the concept of responsible-use education to prevent health problems was advocated by a few health professionals in the United States. This is represented in a book, *Responsible Alcohol and Drug Use* (1979). However, it was published at the beginning of the Reagan administration, which advocated "just say no," the elimination of all illegal drugs from society, and prison sentences for even small-time distributers and users, and later, a panic over a perceived "crack cocaine" epidemic. The concept of responsible use (now called harm reduction) was banned. In contrast, in Europe during the 1980s, health professionals saw the strict global

To minimize the impact of illegal drug use on the HIV/AIDS and hepatitis C epidemics, several nations instituted needle exchange programs. Here, a volunteer gives needles to an addict in Odessa, Ukraine, August 2005. (Brent Stirton/Getty Images)

enforcement system as harmful to the health and welfare of their societies. In response, in addition to education, the concept of harm reduction emerged. It evolved in the 1980s and 1990s to include needle exchange programs (NEP), safe injection facilities (SIF), and decriminalization of illicit drugs, particularly in Western Europe.

For example, around 1984 in Amsterdam, Holland, a drug users' organization established a NEP to prevent hepatitis B among intravenous (IV) drug users who shared needles. Switzerland, around the same time, besides offering a NEP, also had methadone programs, supervised injection rooms, housing, and job programs. These harm reduction efforts were found to reduced blood-borne diseases and overdose. Likewise, Liverpool, England, began a NEP in the late 1980s and held a conference in 1990 at which time the term "harm reduction" for these types of prevention methods was coined. Australia and New Zealand also operated NEPs in the late 1980s as did most European nations. In the United States, a few private NEPs started in the 1990s; however, it was not until 2016 that government funds were allowed to support such programs, although not all states have them as of 2017.

In the developing nations, however, due to legal and political considerations, few have NEP programs. When they do, equipment is generally sold by pharmacies. Asian countries such as China and Bangladesh, for instance, did not begin a program until the late 1990s, and most others have not instituted it resulting in an increase in HIV. Few Middle Eastern nations and only one sub-Saharan African nation offer NEP. In Latin America, only Mexico and four South American nations have a NEP.

In addition, supervised injection facilities (SIF) are almost nonexistent in developing countries. However, as nonmedical drug use was increasingly seen as a serious problem in the late 20th century in Europe, a SIF for IV users was established in Berne, Switzerland, in 1986. These facilities were found to decrease not only blood-borne infections but to reduce overdose fatalities. By the early 21st century they are now found in 10 European nations. On the other hand, in North America, Vancouver and Toronto, Canada, are the only places that in 2017 provided a legal facility for IV drug users that are both government sanctioned and funded. The Vancouver site was established as an experiment in 2003. After three years, it was found to decrease the spread of infection and drug overdose. Some other Canadian cities are debating whether or not to have these facilities. In the United States, New York City in 2016 began to advocate for a SIF site as a public health measure. However, this harm reduction innovation at the present time is still fraught with political controversy not only in the United States but also in China and Russia as some feel that these types of programs condone illicit drug use.

Another harm reduction method adopted first in Europe was decriminalization of illicit drugs. In 1976, the Dutch government decriminalized the possession of less than five grams of cannabis, which is considered a "soft drug." All cannabis products in addition to some magic mushrooms (such as psilocybin) could be bought in "coffee shops." By the 21st century, a low percentage of the Dutch population had smoked marijuana leading professionals to note that soft drugs—when widely accessible—seem to lose much of their appeal. Holland also has one of the lowest heroin rates due to its methadone and other intervention programs.

Portugal was the first European nation to decriminalize all illicit drugs and make it an "administrative" issue in 2001. In 1999, after the country was found to have the highest HIV rate in Europe, it expanded harm reduction efforts. A 2009 follow-up study found no adverse effect on drug usage rates from their policies. Moreover, drug-related illnesses including HIV and deaths from drug use decreased dramatically, resulting in the country having one of the lowest non-medical drug use rates in Europe.

By the turn of the 21st century, other nations began to decriminalizing marijuana and other drugs because health workers, law enforcement, and lawmakers began to question the wisdom of the decades-old global treaties to eradicate illegal substances and punish those who produce and consume them. Consequently, a number of political entities changed their laws in the second decade of the century. In 2013, Canada required medical marijuana patients to get their cannabis from licensed producers. However, in 2016, the courts allowed patients with a prescription to grow their own and in 2017 were discussing making it legal. By 2014, other nations had changed their laws. Uruguay became the first country in the world to formally legalize marijuana for its citizens. The Czech Republic allows people to grow up to five marijuana plants and possess a small amount of other illicit drugs, and marijuana was decriminalized in Switzerland. Some states in the United States began to allow marijuana for medical use. California was the first to do so in 1996. Over the next 20 years, 21 states either voted to allow the use of marijuana for medical or recreational purposes although it is still illegal on the federal level. On the international level, concern about the ineffectiveness of current laws led to a special United Nations session in April 2016 to discuss the global drug issue. Their report asked countries to review their current policies and aim to minimize the adverse public health and social consequences of drug abuse.

From the early 20th century to the early years of the 21st century, both prescription and recreational drug use increased often parallel with the expansion of the pharmaceutical industry and the development of new drugs and advertisement. More restrictive international treaties against drugs occurred over this time period, and clinical trials were accomplished in low-income countries that also supplied drugs to high-income nations. By the 21st century, health professions began to look at drug use as a medical and not criminal problem.

11

War, Health, and Medicine

Over the 20th century and into the 21st century, numerous wars and conflicts have erupted. Developments in military trauma care, in particular, have greatly influenced civilian emergency medicine globally. The development of more deadly weapons and warfare since the early 20th century created new challenges for military medicine in each war situation. Advances from the battlefields were incorporated into civilian medical and surgical practice and served to advance public health, medicine, and patient care as a whole. These advances have included rapid transportation of seriously wounded individuals to hospitals, better organization of medical systems, blood banking, and rehabilitation. Some surgical and technological methods cycled in and out of fashion. A few ancient techniques that were effective in saving lives were temporarily overlooked leading to increased deaths, and what was effective in one situation did not necessarily work in another. From the beginning of the 20th century, mortality from battlefield diseases decreased through better personal hygiene and sanitation, insect control, clean water, immunizations, and later antibiotics. Mortality from wounds also decreased due to personal upper-body armor, antibiotics, safer anesthesia, and various surgical techniques—including plastic surgery. By the end of the century, a symbiosis existed between advances in civilian and military medicine in industrialized societies. New techniques in one sector were quickly adopted by the other. In this chapter, selected major conflicts that led to advances in public health and medical care will be discussed.

WARS AT THE TURN OF THE 20TH CENTURY

At the turn of the 20th century, conflict arose between several nations around the world. These wars led to advancements in wound care, hygiene, and public health.

Boer War (October 11, 1899–May 31, 1900)

The Boer War resulted from British colonizers attempting to control the Boers of South Africa, who wanted independence. During this war, new rifles allowed a bullet to pass through a person resulting in a "clean wound" with little wound contamination. Rather than applying antiseptic dressings, wounds were found to heal better uncovered in the hot dry climate. Physicians also stopped the centuries-honored technique of debriding—removing unhealthy tissue and dirt—from the wound. After the war, this uncovered-wound treatment became the standard of military medicine. However, during WWI when this conservative approach was tried, it resulted in disaster as more than 60 percent of wounds were caused by shrapnel that carried in soil contaminated with manure from centuries of pasturing and farming in Western Europe. The surgeons forgot about debriding the wounds resulting in thousands of wounded soldiers dying from infections in these pre-antibiotic days. Due to inadequate field sanitation in the Boer War, typhoid was also a major cause of disease for British troops. However, after the war, standards of training and practice for medical officers were improved along with public health practices. On the eve of WWI, Col. William Horrocks (1858–1941), a physician in the British Royal Army Medical corps, developed a sand filtration and chlorine process for decontaminating water for field use that was widely adopted. The British gave typhoid vaccine as a trial with Indian troops with good results; the Germans and Japanese also tested typhoid and other vaccines.

Spanish-American War (April 1898–August 1898)

During the Spanish-American war, more American soldiers died from typhoid, yellow fever, and malaria than from combat. This brief war with Spain resulted in America's support for the ongoing struggle by Cubans, Puerto Ricans, and Filipinos against Spanish rule. It was precipitated by the battleship USS *Maine* being mysteriously blown up in Havana, Cuba's harbor. Due to the high death rate from typhoid, in 1911, American physicians, who were aware of other countries' developments of various antitoxins and immunizations, ordered mandatory vaccination of military personnel for typhoid fever, resulting in the disease almost disappearing in the peacetime army. Immunization against typhoid was suggested for individuals traveling from industrialized to typhoid-endemic regions with inadequate sanitation and clean water. This is also recommended today.

After the end of this war, yellow fever and malaria continued to ravage both Cubans and the American-occupation force in Cuba. In addition, the disease was making it impossible to build the Panama Canal. Therefore, in 1900, a Yellow Fever Commission was appointed by the surgeon general of the U.S. Army. The commission was headed by army surgeon Maj. Walter Reed (1851–1902) whose mission was to investigate the cause and prevention of yellow fever. Cuban physician Carlos Juan Finlay (1833–1915) had suggested that the disease was transmitted between people by mosquito bites and not through the air or contaminated clothing from fever victims. Reed tested the mosquito theory by having mosquitoes that had previously bitten fever patients bite volunteers in a series of experiments beginning in June 1900. Reed's commission confirmed the theory that yellow fever was spread by the female *Aedes aegypti* mosquito (see chapter 6 for more information on yellow fever and malaria).

In addition, the U.S. Army's chief sanitation officer and physician, Maj. William C. Gorgas (1854–1920) contributed to the elimination and prevention of yellow fever. Gorgas was stricken with the fever as a young man as was his wife. Since after contracting it, they were now both immune to the disease, they were posted to Havana during the occupation of Cuba. While there, he implemented an experimental program of inoculations against the disease. However, many of the volunteers died from the vaccine, so the experiment was canceled. The vaccine was later perfected. Gorgas successfully eradicated yellow fever from Havana by destroying larval breeding sites with an insect-control program that included spraying and putting oil on swamps. Use of mosquito nets over beds was also implemented. These interventions also resulted in a decreased incidence of malaria. The success of this military research led many nations to follow these procedures to eliminate mosquito-borne diseases. Only after mosquito control was obtained was construction of the Panama Canal possible in the first decade of the 20th century.

The Russo-Japanese War (February 8, 1904–September 5, 1905)

The Russo-Japanese War in terms of the advances in military medicine was one of the most important wars in history. This war involved Japan and Russia's attempt to seize control over Korea and Manchuria. During this war, both the Japanese and Russians generated major medical innovations that set new standards for armies around the world and advances in medicine in general. The Japanese in the late 19th century developed a high level of field sanitation because numerous military medical officers were sent to Germany for training. Germany at the time had the most advanced system in the world. Japanese officers were given extensive training in field hygiene and sanitation along with the bacteriological nature of disease. As a result, Japanese military medicine developed a strong emphasis on disease prevention that was ahead of most Western nations at the time.

During the Russo-Japanese War, this scientifically based training and prevention resulted in the first major war in history where the number of men killed by bullets and war wounds exceeded the number of solders who died from disease in the Japanese military. Japanese military medicine as a result became the envy of the world and many Western military officers went to Japan to learn their procedures. Japan also developed rigorous research programs that led physician Kitasato Shibasaburō (1853–1931) to develop tetanus and diphtheria antitoxins, which saved many lives around the world.

In addition, the Japanese Army became the first army in history that required combat-operation field orders to include a plan for medical support. Japanese soldiers also had good personal hygiene habits, and strict field discipline reduced sexually transmitted disease (STDs) and alcohol problems; "camp followers" were not allowed. The Russian Army, on the other hand, had many deaths from disease and poorly trained medical personnel. They also had disability due to alcoholism and STDs during the conflict.

However, Russians were the first to treat "battle shock" (shell shock in WWI, combat fatigue in WWII, and post-traumatic stress disorder [PTSD] in 1980, and other psychiatric illnesses near the front line). The Russians theorized that battle shock symptoms were due to brain damage from explosions of munitions and not malingering and cowardliness. They discovered that if psychiatric cases were sent to the rear, more soldiers developed "evacuation syndrome"—signs of psychiatric distress so they could be evacuated out of stressful combat areas. Therefore, these casualties were treated near the front line with rest and food. During the Russo-Japanese war, the Russians laid the foundation for modern military psychiatric treatment due to severe stress.

WORLD WAR I: THE GREAT WAR (JUNE 28, 1914–NOVEMBER 11, 1918)

The Great War began June 28, 1914, with the assassination of Archduke Ferdinand (1863–1914), of Austria-Hungary by a Serbian. This war was between Germany, the Austro-Hungarian Empire, Ottoman Empire, and Bulgaria against France, Italy, Russia, Britain, and eventually the United States on April, 6, 1917—after American shipping had been sunk by German submarines. Most modern medical treatments, systems, and methods had their roots in this war. WWI was the most destructive conflict in history up to this point in time. Combatants mobilized 60 million men with 7 million killed and over 19 million wounded. This is the first major war where more died of wounds than by disease. With new military technology and devices, most combatants were injured by shrapnel and exploding armaments, which produced mutilations of various parts of the body, particularly the face. Some were wounded by chlorine and blistering mustard gas attacks and flamethrowers.

Military medicine employed and expanded new techniques to treat casualties of these wounds. For the first time, bacteriology diagnostic labs, improved X-ray machines, saline infusions, better retractors, and surgical lighting were introduced along with the first field blood-transfusion teams. Rapid transportation to get the wounded to treatment faster was developed. Both the American Red Cross and American military began hospital operations (called ambulances) and transportation services in France before the United States' entry into the war. By 1917, Red Cross personnel worked under the auspices of the U.S. Army, now called the American Expeditionary Force. At the beginning of the war, wounded allies in France were carried by litter bearers from the trenches to horse-drawn carts, sometimes to clearing stations, and then to railroad stations and placed in straw-lined cattle cars to be shipped to the nearest hospital. However, by the time they arrived, many had died. At the battle of the Marne in September 1914, thousands of wounded French soldiers were left at the train station outside in the open for want of transportation. To rescue them, American Ambassador Myron T. Herrick (1854–1929) organized his wealthy friends with automobiles to drive the wounded to the newly organized American hospital near Paris. Due to this rapid transportation, many French soldiers received adequate surgery and lived. This marked the beginning of the motor-ambulance corps.

This more rapid transportation led to the establishment of British Casualty Clearing Stations (CCS) approximately 6 to 9 miles behind the front lines. These were advanced surgical units, staffed by surgeons and nurses. The wounded were first moved to waiting ambulances and then to a CCS. Triage, first used by the French, separated patients into three groups; those who would die anyway, those who would live without treatment, and the seriously injured who could be saved by medical treatment. This latter group was treated first. The logistics of triage and establishment of faster transportation in ambulances that emerged out of WWI were soon adopted by civilian medical systems and are commonplace today.

Wounded German and British soldiers wait to be evacuated from a Casualty Clearing Station (CCS) at Grévillers-Bapaume, France, during World War I. (Wellcome Collection)

A major development for the treatment of injuries that saved lives in this pre-antibiotic era emerged. During the first years of the war, the amputation rate was high due to gas gangrene infections from the muddy, manured conditions of the trenches. Those with penetrating abdominal wounds usually died of shock and infection. However, French surgeon Alexis Carrel (1873–1944) and British biochemist Henry Dakin (1880–1952) were sent to a hospital near the front to see if they could reduce infection rates. Dakin had developed a sodium hypochlorite solution, which killed dangerous bacteria such as *Clostridium perfringens*, the cause of gas gangrene, with little damage to healthy tissue. Carrel opened the wounds, rather than closing them, and irrigated them with this solution. The rate of wound infection dramatically decreased along with amputations, including those from "trench foot" from standing in wet filthy trenches. The "Carrel-Dakin Method" was adopted by medical personnel across Europe during the war. Irrigation of wounds is still used today in some surgical procedures.

Most casualties with compound fractures would die from bleeding or infection. However, traction splints—such as the Thomas splint developed by Welsh surgeon Hugh Owen Thomas (1834–1891)—were first routinely used near the end of the war by his nephew, orthopedic surgeon Robert Jones (1857–1933). When transporting soldiers, it kept the compound femoral fracture from further damaging muscle mass and blood vessels. Both irrigation and the splint reduced mortality from compound fractures to less than 20 percent. In addition, the French developed X-ray motor vehicles, called "petite Curies," that allowed physicians to detect broken bones or buried shrapnel and bullets that could introduce bacteria, such as tetanus. Although tetanus had always been a deadly disease, death from tetanus by the war's end was reduced to almost zero by giving tetanus antitoxin as soon as possible to a wounded serviceman.

However, France had little interest in field hygiene, and as a result, soldiers suffered high typhoid rates from unclean water as opposed to the British and Americans who disinfected water supplies with a solution of calcium hypochlorite in a cloth container or what became known as a Lyster bag. Interestingly, one of the major killers during the war was the Spanish influenza epidemic of 1918 that killed millions of young servicemen and civilians worldwide. Although poison gas was used for the first time in war by the Germans, French, and British, the horror of its use led to it being banned in 1925, which was not always adhered to. The Japanese used chemical warfare during WWII as did some Middle Eastern and other nations during 1980–2010. However, gas was not used in the European theater of WWII.

At the beginning of the Great War, the German army was the most medically advanced of all combatants. Not only did soldiers carry first-aid kits but logistics for casualties, such as clearing stations, forward surgery, and a transport system to rear hospital areas by rail, had already been in place for about 10 years. In 1914, the Germany military and civilian surgeons were also using aseptic surgical techniques and had integrated scientific and technical expertise into their practice. The Germans also introduced facilities for rehabilitation of the disabled and wounded. By the end of the war, the German system was adopted by all major militaries.

Standardization of surgical procedures, prosthetic limb development, and the beginning of the rehabilitation profession emerged out of the war for all militaries. With hundreds of thousands of injured soldiers returning home to all combatant nations, unlike previous wars when many died, a new emphasis on rehabilitation, physical therapy, continuing care, and training for reentry into civilian live emerged. This was the beginning of rehabilitative medicine that increased in effectiveness into the 21st century. At Walter Reed Hospital in the United States, for example, the Artificial Limb Laboratory opened in 1917. It aimed to give every amputee soldier a modern artificial limb so he could return to work. In Germany, a similar institute was formed, and after the war many men were trained to reenter civilian life, given education, job training, and placement.

Another major advance in the medical field that had roots in WWI was the beginnings of plastic surgery. Because of new weapons, faces were often mutilated. British Army surgeon Harold Gillies (1882–1960), the father of plastic surgery, invented a number of procedures including the tubular "pedicles" (flaps of skin) to provide blood flow to the reconstructed area from another part of the body. For faces that could not be repaired, he built prosthesis, sometimes including an artificial eye. Artificial limbs were also improved. In the United States, the Dental Corps often did jaw reconstruction.

Psychological testing emerged out of the war. Testing was developed due to low return-to-duty rates that undermined the fighting strength of the allies from "shell shock," or psychiatric, casualties. To address this situation, tests to determine mental fitness to serve in the military were developed. For example, in the United States, recruits were given a battery of psychological tests and physical exams to determine fitness for service. In Germany, tests were used to select for military occupations, but neither Germany nor France tested all recruits or tested for character or mental stability. British recruits were not given psychological tests, but they did undergo physical fitness and medical exams before being accepted as a soldier.

However, psychological screening did little to prevent shell shock among soldiers. Another development dealing with psychological injury during the war was forward psychiatry treatment (within the sound of gunfire) of rest, good food, and the expectation of returning to duty as used by the Russians and Germans. It had about a 40 percent returned-to-service rate. Both Britain and France later established forward neurology centers to diagnose and treat these disorders. In the aftermath of the war, postwar psychological problems of returning veterans stimulated further public health interest in mental health among most of the nations involved with the conflict.

Another major advance that emerged out of the Great War was the use of blood transfusions to prevent shock and save lives. Although blood transfusions had been performed by transferring blood directly from one person to another, this often led to complications such as clotting or incompatibility. In 1901, Viennese physician Karl Landsteiner (1868–1943) discovered the ABO antigens of blood and developed a method of typing and matching donor and recipient for safe transfusions. However, these findings were generally ignored. During 1914–1915, it was found that the addition of sodium citrate to blood prevented it from clotting, and this blood could be stored for 28 days if refrigerated. American army medical researcher Capt. Oswald Robertson (1886–1966) established the first blood depot on the Western Front in 1917 when it was realized that blood needed to be stockpiled for use during battle. Type "O," the universal donor, was used to prevent incompatibility (type O Rh positive blood cannot be given to someone with the rarer Rh negative factor, however). The use of stored blood was adopted by the Canadian and British medical corps and saved the lives of untold number of soldiers. The idea of storing blood led to the creation of civilian blood banks in Britain in 1921, a network of blood facilities for hospital transfusions in 1930 in the Soviet Union, and the first in-hospital blood facility at the Mayo Clinic in the United States in 1935.

THE SPANISH (1936–1939) AND CHINESE (1927–1937) CIVIL WARS

These two civil wars also advanced medical techniques. The Spanish Civil War (July 17, 1936–April 1, 1939) was the first war in which civilian losses exceeded those of combatants. The conflict began with a military coup in which the Nationalist forces under General Francisco Franco (1892–1975) gained control of much of the country. The government (Republicans) responded by turning the militia into a popular army. Out of this conflict, several areas of medical science advanced.

These included the development of mobile blood banks, aseptic treatment of wounds and injuries, and the use of sulfa drugs. One of the first transportable climate-controlled blood banks was established by Spanish physician Frederic Durán-Jordà (1905–1957). Blood was put in refrigerated trucks, which transported the blood to wounded soldiers. Another advance in medicine emerged when French biologist and veterinarian Gaston Ramon (1886–1963) introduced a new tetanus immunization in 1931 that received its first large-scale field test in the war. It was also the first time that the new sulfonamides (sulfa drugs) were used to prevent infections. Both sides in the conflict adopted the German methods of antiseptic and aseptic surgery. This overall care resulted in a dramatic decline in wound infections and amputation rates. These advances were adopted by the allies in WWII and emerged as a part of Western medical practice.

In addition, during the Chinese Civil war, Canadian Marxist physician Norman Bethune (1890–1939), who had served in Spain during its civil war, learned of the blood-bank system. He went to China during the Chinese Civil and Second Sino-Japanese wars and joined the Chinese Communists led by Mao Zedong (1893–1976). Bethune developed a similar blood-bank system service for the Maoists, which saved many lives. This system was adopted by the allies in WWII. After WWII, blood collection and banks became common in many cultures and are an essential part of surgery and trauma treatment today.

WORLD WAR II (JULY 7, 1937–SEPTEMBER 2, 1945)

WWII in the Pacific began when Imperial Japan invaded China July 7, 1937. On September 1, 1939, Nazi Germany invaded Poland, initiating WWII in Europe. On December 8, 1941, the United States declared war on Japan after an unprovoked attack on Pearl Harbor the previous day. For this worldwide conflict, the Allies included Britain and its commonwealth nations, the United States, Soviet Union, China, and France while the Axis included Germany, Japan, and Italy, who had formed a Tripartite Pact in September 1940. The war in Europe (V-E Day) ended May 8, 1945, and the war against Japan (V-J Day) ended September 2, 1945.

Brig. Gen. John W. Mountcastle, former Chief of Military History of the United States, suggests that "World War II was the largest and most violent armed conflict in the history of mankind." (Mountcastle 1996, 1) About 1.9 billion combatants served in WWII and from 70 to 85 million people were killed. Out of this war came deadly nuclear weapons and also medical innovations that advanced the medical field. The British created forward surgical centers to deal with serious casualties. New units such as airborne and special forces were given independent medical support. Casualties were transported by vehicle, train, ship, and aircraft. The Allies all had essentially the same medical-service structure with the exception of the Soviets. The medic or aid man (corpsman for the navy and the marines) gave first aid and directed the wounded to be transferred to the battalion aid station.

In terms of medical-service structure, the "backbone" of the evacuation system was the litter bearer. The next step was transportation by ambulance, if possible, to clearing stations with triage and then the mobile field hospital for uncomplicated surgery. More seriously wounded were transferred to a station or general hospital where complex surgery was rendered and finally hospitals in the "zone of interior," which was out of the combat theater for rehabilitation. Hospital ships were also used. The German army was similar, but medical officers would render aid at the battalion-aid station rather than a medic or corpsman.

Increased survival from the prevention and treatment of infection emerged from the war. Bacteriological testing was done prior to wound closure, and new drugs emerged to combat infection. Although sulfonamides were first identified in 1908, they were not used as antibacterial medication until the Spanish Civil War. In 1935, the sulfa drug, Prontocil, was developed by German chemist Gerhard Domagk (1895–1964) and received worldwide notice. The combatants used these drugs against sexually transmitted diseases and war wounds.

Increased burn wounds in WWII from flamethrowers used by all combatants led to the development of dressings impregnated with surgical jelly and sulfanilamide. In 1941, American soldiers were given pouches of powdered crystalline sulfanilamide to sprinkle on wounds and oral sulfadiazine tablets to take if wounded. However, as the war progressed, the policy of sprinkling sulfa on wounds was recognized as useless, and even harmful, and was stopped by July 1944. Oral sulfonamides often produced toxic reactions and were replaced by the newly developed and less toxic penicillin. British physician Alexander Fleming (1881–1955) had discovered penicillin in 1928. Its perfection and mass production was not forthcoming until the early 1940s, and its use in 1944 dramatically decreased wound infections and death. By the Normandy invasion in June 1944, the Allies had sufficient penicillin to treat all casualties. The Japanese troops had limited supplies of antibiotics near the end of the war and suffered many jungle diseases. Widespread use of penicillin—later other antibiotics—that emerged from the war was first used with civilian populations during 1945 in Australia.

To prevent infectious diseases, Allied troops, depending upon where they were deployed, were given various immunizations including typhus, cholera, plague, typhoid, smallpox, and tetanus. Tetanus antitoxin, as used in WWI, had been phased out in the interwar period as a vaccine, as immunization against the disease was developed, which saved a multitude of lives on all sides during WWII. Routine tetanus immunization for everyone after injury or in childhood and every 10 years emerged as part of standard medical practice in most nations.

Advances in malaria prevention and eradication also emerged. Combatants in malaria-prone areas used mosquito netting. However, since the Japanese had cut off supplies of quinine, the Allies took Atabrine, a synthetic drug developed in Germany in 1931. But the high dose of the drug often caused problems, so after the war it was replaced with chloroquine, discovered in Germany in the mid-1930s. DDT (dichlorodiphenyltrichloroethane) insecticide, discovered by Swiss chemist Paul Hermann Müller (1899–1965) in 1939, was used in the second half of the war to kill insects to control malaria-causing mosquitoes and typhus lice among civilians and troops. However, when DDT was later found to be toxic to various other insects, mammals, and birds, the World Health Organization recommended its limitation. Moreover, some malaria protozoa became resistant to chloroquine, and mosquitoes to DDT.

Malaria was a serious problem in battles fought in the jungles of Southeast Asia. For example, in the China-Burma-India theater, the Maoist and Nationalist Chinese were engaged in a civil war along with fighting the Japanese. However, both sides of the Chinese conflict had a poor medical system with little effort for malaria control or sanitation. This resulted in the Allies giving immunizations and treating the allied Chinese Nationalists to prevent the spread of disease among British and American troops.

On the other hand, Imperial Japan had standards of medical services for the evacuation and treatment of casualties similar to the Allies. They had an efficient medical system, used mosquito netting, took quinine or Atabrine, and used insecticide creams to prevent malaria. Strict attention was also paid to the prevention of diseases through immunization. The Japanese military also took great care to prevent epidemics by disinfecting drinking water and had good field sanitation. The STD rate was low among their military personnel. This was due to the fact that women and girls in occupied territories who were forced into sexual slavery by the Imperial Japanese Army were treated with antibiotics when they contracted sexually transmitted diseases. About 75 percent of these "comfort women" died from mistreatment, and many who survived were sterile. However, near the war's end, medical supplies were difficult to obtain by both the Japanese and German military. Moreover, the excellent German medical service of WWI deteriorated under Nazification. German physicians practiced poor hygiene along with a lack of aseptic techniques. They did not store blood and had critical shortages of sulfonamides and high infection rates.

During the interwar era (between WWI and WWII), blood storage procedures and methods to separate blood into different components such as platelets and plasm were further developed. By 1943, whole blood was more frequently used as the British had shown that transfusion of whole blood was better in preventing shock in both civilian and military populations. Pooled plasma was tried but resulted in hepatitis cases, so this was disbanded as no test existed to screen blood at this time for the virus.

Some lessons learned during WWI were forgotten by the allies in WWII. In terms of psychological problems, mental health professionals again believed that thorough screening of volunteers and inductees would weed out those individuals predisposed to psychological breakdown during combat. However, screening had no effect. In fact, the reported rate for what was now called combat fatigue, in the American armed forces, for example, was at least double the rate of World War I; screening was abolished in 1944. In light of this, Britain readopted forward psychiatry for mental breakdown as a battlefield intervention after a manpower crisis in May 1941. American medical officers also reinstituted forward treatment of psychiatric cases again.

Refinement of advances made in WWI also evolved. This included better anesthesia, plastic surgery, and physical therapy and rehabilitation. Sodium pentothal was used and supplemented by safer and better gases, other than ether, for anesthesia. These enabled more complex plastic, abdominal, chest, and other surgeries. Various types of grafts to heal burns and delicate hand surgery procedures evolved. Near the end of the war, specific regional anesthesia blocks were used that allowed the wounded to be transported after surgery without immediate pain. The dropping of two nuclear weapons on Japan by the Americans to end the war resulted in radiation and burn injuries among civilians. Methods for treating these injuries were developed. Physical therapy and rehabilitation were expanded so that the whole person and not just the damaged portion of the body were treated—generally in rehabilitation hospitals. All of these developments that emerged out of the war advanced medical care globally.

KOREAN CONFLICT (JUNE 25, 1950–JULY 27, 1953)

The North Korean Communist Army crossed the 38th parallel and invaded noncommunist South Korea on June 25, 1950. This army, armed with Soviet tanks and also supported by the communist Chinese, quickly overran South Korea. The United States and United Nation members supported noncommunist South Korea forces. The war ended in an armistice on July 27, 1953, with the creation of a demilitarized zone to separate North Korea and South Korea in an uneasy peace. It is estimated that total battle deaths were about 1.2 million. By 2017, international fear that tensions could erupt again into a full blown war as North Korea developed nuclear armaments and missiles emerged.

Several advances in medical care systems emerged out of the Korean War. The UN-backed forces led by the United States developed Mobile Army Surgical Hospital (MASH) units to provide immediate surgical care within 10 miles of the front lines. These portable medical centers were able to travel with the battle and had a complement of surgeons, nurses, and medics.

The allied forces initially attempted to transport most of the wounded by vehicles over difficult terrain. However, a major innovation of using helicopters with flight nurses to evacuate the wounded from forward medical units to hospitals emerged from this struggle. Helicopters supported the MASH units, which allowed treatment of patients within a few hours of being wounded. After initial treatment, patients were moved to evacuation hospitals. This more rapid care resulted in only 2.5 percent of the patients dying of wounds. The use of helicopters to transport patients to trauma centers became common worldwide for the seriously sick or wounded.

A development to prevent wounds evolved. Personal body armor, "the flak jacket," was field-tested in Korea in 1951, which resulted in a decrease in casualties and also the severity of chest wounds. Since that time, body armor has become standard equipment in most militaries during combat. It also became standard equipment among law enforcement. Into the 21st century, advances in materials made the armor even more effective and reduced thoracic and abdominal wounds.

On the other hand, physicians had to relearn the lessons of previous wars. Due to newly developed antibiotics, young surgeons, in the early days of the war, failed to practice debridement and closed wounds prematurely. This led to an initial high rate of wound infections. However, these experiences did lead to advancement in surgery. Hospitals were now staffed with a variety of surgical specialties. For example, vascular surgeons treated vascular injuries on a routine basis, which reduced the amputation rate. More complex plastic surgery was being carried out.

In terms of the blood-bank system, the American Red Cross was given the responsibility by the military to coordinate blood procurement, transportation, and storage. As part of this process, blood collection and distribution used plastic bags that were light, rather than glass. This resulted in fewer damaged units. The better management of shock was developed along with techniques to treat acute renal insufficiency from crushing wounds, which saved lives.

THE FRENCH-INDOCHINA (1946–1954) AND THE AMERICAN-VIETNAM WARS (1959–1973)

In 1946, a Vietnamese uprising for independence against French rule led to guerilla warfare. The Vietnamese were supported by the Communist Russians and Chinese. This conflict ended at Dien Bien Phu on May 7, 1954, leading to a temporary division of the country between north and south at the 17th parallel. Fearing a communist takeover in Southeast Asia, the "Domino Theory," the United States along with British Commonwealth and other nations first supplied technical supported and then combat troops to South Vietnam. However, the north overran the south in 1975, and the two Vietnams were united as the Socialist Republic of Vietnam, and the Americans and their allies left Vietnam.

During both the French and American interdictions in Vietnam, there was no front line. Therefore, mobilized units, such as MASH used in Korea, were not feasible to treat the wounded. This led to an important innovation in medical care, namely prehospital care by well-trained paramedical professionals during the Vietnam War. This system is now known as EMS (Emergency Medical System) and is in general use in most nations. On the battlefield, new long-range radios enabled calls for medivac helicopters ("dust off"), which delivered the wounded from the battlefield to fixed hospitals or hospital ships that could provide definitive treatment. In Vietnam, small arms and automatic-weapons fire produced about a third of the injuries along with fragmentation missiles from booby traps. Wound mortality for the Vietnam War was about 2.6 percent. Personal body armor continued to improve, which further reduced injury to the torso.

Techniques and therapies advanced, including the use of better topical antimicrobial therapy for the care of burns from napalm and other wounds. Due to frequent blood mismatching, the use of universal donor (Type O) blood—which had been used in previous conflicts—was, again, reintroduced as blood components alone, and saline infusions were found to cause organ failure. Blood was collected from troops, employers, and dependents and was located in various stations throughout Vietnam. The liberal use of whole blood was a major factor in reducing death by shock. Repair of vascular injuries became routine. Disease-control programs were introduced early in the conflict, and these now standard prevention programs such as clean water, immunizations, and mosquito control reduced sickness among troops. As with the French in Vietnam, the major diseases affecting troops were malaria, viral hepatitis, diarrheal disease, skin infections, and sexually transmitted diseases.

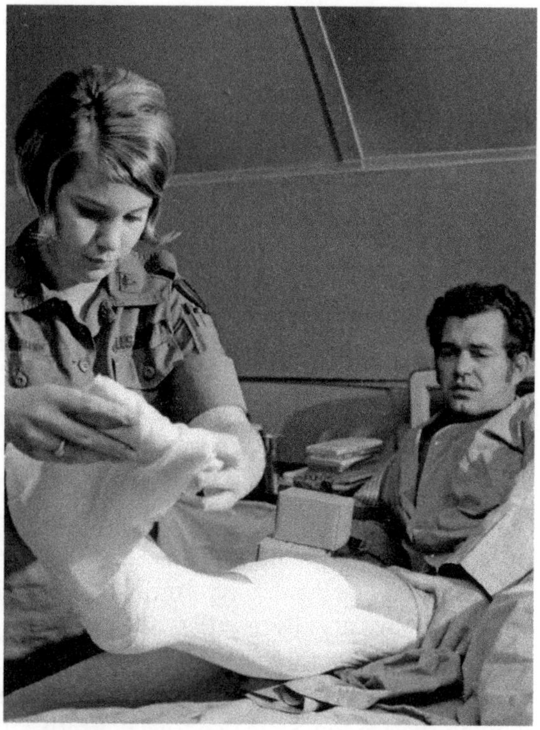

Wounded soldiers in the Vietnam War were transported by medivac helicopters to hospitals for treatment. Here, a U.S. Army nurse changes a patient's bandage at the 24th Evacuation Hospital in Vietnam. (National Archives)

Mental health issues arose from the war. From its inception, extensive psychiatric services were available to treat mentally distressed soldiers. Based upon the recommendations of military psychiatrists during World War II, Vietnam War soldiers had a tour of duty limited to one year. However, this war was unpopular with most Americans and many returning troops encountered hostilities, which made psychological problems worse. Some estimates suggest that about 30 percent of veterans suffered from PTSD, which was classified as a disorder in 1980 by the American Psychiatric Association.

Some of the cases of PTSD might have been caused by a defoliant called "agent orange," which contained dioxin. The chemical was used to eliminate North Vietnamese forests and crops. Dioxin was later found to be linked to type 2 diabetes, immune system dysfunction, nerve disorders, muscular dysfunction, hormone disruption, and heart disease. Vietnamese civilians also suffered from the effects of this chemical. In addition, drug abuse among American servicemen was rampant and spilled over into civilian life upon discharge. Cannabis and opium poppies were common agricultural crops in southeastern Asia leading to easily obtainable and inexpensive marijuana and heroin. Among returning soldiers, it is estimated that around 16 percent used heroin during their final month in Vietnam. In early 1971, the Veterans Administration set up a treatment program for discharged heroin addicts with methadone maintenance as the primary treatment method.

In spite of some negative consequences from the Vietnam War, in addition to the emergency medical system and the use of helicopters to routinely transport patients to appropriate hospitals, further improvement in anesthesia, blood and plasma expanders, treatment of burns, wound healing, shock, and surgical routines along with more advanced-trained physicians, nurses, and other medical personnel emerged. Many emergency medical treatments around the world today evolved from medical experiences in the jungles of Southeast Asia in the late 1960s.

THE GULF WAR AND OTHER WARS IN THE MIDDLE EAST (1990–)

Although the Gulf War and other conflicts in the middle east are complex, the U.S. military along with several NATO and other nations including Australia and New Zealand formed a coalition and have been involved in wars and insurgencies in Afghanistan, Iraq, Yemen, Syria, and Somalia from 1990 to the present time (2019). After 9/11 (September 11, 2001) when Islamic extremist deliberately crashed planes into the twin towers of the New York City World Trade Center and the Pentagon resulting in the death of about 3,000 people, war against these extremist groups has been continuous. Civil war also broke out in these Gulf nations. Combat in Afghanistan and Iraq was the longest military operations since Vietnam for the United States and many coalition nations. Due to advances in trauma care and surgery, U.S. and British army medical teams save 90 percent of casualties, which is the highest in the history of warfare. As of October 2017, there had been 8,391 deaths in Iraq and Afghanistan among NATO and coalition forces. Most deaths were among American (4771), UK (635) and Canadian (180) troops. It is estimated that up to a half million Afghanistan and Iraqi civilian and combatants may have also been killed.

However, out of this conflict as with other wars, advancements in medical services and care emerged. For example, disease and death from disease was low among the United States and its Western allies as they had in general excellent field hygiene. This resulted in few cases of malaria, diarrhea, and heat stroke. The most common killers of the wounded were shock and bleeding. However, a new kind of weapon was used in this conflict by both Iraqi and Afghanistan insurgents, namely the IED (improvised explosive devices). This explosive led to high rates of limb injuries where legs and arms were often partially or fully blown off. To prevent bleeding to death, the ancient method of using a tourniquet was reintroduced. This simple device had been used for centuries; however, it took two hands to apply, and overtightening could cause tissue damage often leading to amputation. Consequently the tourniquet fell out of use in the mid- to late 20th century in many industrialized nations. Combat medics were not even trained in their use and did not carry them. However, in the mid-1990s, to prevent death from bleed out due to injuries of major arteries, the use of the tourniquet became an important life-saving device. They were wider, redesigned to prevent tissue damage and could be placed on a limb with only one hand. This single-handed tourniquet became part of the first-aid kit carried by soldiers, marines, and special forces in battle conditions.

Another advance was the wide spread use of Kevlar flak jackets, which greatly reduced wounds to the chest. However, wounds of the neck, groin, and abdomen could not use a tourniquet to prevent bleeding. Therefore, beginning in 2007, Combat Gauze impregnated with a clotting material, such as kaolin clay, was used. Medics carried a number of these, and they were part of the combatants' first-aid kit. Medics were given advanced training and responsibilities for early treatment of the wounded. By the mid-2010s, they administered tranexamic acid, which causes clotting. Broad spectrum antibiotics were again introduced, and medics applied them on wounds and burns. They also administered new drugs to relieve pain that caused amnesia and did not depress breathing and heart rate, such as ketamine. Research had suggested that this drug could help prevent PTSD. As antibiotic-resistant infections become a growing concern, researchers from the American Navy Medical Research Center announced in 2016 that they had successfully treated a drug-resistant infection with bacteriophage-based therapy (virus that attacks bacteria) and expected this method to be a common treatment in the future among all populations.

Medics were now trained in "permissive hypotension" for bleeding and not to be concerned about low blood pressure. It had been found that raising blood pressure by IV fluids could dislodge clots and restart bleeding. For someone in severe shock, medics now carried special catheters that could be used to push fluids into a vein to raise blood pressure. Cooling the extremity also helped staunch the bleeding. Although the U.S. and British military tried various blood components that could be stored longer than whole blood, they rediscovered—as had been originally found in World War I—that whole blood saved more lives as it did not cause respiratory and organ failure. Extra plasma along with whole blood was also found to save lives. Beginning in 2007, the Damage-Control Resuscitation (DCR) protocol was instituted in most of the allied militaries. This protocol for traumatic bleeding and injury involved early whole blood transfusions, whole blood and additional plasma, or a one-to-one ratio or plasma and red blood cells. In addition, by 2017, several nations including France, Germany, Israel, and the United States also used freeze-dried plasma for battlefield administration.

These procedures became widely used in civilian trauma centers in many higher-income nations. In addition to battlefield medics, selected nonmedic combatants were given additional medical instruction called the Combat Lifesaver Program. These included use of a thoracostomy needle to drain fluid or abnormal accumulation of air in the lungs, training to start intravenous lines (IVs), traction splinting, and fluid resuscitation on the battlefield before evacuation by medivac helicopters to a trauma-treatment facility. These procedures are now being used by first responders in many nations.

Other medical advances in care and transportation emerged. In the U.S. Army, flight medics became fully qualified paramedics, and critical-care nurses were flown to the battlefield to treat wounded service members and accompany them back to hospitals for advanced treatment. On medivac aircraft, using military satellite networks, a telemedicine system recorded and transmitted patient data to the hospital before the patients arrived. The British developed a Medical Emergency Response Team with three to four people that include an ER physician to provide emergency treatment in flight. Anyone with a suspected internal injury also got a full body scan once at the hospital unit.

In addition, due to many concussions, to treat mild traumatic brain injuries, concussion care centers in Afghanistan were established rather than transferring wounded warriors to major hospitals. For combat stress, as has been practiced since the Korean conflict, a two- or three-day rest period near the fighting such as a battalion or regimental headquarters was used. This was because this war required rapid and frequent movement. The service member was told that he was reacting normally to extreme stress and was expected to recover and return to full duty in a few hours or days. He was encouraged to think of himself as a warrior, rather than a patient.

Due to concussion blasts from IEDs, it was estimated that approximately 20 percent of soldiers from the Iraq and Afghanistan wars have suffered brain damage outside of major brain trauma such as penetration wounds and fractured skulls. In addition, within a few months of returning home, it was estimated that from 10 to 30 percent of troops suffered from PTSD. It was speculated that several tours of duty in high-stress combat situations could be a cause of the increased incidence of this condition. However, the causes of PTSD were still controversial. Some believed it had a psychological basis, while others thought it was physical due to minor blast trauma. Treatment for PTSD included group support, medication, individual psychological and psychiatric therapies, and recreational and physical activities.

Another medical advance from the Gulf wars was the development of better prosthetic limbs for amputees. Artificial joints improved and more closely matched the range of motion of natural limbs. Microprocessors embedded in the prostheses were able to adjust for various physical activities such as walking, running, jumping, or climbing. They also became more comfortable to wear. Some troops were even able to return to service with their prosthesis. As part of rehabilitation, various wounded-warrior projects that focused on adaptive physical exercise helped wounded troops integrate back into society.

In summary, out of the many wars from 1900 to the mid-2010s, many advances in health and medicine emerged that are taken for granted today. These included methods for rapid transportation of seriously wounded individuals to hospitals, blood banking and administration systems, treatment of shock and bleeding, methods for wound and psychological care, complex plastic and other surgery, immunizations, antibiotics, and prostheses. All of these developments were quickly incorporated into civilian society in many nations of the world.

12

Medical Institutions

The trend from the early 20th century to the early 21st century in developed countries has been the shift from individual stand-alone health care entities to complex integrated systems. This includes the evolution of individual practicing physicians—with the patient paying "out-of-pocket" for care—to multidiscipline practices with payment ranging from out-of-pocket to all-inclusive insurance or governmental coverage. Practices and various levels of care by the end of the 20th century generally had governmental oversight. Access and quality of care globally ranged from excellent to inadequate. Hospitals also grew from local institutions to complex networks of facilities in developed nations. Although lower-income nations had advanced in health care by the 21st century, they still had major problems. From the early 20th century, various international health organizations developed in an effort to improve health care not only on the domestic level but also globally.

INSTITUTIONS AND HEALTH CARE SYSTEMS IN DEVELOPED NATIONS

In 1900, health care in most higher-income Western nations included general practitioners (GPs), a few specialists, and hospitals. Public or charity hospitals, often run by religious organizations, increasingly became secularized. In France, for example, the Catholic Church operated many public hospitals. However, government policy after 1900 secularized many of these institutions to maintain a better quality of medical care as the hospitals were often antiquated. Hospitals during this time also increasingly became associated with medical schools. In the United States, which never had a state religion, various religious groups including Baptists, Episcopalians, Catholics, Jews, Lutheran, and Methodists established clinics and hospitals. Originally, they were set up for particular religious or ethnic groups but by midcentury served anyone. Private hospitals were also founded by physicians and nurses, and by local charity groups in several nations.

In developed nations, preventative measures became important to decrease illness as part of a progressive "clean-living movement" during the early 20th century. This public health movement embodied sanitation, hygiene, clean water, good diet, exercise, elimination of disease, and eugenics. The eugenics movement involved both positive and negative eugenics, and its programs became part of the health care system and institutions in several nations. Positive eugenics included encouraging the healthy and "fit" to marry, advocated child monetary allowances, well-baby clinics, and health exams. Negative eugenics advocated sterilization and/or institutionalization of the "unfit" to keep them from reproducing. These groups included alcoholics, paupers, rapists, criminals, and those with mental and physical disabilities and illnesses. By late-20th-century standards, these negative eugenic activities were not considered ethical. In the early 20th century, health care systems and institutions primarily consisted of male physicians, community, and long-term hospitals and some dispensaries aimed at poorer people.

During both world wars in Europe, health care institutions were destroyed and the medical system was in shambles. In the post-WWII years, the American Marshal Plan aided economic recovery in Western Europe. Clinics, hospitals, and other health facilities were rebuilt, universal health insurance became common, and the health care delivery systems became more efficient.

In higher-income nations up through the 1960s and 1970s, most surgical procedures were done in hospitals. However, by the 1990s, acute care hospitals and ambulatory surgery centers for minimally invasive surgery emerged. With the advancement of surgical techniques, routine surgeries and procedures were increasingly carried out in these facilities as a method of cost containment and reduction of in-hospital acquired infections. The average length of stay in hospitals for even complex procedures had dramatically decreased by 2010 (see chapter 8 for additional information). In addition, in many nations, to see a specialist or to be referred for surgery, a patient first had to see a primary health provider or GP who acted as a "gatekeeper" for referrals. Physicians in many developed nations by the 1970s rarely made home visits and required patients to be seen at their offices or clinics.

Since 1998, surveys to measure the performance of health care systems have been accomplished by several organizations on an ongoing basis. The World Health Organization (WHO), for example, examines quality, access, efficiency, and equity in treatment along with healthy lives for its rankings of the best to the worse systems. The NGO, the Commonwealth Fund, collects data globally on health care access, the care process, administrative efficiency, equity, and quality along with various economic indicators.

By 2000, it had been observed that adequate health care delivery included universal health coverage (UHC) for all citizens. Everyone had equal access to prevention, screening, treatment, and rehabilitative services for the highest quality health care the country could afford without anyone suffering financial hardship. Most importantly, later studies found that, "Life expectancy [had] a positive correlation with core components of health coverage, as well as overall healthcare resources" (Pearson, et al. 2016, 4). This included a positive relationship of life expectancy with the number of GPs in a region and a positive relationship with the total amount spent on health care—the exception was the United States, which spends the most on health care but has poorer results compared to other high-income nations. However, a negative relationship exists between life expectancy and out-of-pocket payments. In addition, in nations without UHC, the poor often have poorer care compared to richer individuals. Based upon these criteria, in 2017, 11 higher-income nations were ranked from the highest to the lowest: the United Kingdom (UK), Australia, the Netherlands, New Zealand, Norway, Sweden, Switzerland, Germany, Canada, France, and the United States.

Due to the effectiveness of UHC to increase the health of a nation, the United Nations General Assembly in December 2012 passed a landmark resolution for worldwide comprehensive health reforms and universal health coverage. The Rockefeller Foundation, WHO, and the World Bank stressed the importance of universal access to health services to save lives, end extreme poverty, build resilience against the health consequences of climate change, and end deadly epidemics. Among developed nations, examples of three health care systems—the UK, Germany, and the United States—will be discussed. Although the Canadian health care system is ranked higher than the United States, it, like the United States, is not ranked among the top 25 nations and in some ways has a similar system. The three nations discussed range from high to lower efficiency among high-income developed nations.

United Kingdom (UK)

In the UK prior to around 1911, health care was generally available only to the wealthy. Some individuals were able to obtain free treatment through a charity or teaching hospital. Between 1911 and 1946, a National Insurance Act was in place in which a small amount was deducted from employees' pay, which entitled them to free health care. However, it only benefited individuals who were employed. To increase the health of the nation in the early century, the UK embraced the eugenics movement. It only supported positive eugenics, which fostered child monetary supplements, exercise, good nutrition, and marrying a fit and healthy person.

In the post-WWII era during major social reforms, the National Health Service (NHS)—a public health care system—was founded in 1948. Each of its entities (England, Northern Ireland Scotland, and Wales) was "devolved" into four separate systems in the late 1990s. England's NHS is funded directly from the UK Treasury, while the other countries receive block grants and implemented their own health care polices.

The NHS provided universal, comprehensive and free health care (from cradle to grave) and was funded by general taxation. Private insurance was also available for services not covered, such as cosmetic surgery and private hospital rooms. Most hospitals were nationalized and managed by unelected regional hospital boards. GPs, who acted as gatekeepers for secondary care, were under a separate administration. Public health and social care functions were given to local governments within a structure of local and district health authorities. From the very beginning, this three-tiered system and the NHS itself was controversial. For some it was an example of equality for basic medical care, but for others it was the height of an inflexible bureaucracy. A major complaint from patients was long waiting time for specialist appointments and elective surgeries. However, the system shifted from state paternalism to consumerism and from bureaucratic planning to demands from patients for choice, quality, and more individualized services by the mid-2010s.

In the 1960s, group practice for GPs was encouraged, nurses in primary care became more common, and support staff ran appointment systems that improved record keeping. The GP gained more status as they were now better integrated locally with hospital consultants (specialists). The 1970s saw administrative restructuring. The 1974 reorganization of the NHS dismantled the three-tiered system and allowed a region to support all three areas of care. In 1990, the National Health Service and Community Care Act was passed, which set up independent trusts that managed hospital care. Trusts are organizational entities that serve a geographical area. The government also created the "internal market" later, called the NHS Trust, which physicians needed to be part of to acquire patients. Under the Health Act (2006), health legislation and general policy in England is guided by Parliament, the Secretary of State for Health, and the Department of Health.

In 2009, the government permitted patients to pay for additional private health care, mostly paid for by private insurance, while continuing to receive care from

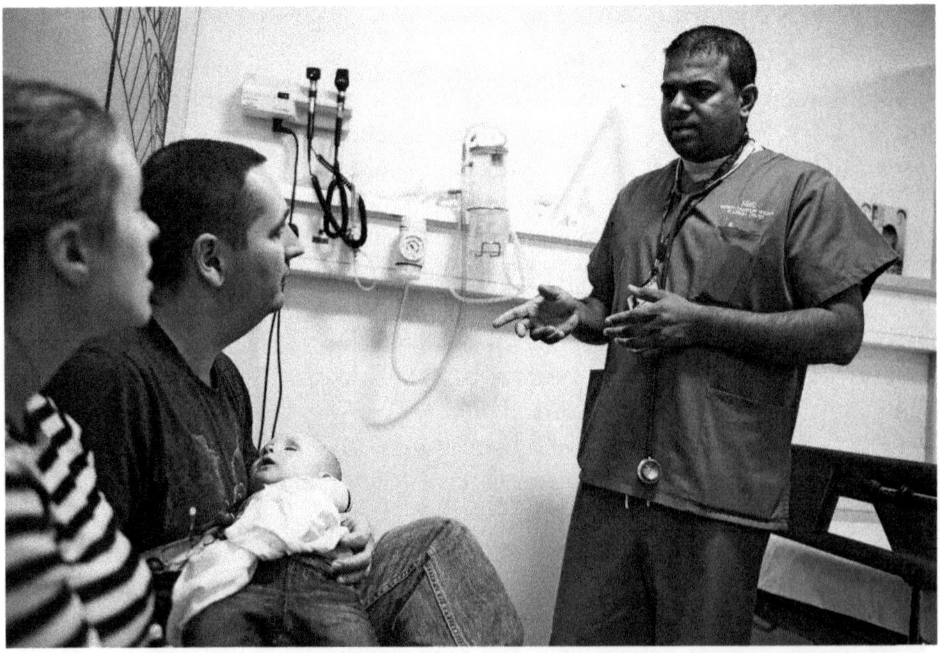

A physician attends to a young patient in the Royal Albert Edward Infirmary in northwest England, April 2015. By the mid-2010s, almost all citizens in the United Kingdom were covered by either public or private health insurance. (Oli Scarff/AFP/Getty Images)

the NHS as long as the NHS was not subsidizing the care. In 2012, the Health and Social Care Act made changes to the structures of the NHS in terms of how providers were regulated and how services were purchased.

Competition was seen as a positive force in England for improving the quality of care. By the mid-2010s, around 10 percent of patients had private insurance, and around 80 percent of this insurance was through their workplace. There were around 500 private hospitals and 500 private clinics. There were 168 NHS "acute trusts" that managed hospitals; some trusts operated hospitals on more than one site. Around two-thirds of GPs operated as private contractors, and most worked together in small group practices to provide different types of services. People were still required to register with a local practice of their choice but in some areas, walk-in centers offered primary care services, for which registration was not required. Nearly all specialists were salaried employees of NHS hospitals, and patients were seen at the outpatient center in a hospital. Some of these consultants also contributed to private health care. By the mid-2010s, the UK's NHS was seen as one of the most efficient in the world. However, patients still complained of long waiting times for specialist appointments and elective surgeries—often up to four or five months. Even with private insurance, the waiting time could be several months.

Germany

Over the 20th century, some developed countries waxed and waned in terms of efficient health care systems and institutions. For example, the German health system, at the beginning of the 20th century under the Bismarck Model of Social Protection was the best in the world as were its aseptic hospitals where safe surgeries were performed. It was the first nation to have health insurance. It had old-age pensions, accident insurance, and sickness insurance for workers. This system was established on a local basis. Cost for insurance was divided between employers and employees. By 1919, health insurance was extended to the unemployed. Most German physicians had private practices. A few hospitals were linked with religious orders, but most were secular and hospitals in larger communities were often associated with medical schools and conducted medical research.

After serious problems in the health care system due to WWI, in the postwar era, the government became increasingly involved with medical care and funding medical research. To improve research, in 1929, the Kaiser Wilhelm Institute for Medical Research was founded. After WWII, it was reestablished as the Max Planck Institute for Experimental Medicine and is today an internationally renowned institution. In the mid- to late 1920s, the focus of medicine shifted from private practice to public health and from treatment to disease prevention. Public health improved under these new laws. However, under increasing governmental control, physicians were required to shift their responsibilities to the health of the nation rather than the health of their individual patients. By the time the National Socialist Party took control in 1933, the state held absolute power over physicians and hospitals.

In the early 20th century, Germany also experienced a health movement that focused upon healthy living. An aspect of the movement was a positive eugenics movement to increase the health and vitality of all Germans. This included advocating the increase of the birth rate of the culturally and economically "fit" and family allowances to encourage large healthy families. However, until Adolf Hitler (1889–1945) took power, negative eugenics was not acceptable in Germany, and eugenic sterilization was not condoned. During the Nazi regime (1933–1945), this practice changed and sterilizations of "unfit" Germans took place. Some physicians engaged in unethical practices that were not acceptable by eugenicists, such as euthanasia of those with chronic mental and physical illnesses or disabilities. In hospitals and research institutions, unscrupulous medical research occurred.

Under Nazi rule, 20 million people were slaughtered. In this Holocaust, the genocide of Jews, the ethnic group called the Roma, and other ethnic groups deemed undesirable was carried out. At the end of WWII, the German health system was in shambles as many hospitals and clinics were destroyed and medical personnel were poorly trained or had been killed in the war.

In the postwar years in western Germany, with the help from the Marshal Plan, hospitals and other health care facilities were rebuilt and the health care system revived. From the late 1950s through the early 2000s, Western Germany developed a strong economy. After German reunification in 1987, former East Germany was assimilated into the health care system. Statutory Health Insurance (SHI) or universal health insurance called "sickness funds," was introduced in 1988. About 89 percent of individuals are in this public system, and the rest in private systems—the Substitutive Private Health Insurance (PHI). Insurance is compulsory for everyone, and payment is through joint employer and employee programs, governmental funds, or individual premiums for private insurance. Copayments were introduced in the 1980s in an attempt to prevent overutilization and to control costs. In 1995, Germany mandated long-term care insurance to provide care for the elderly. In 1989, the Health Care Reform Act to address cost containment was passed.

Primary care under the German system is through GPs or specialists who are reimbursed on a fee-for-service basis by SHI according to an amount negotiated between the physicians and the SHI. Physicians practice in both private and group practices. Unlike some developed nations, registration with a family physician by patients is not required, and GPs have no formal gatekeeping function. By 2000, waiting times were brief for appointments and surgery, although some elective surgeries had longer waits.

In terms of hospitals, around 1900 hospitals were found in Germany in the mid-2010s. About a half of these were public, and around 30 were university clinics. The rest were private not-for-profit or for-profit institutions, which have been increasing. However, the total numbers of hospitals have been decreasing since 2000. Hospitals were staffed by salaried physicians along with nurses and other health care personnel. By 2010, the health industry was one of the largest sectors of the German economy, and the nation was becoming a leader in global health.

United States of America (USA)

In the early 20th century, as part of the Progressive Era, medical and other professionals in the United States, like other developed nations, embraced the eugenics movement to improve the health of their nation. Eugenic remedies became part of health care institutions. Positive eugenic measures in most states included well-baby clinics, prenatal care, and premarital exams including a test for syphilis. Negative eugenics consisted of sterilization or long-term institutionalization of mentally ill and disabled individuals.

Over the century, the practice and perception of physicians changed. By the 1960s, rather than the physician making home visits and often being a friend of middle- and upper-middle-class families, patients were required to go to physicians' offices or newly established clinics, which generally required appointments. There was also a push for physicians to become specialists. Long waiting times in offices and the inability to get an appointment with a preferred physician distanced patients from physicians. By the 1980s, as a result of dissatisfaction by baby boomers, the paternalism of physicians began to crumble and more women were admitted to medical school (see chapter 2 for more details). By 2000, physicians were less authoritarian and more likely to give patients options concerning their treatment rather than mandating a specific course.

By the 2010s, about one-third of physicians practiced in primary care, which included family and general practitioners, general internists, general pediatricians, and geriatricians. They generally did not act as gatekeepers, and patients usually had a choice of what specialist they wished to consult depending on their insurance plan. The majority of physicians operated in small self-or group-owned practices. Physicians were paid through a combination of methods, including negotiated fees with private insurances or set fees through governmental insurance plans. Many practices had advanced nurse practitioners or physician assistants and others on staffs who were salaried.

During the first two decades of the 20th century, small community hospitals for the middle class were founded by physicians, nurses, and local benevolent groups. Charity public hospitals were common in urban areas for the poor. Most hospitals until the post-WWI era operated without much money as physicians donated their time, and costs for nurses and staff were low. In the 1920s, physicians and surgeons began getting paid, the nursing staff was professionalized, and the public began to view hospitals as the technological and scientific centers of medicine. This resulted in many urban public hospitals transforming into prestigious institutions affiliation with universities and medical schools although they were still committed to treating everyone.

Urban public hospitals had a difficult time in the 1930s depression years and during the economic boom years of the post-WWII era when the insured middle-class moved from urban areas to the suburbs. To meet the needs of these insured patients, for-profit and not-for-profit hospitals were built. ERs and outpatient clinics in the urban public hospital cared mostly for indigent people remaining in the increasingly poorer urban centers. To keep standards in all hospitals high, the Joint Commission on Accreditation of Hospitals was created in 1951. By the end of the century, many urban hospitals and their associated medical and allied health schools combined to form vast medical and research complexes. By 2010, these medical centers became associated with smaller regional or community hospitals and physician practices and became one large corporation. Private corporations also purchased and operated hospitals around the nation along with long-term care facilities for the elderly.

By the 1970s, patients finding long waits for appointments, without health insurance, or a regular physician, began to flood hospitals' ER units to receive routine care. This use of hospital ERs for nonemergencies and minor illnesses began to tax the overall health system. To relieve pressure on emergency units, "walk-in" or urgent-care clinics emerged by the late 1980s. These stand-alone facilities were established by physicians or hospitals and were generally open after physician offices had closed. By the 2010s, these walk-in centers were also found in pharmacies or other facilities staffed with physicians, nurse practitioners, or physician assistants who treated common illnesses. By the mid-2010s, about 70 percent of hospital beds were nonprofit; 15 percent, for profit; and about 15 percent, public.

In the 1920s, private insurance coverage emerged when some hospitals offered services on a prepaid basis to pay for increasingly expensive hospitalization or doctors' visits. The first employer-sponsored hospitalization plan was created by teachers in Dallas, Texas, in 1929. The Blue Cross Blue Shield organization was the first to offer a group health plan in 1932. Although it began as a nonprofit entity, due to competition from for-profit plans and surplus funds, by the mid-2010s, many of its franchises became for-profit companies. During the WWII years, as a result of the federal government's wage control, employer-sponsored health insurance was offered as a fringe benefit. Private insurance rapidly increased, and by 1955, nearly 70 percent of the population had health insurance compared to around 10 percent in 1940. All private insurance companies were controlled by varying state and federal regulations.

Some managed care plans, such as health maintenance organizations (HMOs) as in California's Kaiser Permanente Institution, require referral to a specialist by a primary care physician within the system. Other plans such as preferred provider organizations (PPOs) allowed patients direct access to any physician although physicians outside the network could be more expensive. Copayments were generally required, and some specialist would not treat economically disadvantaged Medicaid patients due to low reimbursement rates.

A major difference between health care in the United States and other high-income nations has been a reluctance to institute a national health care system that covers everyone. In the second decade of the 20th century, former President Theodore Roosevelt (1858–1919), as part of the progressive Bull-Moose party, proposed a government-supported national public health care system as part of his platform; however, he was not elected. Democratic presidents since the Truman administration have attempted to create a national health insurance. However, they have encountered fierce opposition from the American Medical Association, American Hospital Association, the insurance industry, and Republican administrations who considered it "socialized medicine."

In 1948, Harry Truman (1884–1972) was reelected on a platform that included the creation of a "single-payer" national health insurance system that would subsidize the poor. In a single-payer system, an agency, generally public or quasi-public, organizes health care financing, but the delivery of care remains largely in private hands. However, Truman encountered much opposition. Curiously, in 1956, under Republican president Dwight D. Eisenhower (1890–1969), a former military general, a military "medicare" (called Tricare beginning in 1988) program was enacted that provided government health insurance for service members and their dependents.

By 1960, private insurers were becoming increasingly incapable of providing comprehensive and affordable health care to older adults. Therefore, in 1965, the Social Security Act Amendments (Medicare) a program of hospital and outpatient insurance for persons aged 65 and older was created and funded by a tax on both employees and employers. Medicaid to aid the poor was also created and funded jointly by the state and federal governments. These amendments were signed into law by President Lyndon Johnson (1908–1973). President William Clinton (1946–) in 1993 attempted to introduce a national health care plan but was unsuccessful. It was not until president Barack Obama (1961–) that a quasi-national health insurance plan was put into place. The Patient Protection and Affordable Care Act (2010) called "Obamacare," or Affordable Care Act (ACA), was signed into law by Obama in 2010. The act established "shared responsibility" between government entities, employers, and individuals for ensuring that everyone had access to affordable and good-quality health insurance. Under this act, low- to moderate-income families could receive financial assistance to obtain health insurance coverage.

The ACA represented the largest health care overhaul since 1965, and by 2016, about 56 percent of Americans were covered by workplace insurance; 19.4 percent, by Medicaid; 16.7 percent, by Medicare; and 16.2 percent, private-individual health plans. About 8 percent were not covered by any insurance and went without needed health care because of cost. Coverage remained fragmented due to numerous private and public plans and was fraught with partisan politics. In 2017, the new Trump administration began attempts to dismantle ACA.

Compared to other developed nations, by the mid-2010s, the United States was weak on universal access to health care and the ability to obtain prompt attention from their primary care physician. Patients often had to wait several weeks for their physician to apprise them of their test results. The United States also had a lower life expectancy at birth and higher rate of infant mortality, diabetes and coronary heart disease, compared to other developed high-income nations. On the other hand, it ranked high on preventative care and shorter waiting times for specialists and elective surgeries.

INSTITUTIONS AND HEALTH CARE SYSTEMS IN DEVELOPING NATIONS

At the turn of the 20th century, as discussed in chapters 2 and 3, the developing lower-income nations, which included nearly all of tropical and subtropical regions of Africa, Asia, and Latin America, relied on local indigenous healers and a few scattered Western medical institutions established by missions. It is estimated that in the late 2010s, approximately 80 percent of people in these countries, particularly those living in rural areas, still used this traditional medicine to meet their primary health care needs due to lack of efficient health care systems and institutions. In these nations, over the 20th century and into the 21st century, massive public health programs such as smallpox eradication, malaria prevention, and immunizations were generally funded by private foundations, WHO, or NGOs.

Since the early 1990s, the Global Burden of Disease (GBD) study helped guide global health policy development and most nations have improved access to and quality of health care. Since 2000, some lower- to middle-income countries, in particular China, Vietnam, India, Colombia, Mexico, Thailand, Kenya, Ghana, and Zambia, have attempted to reform their health systems and institutions based upon the Millennium Development Goals 2000 (MDG). (See chapter 1 for more information.) However, access to health care and poor quality care is still a major problem in many, but not all, developing countries.

A major issue in low- to middle-income nations is the lack of financial coverage for the costs of medical care, which pushes millions of people into poverty each year due to out-of-pocket fees. Many developing nations do not have health insurance, much less universal coverage. About half of all health care is self-paid, which results in poor people not seeking care as they do not have the money. Most funds for public health are still aimed at hospital-based care, which is often distant from poor rural populations. This results in long travel time to health care facilities, especially in Africa and China. However, short travel time and better quality care, even with increased fees, results in more people, even the poor, seeking needed care.

The private sector, as opposed to public governmental managed care, makes up a large part of health care systems in developing nations. The private sector is often contracted to oversee primary care and hospital facilities on behalf of the public sector. Clinics and hospitals in developing countries tend to be used by well-off urban populations with few facilities available for the rural poor. This is because doctors and nurses often refuse to work in remote areas resulting in a two-tiered system of expensive private hospitals and underfunded public hospitals. In some countries, such as Kenya, religious missions are the main suppliers of health care although this practice is controversial as some feel they help to advance the nation, while others suggest it is a vestige of imperial and colonial rule.

Since developing nations have different cultures, poverty levels, general level of health, resources, and climate, "it is unlikely that there is one single blueprint for an ideal health care system design or a magic bullet that will automatically remedy deficiencies. The strengthening of health care systems in low-and middle-income countries must be seen as a long-term developmental process" (Mills, 2014). Examples of health care institutions and system in the two largest nations (China and India) and two global regions (Latin America and sub-Saharan Africa) will briefly be discussed.

China

China in the early 20th century relied on local indigenous healers and a few scattered Western medical institutions established by missions for health care through the 1940s. In the mid-1960s, the rural "barefoot doctors" gave care to local residents in isolated areas. In the 1990s, partnerships between Western university medical schools and health departments were established to improve the standards of health care and education in China. By 2000, health care in China consisted of both public and private medical institutions and insurance programs. However, there was still a rural-urban difference in resources.

State-funded health insurance was based on where people lived and their employment status. The Urban Employed Basic Medical Insurance began in 1998 and was financed by taxing both employee and employers. The New Cooperative Medical Service was launched in 2003 to prevent rural populations from becoming impoverished by catastrophic health costs, and the Urban Resident Basic Medical Insurance that covered the aged, children, and nonemployed was introduced in 2009. These programs were subsidized by the central and provincial governments. Private health insurance was primarily bought by higher-income individuals and by employers for their workers. It often enabled better quality of care and higher reimbursements. By 2014, more than 97 percent of people in China used a public health insurance system, but different plans affected the quality of the services they received.

Hospitals were mainly public in rural areas and both public and private in urban regions. In rural areas, Western primary care was delivered through village doctors and health workers in clinics. After-hour care in rural districts could be obtained through individual physicians or clinics, and at hospitals in urban areas. GPs worked in rural township and in urban community hospitals. Patients generally did not have to register with a GP, and GPs in most regions did not have a gatekeeping function. Private primary care providers were paid by fee-for-services or salaried if employed by hospitals. To be accredited, hospitals needed to obtain a license from the local health authority. Outpatient specialists received their licenses from the hospital where they worked.

The Chinese government continued to work to provide affordable basic health care to all residents by 2030. China had issues with efficiency but was undertaking a systemic reform of institutions including creating a universal health care system, improving public hospitals, and strengthening primary care within an integrated health delivery system. China was considered a developing nation for most of the 20th century and into the 21st century. But, by 2010, it was transitioning from a recipient-of-aid from the West to a donation nation. It is emerging as a major player in global health with the establishment of the International Development Cooperation Agency (IDCA) in 2018 to aid developing nations in Africa and Asia.

India

Until 1947, India was a colony of the British Empire. Although the European scientific model became the official health care system in the 20th century,

Ayurvedic and other traditional medicine systems were still widely used into the 21st century especially by the rural poor (see chapters 2 and 3). In urban areas, medical care in hospitals was often only for Europeans and well-off Indians. As with other developing nations, Western medical care was sometimes available from scattered clinics and hospitals established by religious missions. It was usually a fee-for-service system, and few people could afford quality care.

After independence, the states were responsible for organizing and delivering health services to their residents. The central government was responsible for medical education, national health policy including the regulatory structures, and financial support of the state. Over the years, health insurance coverage has fluctuated between public and private insurance. To attempt a goal of universal health care, in 1948, the Employees' State Insurance Scheme (ESIS) social security and health insurance plan for Indian workers was initiated. The Indian parliament passed the Insurance Amendment Act of 1950 to nationalize the insurance business. In 1954, the Central Government Health Scheme (CGHS) was established to institute universal health coverage for central government employees and families through employee-employer taxes, and most of the services were free under these programs.

In 1972, all Indian insurance companies were nationalized, and by the 21st century, the major public health insurers in India were government run, such as the General Insurance Corporation (GIC) and its subsidiaries. A key program for making health care accessible and affordable was the 2008 Rashtriya Swasthya Bima Yojana (RSBY). It was a government-run program that provided health insurance coverage to poor families in addition to individual workers. However, it was expensive and was limited to inpatient treatment or other hospital-based services. This, in addition to budget constraints and a high level of poverty, resulted in less than 20 percent of the population being covered by any health insurance by the mid-2010s. In 2016, private insurance companies including companies from Germany, Switzerland, and France were allowed to offer health insurance to workers.

Health care services were delivered by a complex network of public and private providers. These ranged from single GPs to multispecialty tertiary care hospitals. In theory, health care at all government facilities was free; however, in practice, severe shortages of staff and supplies often limited access to care. The quality of care in public facilities was often poor, so most people sought out private services, which resulted in high out-of-pocket expenses, or used cheaper traditional healers. Most public hospitals in rural areas were often staffed by inexperienced interns who were required to work in them as part of their educational requirement. Hospitals and clinics were often miles away and had inconvenient operation hours.

From the 1980s, several private hospitals joined medical complexes with modern diagnostic facilities and evolved into high-quality medical centers as Indian institutions incorporated world-class technology and training. As discussed in chapter 2, these became medical tourist destinations for those from higher-income nations because of quality treatment and low cost. In the first two decades of the

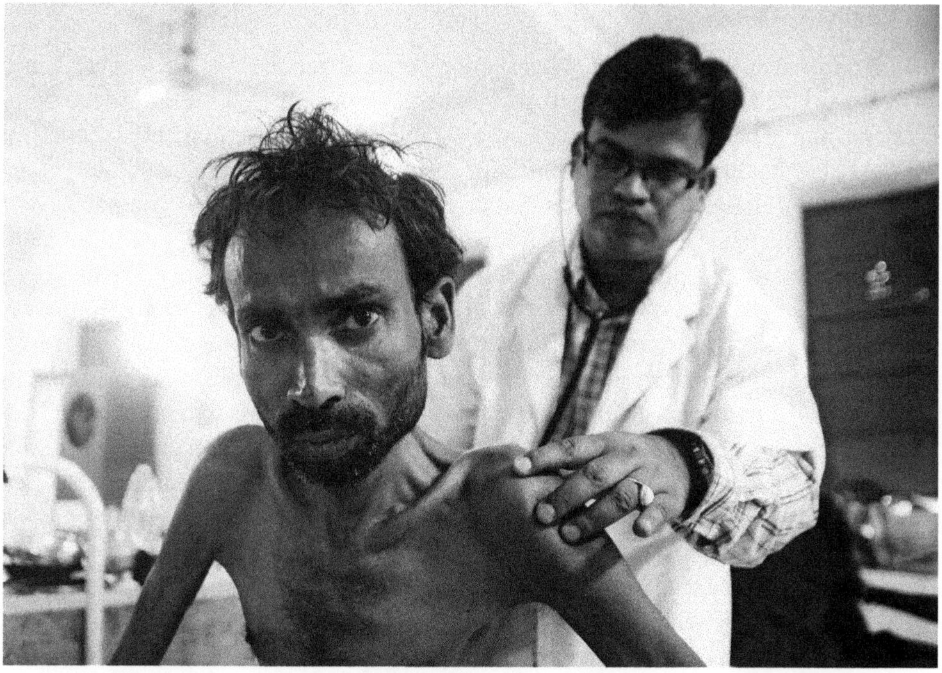

A physician examines a tuberculosis (TB) patient in a government TB hospital on "World Tuberculosis Day" in Allahabad, India, March 2017. In 2018, the Indian government launched an insurance program, popularly known as "Modicare," to cover the poor. (Prabhat Kumar Verma/Pacific Press/LightRocket via Getty Images)

21st century, the private hospital sector expanded rapidly, and government-sponsored health plans used private hospitals as a part of public-private partnerships. By 2010, the private health care sector was responsible for the majority of health care in India. But most medical expenses were still paid out-of-pocket rather than through insurance. Physicians working in government facilities were salaried, and private physicians were generally fee-for-service. Patients were not required to register with a GP, nor were GPs required to have a gatekeeping function.

In 2014, to meet the 2020 Sustainable Development Goals 3.8, the government proposed plans for a nationwide universal health care system known as the National Health Assurance Mission. However, due to budget constraints, other than some public health and sanitation programs, it was only partially implemented. In 2018, the government advanced a program to cover the poor, Ayushman Bharat Yojana, commonly known as "Modicare." It was the most ambitious health care plan in India to date and included the creation of "health and wellness" centers in poorer areas. If this proposal was adequately funded and implemented, it could be a major step toward universal health coverage in India. Although India was attempting to strengthen its health care system and institutions, it still lacked an adequate health care infrastructure due to the unavailability of a universally insured population, high out-of-pocket expenditures, and often poor quality of care.

Latin America

In Latin American nations, health care services ranged from adequate health care in urban areas to poor care in isolated regions. As with many developing nations, native healers are widely used. Colombia by the early 21st century had one of the better health care systems in Latin America. It had a public health insurance company, *Nueva EPS,* and a number of private health insurance companies. All citizens have a basic health care plan that includes medical, dental, and vision care. However, the financially well-off can get private policies that expand basic coverage. Due to high cost of care in 1993, employees and employers were required to contribute to health insurance. This system expanded coverage to about three-fourths of the population. However, as found in other developing nations, the poor and rural inhabitants have a more difficult time gaining access to quality care. Hospitals in urban areas are good and often staffed by medical personnel who often have gone abroad for training. Over a half of all health care institutions are private.

Argentina has quality hospitals and medical care in its cities. However, rural and remote areas have few clinics or hospitals. In Argentina, the health care system is organized around three main providers. The largest is a system of free public hospitals where outpatients only pay for doctor visits and medications. About half of the population is under this public plan. A private plan covers about 5 percent of the population where patients pay for all their medical care. A small number of people are covered by insurance where both employees and employers pay a fixed fee.

In Nicaragua, both private and public institutions are common for health care. The Nicaraguan government guarantees universal free health care for its citizens. However, as found in other developing areas, unequal distribution of institutions, medical personnel, and quality of care between rural and urban areas are found. Overall, health care has improved since 2000.

In 1959, Honduras created a national public health system the *Instituto Hondureño del Seguro Social* (Honduran Social Security Institute) that was supposed to cover all citizens. However, there is still a lack of universal coverage and care. Access to and the quality of health care is dependent upon income. If one can afford to pay the high out-of-pocket cost, adequate health care is available. For the urban or rural poor, care is extremely limited. In isolated areas, there are few health care institutions. These factors result in health institutions and services not being readily accessible to most of the population.

Africa

Most African nations' health care institutions and systems are ranked on the bottom internationally in terms of efficiency, access, and quality of care with little organized systems. Like India, many African nations were under colonial rule, and hospitals were generally in urban areas and catered to white colonials. Scattered hospitals in rural areas were often mission based. However, a few African nations have attempted to make improvements in the health care system and institutions. Since 1991 when the socialist era ended, Zambia developed a private and public health care system—the National Health Policies and Strategies. By 2015, public health facilities were divided into primary (local district), secondary (provincial), and tertiary (central) facilities. However, most were understaffed, had poor work environments, and pay. This resulted in many educated medical personnel leaving for Western nations. Medical supplies were also short. Financing relied mostly on international and private donors, individual households, government subsidies, and, to a lesser extent, employer/employee taxes.

Rwanda introduced a voluntary insurance coverage, although the number of services covered was limited and there was little protection for the poorest groups. Ghana expanded health care coverage by the introduction of a national health insurance program in which enrollment was compulsory. General taxation was the main financing source for this program.

South Africa attempted to improve its health care system. Due to apartheid through most of the 20th century, the black African population had poor health care. In 1994, when apartheid ended, the health system faced massive challenges. Despite continued government efforts to compensate for past issues, limited progress has been made toward achieving the MDG. The large and under-resourced public health sector was also burdened by urban-rural inequalities. National Health Insurance was introduced in 2016, which called for public financing to purchase a comprehensive package of services from accredited public and private providers, but it has only been partially implemented.

INTERNATIONAL HEALTH ORGANIZATIONS AND INSTITUTIONS

As discussed in chapter 2, in the early 20th century, various medical and health organizations were founded, or gained power, in higher-income nations to assure quality in medical education, health care, and hospitals. In the United States, they exerted control over the health care system and institutions into the 21st century. Simultaneously various international organizations emerged that worked on the global level. They ranged from religious mission, official governmental, to charitable NGOs. Most of these organizations have been Western efforts to improve global health by offering aid to eliminate tropical and other diseases and to promote prevention and treatment along with establishing clinics and hospitals in low- to middle-income nations.

At the beginning of 1900, Western health care in developing nations was primarily from Christian missionaries. However, secular organizations also arose such as the Pan American Health Organization established in 1902 to coordinate health issues in the Western Hemisphere. From its beginning, it addressed programs to prevent and control infectious and later noninfectious diseases. It aimed to strengthen health institutions and systems and responded to emergencies and disasters in the Western hemisphere. By 1950, it also served as the regional office for the Americas of WHO and worked in partnership with various health and other government agencies, civil organizations, and other international groups to promote good health.

In 1907, the *Internantional d'hygiene Publique* (IHP), based in Paris, was founded to oversee international rules for the quarantining of ships and ports so as to prevent the spread of cholera and bubonic plague in addition to managing other international public health agreements. It was dissolved in 1946 and incorporated into the newly formed WHO.

In 1919, during the aftermath of WWI, the League of Red Cross Societies—changed to the International Federation of Red Cross and Red Crescent Societies (IFRC) in 1991—was founded in Paris to offer humanitarian aid to prisoners of war and combatants and to assist those countries that had suffered during WWI. It later became involved in worldwide disasters. Founding nations included Britain, France, Italy, Japan, and the United States. By the late 20th century, this international society included almost every nation in the world.

In 1919, the newly organized League of Nations partnered with the IHP and the Red Cross League to focus on surveillance and control of epidemic diseases, particularly in Eastern Europe. The League of Nations disbanded during WWII, but in 1948 at the founding of the United Nations, WHO was formed based upon the League of Nations model. The mission of the WHO was to direct and coordinate international health activities and supply technical assistance to countries. Other international organizations were also created that worked closely with WHO, including the United Nations Children's Fund (UNICEF) and the World Bank, aimed at children's health and financial support, respectively, for low- and middle-income nations.

Many private NGOs also provided international health care. For example, Doctors without Borders (*Medecins Sans Frontieres*) founded in 1968, in Paris, delivers health care to victims of wars and major disasters and also health care to impoverished nations. In the 2010s, it helped with the African Ebola crisis and the Mediterranean migrant/refugee crisis. Several private foundations, particularly from the United States such as the Kellogg, Kresge, and Rockefeller Foundation (RF) have been involved in global health initiatives since the early 20th century. The RF, established in 1903, focused on many infectious diseases and supported medical schools in several developing nations. The Bill & Melinda Gates Foundation, as discussed in chapter 5, has attempted to eliminate polio in regions of the world where it is still endemic in recent years.

In summary, various health systems, institutions, and organizations have been formed from the beginning of the 20th century that dramatically changed health care globally. However, many low- to middle-income nations by the second decade of the 21st century still had major issues in access to quality health care.

13

Disease and Healing in the Arts

Art in many forms including visual, literature, and performance have educated health professionals and the public. It has been used for public health promotion in an effort to prevent diseases and unhealthy conditions and give advice to promote healthier lifestyles. The arts have portrayed the public perception of the medical and other health professionals and health care institutions in different eras since the 20th century. Fiction, among other art forms, has also been created by health professionals. In addition, the arts have often featured patients and diseases, real and imaginary, and have reflected the changes and advancements in society and technology.

VISUAL ARTS

The visual arts include paintings, drawings, photography, carvings, sculptures, and other images. Visual arts have been used in thousands of posters and pamphlets with public health messages worldwide. In the early 20th century, for example, posters on both sides of the Atlantic advised people to cover their mouths when they coughed to prevent the spread of TB. During WWI and WWII, they admonished military men to beware of picking up VD (sexually transmitted diseases) from local women who "looked clean" lest they bring the diseases back to their girlfriends/wives back home. In 1918, posters advised people to wear face masks to prevent catching the Spanish flu. In the 1970s, African posters encouraged people to get smallpox immunization in an effort to wipe out the disease. They showed warriors shooting arrows at the evil-looking smallpox enemy.

Visual arts were used in various health, medical, and anatomy texts. One example is Austrian anatomist Eduard Pernkopf's (1888–1959) *Atlas of Topographical and Applied Human Anatomy* (*Topographische anatomie des menschen*) in seven volumes. Pernkopf, an ardent Nazi, was dean of the medical school in Vienna. He prepared the anatomy atlas along with several artists from 1937–1960. This detailed work likely used executed political prisoner as models. Sometimes his early SS artists wove "SS" into their signatures or wrote it in a corner of a page.

Reprints later in the century airbrushed these out. The drawings were used in medical journals and textbooks into the 21st century. Because of the atlas's association with German National Socialism and the numerous deaths resulting from this regime, the atlas came under criticism by 2000 as to the ethics of its use.

In China beginning in the 1950s, a public health campaign for better sanitation and personal hygiene used posters and drawings. An Indian UNICEF poster and film campaign, *Poo in the Loo*, was introduced in 2014 to encourage Indians to use toilets and not defecate in the streets. During the 2015–2016 Zika crisis in the Americas, cartoon posters in Spanish and English showed people how to take precautions against getting bitten in mosquito-prone areas. Posters and pamphlets were also printed in many languages in regions where Zika was endemic.

In addition to art for public health messages, visual art depicting patients and the medical professionals have been common. They have often reflected societal problems or perception of health professionals of the era. In the early 20th century, for example, German illustrator and artist Käthe Kollwit's (1867–1945) charcoal, *At the Doctor's* (*Beim Arzt*) (1909), shows an older bedraggled pregnant woman knocking at the physician's door. She appears depressed and resigned to her fate.

In contrast, an endearing depiction of a doctor and patient is found in *Before the Shot* (1958). This illustration by American artist Norman Rockwell (1894–1978) for a *Saturday Evening Post* cover shows a boy standing on a chair checking out the doctor's credentials. The physician is filling a hypodermic syringe to immunize the boy. This picture shows a classic image of a general practitioner and his office of the 1950s.

Nurses portrayed in visual art have been found in photos, illustrations, and posters. These works have ranged from photographs showing nurses comforting patients with Spanish influenza to posters recruiting nurses for the armed forces on both sides of the Atlantic during WWI and WWII. Religious paintings with nurses and doctors have also been depicted. In the late 20th century, for example, American Nathan Greene (1961–) painted many illustrations of nurses, physicians, and patients with Jesus in the background giving support and comfort.

Medical themes have also appeared in cartoons or cartoon series. A very popular series has been *Rex Morgan M.D.*, which was first created by American psychiatrist Nicholas P. Dallis (1911–1991) in 1948. This comic strip—read worldwide—continues to show a kind and compassionate family-practice physician. Over the years, the strip has served as an education tool. It has covered diseases and social problems—including drug abuse, domestic violence, HIV/AIDS, diabetes, organ transplants, and sexual harassment—and changes in American medical practice. In the series, Rex's nurse, June, begins as an office nurse; she and Rex eventually marry, have children, and she becomes a nurse practitioner.

LITERARY ARTS

Nonfiction Self-Help Literature

Numerous self-help, health and wellness, exercise and fitness, diet and nutrition, childcare and rearing, and other advice publications have been written since

1900 to help the public achieve a healthy lifestyle. American chemist Wilbur Olin Atwater (1844–1907), the father of nutrition science, wrote *Principles of Nutrition and Nutritive Value of Food* (1904). This booklet for public education advocated variety, moderate proportions, and moderation in consumption of all foods.

Around the same time, American novelist and health fanatic Upton Sinclair (1878–1968) and Michael Williams (1878–1950) wrote *Good Health and How We Won It* (1909). The book promoted yogurt for longevity, daily exercise, fasting, a vegetarian diet, and abstinence from caffeine, tobacco, and alcohol and was based upon the regime followed at surgeon John Harvey Kellogg's (1852–1943) Battle Creek Sanitarium. Kellogg wrote numerous articles and gave presentations on this regime for optimum health. Bernarr MacFadden (1868–1955), a self-styled fitness guru, published the *Physical Culture* magazine (1899–1940). This magazine was a major promoter of physical exercise, good nutrition and a healthy lifestyle in the first three decades of the century.

Popular midcentury fitness, exercise, and nutrition crusader Francois Henri "Jack" La Lanne (1914–2011) preached the health benefits of regular exercise and a good diet. His popular books ranged from *Foods for Glamour* (1961) to *Live Young Forever* (2009). From 1953 to 1985, he also hosted a popular television exercise programs that encouraged everyone including the elderly and women to exercise and join fitness clubs.

Other diet and lifestyle books in the 1990s included *Dr. Dean Ornish's Program for Reversing Heart Disease* (1990) and *Eat More, Weigh Less* (1993). Written by American clinical professor of medicine, Dean Michael Ornish (1953–), these popular books advocated a low-fat diet and lifestyle changes to treat and prevent heart disease. The books promoted whole nonprocessed plant-based foods, nonsmoking, moderate exercise, stress management, exercise, and support groups.

Childrearing advice books have also been popular since 1900. The early 20th century's "seen and not heard" philosophy preached by New Zealand health reformer Frederick Truby King (1858–1938) emphasized discipline and detachment. His book *Feeding and Care of Babies* (1907) was popular in many Western nations until the 1960s. With this method, babies were put on a firm feeding schedule, slept in their own room, cuddled only at playtime, and were left to cry. This was thought to build character. American physician Benjamin Spock (1903–1998) opposed these strict child-rearing practices. He told parents to trust their own instincts, feed the baby on demand, and cuddle and play with the baby frequently. His *Common Sense Book of Baby and Child Care* (1946), which encouraged "indulgence," was one of the best-selling books of the 20th century worldwide. An even more radical position was found in *The Continuum Concept* (1975) by American Jean Liedloff (1926–2011), who lived with a South American Stone Age tribe. She recommends that babies should have "constant contact" with their parents, including sleeping in their bed and being carried around in a sling against the body. She fostered the use of the baby sling still used in the 2010s.

During the feminist movement of the 1960s, a book aimed at women, *Our Bodies Ourselves* (1969), was written by the Boston Women's Health Collective. It touched on many aspects of women's health and sexuality including birth control, abortion, pregnancy, and childbirth. Various editions are still being published.

Doctors in Fiction

Numerous fictional works from 1900 have been written by or featured doctors. As societies and their values changed, so did the stereotypes of medicine and health professionals featured in fiction.

Some fiction writers have been doctors. Their nonprofessional works have ranged from bodies of poetry to science fiction and crime thrillers featuring medical professionals as both heroes and villains. For example, British author and physician W. Somerset Maugham's (1874–1965) novel *Of Human Bondage* (1915) was somewhat autobiographical in nature. The protagonist Philip Carey searched for the meaning of life, and after much travel and many occupations, he became a physician and settled down.

Scottish novelist and physician, Archibald Joseph Cronin's (1896–1981) best-known novel was *The Citadel* (1937). It is a story of a physician from a Welsh mining village who quickly moves up the career ladder in London. It examines moral conflicts between the individual and society and the struggle to balance scientific integrity with social obligations. This novel helped establish the National Health Service (NHS) in the United Kingdom (UK) as it exposed the inequity of medical practices between social classes and incompetence of the medical system in the pre-WWII era.

By the end of the century, physicians blended science fiction, medicine, and the horror genre in their novels, which may have reflected public unease about advancements in medicine and technology. For example, American physician and novelist Michael Crichton's (1942–2008) *The Andromeda Strain* (1969) was a science fiction thriller that portrayed the efforts of a team of scientists that investigated and attempted to stop the outbreak of a deadly extraterrestrial disease brought back to Earth on a military space probe. Crichton also wrote *Jurassic Park* (1990), another science fiction thriller about genetic engineering that recreated extinct dinosaurs. The two books were made into films in 1971 and 1993, respectively.

American ophthalmologist Robin Cook (1940–) wrote medical thrillers. His *Coma* (1977), later made into a film, created the medical thriller genre and changed the public's perception and media's portrayal of medicine and physicians—physicians and hospital systems could be evil. In *Coma*, individuals are brain killed and kept on life support so their organs could be harvested. Another American physician novelist was Michael Stephen Palmer (1942–2013), who also wrote a number of novels in this genre. His most noted thriller was *Extreme Measures* (1991). In this novel, an up-and-coming emergency-room physician is invited into a medical cabal that is doing unethical medical research. It was made into a film in 1996. These novels focused on various ethical, social, and public policy issues in medicine and biotechnology.

Another popular American author was pediatrician Perri Klass (1958–), who wrote several fictional works concerning women physicians. Her most noted was *Other Women's Children* (1990). The plot depicts Amelia Stern, an academic pediatrician and mother of a young son, who is deeply involved with her patients. Her marriage and relationships with her child and others suffer due to the demands of her work.

Fiction by doctors with cultural roots other than Western society emerged by the late 20th century. Japanese physician and author Abe Kōbō, pen name Abe Kimifusa (1924–1993), won international acclaim for *The Woman in the Dunes* [砂の女] (1962), which was later made into a film. It depicts a teacher enslaved with a widow in a sandpit whose job was to keep the sand away from the community.

Egyptian dentist Alaa al-Aswany's (1957–) award-winning novel, *The Yacoubian Building* (عمارة يعقوبيان) (2002), was translated into English in 2004. The action takes place in an older, but once grand, building in Cairo in the early 1990s during the first Gulf War. It examines through various characters moral and political corruption, fundamentalist Islam, ill-gotten wealth, extreme poverty, social class stigma, and religious hypocrisy that was found in modern Egypt. The novel became a bestselling Arabic-language novel and in 2006 was made into a film.

Iranian-born American optometry professor Khashayar Tonekaboni (pen name Terry Pinaud) has written several psychological thrillers and science fiction novels often based on social issues. His novel *The Fixer* (2016) is a science fiction paranormal-thriller about a war damaged Korean veteran with a sixth sense.

Abraham Verghese (1955–), an Indian American physician born in Ethiopia, wrote *Cutting for Stone* (2009), a novel of conjoined twin brothers orphaned by their mother's death at their birth and abandoned by their father. They are surgically separated, brought up in Africa and become physicians. The book portrays their complex family dynamics and relationships along with portraying various diseases and surgeries.

Several novels since the early 20th century have focused on physicians but have not been written by physicians. These have appeared in many genres, and the protagonist often struggles with moral issues. An example of an early work is *The Doctor: A Tale of the Rockies* (1906) written by Canadian Presbyterian minister Charles William Gordon (1860–1937) (pen name Ralph Connor). This historical novel involves the fractured relationship between two brothers. One becomes a physician and the other a minister; both go to the frontier unbeknown to each other. The novel fairly accurately portrays medical education in North America at the time and the difficulties of frontier medicine in the 1890s. It also illustrates both moral and immoral practitioners and practices and was written during the time of upheaval in the medical profession in North America between competing systems.

American socialist writer Upton Sinclair (1878–1968) wrote a sterilized dark novelette, *Society Doctor* (1917) for *Physical Culture* magazine. It shows the ruin of a young idealistic physician, Dr. Orman, as the result of his spendthrift, social-climbing wife. To provide money for her overspending, he finally resorts to dispensing illegal birth control and performing an illegal abortion. He is caught and blackmailed to avoid prison.

Another clergyman, American Lutheran minister Lloyd C. Douglas (1877–1951) wrote *Magnificent Obsession* (1929), made into a film in 1954. The plot is about a reckless young playboy, Robert Merrick, whose life is saved at the expense of the death of the town's physician. Merrick, after searching for forgiveness, decides to go into medicine to make up for this tragedy. He also embarks on a course of anonymous philanthropy by "paying it forward."

Several fiction writers whose protagonists are physicians have won the Nobel Prize for literature. Sinclair Lewis (1885–1951) became the first American to receive this honor for his novel *Arrowsmith* (1925). This work became a classic during the first half of the century and was written in the aftermath of the Flexner Report (1910) to reform medical education (see chapter 2). It deals with Martin Arrowsmith's conflict between striving for prestige, power, and wealth and his original plan to be a medical researcher. The novel was inspirational for several generations of medical students.

Another Nobel Laureate was Russian writer Boris Pasternak (1890–1960), who wrote the epic novel *Doctor Zhivago* (До́ктор Жива́го). It was first published in Italy in 1957—the book could not be published in the Soviet Union as the plot showed more concern for the welfare of the individual than for society. It was made into a film in 1965 and a series on Russian TV in 2006. This historical fiction features Dr. Zhivago over his lifetime and follows the effects of the Russian Revolution and its aftermath on his romances, acquaintances, and family.

The *Good Doctor* (2003) was a novel by South African playwright and novelist Damon Galgut (1963–). The novel's narrator, Frank Eloff, is a white doctor and the son of an apartheid-leaning physician; they both work at an understaffed and undersupplied hospital in an outpost city of one of South Africa's old homelands. A black African female physician runs this facility. Joining the practice is an idealistic young physician just out of medical school who was required to complete a service year in a rural community. Through personality clashes, criminal and immoral behaviors, and general corruption, the health care problems in South Africa of the first decade of the 21st century were dramatically pointed out.

Physicians have also been featured in the romance genre. The Canadian Harlequin company has produced numerous romance novels since the early 1950s. They are now translated into many languages and have often featured both male or female doctors and their love lives. The romance genre has not been limited to Western cultures. For example, Chinese romantic novelist Miao Yi You Xiu, in the mid-2010s, penned *Doctor Unruly*, which features Doctor Shi, a neurologist. The story concerns this neurologist and a nurse, with the usual romance novel complications.

The mystery-suspense-crime genre has also portrayed medical personnel. For example, renowned British mystery author P. D. James (1920–2014), the pen name of Phyllis Dorothy James, wrote several novels that featured physicians or nurses. Her *Shroud for a Nightingale* (1971) was the fourth book of her mystery series featuring Scotland Yard's Chief Superintendent Adam Dalgliesh. In this novel, some nursing students of the hospital nursing school are being murdered in strange ways. Her last Dalgliesh book was *The Private Patient* (2008) about a murder in an isolated old mansion that was transformed into a private plastic surgery clinic. Like traditional crime novels, these works have a group of suspects who possess motive, means, and opportunity to have committed the crime. Many of these novels were turned into a television series.

A brutal war novel by Australian Richard Flanagan (1961–), *The Narrow Road to the Deep North* (2013), features an Australian Army surgeon, Dorrigo Evans, who was attempting to survive in an appalling Japanese POW camp during WWII.

There the Australian prisoners under slave labor conditions are forced to build a railway between Thailand and Burma. Evans also cares for his fellow prisoners. The plot jumps back and forth between the POW camp and contemporary Australia when Evans is an old man.

Most fiction about physicians has featured male doctors. Although some female doctors were portrayed in the early 20th century, most were from the late 20th century onward. An early example was the short story "Mr. Peebles's Heart" (1914). This tale by Charlotte Perkins (1860–1935) involves a general-practice woman physician who comes to live with married relatives while establishing her practice in their town. The relationship between the couple is unhealthy and unhappy, and she uses new psychological methods to cure their domestic and other problems.

Later in the century, *Antonia Saw the Oryx First* (1983) by Roberta Worrick (1941–1989), whose pen name was Maria Thomas, depicts the tension between colonial whites and black Africans in various institutions in post-apartheid Africa. The plot features a white Harvard-trained physician, Antonia Redmond, who returns to the African village where she was raised by American parents. She attempts to establish a medical practice in her African home country that no longer wants her. An indigenous healer, Esther Moro, an illiterate prostitute and daughter of a native healer, has a gift for healing without Western medicine. The novel depicts clashes between healing philosophies and cultural, religious, social, and political views.

A romance war novel that features a female doctor is *Lovesick* (1996) (*Mal de amores*) by Mexican author Ángeles Mastretta (1949–), translated by Margaret Sayers Peden (1927). It reflects the social and political realities and the horrific battlefield medicine during the Mexican War (1910–1920). The novel is also a love story between medical practitioner, Emilia Sauri, and her revolutionary childhood friend, and also a fellow physician she works with and later marries. This novel examines apprentice medical training of the time and the heroine's integration of healing from different sources including local herbal, homeopathic, Chinese medicine, and other treatments.

Chinese American physician and author Tess Gerritsen (1953–) is noted for medical and crime thrillers. Her first medical thriller, *Harvest* (1996), had a similar plot to *Coma*. A woman physician, Abby Di Matteo, discovers that innocents are killed for their organs. Gerritsen's first crime thriller, *The Surgeon* (2001), introduced homicide detective Jane Rizzoli. Rizzoli in 10 more novels joined forces with medical examiner Dr. Maura Isles, and they solved crimes together, often with a medical theme.

Chinese Nobel laureate Guan Moye (1955–) (pen name Mo Yan) wrote *Frog* (蛙) (2009). "Frog" in Chinese sounds like a baby crying, or *wa*. It was translated by Howard Goldblatt (1939–).The plot concerns China's one-child-per-family policy and its implications. The story is told by Tadpole, the nephew of Gugu, a female gynecologist. Gugu's lover defects to Taiwan and to appear as a loyal communist she strictly adheres to the one-child policy and forces contraception and abortions, including her own family, to prevent the birth of extra children, in particular girls. The state sees too many children as leading to overpopulation and social and economic issues. This policy was implemented in 1979 to prevent famine, which had occurred due to overpopulation in the post-WWII years. By 2016, it was replaced by a two child family decree.

Nurses in Fiction

Like physicians, nurses have appeared in fiction since the early 20th century. Until midcentury, nurses were generally portrayed as admirable, hardworking, and independent women. Several series about nurses were written for adolescent girls in different settings with various adventures or mysteries to be solved. They were popular in North America and Britain. For example, the *Ruth Fielding* series of novels were popular among girls from 1910–1934. Three authors wrote the series under the pseudonym of Alice B. Emerson. The 13th book of series was *Ruth Fielding in the Red Cross* (1918) that described her works as a nurse's aide on the battlefield in a sanitized version of the WWI. The novel was an effort to encourage girls to go into nursing for the war effort.

The *Sue Barton* nurse series contains seven novels and follows Barton through her nurse's training and work life in different settings. They were written by American Helen Dore Boylston (1895–1984) between 1936 and 1952. Another American series of 27 mystery novels with medical settings was *Nurse Cherry Ames*. They were popular between 1943 and 1968. The novels trace Ames's life from a student nurse, army nurse in WWII, and nurse in the postwar era in many job settings and were written by several authors. The early novels encouraged girls to become nurses as a way to aid the war effort. Due to the opening of other occupations for women in the late 20th century, novels encouraging the nursing profession waned.

The wholesome perception of nurses began to change by the mid-20th century. A novel early in the century, *The Fruit of the Tree* (1907), by award-winning American author Edith Wharton (1862–1937) depicts a nurse who acts illegally. An upper-class woman, Bessie, who is in constant pain and dying, asks her private nurse, Justine, to let her die. Justine secretly gives her a fatal dose of morphine. Euthanasia, even if requested, has been, and is still, controversial in many cultures.

Nurses seen as sex objects were also found by midcentury. For example, a novel by American physician Hiester Richard Hornberger Jr. (1924–1997), (pen name Richard Hooker), in collaboration with W. C. Heinz (1915–2008), wrote *MASH* (1968). Based on Hornberger's experiences during the Korean War, the work featured many eccentric characters including physicians and nurses at a mobile army surgical hospital. The major nurse character, "Hot lips Hooligan," the head surgical nurse, was depicted as a frivolous sexual object. This comedy/drama was turned into a popular TV series (1972–1983).

By late century, nurses were seen as multidimensional and generally competent. For example, a fantasy romance series of nine novels by American author Diana Gabaldon (1952–) is the *Outlander* (1991–present). It features a happily married ex-WWII combat nurse, Claire Randall. Soon after the war's end, she walks through a stone circle in the Scottish Highlands and is transported back in time where she meets and falls in love with a Scottish rebel, Jamie Fraser, whom she later marries and has a child with. In this historical series, she, and later her family and others, go back and forth in time with many adventures where her nursing skills are also used.

A romance war novel that features a competent nurse is the *English Patient* (1992) by Sri Lankan-born Canadian Michael Ondaatje (1943–). It was made into an Academy Award–winning film in 1996. This is the story of a Canadian nurse, Hana, who cares for a badly burned plane crash victim at the end of WWII in an Italian villa after the rest of her unit has left. Kip, a Sikh bomb-disposal expert, becomes her lover, and Caravaggio, a friend of her father, a criminal-turned spy, joins them. They attempt to discover the identity of the patient. The characters have been deeply wounded by the war and previous love affairs.

The Healer's War: A Fantasy Novel of Vietnam (1988) is by American Elizabeth Ann Scarborough (1947–), who served as an army nurse in Vietnam. In this Nebula Award–winning work, the heroine, Lt. Kitty McCulley, a young and inexperienced nurse, cares for horrendously mentally and physically injured soldiers and Vietnamese civilians. She is given an amulet by a dying Vietnamese holy man and with this object survives a journey through a Vietcong infested jungle. This novel shows the brutality of war and what war does to the people in the middle of it.

Male nurses, other than in wartime, have sometimes been portrayed in fiction as weak and ineffectual. For example, in *Meet the Parents* (2000), an American comedy film, a male nurse Greg is portrayed as hapless and bumbling. His future father-in-law, Jack, does not like Greg and openly criticizes him for his choice of career as a male nurse. However, by 2010, male nurses were portrayed as competent. An example is a Christmas Hallmark TV romance film *Magical Christmas Ornaments* (2017), which featured a handsome and compassionate male pediatric nurse.

PERFORMING ARTS

The performing arts include theater, radio, opera, film, and TV. This media ranges from exercise videos and reality TV to fictional drama related to health and medicine. These arts often reflect health and social issues of the period.

Nonfiction and Reality TV Medical Programs

Nonfiction programs emerged with the advent of TV, videos, and DVDs beginning in the 1960s. For example, American actress, controversial activist, and fitness advocate, Jane Fonda (1937–) produced a number of exercise videos and DVDs for people to use at home. Another fitness and diet guru was Milton Teagle "Richard" Simmons (1948–). This flamboyant American comedian promoted weight loss by exercise and good nutrition and was popular in the late 20th century. He launched several videos on diet and exercise but retired by 2016. The PBS network produced a popular exercise program called *Body Electric* (1984–). It is aimed at baby boomers, particularly women. Margaret Richard, the series host and creator, also produced numerous exercise videos and DVDs for home exercise.

By the late 1990s, reality TV shows with medical themes emerged. They gave viewers an insider's view of emergency-room drama, real-life hospital health personnel, and medical procedures. For example, *Trauma: Life in the E.R.* (1997–2002) showed emergency-room patients with a variety of health and medical issues. It was followed by *Paramedics* (1998–2002), which looked at the activities of EMTs (emergency medical technicians) and paramedics in urban hospitals around North America. Similar shows have included *NY Med* and *Boston Med* that began in the early 2010s.

Mystery Diagnosis (2005–2011), a television docudrama series, focused on a couple of patients in each episode who have a disease that several doctors have not been able to diagnose. The diseases are often rare autoimmune or genetic conditions. Some of the more common conditions diagnosed have included heart disease, Lyme disease, epilepsy, myasthenia gravis, and Crohn's disease. The physician on the show notices a symptom that colleagues have overlooked. Further tests are performed and the correct diagnosis is reached along with proper treatment.

By 2000, health and psychological advice programs were also popular. *Dr. Phil* (2002–) is an American talk show hosted by clinical and forensic psychologist Phil McGraw (1950–). He offers therapy in the form of "life strategies." Guests have various problems including drug and alcohol abuse, obesity, money issues, mental illness, and dysfunctional families. Although this is a popular show, McGraw's therapeutic methods have drawn criticism from some psychotherapists. Another popular talk show that has been criticized by medical experts for advice unsupported by research is *The Dr. Oz Show* (2009–). It features Turkish American cardiothoracic surgeon Dr. Mehmet Oz (1960–). He and his guests give advice about various personal health and wellness issues.

Childrearing shows have been popular. As an example, in 2007 a British BBC television program *Bringing Up Baby* featured three different families. They each tried different methods of child rearing. These included Truby King's "seen and not heard," Benjamin Spock's "be indulgent," and Jean Liedlof's "constant contact" methods. The program followed the families for the first year after birth, and all three methods had advantages and disadvantages.

Fiction

Many endearing medical dramas emerged from the radio age of the 1930s and 1940s into the television era in the 1950s. In the mid-decades of the 20th century, physicians were often godlike and in control, and nurses were subservient to them. By 1914, films were regarded as entertainment, and the first "talkie" appeared in 1927. By 2005, medical dramas included flawed physicians and nurses. In earlier years, physicians were almost exclusively white males. However, by the 1990s, the entertainment industry in North America and the UK—where most films were produced—introduced more women and those with African or Asian ancestry as physician characters.

An example of an early film (late 1930s and early 1940s), radio (1950s) and TV (1960s) series featuring physicians was *Dr. Kildare,* although the name of the medical drama slightly changed over time. In these series, Dr. Kildare, along with his gruff older mentor, Dr. Gillespie, were featured in various medical and interpersonal situations and issues with patients. These physicians, as was common during this era, besides seeing patients in their office, also made house calls to see patients.

Numerous films were produced with a focus on treatments and disease. One of the first films to portray mental illness as something that could be treated with psychiatry was the mystery/drama American film, *The Snake Pit* (1948), loosely based on a semiautobiographical novel. It shows the treatment of a mentally ill woman and an abusive nurse and awful surroundings in a psychiatric institution. The film led to changes in the conditions of mental institutions in the United States. Another mystery/drama film dealing with mental illness, the *Three Faces of Eve* (1957) won its leading lady, Joanne Woodward, an Academy Award. The film, based upon a case study, portrays a woman with multiple personality disorder.

The drama film *Awakenings* (1990) is based upon British neurologist Oliver Sacks's (1933–2015) memoir (1973) of the same name. The film portrays the story of an American psychiatrist, Malcolm Sayer, at a chronic-care hospital. Some of his patients are in a catatonic state. They had survived the 1917–1928 epidemic of encephalitis lethargic, which can also cause Parkinson's-like symptoms. Sacks learns that the drug L-Dopa can help Parkinson's patients and administers it to his patients. They temporarily wake up and become conscious until the drug becomes ineffective, and they go back into their original state. The film was nominated for several Academy Awards.

Television also produced many medical dramas. For example, the A. J. Cronin novella *Country Doctor* was the basis for the long-running BBC television program *Dr. Finlay's Casebook* (1962–1971) and a radio series (1970–1978) of the same name. These series center on Dr. Finlay's general medical practice in a fictional Scottish town during the late 1920s. Another general-practitioner medical drama was *Marcus Welby, M.D.* (1969–1976) set in southern California. Dr. Welby was a family practitioner with a kind bedside manner. He, along with his young assistant and dedicated nurse, became involved in various medical and interpersonal situations. They also made house calls.

By the early 1970s, story lines taking place in hospitals became popular on both sides of the Atlantic. *General Hospital* (1972–1979) was a British hospital drama series with various medical crises and interactions between physicians, nurses, and orderlies. (An American drama series of the same name has existed from 1964 and is considered a classic "soap opera" of afternoon TV). *St. Elsewhere* (1982–1988) was an American medical hospital drama/comedy television series. New residents learned to deal with perfectionist cardiovascular surgeon Mark Craig and patients. It was one of the first American medical drama series to feature an African American physician. *Grey's Anatomy* (2005–) portrays strong, attractive, and smart women doctors who encounter interpersonal and medical issues. *ER* (1992–2009), the longest-running primetime medical drama in

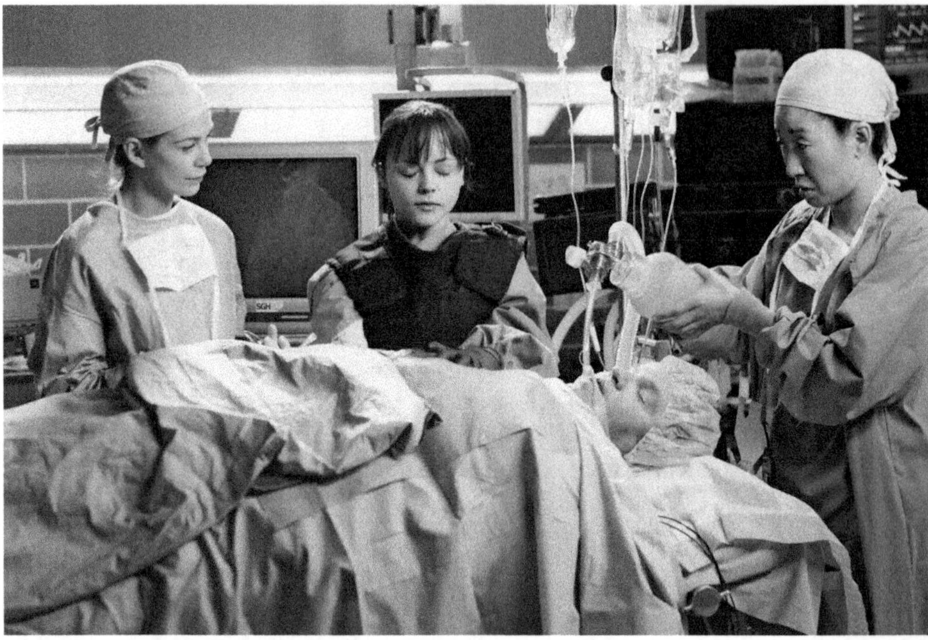

The popular American ABC television drama *Grey's Anatomy* portrays strong, attractive, and smart women physicians. Appearing in this scene from a 2006 episode are, from left, Ellen Pompeo, Christina Ricci, and Sandra Oh. (ABC/Photofest)

American television history, follows various characters and critical issues they face in the emergency room (ER) in a fictional hospital in Chicago.

Saving Hope (2012–2017), a Canadian medical/supernatural TV series, also aired in other countries. The show's central character is Dr. Alex Reid whose fiancé, Dr. Charles, is in a coma after a car accident. When he recovered, he was able to see the spirits of comatose and dead patients. Another Canadian medical TV drama series was *Trauma* (2010–). The series is set in a fictional trauma unit in Montreal. It features Dr. Julie Lemieux, a traumatologist, and her care of trauma patients along with personal and professional interactions.

The science fiction genre for TV and film also featured physicians. Dr. Leonard H. "Bones" McCoy was the physician in the American science fiction television and film franchise *Star Trek* (1966–1969). In *Star Trek: The Next Generation* (1989–1994), science fiction television series and later films, a female physician Commander Beverly Crusher is featured as the lead medical officer. Another science fiction supernatural drama television series was *The X-Files* (1993–2002, 2018–). The hero, Dr. Dana Scully, is a brilliant attractive physician and an FBI agent. In this series, she solves various unusual medical and other cases with her FBI colleague, and later lover, special agent Fox Mulder.

Wild West TV and films also had physicians as main characters. *Gunsmoke* (1955–1975), for example, was an American radio and television western drama series that takes place around Dodge City, Kansas. Dr. Charles Adams was the physician who patched up various characters, including gunshot cases. He starts out as a dark character at the beginning of the series but over time becomes compassionate and caring. Another series with a western theme was *Dr. Quinn, Medicine Woman* (1993–1998). This popular TV series aired in over 100 countries. It featured a strong, attractive, and independent female physician who tends to the various medical and other health and social issues found in a small western town.

By 2004, physicians and nurses with serious flaws began to be portrayed. For example, *House* (2004–2012), an American TV series, featured a physician of the same name who solved mysteries, often related to medical issues. Dr. House, although a genius, has many flaws including being dependent on drugs, grumpy, and rude. In the popular comedy/medical drama TV series, *Nurse Jackie* (2009–2015), hardworking and dedicated emergency department nurse, Jackie Peyton, displays unethical behavior and violates the code of ethics for nurses. She sometimes takes illegal drugs, the drugs of her patients, and changes information on patients' records, along with other questionable behavior. This series resulted in criticism from nursing associations inasmuch as the way nurses are portrayed by the media impacts the public perception of nurses.

A portrayal of strong and competent nurses appeared in a book of memoirs, *Call the Midwife* (2002), by British nurse Jennifer Worth (1935–2011). It became a popular BBC series on both sides of the Atlantic (2012–). This British medical drama series features a group of nurse midwives working in the East End of London in the postwar era of the late 1950s and early 1960s. It focuses on issues surrounding childbirth, reproduction, other medical and social conditions, and interpersonal relationships.

The Good Doctor (2017–), an American TV series, features a young surgeon, Shaun Murphy, with autism and savant syndrome. He uses extraordinary medical perception that saves lives and attempts to fit in with and be accepted by other surgeons and medical personnel.

Medical dramas were made in nations other than English-speaking ones. As an example, *Sob Pressão* (*Under Pressure*) is a Brazilian medical drama television. The series follows the emergency-department doctors and nurses of an underserved and underfunded public hospital in Rio de Janeiro and focuses on physicians.

A Korean TV medical drama, *Romantic Doctor, Teacher Kim* (2016–2017) featured a genius surgeon in a prestigious Seoul hospital who after the death of his junior colleague, changes his name and moves to a small hospital to become the chief surgeon. This drama depicts interactions with patients, junior physicians, nurses, and other personnel along with love interests. It was nominated for several awards.

HEALTH PROFESSIONALS AS VILLAINS

Up through the 1950s, most physicians and nurses were generally shown as caring, dedicated, and ethical. However, in the 1960s, unethical and evil physicians, nurses, and hospital administrators were increasingly found in literature, film, and television. Some of these have already been discussed. The classic evil nurse was depicted in American author Ken Kesey's *One Flew over the Cuckoo's Nest* (1962). Nasty Nurse Ratchet abused the psychiatric patients under her care in a mental hospital. The novel was turned into a film (1975) and won five Academy Awards. The film made lobotomies and mental institutions appear malevolent and suspect to the public. As previously mentioned, Robin Cook is credited for creating the genre of medical thrillers with *Coma* (1977). Likewise, Michael Palmer in his novels features unethical or evil physicians. For example, in *Silent Treatment* (1995), the good protagonist physician's wife mysteriously dies in a hospital, and after much investigation, it is found that a physician for a health care insurance cartel has been hired to kill expensive policyholder patients for "cost containment."

The horror film, *The Silence of the Lambs* (1991) features Dr. Hannibal Lecter, a psychiatrist and cannibalistic serial killer. Although he is committed to a state hospital for the criminally insane, he helps an agent solve a crime. Later he escapes from the hospital. In the crime-horror film *Pathology* (2008), a group of pathology residents after hours at the morgue see who can commit the perfect undetectable murder. Several of the characters end up killing girlfriends and classmates in revenge due to jealousy and infidelity. Nurses in the 2010s have also been portrayed as killers. For example, in the horror film *Nurse 3d* (2013), Abbey, a dedicated nurse during the day is a serial killer of unfaithful husbands in New York City at night.

PATIENTS IN THE ARTS

Patients have been the central characters in all the arts. An example of a visual artwork is Norwegian artist Edvard Munch's (1863–1944) *The Sick Child.* This image was drawn and painted in several renditions between 1885 and 1926. All of them illustrate his sister dying from TB at age 14. Many comic cartoons featured patients in hospital beds or at doctors' offices from the 1920s. For example, a 2010 cartoon shows a doctor telling his patient who is sprouting like a potato that he's been a couch potato too long.

Literature has also featured patients. American novelist Upton Sinclair (1878–1968) wrote several short stories about patients, doctors, and treatments of all kinds. Most were satires. Several previously short unpublished manuscripts were published in *Unseen Upton Sinclair* (2009) edited by Ruth Clifford Engs. In one satire, "The Health Hunters," patients search for cures and are conned into water cures, fasting, raw-food diets, air bathing, milk diets, and other remedies to cure their real and imagined ills. In a novella by Sinclair, *Little Algernon* (1911–1912), which appeared in *Physical Culture Magazine,* a rich young man searching for treatments for an "unruly stomach" and every other ache and pain is fleeced of his money for quack medical devices and cures.

On a more somber note, *As I Lay Dying* (1930), American author William Faulkner's classic southern gothic novel is told by several friends and family members from different perspectives. Addie Bundren is dying and wants to be buried with her own family in another community. After she has died, her impoverished dysfunctional family sets off with her body to get it buried. On the road, the family encounters many problems including mental illness in one of her children, fire, floods, a broken leg and other injuries, and an unwanted pregnancy.

The Sick Child (ca. 1885), by Norwegian artist Edvard Munch, is an example of a visual work of art where the main subject is a patient. (National Museum of Art, Oslo/Fine Art Images/Heritage Images/Getty Images)

A disturbing work is *Hiroshima* (1946) by American journalist John Hersey (1914–1993). This example of New Journalism with a blending of nonfiction reporting and the pace of a novel is based upon many interviews. The book features six nuclear blast victims of the August 6, 1945, bomb, which includes two Japanese physicians, a German Jesuit priest, a minister, a seamstress, and a young woman who worked in a factory. The story examines treatment, health, recovery, and/or deaths over the first year of their lives after the blast. Graphic details of civilians and soldiers who died from radiation and burns within the first day or so are also described. This work brought the horror of nuclear war to the public in many nations leading to bans on using these weapons.

A patient dying of TB is found in South African writer Karel Schoeman's (1939–2017) novel, *Another Country* (1992). The plot features Versluis, a wealthy and educated Dutchman with tuberculosis. He immigrates to Bloemfontein, South Africa, to convalesce from the disease in this frontier town at the end of the 19th century as it was supposedly the right climate for a cure. Although TB is found in all social classes, differences in treatment between various classes are shown. However, all of Versluis's riches and treatments cannot save him, but in this town, he finally accepts his death from the disease.

The ethics surrounding the new eugenics is found in *My Sisters Keeper* (2003). Two patients are depicted in this novel by American author Jodi Picoult (1966–). The heroine is a teenage girl, Anna, who was conceived and selected through in vitro fertilization for the right genetics and was produced to supply cord blood to save her older sister, Kate, who is dying from leukemia. However, over time, Kate relapses, and further demands are made on the younger sister to provide bone marrow and undergo other procedures to save her older sister. As a teenager, Anna now wants out of this mandatory responsibility and seeks emancipation from her parents.

DISEASE IN THE ARTS

Disease has been featured in the visual, literature, and performance art forms for decades and is often an underlying plot in the story line. For example, in a post-WWI novel, when TB was rampant and a major cause of death, German antiwar author Erich Maria Remarque (1898–1970) wrote *Three Comrades* (*Drei Kameraden*) (1936) a romance drama novel. The plot describes a young woman, Pat, who is dying of TB and her two male friends, one her lover. They take her to a mountain sanatorium in Switzerland. As she nears death, her lover, Robert, drives to the institution, and the two spend the remaining weeks together before her death. The novel was made into an American film in 1938.

TB is also featured in visual art. American artist Alice Neel's (1900–1984) painting of a dying patient, *T.B., Harlem* (1940), depicts a gaunt young man in Spanish Harlem who lies propped up on pillows. His right hand points toward a bandage area on his side. The painting evokes sympathy.

Nobel laureate French journalist Albert Camus's (1913–1960) *The Plague* (*Le Peste*) (1947) tells the story of a bubonic plague epidemic sweeping the large city of Oran, Algeria. This allegory of social and other problems that are initially ignored by the authorities features a variety of characters including two physicians, Drs Rieux and Castel, who recognize the seriousness of the disease that needs to be everyone's concern, and they join the antiplague crusade.

Another plague, the "gay plague," of the early 1980s was featured in *An Early Frost* (1985). This film was the first major American made-for-television performance that dealt with AIDS. It features a young gay professional dying of the disease and the reaction of his parents, lover, and medical personnel. At this point, a year after the HIV virus had been identified in the homosexual and hemophilic population, it was still a taboo topic. This film helped bring the disease and its effects on family and society to the general public.

Other performing arts also featured the HIV/AIDS theme in the late 20th century. *Angels in America* (1991) is a play in two parts by American playwright Tony Kushner (1956–). The two parts of the play are entitled *Millennium Approaches* and *Perestroika*. It is a complex drama of homosexual interpersonal relations with AIDs as a central theme. The rock musical *Rent* (1993), which takes place in the East village of New York City in the late 1980s, also features a central character with HIV/AIDS along with homosexual and family relationships. Much of the plot and characters in this production by Jonathan Larson (1960–1996) were loosely based upon Giacomo Puccini's opera *La Bohème* (1895) that takes place in Paris. Both deal with starving artists. Tuberculosis, the plague of Puccini's opera, is replaced by HIV/AIDS in *Rent*.

Theatrical productions have focused on medical issues and patients. French playwright Florian Zeller (1979–) and British translator Christopher James Hampton (1946–) produced *The Father*. It is the story of André, who has Alzheimer's disease. It describes the progression of André first living on his own, then living with his daughter, and finally living in a nursing home. However, what is real and what is not is difficult to determine as audience members also find themselves wondering what is fact or fiction, or past or present.

Contagion (2011) was an American medical-thriller-disaster film. The plot revolves around the spread of a deadly virus and the attempts by medical researchers and public health officials to identify and contain the disease. Worldwide social order and panic results from the pandemic. A vaccine is finally made to halt its spread. This work was praised by medical researchers for its accuracy in terms of the spread of an epidemic and efforts to contain and prevent the disease. The film was inspired by various early 21st century pandemics such as the 2003 SARS and the 2009 flu pandemic.

To sum up, since the early 20th century, many changes in the perception of medical practice, doctors, and nurses have evolved. The arts have reflected these changes in popular health advice and how social consequences of disease, status of health care professionals, and patients are perceived by society. The arts have also been integrated into medical education (discussed in chapter 2).

GLOSSARY

burden of disease
Impact of a health problem as measured by mortality, morbidity, or economic costs to a nation.

cerebral vascular disease (CVA)
Strokes.

congenital anomalies
Birth defects.

consumption
Tuberculosis.

COPD
Chronic obstructive pulmonary disease.

debridement
Cleaning out damaged tissue or containments in a wound such as battle wounds.

Flexner Report
Study of medical education in the United States and Canada that changed Western medical education globally.

healing temples
Sacred places in India that provide mental and chronic illness care.

HIV
Human Immunodeficiency Virus.

ischemic heart disease
Heart disease that often leads to heart attacks.

lower respiratory infections
Pneumonia and tuberculosis.

managed care
Health care where patients can only visit certain doctors and hospitals in order to get insurance coverage.

Medicaid
Health care program that assists low-income families.

microcephaly
Abnormal smallness of the head.

MMWR
Morbidity and Mortality Weekly Report, an American public health newsletter that reports national and global health issues.

morbidity
Illness.

mortality
Death

psychotropic drugs
Mind-altering drugs such as cannabis, alcohol, opiates.

schizophrenia
Mental illness that has faulty perception, hallucinations, and delusion.

thalidomide babies
Birth defects due to exposure to the drug thalidomide in the uterus.

universal health coverage (UHC)
All people in a nation have access to preventative, treatment, rehabilitation, and end-of-life care.

Zika
A virus transmitted by mosquitoes, which causes small heads and brains and babies and retardation.

BIBLIOGRAPHY

Abegunde, Dele O., et al. "The Burden and Costs of Chronic Diseases in Low-Income and Middle-Income Countries." *Lancet* 370, no. 9603 (December 5, 2007): 1929–1938. (Series Chronic Diseases 1) http://www.who.int/choice/publications/p_2007_Chronic_disease_burden_Lancet.pdf (accessed August 4, 2017).

Agrawal, Priya. "Maternal Mortality and Morbidity in the United States of America." *Bulletin of the World Health Organization* 93 (2015): 135. http://www.who.int/bulletin/volumes/93/3/14-148627/en/ (accessed March 4, 2017).

Ahn, Woo-kyoung, et al. "Mental Health Clinicians' Beliefs about the Biological, Psychological, and Environmental Bases of Mental Disorders." *Cognitive Science* 33, no. 2 (March 2009): 147–182. (Author manuscript, available in PMC 2010 April 20. Published in final edited form as: Cogn Sci. 2009 March; 33(2): 147–182.) https://www.ncbi.nlm.nih.gov/pmc/articles/PMC2857376/pdf/nihms177660.pdf (accessed December 16, 2016).

Alarcón, Renato D. "Mental Health and Mental Health Care in Latin America." *World Psychiatry* 2, no. 1 (February 2003): 54–56. https://www.ncbi.nlm.nih.gov/pmc/articles/PMC1525063/ (accessed December 13, 2016).

Albert, Daniel M., and Diane D. Edwards, eds. *The History of Ophthalmology*. Boston: Blackwell Science, 1996.

Albert, Eleanor, and Beina Xu. *China's Environmental Crisis*. Council on Foreign Relations, last updated January 18, 2016. https://www.cfr.org/backgrounder/chinas-environmental-crisis (accessed June 24, 2018).

Ali, Mohammad, et al. "The Global Burden of Cholera." *Bulletin of the World Health Organization* 90 (published online January 24, 2012): 209–218A. http://www.who.int/bulletin/volumes/90/3/11-093427/en/ (accessed July 15, 2017).

Allum, Nick, et al. "Religion and the Public Ethics of Stem-Cell Research: Attitudes in Europe, Canada and the United States." *PLoS One* 12, no. 4 (2017): e0176274. https://www.ncbi.nlm.nih.gov/pmc/articles/PMC5398703/ (accessed March 22, 2018).

Alzheimer's Disease International. *The World Alzheimer Report 2015: The Global Impact of Dementia: An Analysis of Prevalence, Incidence, Cost and Trends*. London: Alzheimer's Disease International, 2015. https://www.alz.co.uk/research/WorldAlzheimerReport2015.pdf (accessed December 5, 2016).

American Association of Medical Colleges. *The State of Women in Academic Medicine: The Pipeline and Pathways to Leadership, 2013–2014*, 2017. https://www.aamc.org/members/gwims/statistics/ (accessed April 1, 2017).

American Cancer Society. "The Burden." *The Cancer Atlas*, 2018. http://canceratlas.cancer.org/the-burden/ (accessed August 13, 2017).

American Dental Association. Dental History, 2018. https://www.ada.org/en/member-center/ada-library/dental-history (accessed May 28, 2018).

American Hospital Association. *Fast Facts on U.S. Hospitals*, 2018. Chicago: AHA, 2018. https://www.aha.org/statistics/fast-facts-us-hospitals (accessed June 2, 2018).

American Psychiatric Association. *Diagnostic and Statistical Manual of Mental Disorders, Fifth Edition.* Arlington, VA: American Psychiatric Association, 2013.

Aminov, Rustam I. "A Brief History of the Antibiotic Era: Lessons Learned and Challenges for the Future." *Frontiers in Microbiology* 1, article 134 (Published online 8 December 2010). https://www.ncbi.nlm.nih.gov/pmc/articles/PMC3109405/ (accessed February 1, 2017).

Amuyunzu-Nyamongo, Mary. "The Social and Cultural Aspects of Mental Health in African Societies" in Commonwealth Secretariat *Commonwealth Health Partnerships 2013*, edited by Andrew Robertson, Rupert Jones-Parry, and Marvin Kuzamba, 59–62. Cambridge: Nexus Strategic Partnerships, 2013. http://www.commonwealthhealth.org/wp-content/uploads/2013/07/The-social-and-cultural-aspects-of-mental-health-in-African-societies_CHP13.pdf (accessed December 22, 2016).

Anderson, Janna, and Lee Rainie. *Millennials will Benefit and Suffer Due to their Hyperconnected Lives.* Pew Research Center. February 29, 2012. http://www.pewinternet.org/2012/02/29/millennials-will-benefit-and-suffer-due-to-their-hyperconnected-lives (accessed June 1, 2017).

Andrews-Speed, Philip. "China's Energy Policymaking Processes and their Consequences." In *Crossroads: Forging a New Energy and Environmental Balance*, edited by Philip Andrews-Speed, Mikkal E. Herberg, and Li Zhidong, 1–18. Seattle, Washington: The National Bureau of Asian Research, 2014. http://nbr.org/publications/specialreport/pdf/sr47_chinas_energy_crossroads_november2014.pdf (accessed June 29, 2018).

Archer, David. *The Long Thaw: How Humans Are Changing the Next 100,000 Years of Earth's Climate.* Princeton, NJ: Princeton University Press, 2009.

Armstrong, Elizabeth M., and Ernest L. Abel. "Fetal Alcohol Syndrome: The Origins of a Moral Panic." *Alcohol and Alcoholism* 35, no. 3 (May 2000): 276–282. https://academic.oup.com/alcalc/article/35/3/276/208920/ (accessed May 19, 2017)

Aung, Steven K. H., et al. "Traditional Chinese Medicine as a Basis for Treating Psychiatric Disorders: A Review of Theory with Illustrative Cases." *Medical Acupuncture* 25, no. 6 (1 December 2013): 398–406. http://www.ncbi.nlm.nih.gov/pmc/articles/PMC3870484/ (accessed December 20, 2016).

Austen, Ian. "Canadian Court Says Some Can Grow Marijuana at Home, with a Prescription." *New York Times.* (24 February 2016) https://www.nytimes.com/2016/02/25

/world/americas/a-new-ruling-on-marijuana-in-canada.html (accessed January 29, 2017).

Australia. Department of Health. "List of Zika virus affected countries." June 9, 2017. http://www.health.gov.au/internet/main/publishing.nsf/content/ohp-zika-countries.htm (accessed June 11, 2017).

Australia. Department of Health. Therapeutic Goods Administration. *Australian Regulation of Over-the-Counter Medicines*, June 3, 2016. https://www.tga.gov.au/australian-regulation-over-counter-medicines (accessed January 8, 2017).

Australian Institute of Health and Welfare. *Overview of Mental Health Services in Australia*. https://www.aihw.gov.au/getmedia/f53e4869-8bb5-44ef-b2e4-6f3981fd3359/Overview-of-mental-health.pdf.aspx (accessed December 15, 2016).

Baker, Michael S. "Military Medical Advances Resulting from the Conflict in Korea, Part I: Systems Advances that Enhanced Patient Survival." *Military Medicine* 177, no. 4 (2012): 423–429. https://academic.oup.com/milmed/article/177/4/423/4283512 (accessed October 11, 2017).

Barnett, Jessica C., and Edward R. Berchick. *Health Insurance Coverage in the United States: 2016.* Publication Number: P60-260, September 12, 2017. United States. Census Bureau. https://www.census.gov/library/publications/2017/demo/p60-260.html (accessed July 30, 2018).

Basch, Paul F. "A Historical Perspective on International Health." *Infectious Disease Clinics of North America* 5, no. 2 (June 1991): 183–96.

Bates, Victoria. "Yesterday's Doctors: The Human Aspects of Medical Education in Britain, 1957–93." *Medical History* 61, no. 1 (January 2017): 48–65. https://www.ncbi.nlm.nih.gov/pmc/articles/PMC5206963/ (accessed December 27, 2017).

Bauerlein, Mark. *The Dumbest Generation: How the Digital Age Stupefies Young Americans and Jeopardises Our Future (Or, Don't Trust Anyone Under 30).* New York: Penguin, 2008.

Beers, Clifford Whittingham. *A Mind that Found Itself: An Autobiography.* New York: Longmans, Green and Co., 1908.

Bennett, J. D. "Medical Advances Consequent to the Great War 1914–1918." *Journal of the Royal Society of Medicine* 83, no. 11 (November 1990): 738–742. https://www.ncbi.nlm.nih.gov/pmc/articles/PMC1292926/ (accessed October 15, 2017).

Betrán, Ana Pilar, et al. "The Increasing Trend in Caesarean Section Rates: Global, Regional and National Estimates: 1990–2014." *PLoS One* 11, no. 2 (February 5, 2016): e0148343 https://www.ncbi.nlm.nih.gov/pmc/articles/PMC4743929/ (accessed June 4, 2017).

Bhugra, Dinesh. "The Global Prevalence of Schizophrenia." *PLoS Medicine* 2, no. 5 (2005): e151. http://journals.plos.org/plosmedicine/article?id=10.1371/journal.pmed.0020151 (accessed December 3, 2016).

Blum, Craig A., and David B. Adams. "Who did the first Laparoscopic Cholecystectomy?" *Journal of Minimal Access Surgery* 7, no. 3 (July–September 2011): 165–168. https://www.ncbi.nlm.nih.gov/pmc/articles/PMC3193755/ (accessed June 1, 2018).

Brauer, Susanne, Nikola Biller-Andorno, and Roberto Andorno, eds. *Country Reports on Advance Directives.* ESF Exploratory Workshop Advance Directives: Towards a Coordinated European Perspective? Institute of Biomedical Ethics, University of Zurich, Switzerland, 18–22 June 2008. [Zurich: University of Zurich, 2008] https://www.ethik.uzh.ch/dam/jcr:00000000-14d5-886d-ffff-fffff1488f30/Country_Reports_AD.pdf (accessed April 10, 2018).

Braunwald, Eugene. "The Ten Advances that have Defined Modern Cardiology." *Trends in Cardiovascular Medicine* 24, no. 5 (July 2014): 179–183.

British Medical Association Board of Science. "Drug Policy in the UK: From the 19th Century to the Present Day" in *Drugs of Dependence. The Role of Medical Professionals*, edited by Penny Howes. 87–96. London: British Medical Association, 2013.

Brown, Phil, ed. *Mental Health Care and Social Policy.* Boston: Routledge & Kegan Paul, 1985.

Brun, Emmanuelle, and Malgorzata Milczarek. *Expert Forecast on Emerging Psychosocial Risks Related to Occupational Safety and Health.* Luxembourg: Office for Official Publications of the European Communities, 2007. https://repository.tudelft.nl/search/tno/?q=title%3A%22Expert%20forecast%20on%20emerging%20psychosocial%20risks%20related%20to%20occupational%20safety%20and%20health%22 (accessed July 5, 2018).

Bryant, Daniel C. "A Roster of Twentieth-Century Physicians Writing in English." *Literature and Medicine* 13, no. 2 (Fall 1994): 284–305.

Bulger, Ruth Ellen, Elizabeth Meyer Bobby, and Harvey Finberg, eds. *Society's Choices: Social and Ethical Decision Making in Biomedicine.* Washington, DC: National Academy Press, 1995.

Busse, Reinhard, and Miriam Blümel. "Germany: Health System Review." *Health Systems in Transition* 16, no. 2 (2014): 142–148. http://www.euro.who.int/__data/assets/pdf_file/0008/255932/HiT-Germany.pdf (accessed July 20, 2018).

Cahill, Sean, and Nathan Schaefer, eds. *Syringe Exchange Programs around the World: The Global Context.* New York: Gay Men's Health Crisis, 2009. http://www.gmhc.org/files/editor/file/gmhc_intl_seps.pdf (accessed January 29, 2017).

Canada. Health Canada. *Best Practices: Concurrent Mental Health and Substance Use Disorders.* Ottawa: Health Canada, 2002. http://www.hc-sc.gc.ca/hc-ps/alt_formats/hecs-sesc/pdf/pubs/adp-apd/bp_disorder-mp_concomitants/bp_concurrent_mental_health-eng.pdf (accessed 27 November 2016).

Canada. Statistics Canada. "Post-Secondary Student Information System, 1992/1993 to 2008/2009." *Women in Canada: A Gender-based Statistical Report.* November 30, 2015. http://www.statcan.gc.ca/pub/89-503-x/2010001/article/11542/c-g/c-g007-eng.htm (assessed April 6, 2017).

Canadian Mental Health Association. *History of CMHA.* http://www.cmha.ca/about-cmha/history-of-cmha/#.WDnFeK1aHMA (accessed November 23, 2016).

Canadian Mental Health Association. *Mental Health and Addiction Legislation*, 2018. https://ontario.cmha.ca/provincial-policy/criminal-justice/mental-health-and-addictions-legislation/ (accessed December 3, 2016).

Canadian Psychological Association. *History of Psychology in Canada*, last updated by the CPA February 2010. http://www.cpa.ca/aboutcpa/archives/ (accessed November 27, 2016).

Canadian Public Health Association. *History of Family Planning in Canada.* https://www.cpha.ca/history-family-planning-canada (accessed March 22, 2017).

Carome, Michael. "Unethical Clinical Trials Still Being Conducted in Developing Countries." *Huffington Post, Blog.* (December 2014). http://www.huffingtonpost.com/michael-carome-md/unethical-clinical trials_b_5927660.html (accessed February 3, 2017).

Charlson, Fiona J., et al. "The Burden of Mental, Neurological, and Substance Use Disorders in China and India: A Systematic Analysis of Community Representative Epidemiological Studies." *The Lancet* 388, no. 10042 (23 July 2016): 376–389. http://www.thelancet.com/journals/lancet/article/PIIS01406736(16)30590-6/abstract (accessed November 22, 2016).

Chasek, Pamela S., David L. Downie, and Janet Welsh Brown. *Global Environmental Politics.* New York: Avalon Publishing, 2016.

Chen, H. H., et al. "Mental Health Law of the People's Republic of China (English translation with annotations); Translated and Annotated Version of China's New Mental Health Law." *Shanghai Archives of Psychiatry* 24, no. 6 (December 2012): 305–321. https://www.ncbi.nlm.nih.gov/pmc/articles/PMC4198897/ (accessed November 22, 2016).

Chen, Lincoln, and Minhui Yang. "New Opportunities for China in Global Health." *The Lancet Global Health* 6, no. 7 (July 2018): e722–e723. https://www.thelancet.com/journals/langlo/article/PIIS2214-109X(18)30263-8/fulltext?dgcid=raven_jbs_etoc_email (accessed June 12, 2018).

Cheng, Tsung-Mei. "Universal Health Coverage: An Overview and Lessons from Asia." *Harvard Public Health Review 4 Global Health* (May 2015). http://harvardpublichealthreview.org/universal-health-coverage-an-overview-and-lessons-from-asia/

Chesler, Ellen. *Woman of Valor: Margaret Sanger and the Birth Control Movement in America.* New York: Anchor Books, 1993.

Chopra, R. N. *Chopra's Indigenous Drugs of India.* Kolkata: Academic Publishers, 2006.

Cleland, John G., Robert P. Ndugwa, and Eliya M Zulu. "Family Planning in Sub-Saharan Africa: Progress or Stagnation?" *Bulletin of the World Health Organization* 89 (2011): 137–143. http://www.who.int/bulletin/volumes/89/2/10-077925/en/ (accessed March 14, 2017).

Climate Central. *The 10 Hottest Global Years on Record.* January 18, 2018. http://www.climatecentral.org/gallery/graphics/the-10-hottest-global-years-on-record (accessed June 30, 2018).

Coates, John Boyd, ed. *Surgery in World War II: Activities of Surgical Consultants.* Volume II. U.S. Army Medical Department. Office of the Surgeon General, 1964. http://history.amedd.army.mil/booksdocs/wwii/actvssurgconvol2/default.htm (accessed October 20, 2017).

Commonwealth Fund. *International Health Care System Profiles: Countries.* New York: The Commonwealth Fund, 1917. https://international.commonwealthfund.org/countries/ (accessed July 22, 2018).

Conference Board of Canada. "Infant Mortality." The data on this page are current as of February 2015. http://www.conferenceboard.ca/hcp/provincial/health/infant.aspx (accessed May 21, 2017).

Coni, Nicholas. "Medicine and the Spanish Civil War." *Journal of the Royal Society of Medicine* 95, no. 3 (March 2002): 147–150. https://www.ncbi.nlm.nih.gov/pmc/articles/PMC1279488/pdf/0950147.pdf (accessed November 15, 2017).

Conifer, Dan, and Francis Keany. "Painkillers with Codeine Won't Be Available over the Counter from 2018." *ABC News*, December 20, 2016. http://www.abc.net.au/news/2016-12-20/codeine-painkillers-won't-beavailable-over-the-counter-2018/8133996 (accessed February 4, 2017).

Connor, Jennifer, Clint Sauer, and Kevin Doll. "Assisted Reproductive Technologies and World Religions: Implications for Couples Therapy." *Journal of Family Psychotherapy* 23, no. 2 (June 2012): 83–98.

Coots, Norvell. "Military Medical Advances in Combat Can Help Civilians at Home." *U.S. Army*, October 9, 2013. https://www.army.mil/article/112860/military_medical_advances_in_combat_can_help_civilians_at_home (accessed November 2, 2017).

Coovadia, Hoosen, et al. "The Health and Health System of South Africa: Historical Roots of Current Public Health Challenges." *Lancet* 374, no. 9692 (September 5, 2009): 817–834. http://depts.washington.edu/sphnet/wp-content/uploads/2013/01/Coovadia.pdf (accessed July 17, 2018).

Corning, Peter A. "The Second Round–1927 to 1940." Chapter 2 in *The Evolution of Medicare: From Idea to Law*. Washington, DC: Social Security Administration, first published 1969. Republished online. https://www.ssa.gov/history/corning chap2.html

Countdown to 2030. *Fulfilling the Health Agenda for Women and Children: The 2014 Report*. http://countdown2030.org/ (accessed March 5, 2017).

Crump, John A., and Eric D. Mintz. "Global Trends in Typhoid and Paratyphoid Fever." *Clinical and Infectious Diseases* 50, no. 2 (Jan 15, 2010): 241–246. https://www.ncbi.nlm.nih.gov/pmc/articles/PMC2798017/#R2 (accessed July 14, 2017).

Cummings, Nicholas A. and William T. O'Donohue. "Psychology's Surrender to Political Correctness." In *Destructive Trends in Mental Health: The Well-Intentioned Path to Harm*, edited by Rogers Wright and Nicholas A. Cummings, 3–28. New York: Routledge, 2005.

Daemmrich, Arthur, and Mary Ellen Bowden. "A Rising Drug Industry." *Chemical and Engineering News* 83, no. 25 (20 June 2005): 28–42. https://pubs.acs.org/cen/coverstory/83/8325/8325intro.html (accessed February 4, 2017).

Davidson, Lauren. "Vaping Takes Off as E-Cigarette Sales Break Through $6bn." *The Telegraph*, June 23, 2015. http://www.telegraph.co.uk/finance/newsbysector/retail andconsumer/11692435/Vaping-takes-off-as-e-cigarette-sales-break-through-6bn.html (accessed December 2, 2016).

Davis, Angela. "Choice, Policy and Practice in Maternity Care since 1948." *History and Policy*. May 30, 2013. http://www.historyandpolicy.org/policy-papers/papers/choice-policy-and-practice-in-maternity-care-since-1948 (accessed March 2, 2017).

Davis, Karen, et al. *Mirror, Mirror on the Wall, 2014 Update: How the U.S. Health Care System Compares Internationally*. New York: Commonwealth Fund, 2014. http://www.commonwealthfund.org/publications/fund-reports/2014/jun/mirror-mirror-wall-2014-update-how-us-health-care-system (accessed March 22, 2018).

Deaton, Angus. *The Great Escape. Health, Wealth, and the Origins of Inequality*. Princeton and Oxford: Princeton University Press, 2013.

Deech, Ruth, and Anna Smajdor. *From IVF to Immortality: Controversy in the Era of Reproductive Technology*. Oxford: Oxford University Press, 2007.

Donohue, Julie. "A History of Drug Advertising: The Evolving Roles of Consumers and Consumer Protection." *Milbank Quarterly* 84, no. 4 (December 2006): 659–699. https://www.ncbi.nlm.nih.gov/pmc/articles/PMC2690298/ (accessed February 5, 2017).

Doshi, Peter. "Trends in Recorded Influenza Mortality: United States, 1900–2004." *American Journal of Public Health* 98, no. 5 (May 2008): 939–945. https://www.ncbi.nlm.nih.gov/pmc/articles/PMC2374803/ (accessed July 25, 2017).

Doskoch, P. "Many Pregnant Women Use Tobacco in Some Developing Countries." *International Perspectives on Sexual and Reproductive Health* 34, no. 4 (December 2008): 199–200. https://www.guttmacher.org/journals/ipsrh/2008/12/many-pregnant-women-use-tobacco-some-developing-countries (accessed February 14, 2017).

Drug Policy Alliance. *Drug Decriminalization in Portugal: A Health-Centered Approach*. New York: Drug Policy Alliance, 2015. https://www.drugpolicy.org/sites/default/files/DPA_Fact_Sheet_Portugal_Decriminalization_Feb2015.pdf (accessed January 28 2017).

Echt, D. S., et al. "Mortality and Morbidity in Patients Receiving Encainide, Flecainide, or Placebo. The Cardiac Arrhythmia Suppression Trial." *New England Journal of Medicine* 324, no. 12 (March 21, 1991): 781–788. https://www.ncbi.nlm.nih.gov/pubmed/1900101/ (accessed January 28, 2017).

Edwards, Griffith. "Cannabis and the Criteria for Legalization of a Currently Prohibited Recreational Drug: Groundwork for a Debate." *Acta Psychiatrica Scandinavica* Supplement 251 (1974): 1–62.

Egenes, Karen J. "History of Nursing." In *Issues and Trends in Nursing: Essential Knowledge for Today and Tomorrow*, edited by Gayle Roux and Judith A. Halstead. Sudbury, MA: Jones and Bartlett Publishers, 2009.

Eisenberg, David M., et al. "Credentialing Complementary and Alternative Medical Providers." *Annals of Internal Medicine* 137, no. 12 (December 17 2002): 965–973. https://www.ncbi.nlm.nih.gov/pubmed/12484712 (accessed June 15, 2017).

Ellis, Harold. *A History of Surgery*. London: Greenwich Medical Media, 2001.

Emanuel, Ezekiel J., et al. "What Makes Clinical Research in Developing Countries Ethical? The Benchmarks of Ethical Research: Perspective." *Journal of Infectious Disease* 189, no. 5 (March 1, 2004): 930–937. https://academic.oup.com/jid/article/189/5/930/810459 (accessed February 7, 2013).

Engelman, Peter C. *A History of the Birth Control Movement in America*. Santa Barbara, CA: ABC-CLIO, 2011.

Engs, Ruth C. *Alcohol and Other Drugs: Self-Responsibility*. Bloomington, IN: Tichenor Publishing Co., 1987.

Engs, Ruth C., ed. *Controversies in the Addiction Field*. Kendal-Hunt: Dubuque, Iowa, 1990. http://www.indiana.edu/~engs/cbook/tabcont.html (accessed June 4, 2018).

Engs, Ruth C. "Controversies in the Addiction Field: Ugly American Politics of Alcohol and Drugs Use, Education, Treatment, and Public Policies." Paper presented at the International Council on Alcoholism and the Addictions Annual Conference. Berlin, Germany, June, 1990. http://hdl.handle.net/2022/17144 (accessed November 19, 2016).

Engs, Ruth C. "Do Traditional Western European Drinking Practices Have Origins in Antiquity?" *Addiction Research* 2, no. 3 (1995): 227–239. https://scholarworks.iu.edu/dspace/handle/2022/17485 (accessed August 30, 2018).

Engs, Ruth C. *Responsible Alcohol and Drug Use*. New York: Macmillan, 1979.

Engs, Ruth C. "Resurgence of a New Clean Living Movement." *Journal of School Health* 61, no. 4 (April, 1991): 155–159. http://hdl.handle.net/2022/17484 (accessed June 4, 2018).

Engs, Ruth Clifford. *Clean Living Movements: American Cycles of Health Reform*. Westfield, CT: Praeger, 2000.

Engs, Ruth Clifford. "Eugenics, Birth Control, and Immigration Restriction." In *A Blackwell Companion to the Harding, Coolidge, and Hoover Presidencies*, edited by Katherine Sibley, 313–337. Wiley-Blackwood, October 2014. http://hdl.handle.net/2022/19003 (accessed June 4, 2018).

Engs, Ruth Clifford. *The Eugenics Movement: An Encyclopedia*. Westport, CT: Greenwood Publishing Co., 2005.

Engs, Ruth Clifford. *The Field Hospital That Never Was: Diary of Lt. Col. Karl D. Macmillan's, MD, 96th Field Hospital in China-India-Burma Theater 1945, WWII*. Bloomington, IN: Magic Farm, 2015.

Engs, Ruth Clifford. *The Progressive Era Health Reform Movements: A Historical Dictionary*. Greenwood Publishing: Westport, CT, 2003.

Fang, Hai. "The Chinese Health Care System." International Health Care System Profiles: Countries. Commonwealth Fund, [2016] https://international.commonwealthfund.org/countries/china (accessed July 22, 2018).

Fass, Paula S. "How Americans Raise Their Children: Generational Relations over Two Hundred Years." 27th Annual Lecture of the GHI, Washington, DC, November 14, 2013. *Bulletin of the GHI* 54 (Spring 2014): 7–19. https://www.ghi-dc.org

/fileadmin/user_upload/GHI_Washington/Publications/Bulletin54/bu54_007.pdf (accessed May 30, 2017).

Field, Marilyn J., ed. *Dental Education at the Crossroads Challenges and Change*. Committee on the Future of Dental Education, Division of Health Care Services, Institute of Medicine. Washington, DC: National Academies Press, 1995.

Fisher, William H., Jeffrey L. Geller, and John A. Pandiani. "The Changing Role of the State Psychiatric Hospital." *Health Affairs* 28, no. 3 (May/June 2009): 676–684. http://content.healthaffairs.org/content/28/3/676.full (accessed December 21, 2016).

Fisk, Donald M. *American Labor in the 20th Century*, January 30, 2003. Originally published in *Compensation and Working Conditions*. (Fall 2001): 1–8. https://www.bls.gov/opub/mlr/cwc/american-labor-in-the-20th-century.pdf (accessed March 17, 2017).

Fleischer, Victoria. "Mentally Ill Shackled and Neglected in Africa's Crisis Regions." *PBS News Hour*, July 10, 2014. http://www.pbs.org/newshour/art/mentally-ill-shackled-and-neglected-in-africas-crisis-regions/ (accessed December 23, 2016).

Frith, John. "The History of Plague—Part 1. The Three Great Pandemics." *Journal of Military and Veterans' Health* 20, no. 2 (April 2012): 8–12. http://jmvh.org/article/the-history-of-plague-part-1-the-three-great-pandemics/ (accessed July 25, 2017).

Fry, Richard. *It's Becoming More Common for Young Adults to Live at Home—and for Longer Stretches*. Pew Research Center. Fact Tank, May 5, 2017. http://www.pewresearch.org/fact-tank/2017/05/05/its-becoming-more-common-for-young-adults-to-live-at-home-and-for-longer-stretches/ (accessed May 25, 2017).

Fulton, John F. "History of Medical Education." *British Medical Journal* 2, no. 4834 (August 1953): 457–461. https://www.ncbi.nlm.nih.gov/pmc/articles/PMC2029428/?page=1 (accessed December 14, 2017).

Funk, Cary, and Brian Kennedy. *The Politics of Climate*. Washington, DC: Pew Research Center. Internet and Technology, October 4, 2016. http://www.pewinternet.org/2016/10/04/the-politics-of-climate/ (accessed June 29, 2018).

Gabriel, Richard A. *Between Flesh and Steel: A History of Military Medicine from the Middle Ages to the War in Afghanistan*. Lincoln, NE: Potomac Books, an imprint of the University of Nebraska Press, 2016.

Gautam, Shiv, and Nikhil Jain. "Indian Culture and Psychiatry." *Indian Journal of Psychiatry* 52, Supplement 1 (January 2010): 309–313. https://www.ncbi.nlm.nih.gov/pmc/articles/PMC3146223/ (accessed December 26, 2016).

Gawande, Atul. "Two Hundred Years of Surgery." *New England Journal of Medicine* 366 (May 3, 2012): 1716–1723. http://www.nejm.org/doi/full/10.1056/NEJMra1202392 (accessed April 21, 2018).

Geffen, Laurence. "A Brief History of Medical Education and Training in Australia." *Medical Journal of Australia* 201, no. 1 Supplement (July 7, 2014): s19–s22. https://www.mja.com.au/journal/2014/201/1/brief-history-medical-education-and-training-australia (accessed May 18, 2017).

Ghendon, Youri. "Introduction to Pandemic Influenza through History." *European Journal of Epidemiology* 10, no. 4 (1994): 451–453.

Gillett, Mary C. "Public Health in Cuba." Chapter 9 in *The Army Medical Department 1865–1917*. Washington, DC: Center of Military History, United States Army, 1995, 229–255. http://history.amedd.army.mil/booksdocs/spanam/gillet3/default.html (accessed October 19, 2017).

Ginchereau, Eugene. "The American Ambulance in Paris, 1914–1917. Part I: The Creation of the American Ambulance." *Military Medicine* 180, no. 12 (2015): 1201–1202.

Ginchereau, Eugene. "The American Ambulance in Paris, 1914 to 1917. Part IV: The American Ambulance and the American Red Cross." *Military Medicine* 181, no. 3 (2016): 191–192.

Glauser, Wendy. "United States Still Too Lenient on 'Faith Healing' Parents, say Children's Rights Advocates." *Canadian Medical Association Journal* 183, no. 11 (August 2011): E709–E710. https://www.ncbi.nlm.nih.gov/pmc/articles/PMC3153535/ (accessed April 7, 2018).

Global Commission on Drug Policy. *War on Drugs: Report of the Global Commission on Drug Policy.* Geneva: Global Commission on Drug Policy, 2011. https://www.globalcommissionondrugs.org/wp-content/themes/gcdp_v1/pdf/Global_Commission_Report_English.pdf (accessed February 6, 2013).

Gochfeld, Michael, and Bernard D. Goldstein. "Lessons in Environmental Health in the Twentieth Century." *Annual Review of Public Health* 20 (May 1999): 35–53.

Gold, Rachel Benson. "Lessons from Before Roe: Will Past Be Prologue?" *Guttmacher Policy Review* 6, no. 1 (March 1, 2003). https://www.guttmacher.org/gpr/2003/03/lessons-roe-will-past-be-prologue (accessed March 3, 2017).

Goldacre, Ben. *Bad Pharma: How Drug Companies Mislead Doctors and Harm Patients.* London: Fourth Estate, 2012.

Goldman, Marlene B., Rebecca Troisi, and Kathryn M. Rexrode, eds. *Women and Health.* 2nd ed. Amsterdam: Academic Press, 2013.

Gole, Sanjay. *Strategies to Reduce Maternal Mortality And Morbidity In Rural India.* Current Articles, Federation of Obstetric and Gynecological Societies of India, June 29, 2015. http://www.fogsi.org/strategies-to-reduce-maternal-mortality-and-morbidity-in-rural-india/ (accessed March 12, 2017).

Gordon, Linda. *The Moral Property of Women: A History of Birth Control Politics in America.* Urbana: University of Illinois Press, 1974.

Gould, Skye, and Lauren F. Friedman. "Something Startling Is Going on with Antidepressant Use around the World." *Business Insider* (February 4, 2016). http://www.businessinsider.com/countries-largest-antidepressant-drug-users-2016-2 (accessed 30 January 2017).

Griffiths, Clare, and Anita Brock. "Twentieth Century Mortality Trends in England and Wales." *Health Statistics Quarterly* 18 (Summer 2003): 5–17. https://www.ons.gov.uk/ons/rel/hsq/health-statistics-quarterly/no--18--summer-2003/health-statistics-quarterly.pdf#page=6 (accessed January 17, 2018).

Griffiths, Sarah. "Drug Map Reveals the Substances Your Country Is Addicted To: Scotland Is Hooked on Cocaine, Iceland Smokes the Most Cannabis and Opiates Are Rife in the US," *The Daily Mail,* November 30, 2015. http://www.dailymail.co.uk/sciencetech/article-3333877/Drug-map-reveals-substances-country-addicted-Scotland-hooked-cocaine-Iceland-smokes-cannabis-opiates-rife-US.html (accessed December 17, 2016).

Grob, Gerald N. *Mental Illness and American Society, 1875–1940.* Princeton, NJ: Princeton University Press, 1983.

Gupta, Indrani, and Mrigesh Bhatia. *The Indian Health Care System.* The Commonwealth Fund. International Health Care System Profiles: Countries, 2016. https://international.commonwealthfund.org/countries/india/ (accessed July 29, 2018).

Gupta, M. C. "What Are the Legal Aspects of Over-the-Counter Sale of Allopathic Medicines?" *Indian Journal of Clinical Practice* 23, no. 12 (May 2013): 864–868. http://medind.nic.in/iaa/t13/i5/iaat13i5p864.pdf (accessed January 6, 2017).

Gureje, O., and A. Alem. "Mental Health Policy Development in Africa." *Bulletin of the World Health Organization* 78, no 4. (2000). http://www.who.int/bulletin/archives/78(4)475.pdf (accessed 20 December 2016).

Guttmacher Institute. Data Center. Regions. https://data.guttmacher.org/regions (accessed March 13, 2017).

Haddad, Lisa B., and Nawal M. Nour. "Unsafe Abortion: Unnecessary Maternal Mortality." *Reviews in Obstetrics and Gynecology* 2, no. 2 (Spring 2009): 122–126. https://www.ncbi.nlm.nih.gov/pmc/articles/PMC2709326/ (accessed March 12, 2017).

Hamel, Ronald P., updated by Kevin O'Rourke. *The Roman Catholic Tradition Religious Beliefs and Healthcare Decisions*. Park Ridge, IL: Park Ridge Center for the Study of Health, Faith, and Ethics, 2002. https://www.advocatehealth.com/assets/documents/faith/roman_catholic3.pdf (accessed February 18, 2018).

Han, Wei. "Health Care System Reforms in Developing Countries." *Journal of Public Health Research* 1, no. 3 (December 2012): 199–207. https://www.ncbi.nlm.nih.gov/pmc/articles/PMC4140377/

Hannam, June, Katherine Holden, and Mitzi Auchterlonie. *International Encyclopedia of Women's Suffrage*. Santa Barbara, CA: ABC-CLIO, 2000.

"A History of China's One-Child Policy." *The Washington Post*, November 15, 2013. https://www.washingtonpost.com/apps/g/page/world/a-history-of-chinas-one-child-policy/596/ (accessed March 12, 2017).

Högberg U., S. Wall, and G. Broström. "The Impact of Early Medical Technology on Maternal Mortality in Late 19th Century Sweden." *International Journal of Gynecology & Obstetrics* 24, no. 4 (August 1986): 251–61. https://www.ncbi.nlm.nih.gov/pubmed/2878833 (accessed March 13, 2017).

Howe, Neil, and William Strauss. *Generations: The History of Americas Future, 1584 to 2069*. New York: William Morrow, 1991.

Hurst, Jillian. "A Modern Cosmas and Damian: Sir Roy Calne and Thomas Starzl Receive the 2012 Lasker-Debakey Clinical Medical Research Award." *The Journal of Clinical Investigation* 122, no. 10 (October 1, 2012): 3378–3382. https://www.ncbi.nlm.nih.gov/pmc/articles/PMC3461936/ (accessed May 3, 2018).

Hurwitz, Brian. "Medical Humanities and Medical Alterity in Fiction and in Life." *Journal of Medical Ethics* 41, no. 1 (January 2015): 64–67. https://www.ncbi.nlm.nih.gov/pmc/articles/PMC5146638/ (accessed December 12, 2017).

icasualties.org. (Iraq Coalition Causality Count) "Operation Iraqi Freedom: Iraq Coalition Military Fatalities by Year" and "Operation Enduring Freedom/Afghanistan: Afghanistan Coalition Military Fatalities by Year," 2009. http://icasualties.org/ (accessed November 4, 2017).

Ighobor, Kingsley. "Improving Maternal Health in Africa." *Africa Renewal. (December 2014).* http://www.un.org/africarenewal/magazine/december-2014/improving-maternal-health-africa (accessed March 13, 2017).

Imamura, F., et al. "Efficacy of the Treatment Program for Substance Use Disorder under the Medical Treatment and Supervision Act in Japan." *Nihon Arukoru Yakubutsu Igakkai Zasshi.* 45, no. 5 (October 2010):452–63. https://www.ncbi.nlm.nih.gov/pubmed/21226343 (accessed 24 December 2016).

India. Ministry of Health and Family Welfare. *National Mental Health Programme*. http://164.100.158.44/index1.php?lang=1&level=2&sublinkid=2381&lid=1962 (accessed December 15, 2016).

Inhorn, Marcia C., and Soraya Tremayne. "Islam, Assisted Reproduction, and the Bioethical Aftermath." *Journal of Religion and Health* 55, no. 2 (April 2016): 422–430. https://www.ncbi.nlm.nih.gov/pubmed/26602421 (accessed February 28, 2018).

Institute for Women's Policy Research. "Pay Equity & Discrimination." Employment, Education, & Economic Change. (2017). https://iwpr.org/issue/employment-education-economic-change/pay-equity-discrimination/ (accessed March 16, 2017).

Intergovernmental Panel on Climate Change. *Climate Change 2007: Impacts, Adaptation and Vulnerability. Contribution of Working Group II to the Fourth Assessment; Report of the Intergovernmental Panel on Climate Change,* edited by M. L. Parry et al. Cambridge: Cambridge University Press, 2007. https://www.ipcc.ch/pdf/assessment-report/ar4/wg2/ar4_wg2_full_report.pdf (accessed April 20, 2017).

International Drug Policy Consortium. *The UN General Assembly Special Session on Drugs (UNGASS) 2016*. http://idpc.net/policy-advocacy/the-un-general-assembly-special-session-on-drugs-ungass-2016 (accessed January 30, 2017).

International Labour Office. *Making Progress against Child Labour: Global Estimates and Trends 2000*–2012. Geneva: ILO. International Programme on the Elimination of Child Labour, 2013. http://www.ilo.org/wcmsp5/groups/public/---ed_norm/---ipec/documents/publication/wcms_221513.pdf (accessed April 20, 2017).

International Narcotics Control Board. *Report of the International Narcotics Control Board on the Availability of Internationally Controlled Drugs: Ensuring Adequate Access for Medical and Scientific Purposes*. Vienna: International Narcotics Control Board, 2010. http://www.incb.org/documents/Publications/AnnualReports/AR2010/Supplement-AR10_availability_English.pdf (accessed January 30, 2017).

Irby, David M., Molly Cooke, and Bridget C. O'Brien. "Calls for Reform of Medical Education by the Carnegie Foundation for the Advancement of Teaching: 1910 and 2010." *Academic Medicine* 85, no. 2 (February 2010): 220–227. https://www.ncbi.nlm.nih.gov/pubmed/20107346 (accessed December 26 2017).

Jacob, K. S. "Indian Psychiatry and Classification of Psychiatric Disorders." *Indian Journal of Psychiatry* 52, Supplement 1 (January 2010): 104–109. https://www.ncbi.nlm.nih.gov/pmc/articles/PMC3146213/ (accessed December 26, 2016).

Jatlaoui, Tara C., et al. "Abortion Surveillance—United States, 2013." *Morbidity and Mortality Weekly Report: Surveillance Summaries* 65, no. 12 (November 25, 2016): 1–44. https://www.cdc.gov/mmwr/volumes/65/ss/ss6512a1.htm (accessed March 26, 2017).

Johnson, Owen A., et al. "Electronic Health Records in the UK and USA." *The Lancet* 384, no. 9947 (September 13, 2014): 954. https://www.thelancet.com/journals/lancet/article/PIIS0140-6736(14)61626-3/fulltext (accessed August 29, 2018).

Joint United Nations Programme on HIV and AIDS. *Prevention Gap Report*. Geneva: UNAIDS, 2016. http://www.unaids.org/sites/default/files/media_asset/2016-prevention-gap-report_en.pdf (accessed March 17, 2017).

Joint Working Group. *Mind the Gaps: Meeting the Needs of People with Co-Occurring Substance Misuse and Mental Health Problems. Report of the Joint Working Group.* Scottish Advisory Committee on Drug Misuse (SACDM); Scottish Advisory Committee on Alcohol Misuse (SACAM). Edinburgh: St Andrew's House, 2003. http://www.gov.scot/resource/doc/47063/0013752.pdf (accessed December 13, 2016).

Jones, Edgar, and Simon Wessely. "Battle for the Mind: World War 1 and the Birth of Military Psychiatry." Series: Legacy of the 1914–18 War. *The Lancet* 384, no. 9955 (November 8, 2014): 1708–1714. https://www.thelancet.com/pdfs/journals/lancet/PIIS0140-6736(14)61260-5.pdf (accessed October 25, 2017).

Kane, Penny, ed. *Women and Occupational Health: Issues and Policy Paper Prepared for the Global Commission on Women's Health*. Geneva: WHO, 1999. http://www.who.int/occupational_health/publications/en/oehwomenandoh.pdf (accessed March 16, 2017).

Kantor, Elizabeth D., et al., "Trends in Prescription Drug Use among Adults in the United States From 1999–2012," *Journal of the American Medical Association* 314, no. 17 (November 3, 2015): 1818–1830, https://jamanetwork.com/journals/jama/fullarticle/2467552 (accessed January 30, 2017).

Kaper, James B., J. Glenn Morris, Jr., and Myron M. Levine. "Cholera." *Clinical Microbiology Review* 8, no. 1 (January 1995): 48–86. https://www.ncbi.nlm.nih.gov/pmc/articles/PMC172849/pdf/080048.pdf (accessed July 15, 2017).

Kelley, Edward. *Medical Tourism*. Geneva: WHO. Patient Safety Programme. 2013. http://www.who.int/global_health_histories/seminars/kelley_presentation_medical_tourism.pdf (accessed January 10, 2018).

Kickbusch, Ilona, et al. "Germany's Expanding Role in Global Health." *Lancet* 390, no. 10097 (August 26, 2017): 898–912. https://www.thelancet.com/journals/lancet/article/PIIS0140-6736(17)31460-5/fulltext (accessed July 27, 2028).

Klatsky, Arthur L. "Moderate Drinking and Reduced Risk of Heart Disease." *Alcohol Research & Health* 23, no. 1 (1999): 15–23. https://pubs.niaaa.nih.gov/publications/arh23-1/15-24.pdf (accessed August 29, 2018).

Koizumi, K., and P. Harris. "Mental Health Care in Japan." *Hospital and Community Psychiatry* 43, no. 11 (November 1992): 1100–1103. https://www.ncbi.nlm.nih.gov/pubmed/1490709 (accessed December 26, 2016).

Kugeler, Kiersten J., et al. "Epidemiology of Human Plague in the United States, 1900–2012." *Emerging Infectious Diseases* 21, no. 1 (January 2015): 16–22. https://www.ncbi.nlm.nih.gov/pmc/articles/PMC4285253/ (accessed July 15, 2017).

Lahtinen, Pasi, Helena Leino-Kilpi, and Leena Salminen. "Nursing Education in the European Higher Education Area—Variations in Implementation." *Nurse Education Today* 34, no. 6 (June 2014): 1040–1047. https://www.ncbi.nlm.nih.gov/pubmed/24090615 (accessed January 17, 2018).

Lane, Christopher. *Shyness: How Normal Behavior Became a Sickness*. New Haven: Yale University Press, 2007.

Lehmann, Heinz E., and Thomas A. Ban. "The History of the Psychopharmacology of Schizophrenia." *Canadian Journal of Psychiatry* 42 (1997): 152–162. http://www.edumed.org.br/cursos/neurociencia/lehmann.pdf (accessed November 28, 2016).

Li, Ling, and Fu, Hongqiao. "China's Health Care System Reform: Progress and Prospects." *The International Journal of Health Planning and Management* 32 no. 3 (July 2017): 240–253. https://www.ncbi.nlm.nih.gov/pubmed/28612498 (accessed July 28, 2018).

Lisonkova, S., et al. "Temporal Trends in Maternal Mortality in Canada II: Estimates Based on Hospitalization Data." *Journal of Obstetrics and Gynaecology Canada* 33, no. 10 (October 2011): 1020–1030. https://www.sciencedirect.com/science/article/pii/S1701216316350514 (accessed March 3, 2017).

Liu, Jin, et al. "Mental Health System in China: History, Recent Service Reform and Future Challenges. *World Psychiatry* 10, no. 3 (October 2011): 210–216. https://www.ncbi.nlm.nih.gov/pmc/articles/PMC3188776/ (accessed December 24, 2016).

Loudon, Irvine. "A Brief History of Homeopathy." *Journal of the Royal Society of Medicine* 99, no. 12 (December 2006): 607–610. https://www.ncbi.nlm.nih.gov/pmc/articles/PMC1676328/ (accessed January 10, 2018).

Loudon, Irvine. "Maternal Mortality in the Past and Its Relevance to Developing Countries today." *American Journal of Clinical Nutrition* 72, no. 1 (July 2000): 241s–246s. http://ajcn.nutrition.org/content/72/1/241s.full#F1 (accessed February 27, 2017).

Lucey, Catherine. "Individualization and Standardization in Medical Education: Holy Grail or Third Rail?" Web seminar presented by Catherine Lucey on September 15, 2011. International Association of Medical Science Educators. http://www.iamse.org/websem/individualization-and-standardization-in-medical-education-holy-grail-or-third-rail/ (accessed January 18, 2018).

Ludmerer, K. *Time to Heal: American Medical Education from the Turn of the Century to the Era of Managed Care*. Oxford; New York: Oxford University Press, 1999.

Lund, Crick, et al. Men*tal Health Policy Development and Implementation in South Africa: A Situation Analysis, Phase 1, Country Report.* Cape Town: Mental Health and Poverty Project, 2008. http://www.who.int/mental_health/policy/development/SA%20Country%20Report%20-%20Final%20Draft%20Jan%202008.pdf (accessed December 23, 2016).

Lutheran Church. Missouri Synod. *Christian Care at Life's End. A Report of the Commission on Theology and Church Relations of the Lutheran Church—Missouri Synod.* [St. Louis, Mo.]: The Commission, 1993. https://www.lcms.org/Document.fdoc?src=lcm&id=361 (accessed April 6, 2018).

MacDorman, Marian F., T. J. Matthews, and Eugene Declercq. "Trends in Out-of-Hospital Births in the United States, 1990–2012." *NCHS data brief,* no. 144 (March 2014). https://www.cdc.gov/nchs/data/databriefs/db144.pdf (accessed March 4, 2017).

MacGarrigle, George L. *Central Burma. The US Army Campaign of World War II.* Washington, DC: U.S. Army Center of Military History. CMH Pub 72–3. https://history.army.mil/html/books/072/72-37/CMH_Pub_72-37.pdf (accessed September 26, 2017).

Mandell, Wallace. *Origins of Mental Health: The Realization of an Idea.* [Baltimore]: John Hopkins Bloomberg School of Public Health. Department of Mental Hygiene, 1995. [later posted] http://www.jhsph.edu/departments/mental-health/about-us/origins-of-mental-health.html (accessed December 20, 2016).

Manring, M. M., et al. "Treatment of War Wounds: A Historical Review." *Clinical Orthopedics and Related Research* 467, no 8 (August 2009): 2168–2191. https://www.ncbi.nlm.nih.gov/pmc/articles/PMC2706344/ (accessed October 27, 2017).

Marlatt, G. Alan. "Harm Reduction: Come as You Are." *Addictive Behaviors* 21, no.6 (November–December 1996): 779–788. https://openlab.citytech.cuny.edu/nehhealth2013/files/2013/11/G-Alan-Marlatt-Harm-Reduction-Come-As-You-Are.pdf (accessed March 16, 2017).

Mathers, Colin D., and Dejan Loncar. "Projections of Global Mortality and Burden of Disease from 2002 to 2030." *PLoS Medicine* (November 28, 2006): e442. http://journals.plos.org/plosmedicine/article?id=10.1371/journal.pmed.0030442 (accessed July 24, 2017).

McEwen, John. *A History of Therapeutic Goods Regulation in Australia.* Canberra: Commonwealth of Australia, 2007. https://www.tga.gov.au/sites/default/files/history-tg-regulation.pdf (accessed January 8, 2017).

McGee, Andrew. "In Places Where It's Legal, How Many People Are Ending Their Lives Using Euthanasia?" *The Conversation,* March 2, 2017. http://theconversation.com/in-places-where-its-legal-how-many-people-are-ending-their-lives-using-euthanasia-73755 (accessed March 1, 2018).

Meadows, Michelle. "Promoting Safe and Effective Drugs for 100 Years." *FDA Consumer Magazine,* Centennial Edition, January-February 2006. https://www.fda.gov/downloads/AboutFDA/History/ProductRegulation/UCM593520.pdf (accessed January 10, 2016).

Medco Health Solutions. *America's State of Mind.* Franklin Lakes, NJ: Medco Health Solutions, Inc., 2011. http://apps.who.int/medicinedocs/documents/s19032en/s19032en.pdf (accessed February 2, 2017).

Meisner, Hans. "Milestones in Surgery: 60 Years of Open Heart Surgery." *Thoracic and Cardiovascular Surgeon* 62, no.8 (2014): 645–650. https://pdfs.semanticscholar.org/d0cd/c43a1317f68983f712a416b1257a80ebddad.pdf (accessed February 20, 2018).

Mental Health America. *Our History.* Mental Health America, [n.d.] http://www.mentalhealthamerica.net/our-history (accessed December 3, 2016).

Merikangas, Kathleen R., et al. "Prevalence and Correlates of Bipolar Spectrum Disorder in the World Mental Health Survey Initiative." *Archive of General Psychiatry* 68, no. 3 (March 2011): 241–251. https://www.ncbi.nlm.nih.gov/pmc/articles/PMC3486639/ (accessed December 3, 2016).

Mills, Anne. "Health Care Systems in Low-and Middle-Income Countries." *New England Journal of Medicine* 370 (February 6, 2014): 552–557. https://www.nejm.org/doi/full/10.1056/NEJMra1110897 (accessed August 1, 2018).

Mokgobi, M. G. "Understanding Traditional African Healing." *African Journal for Physical, Health Education, Recreation and Dance* 20, Supplement 2 (September 2014): 24–34. https://www.ncbi.nlm.nih.gov/pmc/articles/PMC4651463/ (accessed January 27, 2018).

Moore, Thomas J. *Deadly Medicine: Why Tens of Thousands of Heart Patients Died in America's Worst Drug Disaster.* New York: Simon & Schuster, 1995.

Moran, James E. *History of Madness and Mental Illness: A Short History of Care and Treatment in Canada*, 2009. http://www.caringminds.ca/history-of-madness-and-mental-illness-a-short-history-of-care-and-treatment-in-canada/ (accessed December 3, 2016).

Nadelmann, Ethan A. "Drug Prohibition in the United States: Costs, Consequences, and Alternatives." *Notre Dame Journal of Law Ethics and Public Policy* 5, no. 3 *Symposium on Drugs and Society.* (February 2014): 783–808. http://scholarship.law.nd.edu/cgi/viewcontent.cgi?article=1511&context=ndjlepp (accessed February 7, 2017).

National Aeronautics and Space Administration. Goddard Institute for Space Studies. *Global Land-Ocean Temperature Index in 0.01 Degrees Celsius Base Period: 1951–1980.* https://data.giss.nasa.gov/gistemp/tabledata_v3/GLB.Ts+dSST.txt January 2018 (accessed June 30, 2018).

National Alliance on Mental Illness. *About NAMI.* https://www.nami.org/About-NAMI (accessed December 14, 2016).

National Center for Education in Maternal and Child Health. *SUID/SIDS. Statistics*, updated October 2013. https://www.ncemch.org/suid-sids/statistics/#international (accessed June 9, 2017).

Nizamie, S. Haque, and Nishant Goyal. "History of Psychiatry in India." *Indian Journal of Psychiatry* 52, Supplement 1 (January 2010): S7–S12. https://www.ncbi.nlm.nih.gov/pmc/articles/PMC3146221/ (accessed December 15, 2016).

NYU School of Medicine. Literature Arts Medicine Database. http://medhum.med.nyu.edu/?action=new (accessed December 12, 2017).

Oberlander, Jonathan. "Long Time Coming: Why Health Reform Finally Passed." *Health Affairs* 29, no. 6 (June 2010): 1112–1116. https://web.archive.org/web/20161205105530/http://content.healthaffairs.org/content/29/6/1112.full (accessed July 31, 2018).

O'Donnell, Owen. "Access to Health Care in Developing Countries: Breaking Down Demand Side Barriers." *Cadernos de Saúde Pública* 23, no.12 (Dec. 2007). http://www.scielo.br/scielo.php?script=sci_arttext&pid=S0102-311X2007001200003 (accessed July 28, 2018).

Okasha, Ahmed. "Mental Health in Africa: The Role of the WPA." *World Psychiatry* 1, no. 1 (February 2002): 32–35. https://www.ncbi.nlm.nih.gov/pmc/articles/PMC1489826/ (accessed December 15, 2016).

"On the Medicalization of Our Culture." *Harvard Magazine*, April 23, 2009. http://harvardmagazine.com/2009/04/medicalization-of-our-culture (accessed January 30, 2017).

Organisation for Economic Co-operation and Development. *Universal Health Coverage and Health Outcomes: Final Report.* Paris: OECD, July 22, 2016. https://www

.oecd.org/els/health-systems/Universal-Health-Coverage-and-Health-Outcomes-OECD-G7-Health-Ministerial-2016.pdf (accessed July 23, 2018).

Our Documents. *Social Security Act Amendments (1965)*. https://www.ourdocuments.gov/doc.php?flash=false&doc=99# (accessed July 7, 2018).

Papac, Rose J. "Origins of Cancer Therapy." *Yale Journal of Biology and Medicine* 74, no. 6 (November–December 2001): 391–398. https://www.ncbi.nlm.nih.gov/pmc/articles/PMC2588755/ (accessed February 2, 2017).

Parker, George F. "DSM-5 and Psychotic and Mood Disorders." *The Journal of the American Academy of Psychiatry and the Law 42* (2014): 182–190. http://jaapl.org/content/jaapl/42/2/182.full.pdf (accessed December 15, 2016).

Patel, Vikram, et al. "The Magnitude of and Health System Responses to the Mental Health Treatment Gap in Adults in India and China." Series: China–India Mental Health Alliance. *The Lancet* 388, no. 10063 (17 December 2016–6 January 2017): 3074–3084. http://www.globalmentalhealth.org/sites/default/files/Patel_Lancet_2016.pdf (accessed December 23, 2016).

Paulozzi, Leonard J., Karin A. Mack, and Jason M. Hockenberry. "Vital Signs: Variation among States in Prescribing of Opioid Pain Relievers and Benzodiazepine—United States, 2012." *Morbidity and Mortality Weekly Report* 63, no. 26 (July 4, 2014): 563–568. https://www.cdc.gov/mmwr/preview/mmwrhtml/mm6326a2.htm?s_cid=mm6326a2_w#Tab (accessed January 30, 2017).

Payer, Lynn. *Disease-Mongers: How Doctors, Drug Companies, and Insurers Are Making You Feel Sick*. New York, John Wiley, 1992.

Perry, Heather R. *Recycling the Disabled: Army, Medicine, and Modernity in WWI Germany*. Manchester and New York: Manchester University Press, 2014.

Pew Research Center. *Abortion Laws around the World*. (Religion & Public Life), September 30, 2008. http://www.pewforum.org/2008/09/30/abortion-laws-around-the-world/ (accessed March 16, 2017).

Pew Research Center. *Religious Groups' Official Positions on Stem Cell Research*. (Religion & Public Life), July 17, 2008. http://www.pewforum.org/2008/07/17/religious-groups-official-positions-on-stem-cell-research/ (accessed March 22, 2017).

Pew Research Center. *Religious Groups' Views on End-of-Life Issues* (Religion & Public Life), November 21, 2013. http://www.pewforum.org/2013/11/21/religious-groups-views-on-end-of-life-issues/ (accessed March 8, 2018).

Pierce, Steven R. "Blood Transfusion in the First World War." *Medicine in the First World War*. University of Kansas Medical Center. Medicine in the First World War, last modified: Aug 26, 2018. http://www.kumc.edu/wwi/essays-on-first-world-war-medicine/index-of-essays/medicine/blood-transfusion.html (accessed September 26, 2017).

Pierik, Roland. "On Religious and Secular Exemptions: A Case Study of Childhood Vaccination Waivers." *Ethnicities* 17, no. 2 (April 1, 2017): 220–241. http://journals.sagepub.com/doi/full/10.1177/1468796817692629 (accessed March 22, 2017).

Plotkin, Stanley A. "The History of Rubella and Rubella Vaccination Leading to Elimination." *Clinical Infectious Disease* 43, Supplement 3 (November 2006): S164. https://academic.oup.com/cid/article/43/Supplement_3/S164/288915/The-History-of-Rubella-and-Rubella-Vaccination (accessed June 9, 2017).

Plotkin, Stanley A., and Susan L. Plotkin. "The Development of Vaccines: How the Past Led to the Future." *Nature Reviews Microbiology* 9 (December 2011): 889–893. http://www.nature.com/nrmicro/journal/v9/n12/fig_tab/nrmicro2668_I1.html (accessed February 6, 2017).

Pols, Hans, and Stephanie Oak. "War & Military Mental Health: The US Psychiatric Response in the 20th Century." *American Journal of Public Health* 97, no. 12 (December

2007): 2132–2142. https://www.ncbi.nlm.nih.gov/pmc/articles/PMC2089086/pdf/0972132.pdf (accessed September 27, 2017).

Popova, Svetlana, et al. "Estimation of National, Regional, and Global Prevalence of Alcohol Use During Pregnancy and Fetal Alcohol Syndrome: A Systematic Review and Aeta-analysis." *Lancet Global Health* 5, no. 3 (2017): e290–e299. http://www.thelancet.com/journals/langlo/article/PIIS2214-109X(17)30021-9/fulltext#secl (accessed May 19, 2017).

Prentice, Andrew M. "The Emerging Epidemic of Obesity in Developing Countries." *International Journal of Epidemiology* 35, no. 1 (February 1, 2006): 93–99. https://academic.oup.com/ije/article/35/1/93/849975 (accessed August 7, 2018).

Prince, M., et al. "No Health without Mental Health." Series: Global Mental Health. *Lancet* 370 (September 4, 2007): 859–877. http://www.thelancet.com/journals/lancet/article/PIIS0140-6736 (07)61238-0/abstract (accessed November 30, 2016).

Prince v. Massachusetts. 321 U.S. 158 (194*).* Justia, 2018. https://supreme.justia.com/cases/federal/us/321/158/ (accessed April 1, 2018).

Prüss-Ustün, Annette, et al. *Preventing Disease through Healthy Environments: A Global Assessment of the Burden of Disease from Environmental Risks.* Geneva: WHO, 2016. http://apps.who.int/iris/bitstream/handle/10665/204585/9789241565196_eng.pdf;jsessionid=A45DB25 DEF5A0B682F258CA2FB4F3C5?sequence=1 (accessed June 23, 2018).

Raguram, R., et al. "Traditional Community Resources for Mental Health: A Report of Temple Healing from India." *British Medical Journal* 325, no. 7354 (July 6, 2002): 38–40. https://www.bmj.com/content/bmj/325/7354/38.full.pdf (accessed December 26, 2016).

Ralston, Michelle, and Elizabeth Podrebarac. "Abortion Laws around the World." (Religion & Public Life). Pew Research Center, September 30, 2008. http://www.pewforum.org/2008/09/30/abortion-laws-around-the-world/ (accessed April 1, 2018).

Ramamurthi, B. "Stereotactic Surgery in India: The Past, Present and the Future." *Neurology India* 48, no. 1 (2000): 1–7. http://www.neurologyindia.com/text.asp?2000/48/1/1/1482 (accessed December 26, 2016).

Ramesh, Aramandla, et al. "Global Environmental Distribution and Human Health Effects of Polycyclic Aromatic Hydrocarbons." In *Global Contamination Trends of Persistent Organic Chemicals*, edited by Bommanna G. Loganathan and Paul Kwan-Sing Lam, 97–126. Boca Raton, FL: CRC Press, 2011.

Rasmussen, Nicolas. "America's First Amphetamine Epidemic 1929–1971, A Quantitative and Qualitative Retrospective with Implications for the Present." *American Journal of Public Health* 98, no. 6 (June 2008): 974–985. https://www.ncbi.nlm.nih.gov/pmc/articles/PMC2377281/ (accessed December 4, 2016).

Ratanawijitrasin, Sauwakon, and Eshetu Wondemagegnehu. *Effective Drug Regulation: A Multicounty Study.* Malta: WHO, 2002. http://apps.who.int/medicinedocs/pdf/s2300e/s2300e.pdf (accessed January 8, 2017).

Raymond, Elizabeth G., and David A. Grimes. "The Comparative Safety of Legal Induced Abortion and Childbirth in the United States." *Obstetrics and Gynecology* 119, 2 pt. 1 (February 2012): 215–219. https://www.ncbi.nlm.nih.gov/pubmed/22270271 (accessed April 9, 2018).

Reuter, Peter, and Alex Stevens. *An Analysis of UK Drug Policy—A Monograph Prepared for the UK Drug Policy Commission.* London: UK Drug Policy Commission, 2007. http://www.ukdpc.org.uk/wp-content/uploads/Policy%20report%20-%20An%20analysis%20of%20UK%20drug%20policy.pdf (accessed January 6, 2017).

Reyes-Ortiz, Carlos A., Michael Rodriguez, and Kyriakos S. Markides. "The Role of Spirituality Healing with Perceptions of the Medical Encounter among Latinos." *Journal of General Internal Medicine* 24, supplement 3 (November 2009): 542–547. https://www.ncbi.nlm.nih.gov/pmc/articles/PMC2764036/pdf/11606_2009_Article_1067.pdf (accessed December 12, 2016).

Rogers, D. J., et al. "The Global Distribution of Yellow Fever and Dengue." *Advances in Parasitology* 62 (2006): 181–220. https://www.ncbi.nlm.nih.gov/pmc/articles/PMC3164798/ (accessed June 28, 2017).

Rogo, Khama O., John Oucho, and Philip Mwalali. "Maternal Mortality." Chapter 16 in *Disease and Mortality in Sub-Saharan Africa*, edited by Dean T. Jamison, Richard G. Feachem, Malegapuru W. Makgoba, et al. Washington (DC): The International Bank for Reconstruction and Development/The World Bank, 2006. https://www.ncbi.nlm.nih.gov/books/NBK2288/ (accessed February 28, 2017).

Roser, Max. *Maternal Mortality, p*ublished online at OurWorldInData.org. (2016). https://ourworldindata.org/maternal-mortality/ (accessed February 28, 2017).

Russell, Dick. "How a West African Shaman Helped My Schizophrenic Son in a Way Western Medicine Couldn't," *Washington Post*, March 24, 2015. www.washingtonpost.com/amphtml/posteverything/wp/2015/03/24/how-a-west-african-shaman-helped-my-schizophrenic-son-in-a-way-western-medicine-couldnt/?client=ms-android-verizon (accessed December 22, 2016).

Sai, Frederick T. "Population, Family Planning, and the Future of Africa." *World Watch Magazine* 17, no. 5 (September/October 2004): 34–37. http://www.worldwatch.org/node/557 (accessed March 13, 2017).

Salize, Hans Joachim, Wulf Rössler, and Thomas Becker. "Mental Health Care in Germany: Current State and Trends." European Archives of Psychiatry and Clinical Neuroscience 257, no 2. (March 2007): 92–103. (accessed December 12, 2016).

Sallam, Hassan N. and N. H. Sallam. "Religious Aspects of Assisted Reproduction." *Facts, Views & Vision in ObGyn* 8, no. 1 (Mar 28, 2016): 33–48. https://www.ncbi.nlm.nih.gov/pmc/articles/PMC5096425/ (accessed March 1, 2017).

Salvador-Carulla, Luis, et al. "Intellectual Developmental Disorders: Towards a New Name, Definition and Framework for 'Mental Retardation/Intellectual Disability' in ICD-11." *World Psychiatry* 10, no. 3 (October 2011): 175–180. https://www.ncbi.nlm.nih.gov/pmc/articles/PMC3188762/pdf/wpa030175.pdf (accessed December 22, 2016).

Samal, Janmejaya, and Ranjit Kumar Dehury. "Family Planning Practices, Programmes and Policies in India Including Implants and Injectables with a Special Focus on Jharkhand, India: A Brief Review." *Journal of Clinical and Diagnostic Research* 9, no. 11 (November 2015): LE01–LE04. https://www.ncbi.nlm.nih.gov/pmc/articles/PMC4668441/ (accessed March 13, 2017).

Samy, Alexander Lourdes, Zahra Fazli Khalaf, and Wah-Yun Low. "Mental Health in the Asia-Pacific Region: An Overview." *International Journal of Behavioral Science* 10, no. 2 (2015): 9–18. https://www.tci-thaijo.org/index.php/IJBS/article/view/37550/pdf_21 (accessed December 20, 2016).

Sandstrom, Aleksandra. "Most States Allow Religious Exemptions from Child Abuse and Neglect Laws." Pew Research Center. *Fact Tank*, August 12, 2016. http://www.pewresearch.org/fact-tank/2016/08/12/most-states-allow-religious-exemptions-from-child-abuse-and-neglect-laws/ (accessed March 6, 2018).

Schneider, Eric C., et al. *Mirror, Mirror 2017: International Comparison Reflects Flaws and Opportunities for Better U.S. Health Care.* The Commonwealth Fund, 2017. https://interactives.commonwealthfund.org/2017/july/mirror-mirror/ (accessed July 22, 2018).

Schuckit, Marc A. "Recognition and Management of Withdrawal Delirium (Delirium Tremens)." *The New England Journal of Medicine* 371, no. 22 (November 27, 2014): 2109–2113. http://www.nejm.org/doi/full/10.1056/NEJMra1407298#t=article (accessed December 3, 2016).

Schütte, Stefanie, Paula N. Marin Acevedo, and Antoine Flahault. "Health Systems around the World—a Comparison of Existing Health System Rankings." *Journal of Global Health* 8, no. 1 (June 2018): 010407. https://www.ncbi.nlm.nih.gov/pmc/articles/PMC5857204/ (accessed August 3, 2018).

Sedgh, Gilda, et al. "Abortion Incidence between 1990 and 2014: Global, Regional, and Subregional Levels and Trends." *The Lancet* 388, no. 10041(July 16–22, 2016): 258–267.

Senthilingam, Meera. "Canada's Safe Injection Center Brings Drug Addicts 'Out of the Alleys'." *CNN* December 17, 2015. http://www.cnn.com/2015/12/16/health/insite-canada-injection-drug-addicts/ (accessed January 26, 2017).

Shaikh, Babar Tasneem, Syed Khurram Azmat, and Arslan Mazhar. "Family Planning and Contraception in Islamic Countries: A Critical Review of the Literature." *Journal of the Pakistan Medical Association* 63, no. 4 (Supplement 3) (April 2013): S-67–S-72. http://jpma.org.pk/supplement_details.php?article_id=122 (accessed April 6, 2017).

Sheldon, Huntington. *Boyd's Introduction to the Study of Disease,* 11th ed. Philadelphia: Lea & Febiger, 1992.

Shephard, Ben. "Psychology and the Great War, 1914–1918." *The Psychologist* 28 (November 2015): 944–947. https://thepsychologist.bps.org.uk/volume-28/november-2015/psychology-and-great-war-1914-1918 (accessed October 16, 2017).

Shorter, Edward. *A History of Psychiatry: From the Era of the Asylum to the Age of Prozac.* New York: John Wiley & Sons, 1997.

Sinclair, Upton. *Unseen Upton Sinclair: Nine Unpublished Stories, Essays and other Works,* edited by Ruth Clifford Engs. Jefferson, NC: McFarland Publishing Co., 2009.

Singh, Akashdeep. "Treatment of Mental Illness in India." (Letter) *Canadian Medical Association Journal* 176, no. 13 (June 19, 2007) http://www.cmaj.ca/content/176/13/1862.1 (accessed December 26, 2016).

Sjöström, Henning, and Robert Nilsson. *Thalidomide and the Power of the Drug Companies.* Harmondsworth: Penguin, 1972.

Solomon, Zahava, R. Shklar, and M. Mikulincer. "Frontline Treatment of Combat Stress Reaction: A 20-Year Longitudinal Evaluation Study." *The American Journal of Psychiatry* 162, no. 12 (December 2005): 2309–2314. https://www.ncbi.nlm.nih.gov/pubmed/16330595 (accessed September 26, 2017).

Stanley, David J. "Celluloid Angels: A Research Study of Nurses in Feature Films 1900–2007." *Journal of Advanced Nursing* 64, no. 1 (October 2008): 84–85. https://www.ncbi.nlm.nih.gov/pubmed/18808595 (accessed December 16, 2017).

Statistica. *Global Cigarette Consumption from 1880 to 2016 (in billion cigarettes)*, 2018. https://www.statista.com/statistics/279577/global-consumption-of-cigarettes-since-1880/ (accessed August 28, 2018).

Steel, Zachary, et al. "The Global Prevalence of Common Mental Disorders: A Systematic Review and Meta-Analysis: 1980–2013." *International Journal of Epidemiology* 43, no. 2 (2014): 476–493. https://www.ncbi.nlm.nih.gov/pmc/articles/PMC3997379/#__abstractid986278title (accessed December 8, 2016).

Swarup, Ishaan, and Joseph F. O'Donnell. "An Overview of the History of Orthopedic Surgery." *The American Journal of Orthopedics* 45, no. 7 (November/December 2016): E434–438. https://www.amjorthopedics.com/article/overview-history-orthopedic-surgery (accessed May 8, 2018).

Tandon, Ajay, et al. *Measuring Overall Health System Performance for 191 Countries.* GPE Discussion Paper Series: No. 30, EIP/GPE/EQC, 2000. Geneva: World Health Organization, 2001. http://www.who.int/healthinfo/paper30.pdf

Tasca, Cecilia, et al. "Women and Hysteria in the History of Mental Health." *Clinical Practice & Epidemiology in Mental Health* 8 (2012): 110–119. https://www.ncbi.nlm.nih.gov/pmc/articles/PMC3480686/ (accessed November 19, 2016).

Tchounwou, Paul B., et al. "Heavy Metals Toxicity and the Environment." *EXS* 101 (2012): 133–164. https://www.ncbi.nlm.nih.gov/pmc/articles/PMC4144270/pdf/nihms414261.pdf (accessed June 17, 2018).

Thomson, Sarah, et al., eds. *International Profiles of Health Care Systems, 2013: Australia, Canada, Denmark, England, France, Germany, Japan, Iceland, Italy, the Netherlands, New Zealand, Norway, Sweden, Switzerland, and the United States.* New York: Commonwealth Fund, 2013. https://www.commonwealthfund.org/sites/default/files/documents/___media_files_publications_fund_report_2013_nov_1717_thomson_intl_profiles_hlt_care_sys_2013_v2.pdf (accessed July 20, 2018).

Tobert, Natalie. *Cultural Perspectives on Mental Wellbeing: Spiritual Interpretations of Symptoms in Medical Practice.* London; Philadelphia: Jessica Kingsley Publishers, 2017.

Tone, Andrea. *The Age of Anxiety: A History of America's Turbulent Affair with Tranquilizers.* New York: Basic Books, 2009.

Torrel, Lindsey A., et al. "Global Cancer Incidence and Mortality Rates and Trends—An Update." *Cancer Epidemiology, Biomarkers & Prevention* 25, no. 1 (2016): 16–27. Published Online First December 14, 2015 https://pdfs.semanticscholar.org/69f7/e9c467ab20837ebd5d605dcfee2b5610f598.pdf (accessed August 27, 2018).

Torrey, E. Fuller, et al. "Documenting the Failure of Deinstitutionalization." Psychiatry 73, no. 2 (Summer 2010): 122–124.

Turcotte, Martin. "Women and Education," In *Women in Canada: A Gender-based Statistical Report.* Chart 7: "Percentage of women among full-time university enrolments, by program level, Canada, 1992/1993 to 2008/2009." Ottawa: Statistics Canada, 2011. https://www150.statcan.gc.ca/n1/en/pub/89-503-x/2010001/article/11542-eng.pdf?st=WuRLyE4c (accessed April 25, 2017).

U.K. National Health Service. *News Analysis: Controversial Mental Health Guide DSM-5,* August 15, 2013. http://www.nhs.uk/news/2013/08August/Pages/controversy-mental-health-diagnosis-and-treatment-dsm5.aspx (accessed December 15, 2016).

U.K. National Health Service. *What is the Law on the Sales of Medicines?* Page last reviewed November 26, 2015. http://www.nhs.uk/chq/pages/1325.aspx?categoryid=73&subcategoryid=101 (accessed January 7, 2017).

Ulrich, Ralf. *Most European Women Use Contraceptives.* Washington, DC: Population Reference Bureau, 2001. http://www.prb.org/Publications/Articles/2001/MostEuropeanWomenUseContraceptives.aspx (accessed March 12, 2017).

UN Department of Economic and Social Affairs. *The World's Women 2015: Trends and Statistics.* New York: United Nations, 2015. https://unstats.un.org/unsd/gender/downloads/worldswomen2015_report.pdf (accessed March 16, 2017).

UN Department of Economic and Social Affairs. Population Division. *World Contraceptive Use 2016,* 2016. http://www.un.org/en/development/desa/population/publications/dataset/contraception/wcu2016.shtml (accessed March 29, 2017).

UN Division for Sustainable Development Goals. *Sustainable Development Goal 6: Ensure availability and sustainable management of water and sanitation for all. Progress of Goal 6 in 2017,* 2017. https://sustainabledevelopment.un.org/sdg6 (Accessed June 21, 2018).

UN Every Woman Every Child. *The Global Strategy for Women's, Children's and Adolescents' Health (2016–2030)*. Every Woman Every Child, 2015. https://data.unicef.org/wp-content/uploads/2017/02/EWEC_globalstrategyreport_200915_FINAL_WEB.pdf (accessed February 20, 2017).
UN Habitat for a Better Urban Future. ACP-EC Joint Parliamentary Assembly, 12–14 February 2014, Mauritius. *Note on Urbanization Challenges, Waste Management, and Development.* http://www.europarl.europa.eu/intcoop/acp/2014_mauritius/pdf/un_habitat_presentation_en.pdf (accessed June 23, 2018).
UN Office of the High Commissioner for Human Rights. *Sexual and Reproductive Health and Rights.* http://www.ohchr.org/EN/Issues/Women/WRGS/Pages/HealthRights.aspx (accessed April 1, 2017).
UN *Sustainable Development Goals: 17 Goals to Transform Our World*, n.d. https://www.un.org/sustainabledevelopment/sustainable-development-goals/ (accessed August 29, 2018).
UN Women. *Progress of the World's Women 2015–2016: Transforming Economies, Realizing Rights.* New York: UN Women, 2015. http://progress.unwomen.org/en/2015/pdf/UNW_progressreport.pdf (accessed March 16, 2017).
UNICEF. *Maternal Mortality Fell by Almost Half Between 1990 and 2015.* (Maternal Mortality), February 2017. https://data.unicef.org/topic/maternal-health/maternal-mortality/ (accessed June 4, 2018).
UNICEF. *UNICEF Data: Monitoring the Situation of Children and Women.* https://data.unicef.org/?s=monitoring (accessed February 28, 2017).
UNICEF. East Asia and the Pacific. Media Centre. *East Asia Boasts Most Progress on Reducing Maternal Mortality*, 2015. https://www.unicef.org/media_24868.html (accessed June 9, 2018).
Unitarian Universalist Association. *The Right to Die With Dignity: 1988 General Resolution.* https://www.uua.org/action/statements/right-die-dignity (accessed April 8, 2018).
United Nations Convention against Illicit Traffic in Narcotic Drugs and Psychotropic Substances, Vienna, 20 December 1988. U. N. Treaty Series, vol. 1582, p. 95: https://treaties.un.org/doc/Publication/MTDSG/Volume%20I/Chapter%20VI/VI-19.en.pdf (accessed January 3, 2016).
United Nations Office of Drugs and Crime. *A Century of International Drug Control.* Vienna: UNODC, 2010. https://www.unodc.org/documents/data-and-analysis/Studies/100_Years_of_Drug_Control.pdf (accessed January 27, 2017).
United Nations Office of Drugs and Crime. *The 1912 Hague International Opium Convention*, January 23, 2009. https://www.unodc.org/unodc/en/frontpage/the-1912-hague-international-opium-convention.html (accessed January 3, 2016).
United Nations Office on Drugs and Crime. *Patterns and Trends of Amphetamine-Type Stimulants and Other Drugs: Challenges for Asia and the Pacific. A Report from the Global SMART Programme.* Bangkok: UNODC, November 2013. https://www.unodc.org/documents/scientific/2013_Regional_ATS_Report_web.pdf (accessed January 17, 2017).
United Nations Office on Drugs and Crime. *World Drug Report 2015.* New York: United Nations, 2015. https://www.unodc.org/documents/wdr2015/World_Drug_Report_2015.pdf (accessed December 20, 2016).
United Nations Office on Drugs and Crime. *World Drug Report 2016.* New York: United Nations, 2016. http://www.unodc.org/doc/wdr2016/WORLD_DRUG_REPORT_2016_web.pdf (accessed February 7, 2016).
United Network for Organ Sharing. *Theological Perspective on Organ and Tissue Donation.* Richmond, VA: UNOS, 2018. https://unos.org/donation/facts/theological-perspective-on-organ-and-tissue-donation/ (accessed April 5, 2018).

U.S. Central Intelligence Agency. "Illicit Drugs." In *The World Fact Book.* Washington, DC: Central Intelligence Agency, 2016. https://www.cia.gov/library/publications/the-world-factbook/fields/2086.html (accessed January 10, 2016).

U.S. Department of Education. National Center for Education Statistics. *Undergraduate Enrollment*, last updated: May 2016. https://nces.ed.gov/programs/coe/indicator_cha.asp (accessed April 5, 2017).

U.S. Department of Health and Human Services. Agency for Healthcare Research and Quality. *The Number of Practicing Primary Care Physicians in the United States. Primary Care Workforce Facts and Stats No. 1.* Publication: 12-P001-2-EF, page last reviewed July 2018. https://www.ahrq.gov/research/findings/factsheets/primary/pcwork1/index.html (accessed July 31, 2018).

U.S. Department of Health and Human Services. Center for Behavioral Health Statistics and Quality. *Behavioral Health Trends in the United States: Results from the 2014 National Survey on Drug Use and Health.* Rockville, MD: Substance Abuse and Mental Health Services Administration, 2015. HHS Publication No. SMA 15-4927, NSDUH Series H-50. https://www.samhsa.gov/data/sites/default/files/NSDUH-FRR1-2014/NSDUH-FRR1-2014.pdf (accessed November 29, 2016).

U.S. Department of Health and Human Services. Centers for Disease Control and Prevention. "Achievements in Public Health, 1900–1999: Control of Infectious Diseases." *Morbidity and Mortality Weekly Report* 48, no. 29 (July 30, 1999): 621–629. https://www.cdc.gov/mmwr/preview/mmwrhtml/mm4829a1.htm (accessed August 29, 2018).

U.S. Department of Health and Human Services. Centers for Disease Control and Prevention. "Achievements in Public Health, 1900–1999: Healthier Mothers and Babies." *Morbidity and Mortality Weekly Report* 48, no. 38 (October 01, 1999): 849–858. https://www.cdc.gov/mmwr/preview/mmwrhtml/mm4838a2.htm (accessed March 3, 2017).

U.S. Department of Health and Human Services. Centers for Disease Control and Prevention. *Burden of Mental Illness*, 2013. https://www.cdc.gov/mentalhealth/basics/burden.htm (accessed November 22, 2016).

U.S. Department of Health and Human Services. Centers for Disease Control and Prevention. *Global WASH Fast Facts.* (Global Water, Sanitation, & Hygiene (WASH), page last updated: April 11, 2016 https://www.cdc.gov/healthywater/global/wash_statistics.html (accessed June 29, 2018).

U.S. Department of Health and Human Services. Centers for Disease Control and Prevention. *The History of Malaria, an Ancient Disease.* (Malaria), page last updated: March 11, 2016. https://www.cdc.gov/malaria/about/history/ (accessed October 2, 2017).

U.S. Department of Health and Human Services. Centers for Disease Control and Prevention. *Measles, Rubella & Congenital Rubella Syndrome (CRS) Elimination.* (Global Health), page last updated April 1, 2015). https://www.cdc.gov/globalhealth/measles/elimination.htm (accessed June 12, 2017).

U.S. Department of Health and Human Services. Centers for Disease Control and Prevention. *Outbreak Chronology: Ebola Virus Disease.* (Ebola Virus Disease), page last updated: April 14, 2016. https://www.cdc.gov/vhf/ebola/outbreaks/history/chronology.html (accessed June 30, 2017).

U.S. Department of Health and Human Services. Centers for Disease Control and Prevention. *Polycyclic Aromatic Hydrocarbons (PAHs)*, November 2009. https://www.epa.gov/sites/production/files/2014-03/documents/pahs_factsheet_cdc_2013.pdf (accessed June 21, 2018).

U.S. Department of Health and Human Services. Centers for Disease Control and Prevention. *Prescription Opioid Data*, page last updated: August 30, 2017. https://www.cdc.gov/drugoverdose/data/prescribing.html (accessed 20 January 30, 2017).

U.S. Department of Health and Human Services. Centers for Disease Control and Prevention. "Ten Great Public Health Achievements—United States, 2001–2010." *Morbidity and Mortality Weekly Report* 60, no. 19 (May 20, 2011): 619–623. https://www.cdc.gov/mmwr/preview/mmwrhtml/mm6019a5.htm (accessed May 20, 2017).

U.S. Department of Health and Human Services. National Institute of Diabetes and Digestive and Kidney Diseases. *Overweight and Obesity Statistics*, October 2012. https://www.niddk.nih.gov/health-information/health-statistics/Pages/overweight-obesity-statistics.aspx (accessed March 4, 2017).

U.S. Department of Health and Human Services. National Institute of Health. Eunice Kennedy Shriver National Institute of Child Health and Human Development. *What Can Be Done to Help Someone Who Is Being Bullied?* Last reviewed January 31, 2017. https://www.nichd.nih.gov/health/topics/bullying/conditioninfo/Pages/help.aspx (accessed June 1, 2017).

U.S. Department of Health and Human Services. National Institutes of Health. National Center for Complementary and Integrative Health. *Ayurvedic Medicine: In Depth.* NCCIH Pub No. D287, page last modified April 07, 2016. https://nccih.nih.gov/health/ayurveda/introduction.htm (accessed January 26, 2018).

U.S. Department of Health and Human Services. National Institutes of Health. National Center for Complementary and Integrative Health. *Complementary, Alternative, or Integrative Health: What's In a Name*? NCCIH Pub No. D347, page last modified September 24, 2017. https://nccih.nih.gov/health/integrative-health (accessed January 25, 2018).

U.S. Department of Health and Human Services. National Institutes of Health. National Center for Complementary and Integrative Health. *Traditional Chinese Medicine: In Depth.* NCCIH Pub No. D287, page last modified March 23, 2017. https://nccih.nih.gov/health/whatiscam/chinesemed.htm (accessed January 26, 2018).

U.S. Department of Health and Human Services. National Institutes of Health. National Library of Medicine. *Cesarean Section—A Brief History.* Part 3, last updated July 26, 2013. https://www.nlm.nih.gov/exhibition/cesarean/part3.html (accessed March 16, 2017).

U.S. Department of Health and Human Services. Substance Abuse and Mental Health Services Administration. *Results from the 2011 National Survey on Drug Use and Health: Mental Health Findings*. NSDUH Series H-45, HHS Publication No. (SMA) 12–4725. Rockville, MD: Substance Abuse and Mental Health Services Administration, 2012. https://www.samhsa.gov/data/sites/default/files/NSDUHmhfr2011/NSDUHmhfr2011.pdf (accessed December 12, 2016).

U.S. Department of Health and Human Services. Substance Abuse and Mental Health Services Administration. *Substance Use Disorders,* last Updated: 10/27/2015. http://www.samhsa.gov/disorders/substance-use (accessed December 13, 2016).

U.S. Environmental Protection Agency. *Criteria Air Pollutants.* Last updated on March 8, 2018. https://www.epa.gov/criteria-air-pollutants. (accessed June 26, 2018).

U.S. Food and Drug Administration. "FDA Announces Withdrawal Fenfluramine and Dexfenfluramine (Fen-Phen)." P97-32. (September 15, 1997, page last updated: 12/03/2014). https://wayback.archive-it.org/7993/20170723090512/https://www.fda.gov/Drugs/DrugSafety/PostmarketDrugSafetyInformationforPatientsandProviders/ucm179871.htm (accessed February 2, 2017).

Valenstein, Elliot S. *Great and Desperate Cures: The Rise and Decline of Psychosurgery and Other Radical Treatments for Mental Illness*. New York: Basic Books, 2010.

Van den Berg, Henk, Gamini Manuweera, and Flemming Konradsen. "Global Trends in the Production and Use of DDT for Control of Malaria and Other Vector-Borne Diseases." *Malaria Journal* 16 (October 2017): 401–409. https://malariajournal.biomedcentral.com/articles/10.1186/s12936-017-2050-2 (accessed June 15, 2018).

Van Zee, Art. "The Promotion and Marketing of OxyContin: Commercial Triumph, Public Health Tragedy." *American Journal of Public Health* 99, no. 2 (February 2009): 221–227. https://www.ncbi.nlm.nih.gov/pmc/articles/PMC2622774/ (accessed January 30, 2017).

Ventola, C. Lee. "Direct-to-Consumer Pharmaceutical Advertising: Therapeutic or Toxic?" *Pharmacy and Therapeutics* 36, no. 10 (October 2011): 669–674, 681–684. https://www.ncbi.nlm.nih.gov/pmc/articles/PMC3278148/ (accessed January 3, 2017).

Viner, R. "Putting Stress in Life: Hans Selye and the Making of Stress Theory." *Social Studies of Science* 29, no. 3 (June 1999): 391–410.

Wain, John, et al. "Typhoid Fever." *The Lancet* 385, no. 9973 (March 21, 2015): 1136–1145. http://www.thelancet.com/journals/lancet/article/PIIS0140-6736(13)62708-7/fulltext (accessed July 11, 2017).

Wang, Cuntong. "History of the Chinese Family Planning Program: 1970–2010."*Contraception* 85, no. 6 (December 2011): 563–569. https://www.researchgate.net/publication/51886442_History_of_the_Chinese_Family_Planning_program_1970-2010 (accessed March 13, 2017).

Wasylenki, Donald. "The Paradigm Shift from Institution to Community." In *Psychiatry in Canada: 50 Years, 1951–2000, edited by* Quentin Rae-Grant. Ottawa: Canadian Psychiatric Association, 2001.

Weaver, J. L. "The Politics of Latin American Family-Planning Policy." *Journal of Developing Areas* 12, no 4. (July 1978): 415–37.

Weinmeyer, Richard. "Needle Exchange Programs: Status in US Politics." *AMA Journal of Ethics* 18, no. 3 (March 2016): 252–257. http://journalofethics.ama-assn.org/2016/03/hlaw1-1603.html (accessed January 28, 2017).

Weiss, Sheila Faith. *Race Hygiene and National Efficiency: The Eugenics of Wilhelm Schallmayer.* Berkeley: University of California Press, 1987.

Weisse, Allen B. *Medical Odysseys: The Different and Sometimes Unexpected Pathways to Twentieth-Century Medical Discoveries.* New Brunswick, NJ: Rutgers University Press, 1991.

Whiteford, Harvey A., et al. "Global Burden of Disease Attributable to Mental and Substance Use Disorders: Findings from the Global Burden of Disease Study 2010." *The Lancet* 382, no. 9904 (November 9–15, 2013):1575–1586. Published Online August 29, 2013. http://citeseerx.ist.psu.edu/viewdoc/download?doi=10.1.1.393.7985&rep=rep1&type=pdf (accessed December 2, 2016).

Wickens, Andrew P. *A History of the Brain: From Stone Age Surgery to Modern Neuroscience.* London; New York: Psychology Press, 2015.

Wise, Jacqui. "Pfizer Accused of Testing New Drug without Ethical Approval." *British Medical Journal* 322, no. 7280 (27 January 2001): 194. https://www.ncbi.nlm.nih.gov/pmc/articles/PMC1119465/ (accessed February 3, 2017).

Workman, Daniel. *Drugs and Medicine Exports by Country.* World's Top Exports. (January 6, 2017) http://www.worldstopexports.com/drugs-medicine-exports-country/ (accessed February 6, 2017).

World Bank. *Diabetes Prevalence (% of Population Ages 20 to 79,* 2017. http://data.worldbank.org/indicator/SH.STA.DIAB.ZS?end=2015&start=2015&view=chart (accessed August 12, 2017).

World Bank. *Labor Force Participation Rate, Female (% of female population ages 15+) (modeled ILO estimate)*, 2016. http://data.worldbank.org/indicator/SL.TLF.CACT.FE.ZS (accessed April 25, 2017).

World Health Organization. *Avian and Other Zoonotic Influenza.* (Home/News/Fact sheets/Detail/), updated November 2016). http://www.who.int/mediacentre/factsheets/avian_influenza/en/ (accessed August 7, 2017).

World Health Organization. *Benchmarks for Training in Traditional /Complementary and Alternative Medicine: Benchmarks for Training in Unani Medicine.* Geneva: WHO, 2010. http://apps.who.int/medicinedocs/documents/s17558en/s17558en.pdf (accessed January 10, 2018).

World Health Organization. *Cancer.* (Home/News/Fact sheets/Detail/). http://www.who.int/news-room/fact-sheets/detail/cancer (accessed August 12, 2017).

World Health Organization. *Cardiovascular diseases (CVDs).* (Home/News/Fact sheets/Detail/), May17, 2017. http://www.who.int/mediacentre/factsheets/fs317/en/ (accessed August 11, 2017).

World Health Organization. *Children: Reducing Mortality.* (Home/News/Fact sheets/Detail/) http://www.who.int/mediacentre/factsheets/fs178/en/ (accessed March 7, 2017).

World Health Organization. *Climate Change and Health.* (Home/News/Fact sheets/Detail/), February 1, 2018. http://www.who.int/news-room/fact-sheets/detail/climate-change-and-health (accessed June 29, 2018).

World Health Organization. *Comprehensive Mental Health Action Plan 2013–2020.* Sixty-Sixth World Health Assembly (WHA66.8) Agenda item 13.3, 27 May 2013. http://apps.who.int/gb/ebwha/pdf_files/WHA66/A66_R8-en.pdf (accessed December 6, 2016).

World Health Organization. *Dementia.* (Home/News/Fact sheets/Detail/). http://www.who.int/mediacentre/factsheets/fs362/en/ (accessed December 6, 2016).

World Health Organization. *Diabetes Mellitus.* (Fact Sheet No. 138), 2017. http://www.who.int/mediacentre/factsheets/fs138/en/ (accessed August 12, 2017).

World Health Organization. "Direct-to-Consumer Advertising under Fire." *Bulletin of the World Health Organization* 87, no. 8 (August 2009): 565–64. http://www.who.int/bulletin/volumes/87/8/09-040809/en/ (accessed January 7, 2017).

World Health Organization. *The End TB Strategy: Global Strategy and Targets for Tuberculosis Prevention, Care and Control after 2015.* Geneva: WHO, 2014. http://who.int/tb/strategy/End_TB_Strategy.pdf?ua=1 (accessed July 17, 2017).

World Health Organization. *Global Plan of Action on Workers' Health (2008–2017): Baseline for Implementation: Global Country Survey 2008/2009. Executive Summary and Survey Findings.* Geneva: WHO, 2013. http://www.who.int/occupational_health/who_workers_health_web.pdf (accessed June 29, 2018).

World Health Organization. *Global Status Report on Alcohol and Health.* Geneva: WHO, 2011. http://apps.who.int/iris/bitstream/handle/10665/44499/?sequence=1 (accessed August 25, 2018).

World Health Organization. *Global Status Report on Alcohol and Health, 2014.* Geneva: WHO, 2014. http://www.who.int/substance_abuse/publications/global_alcohol_report/msb_gsr_2014_1.pdf (accessed December 14, 2016).

World Health Organization. *Global Status Report on Noncommunicable Diseases, 2010.* Geneva: WHO, 2011. http://www.who.int/nmh/publications/ncd_report_full_en.pdf (accessed August 12, 2017).

World Health Organization. *Global Status Report on Road Safety 2015.* Geneva: WHO, 2015. http://www.who.int/violence_injury_prevention/road_safety_status/2015/en/ (accessed August 14, 2017).

World Health Organization. *Health Promotion Glossary Update: New Terms.* http://www.who.int/healthpromotion/about/HPR%20Glossary_New%20Terms.pdf (accessed July 10, 2018).

World Health Organization. *HIV/AIDS.* Global Health Observatory (GHO) data, (2017). http://www.who.int/gho/hiv/en/ (accessed August 8, 2017).

World Health Organization. *The ICD-10 Classification of Mental and Behavioural Disorders: Clinical Descriptions and Diagnostic Guidelines.* Geneva: WHO, 1992.

http://www.who.int/classifications/icd/en/bluebook.pdf (accessed December 12, 2016).

World Health Organization. *International Classification of Diseases Information Sheet.* (Classifications). http://www.who.int/classifications/icd/factsheet/en/ (accessed December 6, 2016).

World Health Organization. *Legal Status of Traditional Medicine and Complementary/Alternative Medicine: A Worldwide Review.* [Geneva]: WHO, 2001. http://apps.who.int/medicinedocs/pdf/h2943e/h2943e.pdf (accessed January 24, 2018).

World Health Organization. *Life Expectancy. Global Health Observatory (GHO) data.* http://www.who.int/gho/mortality_burden_disease/life_tables/situation_trends/en/ (accessed August 29, 2018).

World Health Organization. *Malaria.* (Home/News/Fact sheets/Detail/). http://www.who.int/mediacentre/factsheets/fs094/en/ (accessed July 28, 2017).

World Health Organization. *Maternal Mortality.* (Home/News/Fact sheets/Detail/). http://www.who.int/mediacentre/factsheets/fs348/en/ (accessed March 2, 2017).

World Health Organization. "Mental and Behavioural Disorders." Chapter V in *International Statistical Classification of Diseases and Related Health Problems 10th Revision.* (ICD-10 Version: 2016). http://apps.who.int/classifications/icd10/browse/2016/en#/V (accessed December 12, 2016).

World Health Organization. *Nutrition 2. Background.* (WHO> Programmes and projects> Nutrition> Nutrition health topics) http://www.who.int/nutrition/topics/2_background/en/ (accessed August 10, 2017).

World Health Organization. *Prevalence of Tobacco Smoking.* (Global Health Observatory (GHO) data). http://www.who.int/gho/tobacco/use/en/ (accessed December 5, 2016).

World Health Organization. *Smallpox.* (Emergencies Preparedness, Response). http://www.who.int/csr/disease/smallpox/en/ (accessed August 90, 2017).

World Health Organization. *10 Facts on Noncommunicable Diseases*, Updated March 2013. http://www.who.int/features/factfiles/noncommunicable_diseases/en/ (accessed August 10, 2017).

World Health Organization. *10 Leading Causes of Death in Females.* Global Health Observatory (GHO). http://www.who.int/gho/women_and_health/mortality/situation_trends_causes_death/en/ (accessed March 7, 2017).

World Health Organization. *The Top 10 Causes of Death.* (Home/News/Fact sheets/Detail/), May 24, 2018. http://www.who.int/en/news-room/fact-sheets/detail/the-top-10-causes-of-death (accessed July 28, 2018).

World Health Organization. *Trends in Maternal Mortality: 1990 to 2013. Estimates by WHO, UNICEF, UNFPA, The World Bank and the United Nations Population Division.* Geneva: WHO, 2014. http://apps.who.int/iris/bitstream/10665/112682/2/9789241507226_eng.pdf?ua=1 (accessed February 22, 2017).

World Health Organization. *Tuberculosis.* (Home/News/Fact sheets/Detail/). http://www.who.int/mediacentre/factsheets/fs104/en/ (accessed July 17, 2017).

World Health Organization. *Yellow Fever.* (Home/News/Fact sheets/Detail/), May 1, 2018. http://www.who.int/en/news-room/fact-sheets/detail/yellow-fever (accessed July 25, 2017).

World Health Organization. *Yellow Fever Outbreak, Global Response.* (Emergencies). http://www.who.int/emergencies/yellow-fever/response/en/ (accessed July 25, 2017).

World Health Organization. Country Office for South Africa. *WHO-AIMS Report on Mental Health System in South Africa.* Cape Town, South Africa: WHO and Department of Psychiatry and Mental Health, University of Cape Town, 2007.

http://www.who.int/mental_health/evidence/south_africa_who_aims_report.pdf (accessed December 20, 2016).

World Health Organization. Department of Reproductive Health and Research. *Unsafe Abortion: Global and Regional Estimates of Incidence of Unsafe Abortion and Associated Aortality in* 2003. Fifth edition. Geneva: WHO, 2007. http://apps.who.int/iris/bitstream/handle/10665/43798/9789241596121_eng.pdf;jsessionid=3EF8606B15DEAB96A01A113678182BDD?sequence=1 (accessed March 4, 2017).

World Health Organization. Regional Office for Africa. *Countries.* WHO: Regional Office for Africa, 2018. https://www.afro.who.int/countries (accessed July 20, 2017).

World Health Organization. Regional Office for Africa. African Health Observatory. *Comprehensive Analytical Profile: Zambia.* http://aho.afro.who.int/profiles_information/index.php/Zambia:Index (accessed July 9, 2017).

World Health Organization. Regional Office for South East Asia. *Climate Change and Health.* Meeting of the Advisory Committee (ACM) to review technical matters to be discussed at the Sixty-first Session of the Regional Committee WHO/SEARO, New Delhi, June 30–July 3, 2008. Agenda item 7.2 SEA/ACM/Meet.1/7.2 (Rev.1), June 18, 2008 http://apps.who.int/iris/bitstream/handle/10665/126809/SEA_ACM_Meet.%201_7.2%20(Rev.1).pdf;jsessionid=28E1B86A7190A61E7CAC641940F444A7?sequence=1 (accessed June 19, 2018).

World Health Organization, UNICEF, UNFPA, World Bank Group, and the United Nations Population Division. "Maternal mortality ratio (modeled estimate, per 100,000 live births)" in "*Trends in Maternal Mortality: 1990 to 2015.* Geneva: WHO, 2015. http://data.worldbank.org/indicator/SH.STA.MMRT (accessed February 22, 2017).

Wynbrandt, James. *The Excruciating History of Dentistry: Toothsome Tales & Oral Oddities from Babylon to Braces.* New York: St. Martin's Griffin, 2000.

Xanthos, Dirk, and Tony R. Walker. "International Policies to Reduce Plastic Marine Pollution from Single-Use Plastics (Plastic Bags and Microbeads): A Review." *Marine Pollution Bulletin* 118, nos.1–2 (May 15, 2017):17–26. https://www.sciencedirect.com/science/article/pii/S0025326X17301650 (accessed July 7, 2018).

Yan, R. Y. "Maternal Mortality in China." *World Health Forum* 10, no.3–4 (1989): 327–30. https://www.ncbi.nlm.nih.gov/pubmed/2637703 (accessed March 5, 2017).

Yap, Kiryu K. "Stem Cells and Religion." *Stem Cells Translational Medicine* 3, no. 8 (August 2014): 977. https://www.ncbi.nlm.nih.gov/pmc/articles/PMC4116252/ (accessed March 21, 2018).

Young, James Harvey. *The Medical Messiahs: A Social History of Health Quackery in Twentieth-Century America.* Princeton, NJ: Princeton University Press, 1992.

Young, James Harvey. *The Toadstool Millionaires: A Social History of Patent Medicines in America before Federal Regulation.* Princeton, NJ: Princeton University Press; 1961. https://www.quackwatch.com/13Hx/TM/00.html (accessed January 3, 2017).

About the Editor and Contributors

Editor

Ruth Clifford Engs, PhD, is Professor Emerita, School of Public Health, Indiana University, Bloomington, Indiana. Her research has focused upon student drinking patterns in addition to social reform movements of the early 20th century. Her many works include *The Field Hospital That Never Was* (2015), *Unseen Upton Sinclair* (2009), *The Eugenics Movement* (2005), *The Progressive Era's Health Reform Movement* (2003), and *Clean Living Movements: American Cycles of Health Reform* (2000). Other major works include two oral histories, *Conversations in the Abbey: Senior Monks of Saint Meinrad Archabbey Reflect on their Lives* (2008) and *Conversations in the Abbey, Volume 2* (2016).

Contributors

Deborah Brunton was awarded a doctorate from the University of Pennsylvania in 1990 and was, until recently, senior lecturer in the history of medicine at the Open University in Milton Keynes in Britain. She has researched extensively on public health, particularly smallpox prevention. She is author of *The Politics of Vaccination: Practice and Policy in England, Wales, Ireland and Scotland, 1800–1874* and of *Medicine in Modern Britain: 1780–1950.*

Joseph P. Byrne, PhD, is a historian and professor of humanities in the honors program at Belmont University in Nashville, Tennessee. He has written *The Black Death* (Greenwood, 2004), *Daily Life during the Black Death* (Greenwood, 2006), the *Encyclopedia of the Black Death* (ABC-CLIO, 2012), and *The World of Renaissance Italy: A Daily Life Encyclopedia* (Greenwood, 2017). He has also edited the *Encyclopedia of Pestilence, Pandemics, and Plagues* (Greenwood, 2008).

William H. York, PhD, earned his doctorate in the history of science, medicine, and technology from the Johns Hopkins University with a focus on medieval and early modern European history. He is a member of the faculty in the Honors College at Portland State University, where he teaches courses on the history of science and medicine, environmental history, and the history of animals. He is currently serving as the president of Medica: The Society for the Study of Healing in the Middle Ages.

Index

Boldface numbers refer to volume numbers.